43

The percentage of students surveyed who believe you don't need a textbook to pass a course.

Instructors understand a textbook helps reinforce concepts for students outside the classroom. *LIFE* provides valuable context to engage students and help foster understanding through its student-friendly, accessible design and by providing real-life examples they can relate to.

89

Percentage of Students Who Look for Highlighted Key Terminology.

LIFE was designed with instructor and student feedback. Students asked for well highlighted terminology and they can find it easily!

The book you are holding is the answer to questions we have asked hundreds of students like you: How do you study? How do you use your textbook? Do you use online homework problems to help you succeed? Many students told us they don't buy any textbook, new or used. That didn't surprise us, and we know it won't surprise you.

After listening to you, we created briefer chapters, end-of-chapter review cards, and a clear and colorful design. Faculty from schools across the country joined us online and in face-to-face conversations to help us refine these solutions into a text students could relate to and benefit from.

LIFE is the result of those conversations: content you expect, presented in a format that students prefer. The student website tools include chapter summaries, flashcards, animations, interactive quizzing, games, and much more.

Thanks for your time – we look forward to your thoughts about **LIFE**.

Peggy Williams
Senior Acquisitions
Editor

Tom Ziolkowski
Senior Marketing
Manager

Amy Cohen
Senior Media
Editor

Michelle Lockard
Senior Project
Manager, 4LTR Press

LIFE with Physiology REVISED

includes Bind-In Printed Access Card and BIO 141 Labs
Drexel University

John H. Postlethwait | Janet L. Hopson | James W. Perry
David Morton | Joy B. Perry

 CENGAGE
Learning·

Australia • Brazil • Japan • Korea • Mexico • Singapore • Spain • United Kingdom • United States

**LIFE with Physiology REVISED
includes Bind-In Printed Access Card and
BIO 141 Labs
Drexel University**

Executive Editors:
 Maureen Staudt
 Michael Stranz

Senior Project Development Manager:
 Linda deStefano

Marketing Specialist:
 Courtney Sheldon

Senior Production/Manufacturing Manager:
 Donna M. Brown

PreMedia Manager:
 Joel Brennecke

Sr. Rights Acquisition Account Manager:
 Todd Osborne

Cover Image:
 Getty Images*

*Unless otherwise noted, all cover images used by Custom
Solutions, a part of Cengage Learning, have been supplied
courtesy of Getty Images with the exception of the Earthview
cover image, which has been supplied by the National
Aeronautics and Space Administration (NASA).

LIFE 2010-2011 Edition
John H. Postlethwait | Janet L. Hopson

© 2011 Brooks/Cole, Cengage Learning. All rights reserved.

Library of Congress Control Number: 2009943808

Laboratory Manual for General Biology, 5th Edition
James W. Perry | David Morton | Joy B. Perry

© 2013, 2007, 2002, 1995, 1992 Brooks/Cole, Cengage Learning.
All rights reserved.

For product information and technology assistance, contact us at
Cengage Learning Customer & Sales Support, 1-800-354-9706

For permission to use material from this text or product,
submit all requests online at **cengage.com/permissions**
Further permissions questions can be emailed to
permissionrequest@cengage.com

This book contains select works from existing Cengage Learning resources and
was produced by Cengage Learning Custom Solutions for collegiate use. As such,
those adopting and/or contributing to this work are responsible for editorial
content accuracy, continuity and completeness.

Compilation © 2012 Cengage Learning

ISBN-13: 978-1-133-87148-4

ISBN-10: 1-133-87148-8

Cengage Learning
5191 Natorp Boulevard
Mason, Ohio 45040
USA
Cengage Learning is a leading provider of customized learning solutions with
office locations around the globe, including Singapore, the United Kingdom,
Australia, Mexico, Brazil, and Japan. Locate your local office at:
international.cengage.com/region.

Cengage Learning products are represented in Canada by Nelson Education, Ltd.
For your lifelong learning solutions, visit **www.cengage.com/custom.**
Visit our corporate website at **www.cengage.com.**

Printed in the United States of America

Brief Contents

LIFE

Enrichment Chapters

Laboratory Manual – General Biology

Cells
and the
Chemistry
of Life

Learning Outcomes

LO[1] Describe the general structure of HIV

LO[2] Differentiate among elements, atoms, molecules, isotopes, and ions

LO[3] Explain the biological importance of chemical bonds

LO[4] List the properties of water that make it so critical to life

LO[5] List and describe the four main types of biological molecules found in all living organisms

LO[6] Compare the characteristics of a virus and a cell

LO[7] List the organelles and structures found in cells, and discuss their functions

LO[8] List the seven steps in HIV's infective cycle

> ## 66 *It is remarkable that a simple, nonliving particle can wreak such havoc in the lives of infected people.* 99

A Threat to Cells and Lives

In his years at the University of California at San Francisco, Dr. Jay Levy has watched acquired immune deficiency syndrome, or AIDS, grow from a seemingly isolated threat into a global epidemic affecting more than 33 million people. "I can't believe where the time has gone," he says, "and that today we still don't have a really long-lasting treatment." That, he says, is because the **human immune deficiency virus (HIV)** that causes AIDS keeps evolving drug-resistant forms. By now, some of Levy's research subjects have been able to stay relatively healthy for many years. But in other patients initially helped by various combinations of antiviral medicines, "the virus is coming back and there are no more drugs to use. I think these are going to be sad cases," he says, "and we're seeing up to 40 percent of the people at San Francisco General Hospital with this."

The ongoing fight against HIV and AIDS make an ideal case study for this chapter. Our subjects here are the chemistry of life and the structure and function of cells, the fundamental units of life. By studying the human immune deficiency virus, you will see how virus particles contain different kinds of building blocks called biological molecules. We will compare viruses, which are nonliving, to bacterial, plant, and animal cells to reveal their basic differences and unique characteristics. By following the entry of an HIV particle into a human cell, as Levy and others have investigated in great detail, you will get an intimate tour of a functioning cell and its many internal organelles. From this, you will see for yourself why AIDS is such a deadly disease and come to understand the efforts now underway to control this global threat through drugs and vaccines.

As we go through the chapter, you'll find out why you can pick up a cold virus—but not HIV—from a doorknob. You'll see why health experts fear that AIDS could annihilate 40 percent of the population of Africa before a solution is found. You will also find the answers to these questions:

- ☑ How are atoms structured and how do they function?
- ☑ What are the special properties of water?
- ☑ What are the main kinds of biological molecules and their roles?
- ☑ How is a living cell different from a virus?
- ☑ How do the various cell parts function and how does HIV sabotage them?

What do you know?

Could a single-celled, amoeba-like creature ever be as big as a truck? Why or why not?

AIDS (acquired immune deficiency syndrome)
a partial or total loss of immune function based on infection by the human immune deficiency virus (HIV)

HIV (human immune deficiency virus)
the causative agent in acquired immune deficiency syndrome (AIDS)

element
a pure substance that cannot be broken down into simpler substances by chemical means

atom
(Gr. *atomos,* indivisible) the smallest particle into which an element can be broken down and still retain the properties of that element

molecule
a cluster of two or more atoms held together by specific chemical bonds

proton
a positively charged subatomic particle found in the nucleus of an atom

neutron
(L. *neuter,* either) a subatomic particle without any electrical charge found in the nucleus of an atom

electron
a negatively charged subatomic particle that orbits the nucleus of an atom; the negative charge of an electron is equal in magnitude to the proton's positive charge, but the electron has a much smaller mass

LO¹ What Is HIV?

HIV is a nonliving particle that infects human cells. Biologists consider HIV to be *nonliving* because it has some but not all of the life characteristics we discussed in Chapter 1. A virus has internal order, based on the same groupings of atoms or biological molecules that make up living things. Viruses have genetic material that can change over time, and thus they can evolve. Finally, parts of the virus particle can move, so we can consider them to display the living trait of motility. However, a virus has no metabolism, it is unresponsive in the biological sense, and it lacks the ability to reproduce (without help from living cells). While virus particles do assemble themselves, this construction requires the machinery inside a host cell and so cannot be considered true growth or development. Virus particles are clearly not alive by our definitions in Chapter 1. Yet their structure and behavior inside the human body are still governed by the same set of chemical and physical laws that determine how all biological molecules form and act and how all living cells function.

It is remarkable that a simple, nonliving particle made up of just a few chemicals can wreak such havoc in the lives of infected people. Our goal in this chapter is to look more closely at our lethal yet nonliving enemy HIV, and at the atoms and molecules that make up all viruses, cells, and larger organisms.

LO² What Are Atoms?

All matter, including HIV particles and the cells they infect, are based on atoms of distinguishable types. That's where the elements come in and they take us back to some of history's earliest students of life and matter.

Elements

Ancient Greek philosophers realized that some materials, such as rocks, wood, and soil, are composed of more than one substance, while other materials, such as chunks of iron, gold, and sulfur appear to be pure materials. Chemists call pure substances like these that can't be broken down further into different constituent **elements**. Chemists also assign each known element a chemical symbol; for example, the symbols for the main elements found in an HIV particle are C (carbon), H (hydrogen), and O (oxygen).

Chemists have discovered 118 elements. Of these, 89 occur in nature, while scientists have created the rest in the laboratory. The properties of different elements vary widely. For example, carbon is a black solid, sulfur is a yellow solid, and helium is a colorless, odorless gas. Although the Earth contains dozens of elements, only seven elements, headed by oxygen, silicon, and aluminum, make up about 98 percent of Earth's surface layer. Researchers have found more than three dozen elements in living things, but most occur only in traces. Just three elements make up 98 percent of the body of a human or a fern—hydrogen, oxygen, and carbon. In our later discussion of water and carbon, we'll see why living tissue is a unique and special form of matter.

Atoms and Molecules

Never satisfied by superficial discoveries, early scientists wondered what makes each element distinct: How is gold, for example, fundamentally different from oxygen? (Knowing this might, among other things, have helped them turn iron or carbon into gold—or so they hoped!) In the 1800s, the English chemist John Dalton concluded that each element is composed of identical particles called atoms (Greek, *atomos* = indivisible). Atoms are the smallest particles of an element that still display that element's chemical properties. A **molecule** is the chemical combination of two or more atoms. In a molecule of water, for example, two hydrogen atoms are combined with one oxygen atom.

Atoms are extremely tiny. About a million carbon atoms could sit side by side on the period ending this sentence. A small gold nugget consists of billions of gold atoms. Tiny as they are, though, atoms themselves have an internal structure.

Structure of Atoms

Whether found in a lifeless rock or in a biological entity, such as a person, all atoms are composed of protons, neutrons, and electrons (Fig. 2.1). A **proton** is a subatomic particle with a positive electrical charge, and a **neutron** is a particle with no electrical charge. **Electrons** are much smaller (have less mass) and they have a negative electrical charge.

A Model of the Atom

Think of an atom as resembling a miniature solar system. The atomic nucleus at the center contains protons and neutrons and accounts for most of the atom's mass. A specific number of electrons, equal to the number of protons, orbit the nucleus at a relatively great distance. Figure 2.1a shows the simplest atom, hydrogen, with its single proton, single electron, and no neutron. If a somewhat larger atom like carbon (Fig. 2.1b) were the size of the Houston Astrodome, the nucleus would be a small marble on the 50-yard line.

What Gives Atoms Their Properties?

Why is a chunk of the element carbon black and solid, while the element oxygen is a clear, colorless gas? The answer is that each type of atom contains a unique number of protons in its nucleus. All carbon atoms have six protons, for example, and all oxygen atoms have eight protons (Fig. 2.1b, c). The number of protons affects the atom's mass and its attraction for electrons, and these two features, in turn, determine the atom's physical and chemical properties.

Electrons and Energy Levels

The attraction between the positively charged nucleus and the orbiting electrons, with their negative charge, sets up conflicting forces: The opposite charges pull the electrons toward the nucleus, but their rapid circling tends to throw them outward, away from the nucleus, the way a rock tied to a twirling string pulls outward.

Electrons are too small to be seen with the eye or most instruments, of course, but scientists picture them whizzing about in **energy shells** at specific distances from the nucleus, with higher energy levels the farther they orbit from the nucleus. Each shell can contain a certain maximum number of electrons, and the bonding of atoms into molecules depends on the order of shell-filling. The ring or electron shell nearest the nucleus can hold either one electron, as in hydrogen, or two, as in helium. The second shell can accommodate up to eight electrons, and will be filled before any electrons appear in the higher-energy third shell, which also holds up to eight electrons. Subsequent shells also become filled with set numbers of electrons, and tend to fill in order.

Variations in Atomic Structure

Slight exceptions to the standard structure of atoms—either in the number of neutrons or the number of electrons—help explain phenomena as diverse as atomic bombs, acid rain, and the actions of your nerve cells.

An atom of a given kind contains a set number of protons, but the number of neutrons can vary. Atoms with the same number of protons but different numbers of neutrons are different **isotopes** of the same element. The most common carbon isotope is ^{12}C with six neutrons and six protons. Other carbon isotopes are ^{13}C and ^{14}C, with seven and eight neutrons, respectively. Both ^{12}C and ^{13}C are stable, nonradioactive forms, but ^{14}C is radioactive—it tends to break down and emit radiation. In 1991, hikers high on a ridge in the Swiss Alps found an unfortunate hiker's head and shoulders sticking out of a chunk of melting ice. Researchers used radioactive carbon 14 (^{14}C) to determine the age of the ice man. When an organism dies, it stops incorporating ^{14}C from the environment, and the isotope begins to decay into the isotope nitrogen 14 (^{14}N). (^{14}C has six protons

atomic nucleus
the central core of an atom, containing protons and neutrons

energy shells
energy levels occupied by electrons in orbit around an atomic nucleus; each shell can contain a maximum number of electrons, for example, two electrons for the first shell, eight for the second

isotopes
an alternative form of an element having the same atomic number but a different atomic mass due to the different number of neutrons present in the nucleus

Figure 2.1

Models of an Atom

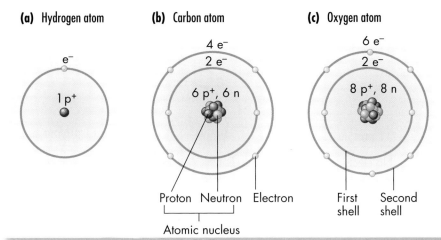

(a) Hydrogen atom

e⁻

1 p⁺

(b) Carbon atom

4 e⁻
2 e⁻
6 p⁺, 6 n

Proton Neutron Electron

Atomic nucleus

(c) Oxygen atom

6 e⁻
2 e⁻
8 p⁺, 8 n

First shell   Second shell

and eight neutrons, while ^{14}N has seven protons and seven neutrons.) As a result of this decay, the concentration of ^{14}C relative to ^{12}C decreases. One-half of the original amount of ^{14}C decays in 5,730 years; this is known as the half-life of ^{14}C. Through ^{14}C dating, scientists concluded that the ice man lived about 5,300 years ago, and that he was the oldest well-preserved human body yet found.

While in the case of isotopes, neutron numbers vary, in ions, electron numbers vary (Fig. 2.2). This means the entire atom has a specific positive or negative electrical charge; the number of electrons in an ion does *not* equal the number of protons. For example, the most common form of the hydrogen atom has one proton and one electron: Because the electrical charges cancel each other out, the atom has no net charge (Fig. 2.2a). A hydrogen ion is missing its electron; as a result, it has only one pro-ton, and is positively charged (Fig. 2.2b). A chlorine ion (Cl^-), on the other hand, has a negative charge.

The properties of the elements emerge from both the structure of the atomic parts and the way those parts are arranged. As we'll see in the next sections, this idea of emergent properties also holds for the way atoms make up molecules and the way molecules make up living things.

LO³ How Do Atoms Form Molecules?

The atoms of life—carbon, hydrogen, oxygen, and the others—are joined in tens of thousands of combinations to form the molecules in your food, in other animals and plants, and in your body. How atoms combine to form different kinds of molecules helps determine their properties in living things.

In molecules, two or more atoms are linked by an attractive force called a chemical bond. The bonds that link atoms are not actual physical connections, like the couplings between railroad cars. Instead, they are links of energy acting like "energy glue," often based on shared or donated electrons. Bonds act like invisible springs; once a bond forms between

Figure 2.2
Ions

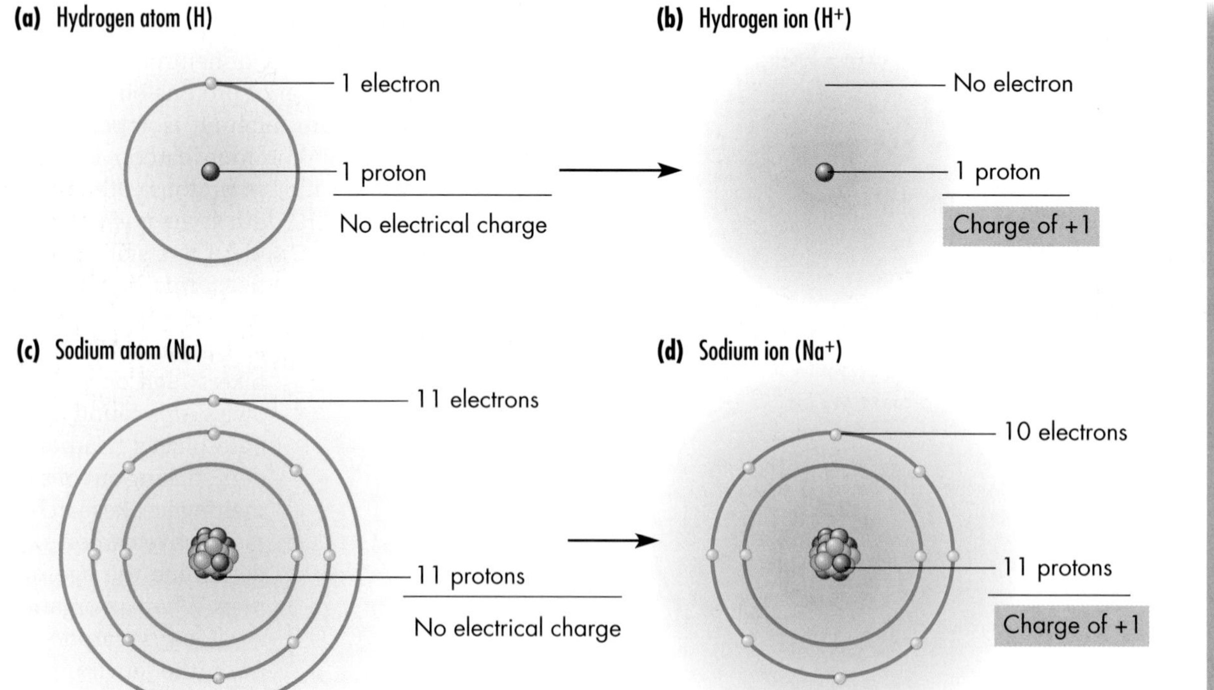

(a) Hydrogen atom (H)

1 electron

1 proton

No electrical charge

(b) Hydrogen ion (H⁺)

No electron

1 proton

Charge of +1

(c) Sodium atom (Na)

11 electrons

11 protons

No electrical charge

(d) Sodium ion (Na⁺)

10 electrons

11 protons

Charge of +1

two atoms, it requires energy to pull the atoms apart or to push them closer together. We'll see three kinds of bonds in our exploration of biology: covalent bonds, hydrogen bonds, and ionic bonds.

Covalent Bonds

When two atoms share a pair of electrons, the most common type of chemical bond forms—a covalent bond (Fig. 2.3a on the next page). In a water molecule (chemical formula, H_2O), two hydrogen atoms each share a pair of electrons with one oxygen atom. As each hydrogen atom approaches the oxygen atom, its positively charged nucleus begins to attract electrons orbiting the other nucleus. Eventually, the electron orbits overlap and fuse, and the two atoms—the hydrogen atom and the oxygen atom—share a pair of electrons.

In some molecules, the electrons spend as much time orbiting one nucleus as the other, and the electrical charge is evenly distributed about both ends, or *poles*, of the molecule. A molecule with this equal sharing of charge is said to be nonpolar. In a molecule like water, however, the electrons spend more time orbiting the oxygen than the hydrogen. This leaves the oxygen pole of the molecule with a slightly negative charge, and the hydrogen pole of the molecule with a slightly positive charge, making H_2O a polar molecule.

Hydrogen Bonds

With their charged ends, some polar molecules can form another kind of chemical bond—a hydrogen bond. In liquid water, for example, a hydrogen atom from one water molecule can electrically attract an oxygen atom from an adjacent water molecule (Fig. 2.3b). The attraction of a hydrogen atom to an atom (usually oxygen or nitrogen) in another molecule is called a hydrogen bond.

Hydrogen bonds are much more easily broken and reformed than covalent bonds. Some of water's unusual properties (such as the tendency for ice to float) are based on hydrogen bonds, and some important biological molecules are held together by hydrogen bonds. Hydrogen bonds, for example, are involved in the interaction between the bead-like proteins on the surface of HIV particles and the surface of a human cell about to become infected. Hydrogen bonds also hold together the nucleic acids that give DNA molecules their "meaning" as the code of life. (We'll encounter this code in Chapter 6.)

Ionic Bonds

In the third type of chemical bond—an ionic bond—electrons from one atom are completely transferred to another atom rather than shared. Salt (NaCl) is a good example: a sodium ion is positively charged (Na^+), and a chlorine ion is negatively charged (Cl^-) (Fig. 2.3c). These oppositely charged ions can attract each other, rather like magnets, and an ionic bond forms between the Na^+ and Cl^- and holds the atoms together. Ionic bonds are much stronger than hydrogen bonds but still not as strong as covalent bonds. That explains why ionically bonded compounds dissociate (break down) into their component ions when dissolved in water, as when table salt dissolves in a pot of soup.

LO⁴ What Makes Water So Special for Life?

Let's look at the many properties of water molecules that make them so special for life.

Physical and Chemical Properties of Water

The tendency of water molecules to form hydrogen bonds gives water several of its important physical characteristics—all of which are important for living organisms. For example, hydrogen bonds make water molecules stick to each other and to soil, glass, and other substrates. This explains the capillary action and transport processes that draw water up into plants—even towering trees. Water's stickiness also creates surface tension or a "skin" on liquid water that some insects can glide across. Hydrogen bonds in frozen water make ice float. And because of hydrogen bonds, it takes a large amount of heat to increase the temperature of water, and this helps living organisms sustain steady internal temperatures.

Water also has chemical properties that explain why things dissolve and why some substances are acidic and some are basic (alkaline). In one sense, living things are forms of water moving about the planet: Our bodies, for instance, contain more than 60 percent H_2O, and so the movement and bonding

covalent bond
(L. *co,* together + *volere,* sharing) a form of molecular bonding characterized by the sharing of a pair of electrons between atoms

nonpolar
having a symmetrical distribution of electrical charge; i.e., a nonpolar molecule like most lipids will not dissolve readily in water

polar
having an asymmetrical distribution of electrical charge; i.e., a polar molecule like glucose will dissolve readily in water

hydrogen bond
a type of weak molecular bond in which a partially negatively charged atom (oxygen or nitrogen) bonds with the partial positive charge on a hydrogen atom when the hydrogen atom is already participating in a covalent bond

ionic bond
a type of molecular bond formed between ions of opposite charge

Figure 2.3
Automic Bonding

(a) Covalent bonds

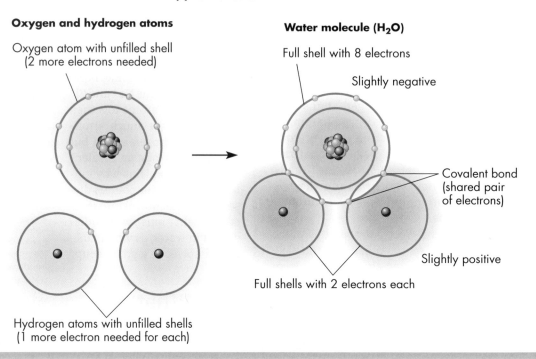

Oxygen and hydrogen atoms

Oxygen atom with unfilled shell
(2 more electrons needed)

Water molecule (H₂O)

Full shell with 8 electrons

Slightly negative

Covalent bond
(shared pair
of electrons)

Slightly positive

Full shells with 2 electrons each

Hydrogen atoms with unfilled shells
(1 more electron needed for each)

(b) Hydrogen bonds

(c) Ionic bonds

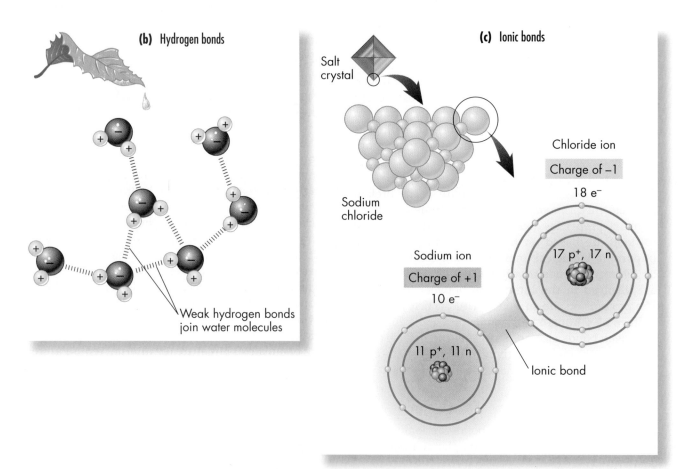

Weak hydrogen bonds
join water molecules

Salt
crystal

Sodium
chloride

Chloride ion

Charge of –1

18 e⁻

17 p⁺, 17 n

Sodium ion

Charge of +1

10 e⁻

11 p⁺, 11 n

Ionic bond

of water molecules is crucial to blood flow, food digestion, and so on. Life itself would be very different if water's chemical behavior was other than it is. Let's see why.

Why Water Dissolves Things

Washing dishes illustrates some of water's important chemical properties. Dishwater—in fact, all water—is a **solvent**, a substance capable of dissolving other molecules. Dissolved substances are called **solutes**. Water can dissolve polar compounds, such as table sugar, and most kinds of ionic compounds, such as table salt. When a polar solute such as sugar—say, syrup on dirty plates, or glucose molecules inside cells—becomes surrounded by water molecules, hydrogen bonds form. With an ionic solute like salt, the component ions dissociate, and each becomes surrounded by a cloud of water molecules (Fig. 2.4a).

Compounds such as sugar and salt that dissolve readily in water are called **hydrophilic**, or "water-loving," compounds. In contrast, nonpolar compounds, such as cooking oils and animal fats on dirty dinner dishes, do not dissolve readily, and are called **hydrophobic**, or "water-fearing," compounds. Instead of dissolving in water, hydrophobic compounds form a boundary (or interface) with the water (Fig. 2.4b). As we will see shortly, the membranes that surround all living cells are just such boundaries.

Acids and Bases

Water has another chemical property with significant implications for living things: Its molecules have a slight tendency to break down into a positively charged hydrogen ion (H^+) and a negatively charged hydroxide ion (OH^-):

$$H_2O \rightarrow H^+ + OH^-$$

solvent
a substance capable of dissolving other molecules

solute
a substance that has been dissolved in a solvent

hydrophilic
compounds that dissolve readily in water, such as salt

hydrophobic
compounds that do not dissolve readily in water, such as oil

Figure 2.4
Hydrophilic Substances Dissolve Well in Water, Hydrophobic Ones Don't

(a) Salt dissolves in water

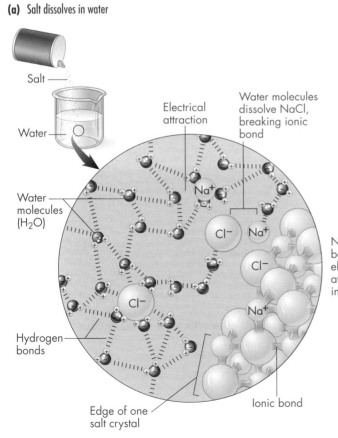

Salt
Water
Electrical attraction
Water molecules dissolve NaCl, breaking ionic bond
Water molecules (H_2O)
Na^+
Cl^- Na^+
Cl^-
Cl^-
Na^+
Hydrogen bonds
Edge of one salt crystal
Ionic bond

(b) Oil and water don't mix

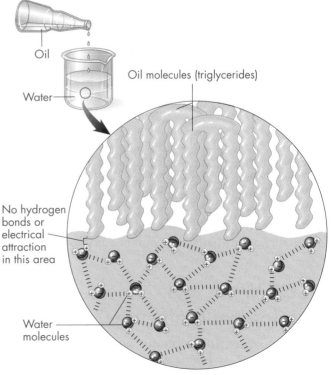

Oil
Water
Oil molecules (triglycerides)
No hydrogen bonds or electrical attraction in this area
Water molecules

acid
a proton donor; any substance that gives off hydrogen ions when dissolved in water, causing an increase in the concentration of hydrogen ions; acidity is measured on a pH scale, with acids having a pH less than 7; the opposite of a base

base
any substance that accepts hydrogen ions when dissolved in water; basic solutions have a pH greater than 7

pH scale
a logarithmic scale that measures hydrogen ion concentration; acids range from pH 1 to 7, water is neutral at a pH of 7, and bases range from pH 7 to 14

buffer
a substance that resists changes in pH when acids or bases are added to a chemical solution

biological molecules
molecules derived from living systems; the four major types are carbohydrates, lipids, proteins, and nucleic acids

organic
molecules that are based on carbon and contain hydrogen

inorganic
molecules that are not based on carbon

This breakdown, however, is a relatively rare event in pure water. By definition, an acid is any substance that gives off hydrogen ions when dissolved in water, thereby increasing the H$^+$ concentration of the solution. A base is any substance that accepts hydrogen ions in water. This property allows a base to reduce the H$^+$ concentration of a solution.

The concentration of hydrogen ions is important to living cells because many of the chemical reactions that drive life's processes—the digestion of foods, for example—depend on specific concentrations of these ions. Biologists measure hydrogen ion concentration on the pH scale, which ranges from 1 to 14 (see Appendix A). On the pH scale, water has the neutral value of 7, in the middle of the scale. Acidic solutions like stomach acid or coffee have pH values between 0 and 7. Basic solutions like drain cleaners or baking soda in water have pH values between 7 and 14. The pH inside most cells stays fairly neutral, between about 6.5 and 7.5, and it is only within this narrow range that many vital cellular reactions take place at optimum speed. A subject related to acids and bases concerns buffers, agents that soak up or dole out hydrogen ions and help control pH level. Antacids buffer your stomach acid, for example, and cells contain natural buffering agents.

Water is clearly a key to life, but so is the element carbon and the biological compounds it forms.

LO^5 What Are Biological Molecules?

All the living things on our planet contain four main types of biological molecules—carbohydrates, lipids, proteins, and nucleic acids—as well as millions of smaller molecules, all based on the special properties of the carbon atom. Why are carbon atoms so crucial for living things? And how do its bonding properties allow the raw materials of life to form?

Carbon Compounds

Our bodies may be mostly water, but a full 18 percent of our weight comes from carbon atoms. For a large tree, the figure can approach 50 percent. Carbon and its chemical bonds are so interesting that chemists divide all molecules into two broad types—those that contain carbon, organic molecules, and those not primarily based on carbon, or inorganic (lifeless) molecules.

Interestingly, there are far more organic than inorganic compounds. Why? Because carbon, with its unique structure, can form millions of different combinations with other atoms. This versatile bonding is carbon's key characteristic, and it explains why carbon is the "stuff of life."

Carbon Backbones

Carbon is "hungry" for electrons and can form covalent bonds with up to four atoms at a time (review Fig. 2.3a). A simple example of a "satisfied" carbon atom is methane gas (CH$_4$), sometimes called *swamp gas* (Fig. 2.5). Many biological compounds are much

Figure 2.5
The Versatility of Carbon

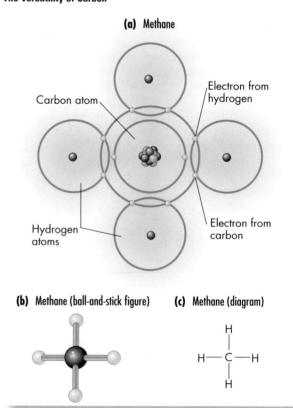

(a) Methane

Carbon atom

Electron from hydrogen

Hydrogen atoms

Electron from carbon

(b) Methane (ball-and-stick figure)

(c) Methane (diagram)

larger than methane and have a backbone of several carbon atoms bonded to each other in long, straight chains, branched chains, or rings—a sculptural property, again, based on forming up to four bonds per carbon atom.

Functional Groups

The chemical sculpturing of an organic molecule's shape contributes to its role in a cell, whether as water-tight seal, storage compound, messenger, protector, or reference library. But a molecule's specific activities often come from small clusters of atoms called functional groups that hang from the carbon backbone. Functional groups usually contain atoms other than carbon and hydrogen, and they give special properties to the molecules they are part of. The presence of a methyl group (CH_3), for example, prevents a molecule from quickly dissolving in water, and the hydroxyl group (OH) gives wood alcohol some of its properties like low boiling point and solvent activity.

The functional groups help explain why the four classes of large biological molecules—carbohydrates, lipids, proteins, and nucleic acids—form and act as they do. Together with a few other materials, these four types of compounds account for the diverse shapes, colors, and textures of organisms.

Figure 2.6
Carbohydrates

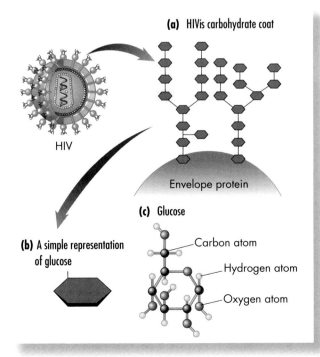

(a) HIV's carbohydrate coat

HIV

Envelope protein

(c) Glucose

(b) A simple representation of glucose

Carbon atom

Hydrogen atom

Oxygen atom

Carbohydrates

An HIV particle looks like a basketball studded with beads tipped with little threadlike branches (Fig. 2.6a). These branches are made of carbohydrates, and together they form a fuzzy coat that helps an HIV particle to recognize a target cell to infect. In addition to their role in recognition, carbohydrates are also crucial to cell structure and to energy storage. Carbohydrates include sugars and starches, and the term itself literally means "carbon-water." Indeed, carbohydrates usually contain carbon, hydrogen, and oxygen in a ratio of 1:2:1 (CH_2O). The formula for the sugar glucose, for example, is a multiple of that CH_2O subunit: $C_6H_{12}O_6$ (Fig. 2.6b,c). The same generally holds true for both simple and more complex carbohydrates.

Simple Carbohydrates: Mono- and Disaccharides

The simple sugars, including glucose and fructose, contain three to six carbon atoms. They share the same molecular formula, $C_6H_{12}O_6$, but have slightly different properties because their −OH functional groups are attached in different places. As a group they are called monosaccharides (*mono* = one), and their simple structures form the subunits of more complex carbohydrates.

A molecule with two simple sugars joined together is a disaccharide (*di* = two). For example, the joining of glucose and fructose makes the disaccharide sucrose. Sucrose is abundant in the saps of sugarcane, maple trees, and sugar beets—our major sources of sugar for refining.

Complex Carbohydrates: Polysaccharides

Many carbohydrates consist of thousands of simple sugar subunits joined into long chains or polysaccharides (*poly* = many). A polysaccharide molecule is like a string of beads, where each bead is a simple sugar, often glucose.

Starch is the polysaccharide stored as an energy reserve in plants. Glycogen is the polysaccharide

functional group
a group of atoms that confers specific behavior to the (usually larger) molecules to which they are attached

monosaccharide
a simple sugar that cannot be decomposed into smaller sugar molecules; the most common forms are the hexoses, six-carbon sugars such as glucose, and the pentoses, five-carbon sugars such as ribose

disaccharide
a type of carbohydrate composed of two linked simple sugars

polysaccharide
a carbohydrate made up of many simple sugars linked together; glycogen and cellulose are examples of polysaccharides

starch
a polysaccharide composed of long chains of glucose subunits; the principal energy source of plants

glycogen
a polysaccharide made up of branched chains of glucose; an energy-storing molecule in animals, found mainly in the liver and muscles

cellulose
(L. *cellula,* little cell) the chief constituent of the cell wall in green plants, some algae, and a few other organisms; cellulose is an insoluble polysaccharide composed of straight chains of glucose molecules

chitin
a complex nitrogen-containing polysaccharide that forms the cell walls of certain fungi, the major component of the exoskeleton of insects and some other arthropods, and the cuticle of some other invertebrates

alpha-helix
one possible shape of amino acids in a protein that resembles a spiral staircase

pleated sheet
secondary protein structure in which hydrogen bonds link two parts of a protein into a shape like a corrugated sheet

disordered loop
regions of a less specific but constant shape that link other parts of a protein

amino acid
a molecule consisting of an amino group (NH_2) and an acid group (COOH); the 20 amino acids are the basic building blocks of proteins

peptide bond
a bond joining two amino acids in a protein

polypeptide
(Gr. *polys,* many + *peptin,* to digest) amino acids joined together by peptide bonds into long chains; a protein consists of one or more polypeptides

storage molecule in animals. **Cellulose** and **chitin** (KYE-tin) are structural polysaccharides that give form and rigidity to plants and insects, respectively.

Proteins

The complexities of our bodies and the rich diversity of life in general—the millions of organisms of different textures, colors, and life styles—depend on different types of proteins in different types of cells. Proteins come in such a wide variety of forms (at least 10 to 100 million different kinds in the spectrum of the earth's organisms) that they can easily explain the myriad shapes and functions of specific cells and whole living things.

Proteins have many functions. They can:

- form structural parts of cells (e.g., the contractile machinery in a muscle cell)

- control cell processes (e.g., the steps involved in metabolism)

- act as messengers that move through fluids (e.g., hormones)

- carry other substances (e.g., the hemoglobin in red blood cells)

- protect animals from disease (e.g., antibodies)

- speed life processes (e.g., enzymes), and

- act as receptors on cell surfaces (e.g., the receptors for HIV).

Protein Structure: An Overview

The overall shape of a protein determines its function. A protein region shaped like a spiral staircase is called an **alpha-helix** and provides rigidity. A **pleated sheet** region (often represented by a broad flat arrow) gives proteins flat, box-like sides. The two types of regions within the protein ribbons are connected by **disordered loops**, which are usually gently curved. The helix, sheet, and loop regions occur in specific positions along the length of the protein and help provide each protein's unique overall shape.

Amino Acids: Building Blocks of Proteins

The long ribbon of a protein not only has coiled, looped, and pleated regions, but it can also be represented in finer detail as beads on a string, where each bead is an **amino acid** with the general structure shown in Figure 2.7a and b.

Proteins consist of hundreds of amino acids strung together. A single amino acid consists of an amino part, an acid part, and a side chain. The side chains of the 20 amino acids commonly found in proteins differ in chemical composition. Different side chains have different properties; for example, some attract water, some repel water, some are acidic, and some are basic.

Each amino acid "bead" links to the next one by means of covalent bonds called **peptide bonds**. The *order* of the beads is distinctive in each protein and is determined by the organism's genes.

Just as simple sugar units are joined into a polymer called a polysaccharide, amino acid subunits are joined into a polymer called a **polypeptide** (Fig. 2.7c).

The 20 types of amino acids with their different side chains function as subunits in a biological alphabet, forming complex proteins much as the 26 letters of our alphabet can form a nearly infinite array of words. And just as the order of letters in a word determines the word's meaning, the identity of a protein—its shape, properties, and functions—depends on the exact order of its amino acid "letters." Biologists refer to the order of these letters as the protein's primary structure. They call the specific helical portions, sheets, and loops we discussed earlier the protein's secondary structure. A protein's tertiary structure is the particular way these helices, sheets, loops, and intervening parts pack together into a three-dimensional ball like the HIV matrix protein or the long, fibrous shape of the keratin protein. Some proteins consist of more than one amino acid chain—the oxygen-carrying protein in your blood, hemoglobin, is an example—and the protein's quaternary structure is the way these chains pack together. Within the human body, there are over 50,000 different proteins, each with a unique shape. In the living world collectively, there are tens of millions of unique sequences of amino acids, giving rise to an enormous array of specific proteins that make possible life's amazing diversity.

To some, the chemistry of biological molecules and structures may seem detached from the living world they inhabit, but in fact, it's actually the basis for life.

1. The variable side chains (functional groups) on each of the 20 different amino acids found in proteins determine how those amino acid "beads" behave within their protein chains.
2. The order of the amino acid beads determines the shape of the overall protein molecule.
3. The overall shape of the protein molecule determines its function in the organism.
4. Collectively, the functions of an organism's proteins determine what the organism looks like and how it lives.

For an HIV particle, amino acid properties and sequences determine the shape of the matrix protein, which in turn helps strengthen the virus particle. Other proteins with their own sequences and shapes protect the virus's genetic instructions and help make new copies that will infect additional cells and eventually destroy a patient's immune system. The virus contains not just protein but another category of biological molecules—lipids. So let's look at that type next.

Lipids

The smooth surface of the HIV "basketball"—beneath the protein "beads" with their fuzzy carbohydrate extensions—is made of lipid molecules. Lipids are a class of biological molecules that tend not to dissolve in water. Thus they can keep water from rushing into cells and diluting their contents.

Lipids can serve as energy-storage molecules in plants and animals, just as carbohydrates do. Solid storage molecules are **fats**. Liquid storage molecules are oils. **Waxes** are semisolid types of lipids. Another important class of lipids, the **steroids**, includes certain vitamins, some hormones, and cholesterol.

fat
an energy storage molecule that contains a glycerol bonded to three fatty acids; fats in the liquid state are known as oils

wax
a sticky, solid, waterproof lipid that forms the comb of bees and waterproofing of plant leaves .

steroid
(Gr. *stereos,* solid + L. *oi,* having the form of + *oleum,* oil) a major class of lipids based on a 4-carbon-atom ring system and often a hydrocarbon tail; cholesterol and sex hormones are steroids

nucleic acid
a polymer of nucleotides, e.g., DNA and RNA

Nucleic Acids and Nucleotides

The fourth major class of biological molecules, the **nucleic acids,** include DNA and RNA, which carry the chemical "code of life" and transmit genetic information from one generation to the next (Fig. 2.8a,b). The

Figure 2.7
The Overall Shape of a Protein and Amino Acids

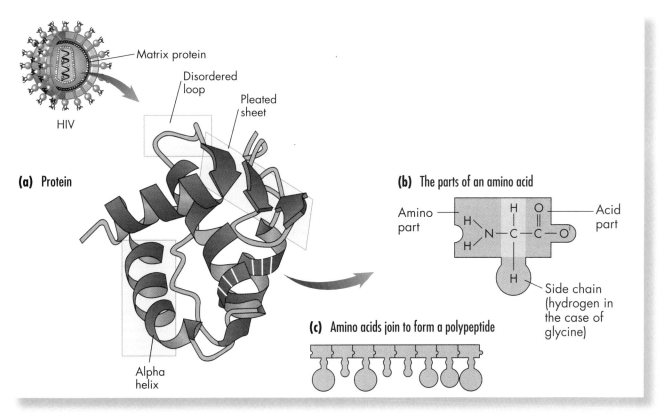

HIV

(a) Protein

Matrix protein

Disordered loop

Pleated sheet

Alpha helix

(b) The parts of an amino acid

Amino part

Acid part

Side chain (hydrogen in the case of glycine)

(c) Amino acids join to form a polypeptide

RNA (ribonucleic acid)
a nucleic acid similar to DNA except that it is generally single-stranded and contains the sugar ribose and the base uracil replaces thymine

DNA (deoxyribo-nucleic acid)
the twisting, ladderlike molecule that stores genetic information in cells and transmits it during reproduction; DNA consists of two very long strands of alternating sugar and phosphate groups that form a double helix; each "rung" of the ladder is a base (either adenine, guanine, cytosine, or thymine) that extends from the sugar and bonds with a base from the other strand; genes are made of DNA

reverse transcriptase
the enzyme that facilitates "reverse" transcription of RNA to DNA

information necessary for building new HIV particles lies in the viral RNA molecule.

Nucleic Acids: Molecules of Information Storage and Processing

Ribonucleic acid, or RNA, is present in living cells and helps in the processing and use of the information stored in deoxyribonucleic acid, or DNA, which stores hereditary information in all living cells and most types of viruses. (Chapter 6 covers RNA and DNA in detail; here we'll just explore enough to understand the basic story of HIV, AIDS, and the chemistry of living cells.)

Nucleic Acids and HIV Infection

When a person is exposed to HIV, viral RNA molecules enter his blood cells and are copied into molecules of DNA (see Chapter 6). This so-called reverse transcription of RNA to DNA was facilitated by the enzyme reverse transcriptase. (The process is called "reverse" because in living cells, genetic information is copied from DNA to RNA, not RNA to DNA.)

The RNA molecule in an HIV particle carries three major genes, laid out one after the other. Each gene provides all the instructions for making a single type of protein. The three proteins initially made are then chopped into the smaller proteins that make up the virus. Chapter 6 explains how nucleic acids store the instructions for making proteins. For now, just remember that your DNA, by determining the shape of your proteins, has played a central role in shaping the way you look and the way your body functions, and the same is true for all plants, animals, and other living organisms.

You've seen how atoms join to form biological molecules and how an HIV particle is built of all four kinds. But why do we keep insisting that HIV is nonliving, while cells are alive? What makes a cell a cell and a virus . . . different?

LO⁶ What Is a Living Cell, and What Makes HIV a Nonliving Enemy?

What makes cells alive and susceptible to being killed by HIV particles, which themselves are not alive and are so very difficult to fight? Answering this requires an explanation of cells—including those found in animals, plants, and single-celled organisms like bacteria and protozoa—as well as a discussion of viruses. How big are both entities? What are their parts? How do they function? Size is a good place to start, and that leads us to the story's 17th-century beginnings.

The Discovery of Cells

More than 300 years ago, English scientist Robert Hooke focused one of the very earliest microscopes on some everyday objects from his home: the point of a pin, the surface of a nettle leaf, and the body of a flea. Hooke was astonished by the fine detail he could make out in this new, previously unseen world. When Hooke looked at a thin slice of cork through his microscope, he saw what he called "cells," which reminded him of the small rooms inhabited by monks.

Hooke was apparently the first person to publicize seeing cells, but he could not fully define what he was observing. Modern biologists know that a *cell* is the smallest entity completely surrounded by a membrane and capable of reproducing itself independent of other cells. It is also the smallest unit dis-

Figure 2.8
Nucleic Acids and Nucleotides

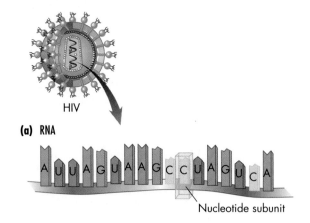

HIV

(a) RNA

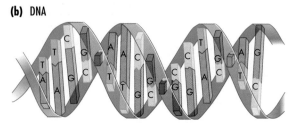

A U U A G U A A G C C U A G U C A

Nucleotide subunit

(b) DNA

playing all the properties of life listed in Chapter 1, including the orderly chemical activities of metabolism, the capacity of self-propelled motion, the ability to reproduce and develop, and the potential to evolve over many generations.

Cells versus Viruses

Biologists have found that cells have three fundamental parts:

1. A surface envelope of lipid and protein (a *plasma membrane*) that controls the passage of materials into and out of the cell.
2. A central genetic region that controls all the cell's functions and stores DNA, the repository of the cell's hereditary information.
3. A gel-like substance (called *cytoplasm*) that fills the cell between the surface envelope and the genetic storage region, and surrounds small uniquely structured compartments called *organelles* (see Chapter 1) that carry out specialized functions.

Given these principles, how does a virus like HIV differ from a cell and why is it nonliving rather than living? HIV has a membrane made up of lipid and protein, and it has a central genetic region that contains RNA rather than DNA. Both of these features embody the life characteristic of order. (In many viruses, the genes are DNA.) HIV can also evolve or change and adapt over time; recall that HIV has evolved resistance to some drugs.

However, as we saw earlier, viruses lack metabolism, responsiveness, and independent reproduction. HIV, for example, is not filled with cytoplasm, and this material is integrally involved in a living cell's ability to carry out metabolic functions such as harvesting energy, generating self-powered movement, and building proteins. Virus particles are tiny compared to the living cell. There's simply not enough space inside a virus for the machinery of the cytoplasm that gives cells their capacity for independent life, including metabolism, motion, and reproduction. Instead, viruses have evolved to use a cell's machinery. Viruses in fact may once have been complete cells that lost elements and became parasites on true cells.

Cell Size: An Import-Export Problem

Even though a cell is thousands of times bigger than an HIV particle, cells are still minuscule. The average cell in your body is just one-fifth the thickness of the paper in this book. Why are cells so small? The answer is that cells have an import-export problem based on the physical relationship between surface area and volume.

A cell's active cytoplasm needs to take in materials to fuel activities and build cell parts, and it needs to get rid of wastes it produces as by-products—in general, the more cytoplasm, the more materials and wastes. A cell imports materials and exports wastes across its plasma membrane. The greater the surface area of this plasma membrane, the more rapidly the cell exchanges substances with its environment. When a cell increases in size, its volume increases more rapidly than its surface area, and its import-export needs outstrip its ability to exchange these items with the surroundings. If a cell got much larger than a certain typical size (for a bacterium, under 10 micrometers; for an animal cell, 5 to 30 micrometers; for a plant cell, 35 to 80 micrometers), it couldn't meet its material and waste needs quickly enough to survive. (Note that the abbreviation μm is frequently used for a micrometer, one millionth of a meter.) This is why an elephant's liver is hundreds of times bigger than a mouse's liver, but its *cells* are the same size. There are just millions more of them.

Viruses have one solution to this surface-to-volume problem and cells have others. Since viruses don't metabolize, particles like HIV don't have to "worry" about their surface-to-volume ratio; living cells import, export, and stockpile all their needed materials, and the viruses simply have to enter and use it. This strategy clearly wouldn't work for most living cells, and so one primary means of solving their surface-to-volume problem is through altered cell shape or contents. A long, thin cell, such as a nerve cell that reaches from a giraffe's spine down to its hoof, can have the same volume as a round or cube-shaped cell but a greatly expanded surface area.

The Cell Theory

Because cells are so small, large organisms such as people and trees consist of trillions of cells. About 160 years ago, biologists were trying to understand how cells could be so small and yet how billions of them could function in a coordinated way inside a plant or animal organ. Their efforts resulted in the cell theory, which illuminated the cell's significance to life for all of us who came later. According to the cell theory:

1. All living things are made up of one or more cells.

For an analogy to the surface-area-to-volume problem, think of a pile of wet laundry. If left in a heap, this soggy pile takes a long time to dry because its exposed surface area is small compared with its volume. But if you hang the items on a line to dry, the surface area is large, while the volume is unchanged, and the laundry can dry much faster.

2. Cells are the basic living units within organisms, and the chemical reactions of life take place within cells.

3. All cells arise from pre-existing cells.

What makes these simple statements so important? First, there are no living organisms made up of anything other than cells. Organisms such as bacteria consist of just one cell, while people and trees contain trillions, but the living subunits are always still cells. Viruses are considered particles not cells, because they don't carry on their own energy metabolism and can't reproduce independently.

Second, cells are the basic units of life because the individual components that make up cells lack the complete properties of life. For example, if you take the nucleus out of a cell, it can't carry out life functions or replicate on its own anymore.

Third, new cells arise today only from preexisting cells that divided into daughter cells. Each cell in your body can be traced back to a single fertilized egg cell generated when your mother's egg cell fused with your father's sperm cell. These sperm and egg, in turn, were produced by other cells in your parents' bodies; each of your parents arose from a single fertilized egg cell produced by your grandparents, and so on back in time. Virus particles do not arise from the division of a pre-existing particle into two new particles. The end of this chapter explores not only how new HIV particles are assembled from parts like the manufacture of cars on an assembly line, but also, why a living cell is required for the assembly.

Cell Types in Life's Kingdoms and Domains

Biologists have never found a cell they can't assign to just one of two basic types: prokaryotic or eukaryotic.

A cell's most obvious distinguishing feature is the presence or absence of a cell nucleus. **Eukaryotic cells** (*eu* = true *karyo* = nucleus) contain a prominent, roughly spherical, membrane-enclosed body called the nucleus, which houses DNA, the cell's hereditary material. In contrast, in **prokaryotic cells** (*pro* = before *karyo* = nucleus) the DNA is loose in the cell's interior and not separated from the rest of the cell's contents by a membrane (Fig. 2.9). An organism made up of a prokaryotic cell is called a **prokaryote**; an organism made up of one or more eukaryotic cells is called a **eukaryote**.

Our own cells are eukaryotic and so we humans are eukaryotes, belonging to the domain Eucarya (see Chapter 1). So are all the members of the animal and plant kingdoms, the mushrooms and other fungi, and the algae and other protists. The two remaining domains of life, the Eubacteria (also called simply Bacteria) and Archaea, contain thousands of species in which each individual is made up of a single prokaryotic cell lacking a cell nucleus. Because HIV and other viruses are not cells, they're neither prokaryotic nor eukaryotic.

eukaryotic cell
a cell whose DNA is enclosed in a nucleus and associated with proteins; contains membrane-bound organelles

prokaryotic cell
a cell in which the DNA is loose in the cell; eubacterial and archaebacterial cells are prokaryotic; prokaryotic cells generally have no internal membranous organelles and evolved earlier than eukaryotic cells

prokaryote
an organism made up of a prokaryotic cell

eukaryote
an organism made up of one or more eukaryotic cells

Prokaryotic Cells

Prokaryotes are the smallest cells, and some bacteria are no more than 0.2 µm in length, just twice as big as an HIV particle. (For comparison, the thickness of this page is about 100 µm.) Prokaryotes exploit environments not open to eukaryotes, with their more complex cells. Some prokaryotes, for example, thrive in the boiling waters of hot springs.

Eukaryotic Cells

Because they house nuclei and other compartments or organelles that perform specific tasks, eukaryotic cells are generally much larger than prokaryotic cells. An average-sized animal cell (Fig. 2.10a on the next page) is about 20 µm in length—about five animal cells could be lined up across the thickness of a sheet of paper. A typical plant cell (Fig. 2.10b) (also a eukaryote) is a bit larger at about 35 µm across.

LO⁷ What Are the Parts of the Cell, and How Does HIV Sabotage Them?

If HIV is not a cell and is not alive, how can it destroy white blood cells and cause the other devastating consequences of AIDS? More specifically, how can HIV take over the various organelles inside the cell and replicate more deadly particles of itself? This section gives the answers by following the way HIV infects a cell, step by step, cell part by cell part. This will serve as an introductory tour of the cell and how it functions, while at the same time explaining the dangers of HIV and AIDS.

HIV Infection and the Cell Surface

HIV enters a cell by injecting its contents through the cell surface and into the cell's interior. An animal cell contains many organelles, including those responsible for its metabolism and reproduction (Fig. 2.10a). But we'll start our tour of the eukaryotic cell at the cell's outer envelope, then see how HIV overcomes a component of that protective barrier to gain entry.

Crossing Plasma Membranes

As a flexible fatty boundary studded with proteins and carbohydrates, the cell's plasma membrane tends to keep the watery cell contents in and moisture,

Figure 2.9

HIV, Prokaryotic Cells, and Eukaryotic Cells Compared

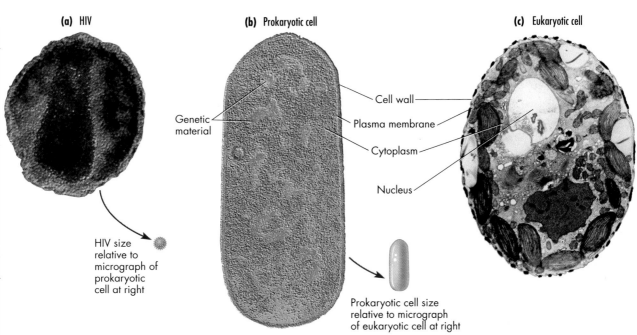

(a) HIV

(b) Prokaryotic cell

(c) Eukaryotic cell

Genetic material

HIV size relative to micrograph of prokaryotic cell at right

Prokaryotic cell size relative to micrograph of eukaryotic cell at right

Cell wall

Plasma membrane

Cytoplasm

Nucleus

Figure 2.10
Generalized Animal and Plant Cells

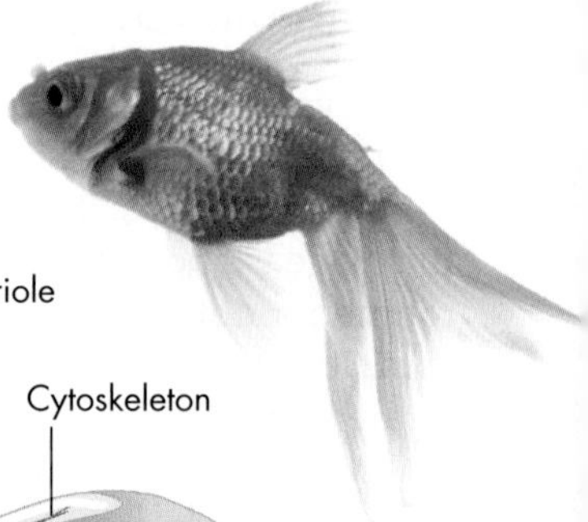

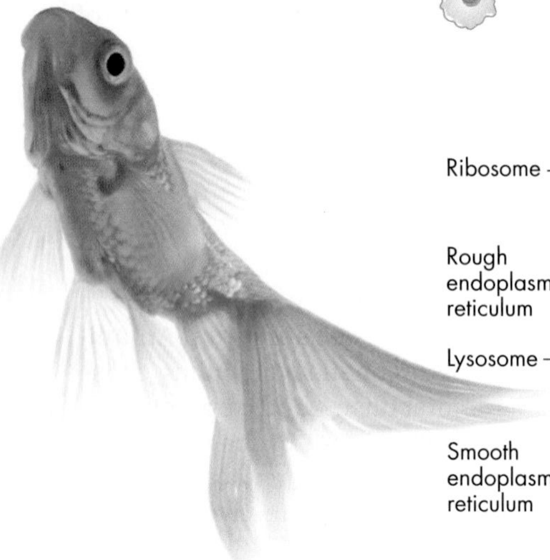

(a) Animal cell

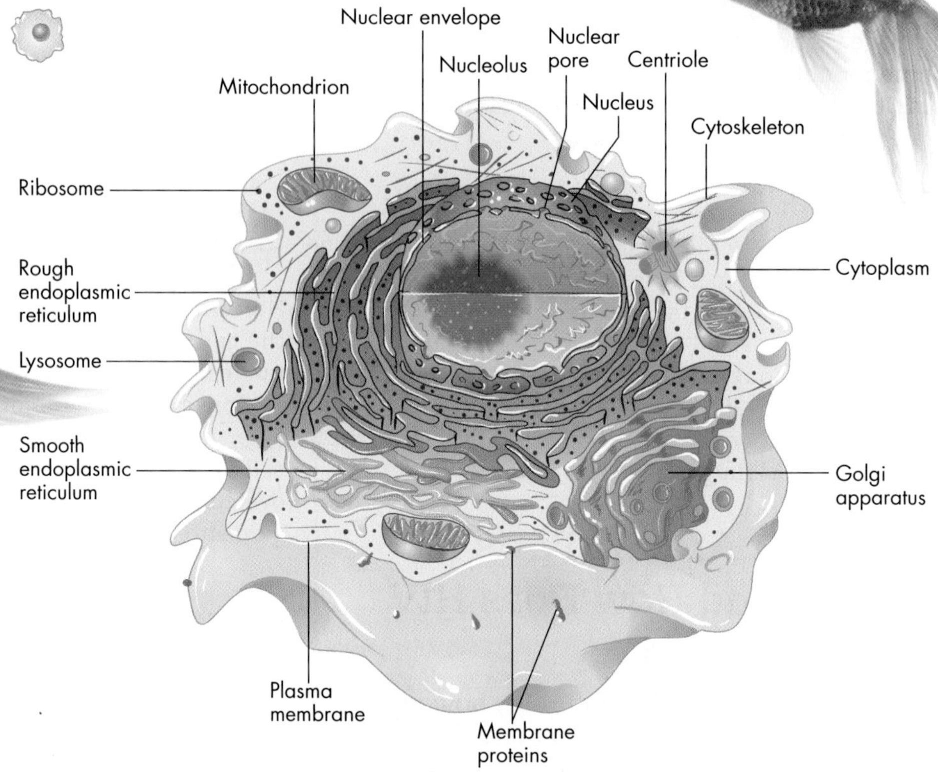

Mitochondrion

Nuclear envelope

Nucleolus

Nuclear pore

Nucleus

Centriole

Cytoskeleton

Ribosome

Rough endoplasmic reticulum

Cytoplasm

Lysosome

Smooth endoplasmic reticulum

Golgi apparatus

Plasma membrane

Membrane proteins

© JOHANNA GOODYEAR/ISTOCKPHOTO.COM

(b) Plant cell

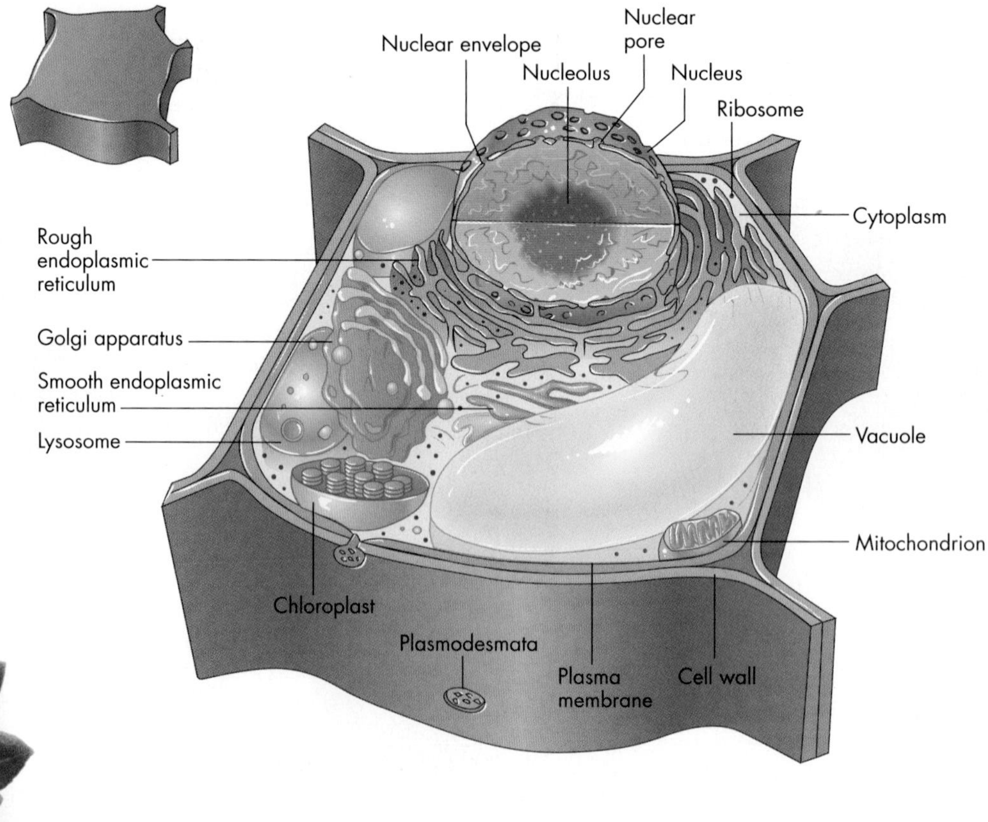

Nuclear envelope

Nuclear pore

Nucleolus

Nucleus

Ribosome

Rough endoplasmic reticulum

Cytoplasm

Golgi apparatus

Smooth endoplasmic reticulum

Lysosome

Vacuole

Chloroplast

Mitochondrion

Plasmodesmata

Plasma membrane

Cell wall

© DANE WIRTZFELD/ISTOCKPHOTO.COM

chemicals, and other elements of the external environment out (Fig. 2.11a on the next page). Recall, though, that nutrients must pass into cells and waste products must pass out. To be infective, HIV and other viruses must gain entry to the cell. The plasma membrane is *selectively permeable*, that is, permeable (penetrable) to certain substances but not all. So what accounts for the selectivity that allows nutrients, wastes, and viruses to pass through plasma membranes while most other substances are barred?

Fat-Soluble and Water-Soluble Molecules

Passage through plasma membranes depends first on size. Some very small inorganic molecules such as oxygen, carbon dioxide, and water pass through plasma membranes by simple diffusion—they move from a region of high concentration to one of low concentration (Fig. 2.11b).

Organic molecules tend to be larger, so instead of diffusing, they pass into cells in two other ways, depending on whether they dissolve in fat or water. Some organic substances are fat-soluble: They can dissolve in fats, and thus they can pass directly through the fatty plasma membrane.

Most organic molecules, however, are water-soluble, including nutrients such as sugars and amino acids, and cellular wastes such as urea. A plasma membrane made of pure lipid molecules (fat or oil) would act like a perfect raincoat, blocking out all water-soluble materials and eventually starving or poisoning the cell. Instead, small water-soluble organic compounds enter the cell by passing through proteins floating in the plasma membrane. Some membrane proteins allow only particular sugars, ions, or amino acids to pass, often through a channel in the protein. If the protein helps the substance pass down its concentration gradient without the expenditure of energy, we call the process facilitated diffusion (Fig. 2.11c). If a substance is too large to simply diffuse through the membrane or slip through a channel, the cell may have to expend energy to pump materials in or out by means of a process called active transport (Fig. 2.11d).

Large Materials

A cell's outer membrane obviously has lots of "gates" and lots of traffic in and out. Really large materials, though, such as virus particles and large protein molecules usually can't get through those gates. Often, soldiers of the body's immune defense system—for example, large, mobile blood cells—engulf debris left over from a dying cell or surround whole parasites such as bacteria or viruses within pockets of the cell membrane. The engulfment of solid material is called phagocytosis (FAJ-oh-sigh-toh-sis) (literally "cell eating"; see Fig. 2.12a on page 37). Jay Levy was the first scientist to show that these large cells or phagocytes can themselves be infected by HIV.

Cells can move substances in across the plasma membrane by the import process of endocytosis (of which phagocytosis is one type) or out across the plasma membrane via the export process of exocytosis (Fig. 2.12b). Some cells discharge wastes this way or secrete proteins, such as hormones or digestive enzymes, into the bloodstream or into a food-digesting organ like the stomach or small intestine.

How HIV Gets into a Cell

Recall that HIV looks like a basketball studded with beads and that the skin of the "basketball" is made of lipids while the beads are a type of envelope protein. To explain in a simplified way the lipid membrane surrounding the HIV particle is suddenly able to fuse with the lipid membrane of a white blood cell like two soap bubbles converging. The contents of the HIV particle can then spill into the cell and infect it.

Once the HIV membrane has fused with the cell membrane, the virus releases its genetic material, RNA. This gets copied into the cell's own genetic language, DNA, and this new viral DNA enters the cell's central repository of genetic information, the nucleus. We'll take a closer look at this process as we examine the nucleus.

The Nucleus

When you look through a microscope at a typical animal or plant cell, often the most conspicuous organelle you will see is the nucleus (Fig. 2.10). This roughly spherical structure contains genetic information that controls most of the cell's activities. Just as an

---

diffusion
(L. *diffundere,* to pour out) the tendency of a substance to move from an area of high concentration to an area of low concentration

facilitated diffusion
a type of transport in which a protein helps a substance pass across a cell membrane down its concentration gradient without energy expenditure by the cell

active transport
movement of substances against a concentration gradient requiring the expenditure of energy by the cell

phagocytosis
the type of endocytosis through which a cell takes in food particles

phagocyte
a specialized scavenger cell that devours debris

endocytosis
the process by which a cell membrane invaginates and forms a pocket around a cluster of molecules; this pocket pinches off and forms a vesicle that transports the molecules into the cell

exocytosis
the process by which substances are moved out of a cell by cytoplasmic vesicles that merge with the plasma membrane

nucleus
the membrane-enclosed region of a eukaryotic cell that contains the cell's DNA

Figure 2.11

The Plasma Membrane and Movement of Molecules Into and Out of Cells

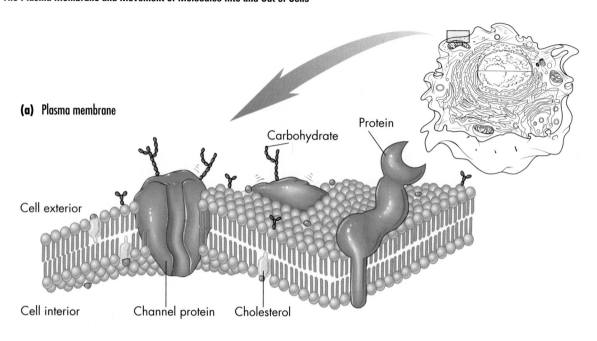

(a) Plasma membrane

Carbohydrate

Protein

Cell exterior

Cell interior

Channel protein

Cholesterol

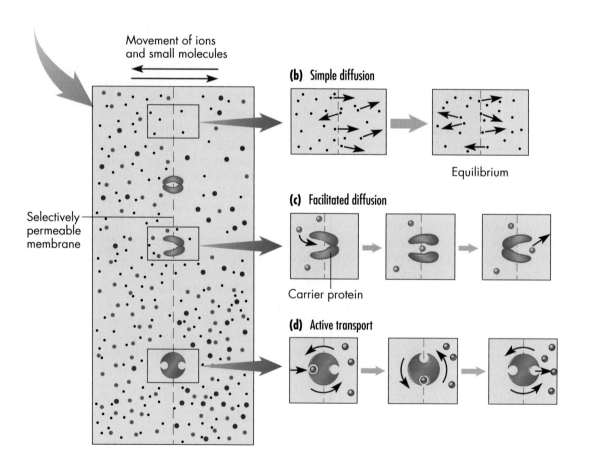

Movement of ions
and small molecules

(b) Simple diffusion

Equilibrium

Selectively
permeable
membrane

(c) Facilitated diffusion

Carrier protein

(d) Active transport

Figure 2.12
Cell Engulfing Large Materials

(a) A white blood cell engulfs a yeast cell

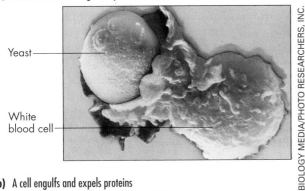

Yeast

White
blood cell

© BIOLOGY MEDIA/PHOTO RESEARCHERS, INC.

(b) A cell engulfs and expels proteins

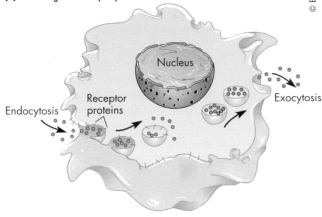

Nucleus

Endocytosis — Receptor proteins — Exocytosis

enemy tries to take over an opposing army's central command post, HIV must get into the nucleus if it's going to take over the cell's activities and commandeer them for its own purpose: making new virus particles.

Information Flow in the Nucleus

In the nucleus of all eukaryotic cells the information in DNA is copied into RNA, the RNA then moves out of the nucleus into the cytoplasm, and its information is used to make proteins, which carry out the work of the cell. This flow of information can be diagrammed:

> DNA → RNA → Protein

We've said that when HIV enters the cell, its RNA is copied into DNA and this viral DNA enters the cell nucleus. Once inside, however, and once integrated into the cell's chromosomes, it follows the DNA→RNA information flow characteristic of healthy, uninfected cells. Thus new viral RNA is once again made and moves back out of the nucleus into the watery cytoplasm to begin diverting the cell to act as an HIV-manufacturing factory. This takeover involves a number of cell organelles.

Cytoplasm and Organelles

All living cells are filled with cytoplasm, a semifluid, highly organized pool of raw materials and fluid in which the cell's internal organelles are suspended. Cytoplasm is about 70 percent water, 20 percent protein molecules, and 10 percent carbohydrate, lipid, and other types of molecules. An average cell contains 10 billion or so protein molecules of about 10,000 different kinds! Many of these proteins are highly active *enzymes,* substances that speed biochemical reactions, while others are structural proteins that assemble into various cell parts. Suspended in the cytoplasm are numerous kinds of organelles—many of which HIV uses for its own ends.

Ribosomes

In order for new virus particles to form inside a cell, HIV needs new proteins. So it usurps the cell's protein-sythesizing machinery, the ribosomes. Thousands of ribosomes are embedded throughout the cell's cytoplasm. There are no functional ribosomes inside the nucleus, so protein building occurs only in the cytoplasm. We'll see more about how HIV takes over ribosomes shortly.

Rough Endoplasmic Reticulum

Most of a cell's ribosomes float freely in the cytoplasm, but some are attached to flattened membranous sacs within the cell—the endoplasmic reticulum, or ER (*endo* = inside; *plasmic* = cell; reticulum = network) (Fig. 2.13 on the next page). Part of the endoplasmic reticulum looks rough because it is so heavily studded with ribosomes; biologists call this the rough ER. This rough region makes many proteins that wind up being exported from the cell. For example, the rough ER helps produce the enzymes that digest most of the foods you eat. Since HIV takes over the rough ER, tracing how the membranous network makes and transports viral protein is a good way to see how the ER functions.

In a white blood cell infected with HIV, viral RNA made inside the nucleus attaches to floating ribosomes and then docks with the rough ER (Fig. 2.13, Step ①). Next, the ribosomes make some of HIV's bead-shaped proteins, which enter the interior

ribosome
a structure in the cell that provides a site for protein synthesis; ribosomes may lie freely in the cell or attach to the membranes of the endoplasmic reticulum

endoplasmic reticulum (ER)
a system of membranous tubes, channels, and sacs that forms compartments within the cytoplasm of eukaryotic cells; functions in lipid synthesis and in the manufacture of proteins destined for secretion from the cell

Golgi apparatus
in eukaryotic cells, a collection of flat sacs that process proteins for export from the cell or for shunting to different parts of the cell

smooth ER
the part of the endoplasmic reticulum folded into smooth sheets and tubules, containing no ribosomes; synthesizes lipids and detoxifies poisons

cavity of the rough ER (Step ②). Eventually, the proteins enter transport vesicles—little membranous bubbles that pinch off from the rough ER (Step ③). Most of these transport vesicles then fuse with membranes of another cell organelle, the Golgi apparatus (Step ④).

Golgi Apparatus

The Golgi apparatus (GOAL-gee) is a series of flattened membranous sacs resem-

Figure 2.13

The Endoplasmic Reticulum and the Golgi Apparatus

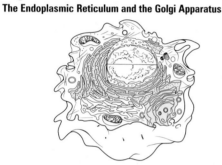

bling a pile of empty hot-water bottles. Some cells have just one Golgi apparatus, but others may have hundreds.

The Golgi apparatus acts like a traffic cop, directing different proteins to different parts of the cell, where they perform their functions. For example, it sends vesicles carrying the new HIV proteins to the cell surface, where they fuse with the cell's plasma membrane (Step ⑥). The HIV proteins then embed in the cell's membrane, so that the infected cell's surface now has the bead-studded appearance that usually characterizes an HIV particle (Step ⑦). Usually, when other proteins reach the cell surface, they just diffuse away and enter the bloodstream. The HIV proteins have their "tails" stuck into the cell membrane, so when they move to the surface, they remain embedded.

Smooth ER

Another part of the endoplasmic reticulum, the **smooth ER**, is folded into smooth tubes and small sacs. Smooth ER makes the lipids that line up side-by-side in cell membranes. When commandeered, they also make the HIV particle's lipid "basketball" or envelope. Smooth ER makes other familiar lipids, as well, including cholesterol, and the steroid sex

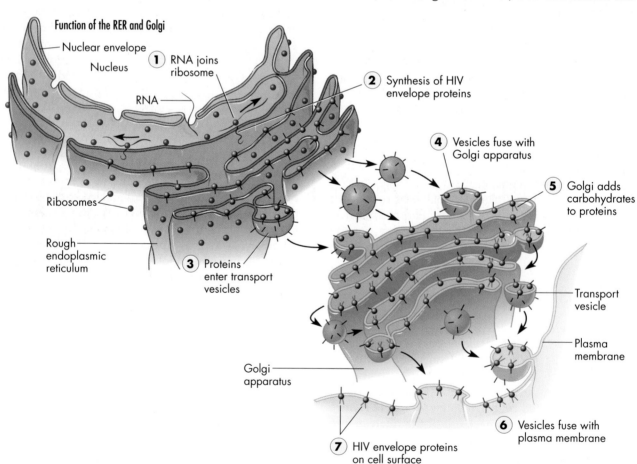

Function of the RER and Golgi

- Nuclear envelope
- Nucleus
- RNA
- Ribosomes
- Rough endoplasmic reticulum

① RNA joins ribosome
② Synthesis of HIV envelope proteins
③ Proteins enter transport vesicles
④ Vesicles fuse with Golgi apparatus
⑤ Golgi adds carbohydrates to proteins
⑥ Vesicles fuse with plasma membrane
⑦ HIV envelope proteins on cell surface

- Golgi apparatus
- Transport vesicle
- Plasma membrane

hormones estrogen and testosterone. Smooth ER in liver cells is especially active at detoxifying harmful lipids, making them more water soluble so that they can eventually be excreted in the urine.

Lysosomes: The Cell's Recyclers

Lysosomes are tiny spherical bags of powerful digestive enzymes that can digest invading bacteria or debris the cell has engulfed, or cell parts that have worn out internally. Digestive enzymes in the lysosome generally break down the refuse into smaller molecules, which then reenter the cytoplasm for reuse by the cell.

Cytoskeleton

The cytoskeleton is a structure of thin protein fibers forming a lattice throughout the cytoplasm, suspending the organelles and allowing cell parts to move. Protein fibers in the cytoskeleton also help maintain a cell's shape and transport cell organelles.

When cells divide in two, they use another cytoskeleton organelle called the centriole (see Fig. 2.10). Pairs of these short rod-shaped organelles organize certain cytoskeletal fibers that guide the separation and movement of chromosomes into the two new cells.

Mitochondria: Harvesters of Energy

Mitochondria (sing., mitochondrion) are cellular organelles that harvest energy from food by breaking down carbon-containing molecules and that release energy packets, or ATP. In this way mitochondria provide chemical fuel for cellular activities such as building proteins, copying DNA, and moving cells and cell parts.

Mitochondria have their own DNA and make some of their component proteins on their own ribosomes. The cell's DNA encodes the rest. They can also divide in half independently of the cell's normal division cycle.

The HIV drug AZT blocks the copying enzyme that translates HIV's RNA genes into DNA. Experiments show that AZT can also inhibit the enzyme that copies mitochondrial DNA before the organelle divides. This blockage slows HIV replication but also slows mitochondrial DNA. This, in turn, may interfere with the way the energy organelles function and lead to the weakness and fatigue of AIDS patients taking AZT.

Specialized Organelles

So far, all the cell structures we've talked about can be found in human cells and in most other eukaryotic cells, and are commandeered by HIV and contribute to AIDS. No exploration of cell biology would be complete, however, without examining a few specialized organelles for movement and storage found only in certain cell types. (These specialized organelles play no known role in HIV or AIDS.)

Organelles of Cell Movement. For some mobile cells throughout the kingdoms of life, movement is made possible by propelling extensions of the cytoskeleton. A whiplike organelle called a flagellum (Latin, small whip; pl., *flagella*) extends from the cell surface and pulls or pushes the cell through a liquid medium. Many kinds of sperm rely on propulsion by flagella.

Certain single-celled protists have thousands of projections called *cilia* (Latin, eyelashes; sing., *cilium*) that look and act much like flagella. Cilia beat in concert like the oars of a medieval galley ship, allowing the cell to swim quickly. In cells that line the human breathing passages, cilia sweep dust particles out toward the mouth and nose, where they are eventually expelled in mucus or swallowed.

Links between Cells. Most animal cells are attached to neighboring cells by links called *intercellular junctions,* which help weld cells together into functional tissues and organs (Fig. 2.14 on the next page). These junctions also allow free communication between cells and the coordination of cells in tissues and organs. Some linkages allow materials to flow between cells; others prevent leaks between cells and help organs like the urinary bladder hold fluid.

Junctions at the base of many cells attach fibrous proteins or an extracellular matrix that surround and support the cell and glue it to adjacent cells.

lysosome
spherical membrane-bound vesicles within the cell containing digestive (hydrolytic) enzymes that are released when the lysosome is ruptured; important in recycling worn-out mitochondria and other cell debris

cytoskeleton
found in the cells of eukaryotes, an internal framework of microtubules, microfilaments, and intermediate filaments that supports and moves the cell and its organelles

centriole
pairs of short, rod-shaped organelles that organize the cytoskeletal fibers called microtubules into scaffolds; these intracellular frameworks help maintain cell shape and move chromosomes during cell division

mitochondrion
(pl. mitochondria) organelle in eukaryotic cells that provides energy that fuels the cell's activities; mitochondria are the sites of oxidative respiration; almost all of the ATP of nonphotosynthetic eukaryotic cells is produced in the mitochondria

flagellum
(pl. flagella) long whiplike organelle protruding from the surface of the cell that either propels the cell, acting as a locomotory device, or moves fluids past the cell, becoming a feeding apparatus

extracellular matrix
a meshwork of secreted molecules that act as a scaffold and a glue that anchors cells within multicellular organisms

plastid
an organelle found in plants and some protozoa that harvests solar energy and produces or stores carbohydrates or pigments

vacuole
large fluid-filled sac inside cells surrounded by a single membrane; in plant cells, it is important for maintaining cell shape

cell wall
a fairly rigid structure that encloses some protists, and all prokaryotic, fungal, and plant cells

plasmodesmata
specialized junctions between plant cells that facilitate cell-to-cell communication

The most common of these fibrous proteins is collagen, which constitute 25 percent of all the protein in a typical mammal, including most of the material in tendons, the cables that enable muscles to move bones.

Specialized Organelles in Plant Cells. Some special organelles account for the successful stationary, light-harvesting lifestyle of plants.

Plastids are oval organelles surrounded by a double-layered membrane. They harvest solar energy, manufacture nutrient molecules, and store materials. *Chloroplasts* are one type of plastid that trap the energy of sunlight in a chemical form—generally, sugar molecules—in the process of photosynthesis (see details in Chapter 3). All animals and fungi, as well as most of Earth's other organisms, depend on photosynthesis—directly or indirectly—to supply the nutrients, materials, and energy compounds they need for survival.

Chloroplasts share several features with mitochondria, an organelle that plant cells also have. Both have an outer membrane and a convoluted inner membrane (see Fig. 2.10b). Both organelles house their own DNA molecules and make some

of their own proteins. A major difference, though, is that the convoluted innermost set of chloroplast membranes contains the green, light-absorbing pigment *chlorophyll*.

Many plant cells have large fluid-filled sacs in the center called vacuoles. Plant vacuoles contain water and nutrients; they have a single surrounding membrane and can fill up to 95 percent of the total cell volume. That's a lot of space, and in fact, taking up space is the vacuole's main role. Essentially a bag of water that fills up a plant cell, the vacuole presses a small amount of cytoplasm and all the cell's organelles into a thin layer with a favorable surface-to-volume ratio (see Figure 2.10b). Full vacuoles keep plant cells plump and give firm shape to the leaves, stems, and other structures.

Cell walls surround most plant cells just outside the plant cell's plasma membrane. Cell walls are composed largely of cellulose. They remain stretchable and flexible until the cell has stopped growing and has begun to mature, then they harden. The porous wall allows water, gases, and some solid materials to pass through to the plasma membrane, and specialized junctions between plant cells called plasmodesmata facilitate cell-to-cell communication (Fig. 2.10b). If you are reading this book at a wooden desk, your work is being supported by thickened, dead cell walls—all that remains of a once-living tree.

LO⁸ How Does HIV Complete Its Infective Cycle?

Our complete tour of cell parts puts us in position to return to HIV and understand its whole cycle of infection; how it involves the biological molecules and cell parts we discussed in this chapter; how it harms a patient; and how the drugs called protease inhibitors are helping many people with AIDS.

We've already seen:

- How HIV works its way into the cell (Fig. 2.15 Step ①).

- How the viral RNA is copied onto DNA (Step ②).

- How that DNA enters the nucleus and leads to new viral RNA being formed (Step ③).

- How the cell makes viral proteins on its own ribosomes (Step ④).

- How these proteins are transported to the cell surface (Step ⑤).

Figure 2.14
Junctions between Cells

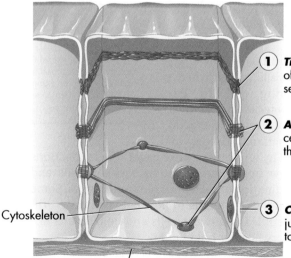

Cytoskeleton

Extracellular matrix

① **Tight junctions** block movement of chemicals through the spaces separating cells

② **Adhering junctions** attach a cell to an adjacent cell or to the extracellular matrix

③ **Communicating junctions** (gap junctions) allow small molecules to pass from one cell to another

We haven't seen, however, how new viruses are assembled. This last step is crucial because it provides the target for the protease inhibitor drugs that help patients return to relative health. Here, then, is the final part of the HIV infection story.

Assembly of new HIV particles requires additional large viral proteins produced on cellular ribosomes floating free in the cytoplasm. After they're made, the active viral protein called protease cuts the large proteins into smaller proteins (Step ⑥). These proteins eventually surround the viral RNA, move toward the surface, and help assemble hundreds, even thousands of complete viral particles (Step ⑦). The role of protease in chopping large proteins into smaller ones explains why blocking that process with protease inhibitor drugs helps so many AIDS patients so dramatically.

Who knew?

As cells increase in size but maintain the same shape, their volume enlarges more than their surface. An amoeba-like creature the size of a truck would have too much internal volume to be supplied adequately by the area of its outer membrane. It couldn't support the intake of nutrients and excretion of wastes.

Figure 2.15
The Infective Cycle of HIV

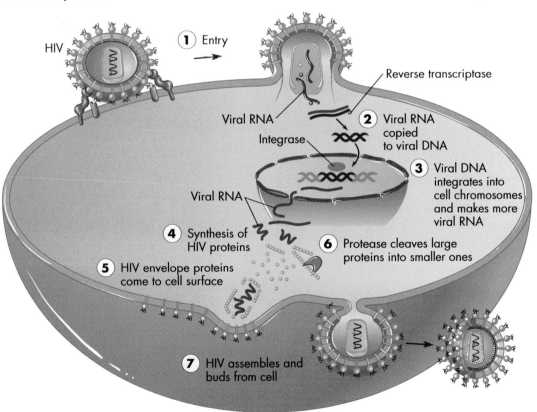

How Cells
Take in and
Use Energy

Learning Outcomes

LO **1**   Identify the universal laws of energy conversions

LO **2**   Explain the energy flow in living things

LO **3**   Understand how living things harvest energy

LO **4**   Identify the energy systems used for exercise

LO **5**   Explain how plants trap and convert light energy

> ## "Energy flows from the nonliving physical world to the living world and back."

The Highly Improbable Hummingbird

Hummingbirds have a problem when it comes to energy use: Their bodies have to be very small in order to hover in front of delicate flowers and thus extract an energy resource not readily available to most other species. Their small size, however, means that they lose heat faster than bigger animals because hummingbirds have a larger surface area relative to their body mass. To maintain a high body temperature and still generate enough energy to hover, their rate of food use and calorie expenditure—for their size, anyway—far exceeds that of any other animal with a backbone. How do they do it? What mechanisms do they share with all other organisms for extracting energy from food? What special tricks do they have up their feathery sleeves that allow them to harvest energy fast enough so they can hover like nature's helicopters? These discoveries are related to, and require an understanding of, energetics, the study of energy intake, processing, and expenditure. So do each of the bird's other amazing adaptations. Energetics is part of our exploration of how animals, plants, bacteria, and other living things acquire energy and use it to fuel the ongoing enterprise of maintaining order and staying alive. Energy metabolism is a complex subject. But it helps us appreciate life's intricate beauty and its important biochemical symmetry and balance. It also allows us to explore other subjects later in the book, including how our cells build the proteins they need, how we digest the food we eat, how we burn that fuel during exercise, and—on a much bigger scale—what we must do to keep our global ecosystems healthy. In the course of this chapter, you'll find the answers to these questions:

What do you know?

Our planet can support a larger number of vegetarians than meat eaters. Why?

- ☑ What universal laws govern how the cells of living things gather and use energy?
- ☑ What are the energy routes and carriers in living things?
- ☑ How do oxygen-dependent organisms harvest energy?
- ☑ How do organisms that can survive without oxygen harvest energy through alternative pathways?
- ☑ How do we get the energy for exercise?
- ☑ How do plants trap solar energy and form sugars and other biological molecules?

> **energetics**
> the study of energy intake, processing, and expenditure

LO¹ What Universal Laws Govern How Cells Use Energy?

All cells need energy to live. That's true whether they are muscle cells driving a hummingbird's wing beat, nectar-producing cells in the red columbine flower the hummingbird sips from, or bacterial cells decomposing leaves that have fallen off the plant. Regardless of type, however, no cell can "make" energy; instead, it must get energy from some outside source in the environment. Let's follow the flow of energy through a mountain ecosystem that includes hummingbirds and the flowers on which they depend.

Sunlight arriving from space strikes the leaves of the red columbine plant, and they carry out photosynthesis, the trapping of energy in a series of metabolic steps that eventually stores energy in the chemical bonds of sugars. The sugar molecules are transported inside the plant, which uses some of the energy to build the delicate, tubular blossoms that attract the hummingbird. Other sugar molecules become concentrated in the flower's nectar. After a hummingbird sips and swallows the nectar, the sugars in the sweet droplets leave the bird's stomach and intestines, flow through the bloodstream, and enter muscle, brain, lung, and other tissue cells. The millions of cells then break down the sugar molecules in the presence of oxygen and release some of the energy in the process called cellular respiration. That energy is now available to power the hummingbird's breathing, heartbeat, hovering, and other activities. This represents an energy transformation from solar energy to chemical energy. Such transformations are never 100 percent efficient, however, and some energy is inevitably lost as heat. As a result, the hummingbird warms up as it hovers over one columbine flower then another. The bird's excess body heat dissipates in the cool mountain air around it. Eventually, when the bird dies, bacteria and fungi break down the little body and the rest of the energy still trapped in its tissues fuels the decomposer's activity or is lost as heat. We will explore the processes of photosynthesis and cellular respiration in more detail later in this chapter.

Our main message for now is that energy flows from the nonliving physical world to the living world and back, and it is essential for the activities and survival of all living cells. There are a few basic physical laws that underlie energy transactions in nature. Let's look at them now.

> How can I transform this book's *potential energy* into *kinetic energy*?

© ISTOCKPHOTO.COM

The Laws of Energy Conversions

Lift this book and hold it parallel to the floor at head level. Now drop it. What seemed like nothing but a slam on the floor is really a series of energy conversions, energy being officially defined as the ability to perform work or to produce change.

States of Energy

The lifted book contained stored energy in the form of potential energy—energy that is available to do work. Likewise, water saved up behind a dam contains stored energy. This potential energy can be released and accomplish work, such as turning the turbines of a hydroelectric generator. When you dropped the book, it began falling and potential energy was transformed into kinetic energy, the energy of motion. These two forms of energy, potential and kinetic, are the two major states of energy in the universe, and each can be converted into the other.

© VLADIMIR MELNIKOV/ISTOCKPHOTO.COM

The Law of Energy Conservation

As the book fell and hit the floor, energy changed in form but not in amount. This is because *energy is conserved in energy transformations*; it is neither created anew nor destroyed. When the falling textbook loudly met the floor and abruptly stopped moving, the amount of energy released as sound waves in the air, plus the amount of energy that warmed the floor, book, and surroundings, exactly equaled the kinetic energy in the moving book.

The Law of Inefficient Energy Changes

The amount of energy is the same before and after an energy conversion, but *the amount available to do useful work always decreases during the change.* For example, energy in the sound waves from the book slapping the floor is less than the total kinetic energy of the falling book. Energy conversions are never completely efficient because some energy is always lost as heat, the random movement of atoms and molecules.

Random movement is the opposite of order, so the inefficient conversion of energy from one form into another increases disorder in the system. Scientists use the term entropy (EN-tro-pee) to describe the disorder or randomness in a system. The more disorder, the greater the entropy.

Cells and Entropy

The law of inefficient energy transformations most directly affects an organism's cells. Cells remain healthy only if they obtain enough energy to fuel all their synthesizing and repair activities, over and above the loss of energy to inefficiency and heat. A living cell is just a temporary island of order supported by the cost of a constant flow of energy. If energy flow is impeded, order quickly fades, disorder reigns, and the cell dies.

LO² How Does Energy Flow in Living Things?

If a cell is a temporary island of order, then hummingbirds are temporary archipelagoes with millions of islands, all maintained and orderly—at least so long as the animal is alive. What maintains that order? The answer is chemical energy, trapped and released through chemical reactions. Recall from Chapter 2 that chemical bonds are a type of "energy glue" that joins atoms together. In a chemical reaction, energy in chemical bonds shifts and atoms rearrange, forming new kinds of molecules. As a kid, did you ever mix vinegar with baking soda? The resulting chemical reaction is a vigorous release of energy in the form of fizzing and heat. The starting substances, or reactants, interact to form new substances, the products. The reactants are hydrogen

ions (H^+), from the acetic acid in the vinegar, and bicarbonate ions (HCO_3^-), from the baking soda. Chemical bonds break, allowing the OH^- group to leave the bicarbonate ion, which becomes CO_2, or carbon dioxide gas, bubbling in the water. The OH^- combines with a hydrogen ion (H^+), producing H_2O, water. This reaction takes place spontaneously, and releases energy in the form of heat because the energy conversion is inefficient. The entropy (disorder) of the system increases as the carbon dioxide molecules bubble off into the air randomly.

The reaction of vinegar and baking soda satisfies the law of inefficient energy exchanges: The products contain less energy and are more disordered than the reactants. Some reactions release energy like the one we just discussed, but need some energy input before they will proceed, just as a rock poised at the top of a hill needs a shove before it will start rolling downhill and release potential energy. Even with this needed initial energy to get the reaction started, however, the overall result is a *release* of energy. Reactions of these two types that proceed spontaneously or need a starting "push" but eventually release energy are called energy-releasing reactions.

An entirely different set of reactions called energy-absorbing reactions will not proceed spontaneously and do not give off heat. Think about an egg cooking in a pan. The added energy (heat) causes the egg white proteins to form new chemical bonds with each other and to change into a white rubbery solid. Another example is the way red columbine or purple lupine leaves trap energy from sunlight and use it to power the building of carbohydrate molecules in flower nectar, cell walls, pollen, or other plant parts. Energy-absorbing reactions underlie most of the transformations that maintain order in the cell, such as the building of proteins and the replacement of worn-out cell parts.

So where, then, does the energy come from to fuel a cell's huge number of energy-absorbing reactions? The answer involves a beautiful symmetry: The power for *energy-absorbing reactions* comes from the cell's *energy-releasing reactions.* The two kinds of reactions are energetically *coupled,* so that the leftover energy of a releasing reaction provides the energy

heat
the random motion of atoms and molecules

entropy
a measure of disorder or randomness in a system

chemical reaction
the making or breaking of chemical bonds between atoms or molecules

reactant
the starting substance in a chemical reaction

product
a substance that results from a chemical reaction

energy-releasing reactions
reactions that proceed spontaneously or need a starting "push" but eventually release energy

energy-absorbing reactions
reactions that will not proceed spontaneously and do not give off heat

needs of an absorbing reaction, and so on down a chain of linked reactions called a metabolic pathway (more on this shortly).

ATP: The Cell's Main Energy Carrier

Most of the energy given off during an energy-releasing reaction is quickly trapped in the chemical bonds of a compound that can carry energy from one molecule to another. The most common energy-carrying molecule within a living cell is ATP (adenosine triphosphate). ATP is a *nucleotide,* a two-part molecule with a head com-

posed of three molecular rings and a tail made up of three phosphate groups (PO_4^-, a phosphorus atom bonded to four oxygen atoms) (Fig. 3.1a). Living cells make the energy carrier ATP from ADP (adenosine diphosphate), a related molecule with only two phosphate groups (Fig. 3.1b). Cells can use the energy freed from an energy-releasing reaction to add a phosphate group to ADP and thus make ATP, with a higher level of stored energy in its chemical bonds.

Cells can then "spend" their ATP currency, because the release of a phosphate from ATP delivers energy in a controlled way. The cleavage of ATP releases ADP, a phosphate, and a small amount of energy (Fig. 3.1c). A cell can then use that energy to do work. A hummingbird flaps its wings 40 to 80 times per second and the muscle cells that contract to move those wings carry out millions of energy-absorbing reactions every second to keep up with that hard, fast work. An energetic phosphate released from ATP will often transfer to another molecule, energizing that molecule (Fig. 3.1d). When phosphate is split off an ATP, ADP forms; that ADP can itself lose another phosphate group and

Figure 3.1
ATP: The Cell's Main Energy Carrier

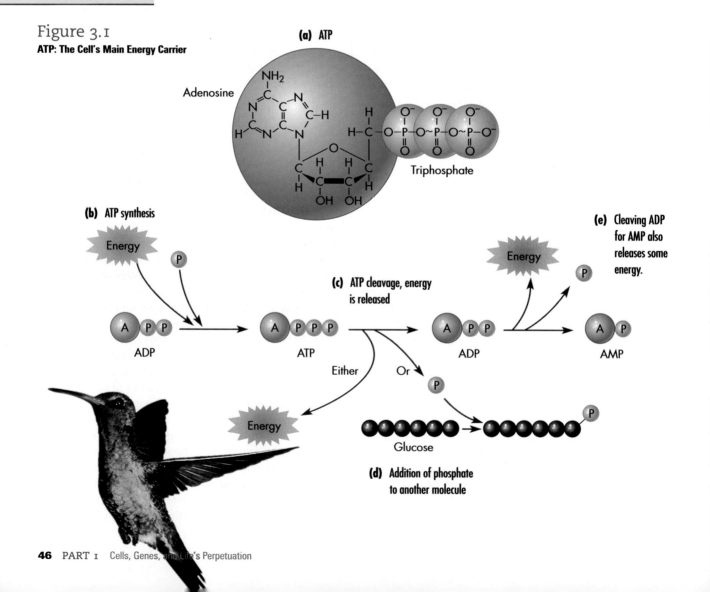

(a) ATP

Adenosine

Triphosphate

(b) ATP synthesis

Energy

ADP → ATP

(c) ATP cleavage, energy is released

ADP

(e) Cleaving ADP for AMP also releases some energy.

AMP

Either / Or

Energy

Glucose

(d) Addition of phosphate to another molecule

release more energy plus the molecule AMP (adenosine monophosphate) (Fig. 3.1e). Cells only use this second release and formation of AMP when energy demands are unusually high. The significance of ATP and its less energetic relatives ADP and AMP is that they function as links between energy exchanges in cells.

How Enzymes Speed Up Chemical Reactions

Chemical reactions rearrange chemical bonds and release or absorb energy. But how fast does this take place? For example, if you collected some flower nectar and allowed it to dry in a cool, arid place, the high-energy food (sucrose) would sit there intact for decades, like sugar in a jar, rearranging its chemical bonds very slowly and releasing energy at a nearly undetectable rate. When a hummingbird takes that same nectar into its digestive tract, however, special digestive proteins can break down the chemical bonds in the sucrose within seconds into simpler sugars. Clearly, these proteins can speed up chemical transformations. Let's look at how they do it.

Within living cells, most chemical transformations are facilitated by enzymes. Digestive enzymes are just one type. Enzymes are proteins that function as biological catalysts, agents that speed up specific chemical reactions without themselves being permanently changed by the reaction. Without dozens of kinds of enzymes to speed the breakdown of sugars, hummingbirds would not be able to maintain their high metabolic rates.

AMP (adenosine monophosphate)
an energy molecule related to ATP but having only one phosphate group instead of two (ADP) or three (ATP)

enzyme
a protein that facilitates chemical reactions by lowering the required activation energy but is not itself permanently altered in the process; also called a biological catalyst

catalyst
a substance that speeds up the rate of a chemical reaction by lowering the activation energy without itself being permanently changed or used up during the reaction

transition state
in a chemical reaction, the intermediate springlike state between reactant and product

Enzymes Lower Activation Energy

In chemical reactions, there is an energy barrier separating the reactants and products. For a pair of reactants such as bicarbonate and hydrogen ions to be converted into products such as carbon dioxide and water, the reactants must collide with each other hard enough to break chemical bonds in the reactants and form new bonds in the products. For a fleeting instant during the conversion, chemical bonds in the reactants are distorted like springs being stretched, and this fleeting intermediate state cannot be reached without a very energetic collision between the molecules. We call the momentary, intermediate springlike condition a transition state. Because energy input is required to achieve it, the transition state is often characterized as an energy hill or barrier that separates reactants and products (Fig. 3.2).

Most molecules jostling about and colliding randomly lack the energy

Figure 3.2
Activation Energy and Enzymes

(a) Activation energy

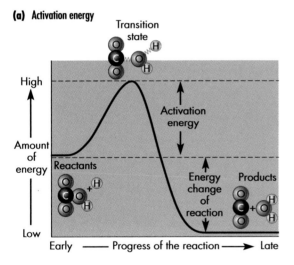

(b) Analogy for enzyme action

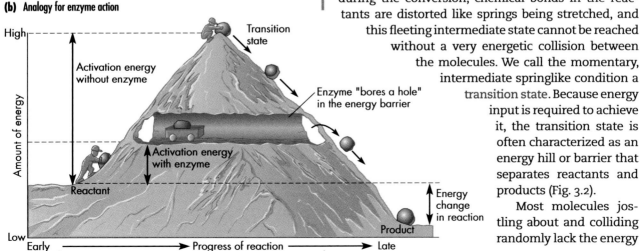

of motion they need to overcome the energy barrier; they simply bounce off each other. Some individual molecules, however, do jostle about with enough kinetic energy so that they achieve a productive collision, an impact that generates the springlike transition state, from which reactants change into products. An energy of impact great enough to cause molecules to cross the energy barrier is called the activation energy (Fig. 3.2).

In a living cell, most molecules need help in overcoming the energy barrier that prevents the start of many reactions. Heat, of course, speeds up colliding molecules, but high temperatures would speed *all* the reactions in a cell, not just those special ones that help a cell function. This overall temperature increase would disorganize the cell and kill it. Luckily, enzymes can lower the level of activation energy enough so that biochemical reactions can take place without an increase of temperature. The action of an enzyme, in effect, bores a tunnel through the energy hill, allowing the reactants to become products without needing to roll like a heavy boulder up and over the high barrier represented by activation energy.

Enzymes not only allow reactions to proceed at the relatively low temperatures compatible with life processes, but they act only on specific reactions. For example, one specific enzyme speeds up a reaction that helps red blood cells transport CO_2 from tissues

Figure 3.3
How an Enzyme Works

(a) Enzyme binds substrate

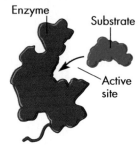

Enzyme

Substrate

Active site

(b) Enzyme-substrate complex

(c) Active site's new shape induces a better "fit"

Changed enzyme shape

Strained bond

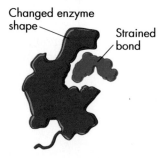

(d) Enzyme unchanged

Products

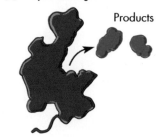

that produce it, such as active muscles, to the lungs, from which the waste gas can be exhaled. Each single molecule of this enzyme facilitates this change at the amazing speed of 600,000 times per second, nearly a million times faster than the reaction would occur without a catalyst. Biologists estimate that every second, a hummingbird's blood makes an entire circuit of its heart, lungs, and body and the animal breathes in and out four to eight times. Without this red blood cell enzyme working at near top speed, carbon dioxide produced in working cells could not possibly get transferred fast enough to the lungs to ensure the bird's survival.

Induced Fit Model of Enzyme Action

Like other proteins, each enzyme has its own unique three-dimensional shape, but most share an important feature: a deep groove, or pocket, on the surface called the active site. The shape of the enzyme's active site fits a specific reactant, or substrate. The substrate fits into the active site forming an enzyme-substrate complex (Fig. 3.3a,b). The active site of the enzyme can change shape as the substrate binds to it, improving the "fit" (Fig. 3.3c). (For this reason, biologists sometimes call it the "induced fit" model of enzyme action.) In fitting to the active site, the substrate's bonds are strained, which makes it possible for the substrate to reach a transition state, which in turn lowers the activation energy that is needed for the substrate to react and form products (Fig. 3.3d).

Enzymes accelerate a huge number of processes in living cells. Among these processes are the ones that allow organisms to transform energy in food molecules, light, or other nonliving sources into forms of energy that can do work for the cell. These enzyme-catalyzed reactions, along with all the other reactions of the body that sustain life, constitute metabolism. Metabolic reactions can break down or build up molecules, and can give off or use energy. As we saw earlier, metabolic reactions are interlinked within cells in metabolic pathways. These pathways allow living cells to subdivide a big chemical change into a number of smaller steps. One such change might, for example, release a tremendous amount of heat. This, in turn, would liberate energy in packets small enough for the cell to use efficiently.

LO³ How Do Living Things Harvest Energy?

Some of the busiest molecules in the living world are the enzymes within hummingbird muscles that keep those flight "motors" whirring. They have to be amazingly active to keep up with the animals' constant energy needs for hovering, flying, defending territory, and staying warm. The energy comes primarily from sugars present in flower nectar. In this section, we'll examine the mechanisms that cells use to obtain energy from food molecules. In the next section, we'll go on to see how plants, algae, and some bacteria trap solar energy in energy-rich molecules. These are challenging subjects, but they're central to all that goes on in cells and organisms and crucial to understanding biology. The subject is as personal as how your body is currently utilizing what you ate for your previous meal. On a larger scale, the subject of cellular energy harvest is also a key to understanding ecology, including how energy flows in the environment as one organism feeds on another. We'll return to it in Chapter 15.

An Overview of Energy Harvest

A hummingbird lighter than a tea bag can migrate all the way across the Gulf of Mexico without stopping. Think about this animal's exertion as it migrates nonstop, and then contrast it with the rapid burst of effort the bird would make as it accelerated to escape a swooping predator. These exertion levels are similar to you strolling for miles through the fall leaves versus running to catch the bus. Where does the hummingbird's (or your) energy come from?

There are two pathways of energy harvest that take place in living cells: energy harvest with plenty of oxygen, the aerobic pathway, and energy harvest with minimal oxygen or none at all, the anaerobic pathway. Many living cells are committed to one type or the other. However, some cells, such as muscle cells, are somewhat special in their ability to obtain energy from either pathway, depending on oxygen availability at any given moment.

Consider a man hiking up a low hill. As he walks, his lungs and blood circulation deliver enough oxygen to his muscles so that the cells can use the aerobic pathway (the yellow arrows in Fig. 3.4). During a more strenuous climb, his heart, lungs, and blood vessels cannot provide oxygen as fast as muscle cells require it. For this reason, muscle cells switch to the anaerobic pathway (the orange arrows in Fig. 3.4).

The Aerobic Pathway

The aerobic energy harvesting pathway, also called *cellular respiration*, consists of three main parts (follow the yellow arrows in Fig. 3.4). The first part, glycolysis, begins the breakdown of glucose and produces just a few ATP molecules. The second part of the aerobic pathway, called the Krebs cycle, completely dismantles glucose to individual carbon atoms while capturing high-energy electrons. The third part of the aerobic pathway, the electron transport chain, is where the oxygen comes in: The high-energy electrons captured in the Krebs cycle join with oxygen and hydrogen. This produces water molecules and a large number of ATP molecules—a big energy payoff for the cell. Most cells in animals, plants, algae, and fungi, and most kinds of bacteria carry out a strictly aerobic energy harvest.

The Anaerobic Pathway

The anaerobic pathway consists of two main parts (follow the orange arrows in Fig. 3.4). The first, glycolysis, is the same as in the aerobic pathway. The second, fermentation, doesn't release any useful energy, but it does recycle materials necessary for glycolysis to continue. Without fermentation, a cell could not even use glycolysis to produce its meager amount of ATP. Animal muscle cells, yeasts in low-oxygen environments, and many kinds of bacteria harvest energy through this anaerobic pathway some or all of the time.

aerobic pathway
energy harvest in the presence of oxygen; also called cellular respiration

anaerobic pathway
the series of metabolic reactions that results in energy harvest in the absence of oxygen

glycolysis
the initial splitting of a glucose molecule into two molecules of pyruvate, resulting in the release of energy in the form of two ATP molecules; the series of reactions does not require the presence of oxygen to occur

Krebs cycle
the second stage of aerobic respiration, in which a two-carbon fragment is completely broken down into carbon dioxide and large amounts of energy are transferred to electron carriers; occurs in the mitochondrial matrix

electron transport chain
the third stage in aerobic respiration, in which electrons are passed down a series of molecules, gradually releasing energy that is harvested in the form of ATP

fermentation
extraction of energy from carbohydrates in the absence of oxygen, generally producing lactic acid or ethanol and CO_2 as byproducts

How Do Cells Harvest Energy When Oxygen Is Present?

How can the tiny hummingbird store enough energy to make a migration of 800 km or more? What accounts for the hummingbird's tremendous feats of strength and endurance—or for that matter, your own? The answers can be summarized with a simple equation for cellular respiration, the process of energy harvest utilizing oxygen:

Glucose + Oxygen + ADP + Phosphate →
Carbon dioxide + Water + ATP

This equation basically says that in the presence of oxygen, the energy of sunlight trapped in glucose molecules is transferred to ADP along with a phosphate ion, thereby producing the more readily usable energy carrier ATP. Water and carbon dioxide are byproducts of this ATP formation. The arrow in the equation above represents the cellular mechanisms that bring about the phases of this energy harvest: glycolysis, the Krebs cycle, and the electron transport chain (yellow arrows in Fig. 3.4).

Glycolysis

Energy harvest begins with the breakdown of the simple sugar glucose in a sequence of reaction steps called glycolysis (*glyco* = sugar + *lysis* = splitting). Cells can convert other kinds of sugar, such as the sucrose in flower nectar, into glucose and use it as a basic fuel. Energy stored in the chemical bonds of glucose molecules originally came from the sun, and it was trapped in molecular form by photosynthesis taking place in green plants as well as in algae and certain kinds of bacteria.

The reactions of glycolysis split the six-carbon sugar glucose into two molecules of the three-carbon compound, *pyruvate* (ionized pyruvic acid; Fig. 3.5). Pyruvate contains some stored chemical energy and acts as an *intermediate,* a compound that serves as a product for one reaction and a reactant for the next in a metabolic pathway. The splitting of glucose makes available energetic electrons (charged atomic particles) and hydrogen ions (H⁻, also called protons). These electrons and hydrogen ions are transferred to a special electron carrier molecule—a type of biochemical "delivery van" we'll discuss in detail later. The steps of glycolysis take place in the cell's liquid cytoplasm, rather than in an organelle, and they are facilitated by enzymes dissolved in the watery cytoplasmic solution. For each glucose molecule split during glycolysis, there is a net gain of two ATPs and two pyruvate molecules. The ATPs can move through the cytoplasm to places in the cell where energy is immediately needed. The pyruvate molecules leave the cytoplasm and enter the cell organelle called the mitochondrion.

Figure 3.4

An Overview of Energy Harvest

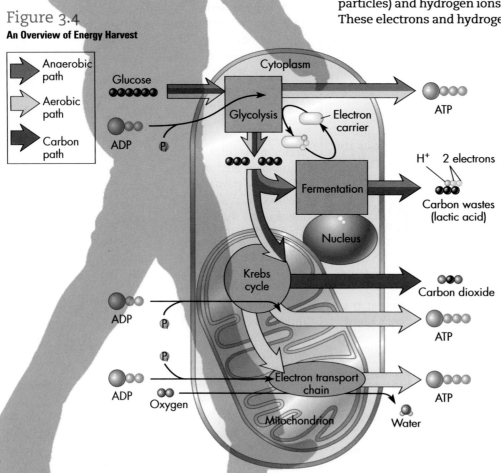

©JAMIE FARRANT/ISTOCKPHOTO.COM

The Mitochondrion

Highly active cells—your own heart muscle cells, for example—contain large numbers of sausage-shaped organelles called *mitochondria*, which we encountered in Chapter 2 and which act as the cell's powerhouses, generating ATP.

Mitochondria consist of two membranes, like a large, uninflated balloon folded up inside a smaller, fully inflated balloon (see the micrograph in Fig. 3.7). A mitochondrion's *outer membrane* is directly bathed by the cell's cytoplasm. Large protein-bound pores perforate the membrane, and molecules up to the size of small proteins can pass through the openings. A mitochondrion's inner membrane is thrown into folds called cristae, which are studded with enzymes and pigment molecules (see Fig. 3.7). Some of these enzymes take part in an energy bucket brigade described below, and one of the enzymes synthesizes ATP.

In all eukaryotic organisms—even lethargic slugs and slow-growing lichens—the mitochondrion's inner membrane is much less permeable than the outer membrane; hence, the area enclosed by the inner membrane, the matrix, is a compartment well isolated from the rest of the cell. The matrix contains many enzyme molecules, including those that carry out the reactions of the Krebs cycle, which is so important in aerobic respiration. The matrix also contains several copies of the circular mitochondrial DNA molecule and hundreds of mitochondrial ribosomes.

Inside the mitochondrion, the pyruvate that formed after glycolysis gets broken down by means of cellular respiration, the breakdown of nutrients and the production of ATP energy using oxygen. Aerobic respiration in mitochondria consumes oxygen and yields carbon dioxide and water plus a large harvest of ATP molecules. That energy harvest, involving the Krebs cycle and the electron transport chain, accounts for the mitochondrion's reputation as a cellular powerhouse, regardless of a cell's metabolic speed.

> **crista (pl. cristae)**
> a fold or folds formed by the inner membrane of a mitochondrion
>
> **matrix**
> in HIV and many other viruses, a sphere of protein inside the envelope and outside the capsid; in a mitochondrion, the area enclosed by the inner membrane

The Krebs Cycle

The Krebs cycle is part of a series of chemical reactions taking place inside mitochondria that break down pyruvate completely into carbon dioxide and water (Fig. 3.6). In several steps, the carbons in pyruvate are cleaved off, one at a time, and released as carbon dioxide (CO_2). Your exhaled breath is the body's way of getting rid of carbon dioxide produced in the Krebs cycle.

The Krebs cycle starts with the end product of glycolysis, the three-carbon substance pyruvate

Figure 3.5

The Aerobic Pathway Part 1: Glycolysis

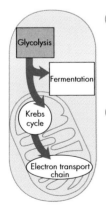

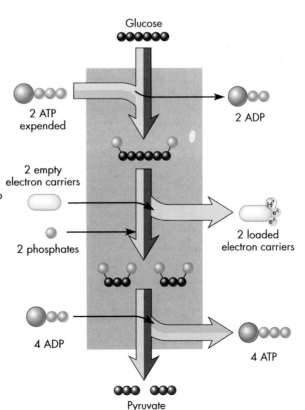

(1) The enzymes of glycolysis i superchargeî glucose by spending two molecules of ATP and adding their phosphates to the six-carbon sugar molecule.

(2) Enzymes chop the six-carbon molecule in half, and then strip two electrons and a hydrogen from each three-carbon compound and add them to an electron carrier while adding another phosphate to each three-carbon compound.

(3) In the final step, enzymes remove both phosphates from each three-carbon compound and use them to make 4 ATPs, giving a net payoff of 2 ATPs.

Glucose

2 ATP expended

2 ADP

2 empty electron carriers

2 loaded electron carriers

2 phosphates

4 ADP

4 ATP

Pyruvate

(review Fig. 3.5), which passes from the cell's watery cytoplasm into the mitochondrion. In the matrix of the mitochondrion, enzymes cleave pyruvate into a molecule of carbon dioxide plus a two-carbon portion (Step ④ of Fig. 3.6). Enzymes in the Krebs cycle join this two-carbon portion to a four-carbon compound to make a six-carbon molecule (Step ⑤). Other enzymes sequentially cleave two carbon dioxide molecules from this six-carbon molecule (a person exhales this in his or her breath) and produce four energized electron carriers. Notice the two electron carriers in Steps ⑥ and ⑦).

In addition, enzymes in Step ⑦ regenerate the original four-carbon compound, completing the cycle. An additional step, not shown, results in one ATP. The end result is that the Krebs cycle converts all the carbons from the original glucose into carbon dioxide and stores the energy in electron carriers.

The Krebs Cycle as a Metabolic Clearinghouse

The various compounds taking part in the Krebs cycle are intermediates, reactants in one metabolic reaction and products in the next. Cells can use these intermediates in several ways. The Krebs cycle can help a cell use lipids or proteins for energy in addition to carbohydrates. When an animal or plant cell's supply of sugar falls, the cell

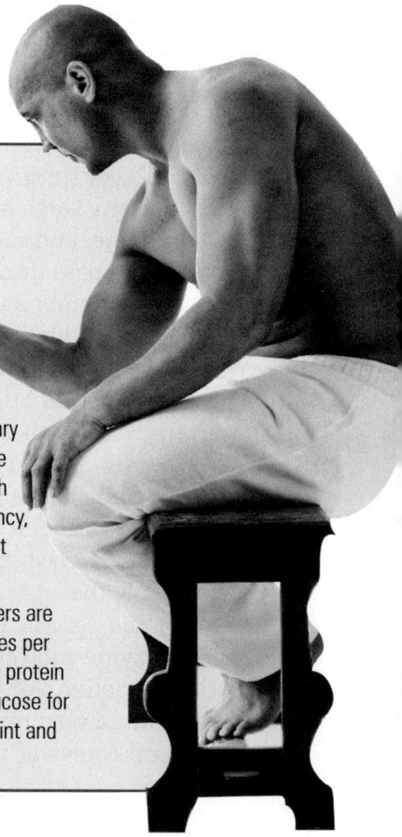

{Give Me Some Sugar}

An important exception to the clearinghouse principle is the human brain cell. For complex reasons, the brain can use only glucose as fuel, and this fact has major implications:

- First, it explains why sugary foods are temporary mood elevators. Soon after you eat a candy bar or drink a sugary soda, glucose molecules are cleaved from sucrose (table sugar) and enter the bloodstream and brain. Infused with their favorite fuel, the brain cells function at peak efficiency, leading one to feel happier, smarter and livelier—at least for a time.

- Second, this property of the brain cell explains why dieters are warned to consume at least 500 calories in carbohydrates per day and not to restrict themselves to liquid or powdered protein diets—the brain alone needs at least 500 calories of glucose for normal functioning, and without it, a person can grow faint and even lapse into unconsciousness.

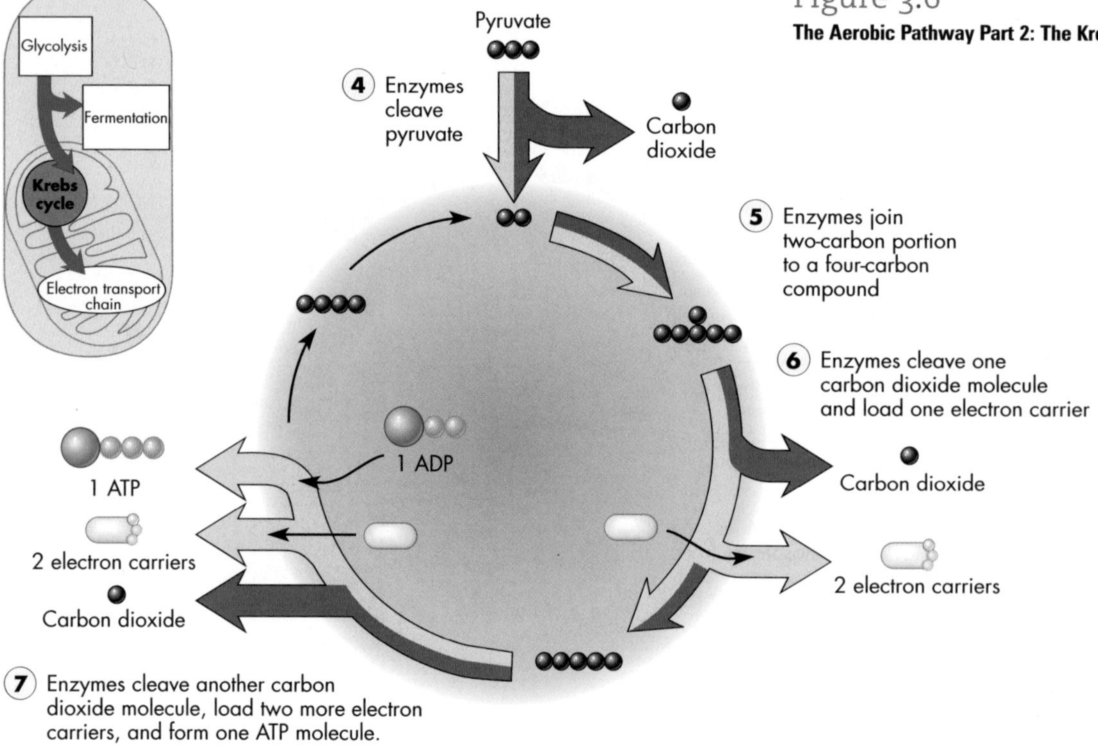

Figure 3.6
The Aerobic Pathway Part 2: The Krebs Cycle

Glycolysis

Fermentation

Krebs cycle

Electron transport chain

Pyruvate

④ Enzymes cleave pyruvate

Carbon dioxide

⑤ Enzymes join two-carbon portion to a four-carbon compound

⑥ Enzymes cleave one carbon dioxide molecule and load one electron carrier

Carbon dioxide

2 electron carriers

1 ADP

1 ATP

2 electron carriers

Carbon dioxide

⑦ Enzymes cleave another carbon dioxide molecule, load two more electron carriers, and form one ATP molecule.

begins to break down lipids or proteins. Some of the subunits from these reactions can then be converted into pyruvate or into Krebs cycle intermediates. These compounds can then enter the Krebs cycle pathway at the appropriate stage and be dismantled for energy harvest. If an organism is starving, this process can provide enough energy to keep the body alive, but the body is literally digesting itself to provide that energy, with the Krebs cycle making it possible. When food once more becomes available, intermediates from the Krebs cycle can become the raw materials for growth: They can serve as skeletons for the synthesis of new fats, proteins, and carbohydrates to restore those broken down during lean times or that wear out and need replacing.

The Electron Transport Chain

Still inside the mitochondrion, eight electron carrier molecules per initial glucose molecule are loaded with electrons from the Krebs cycle. These carriers move to the *electron transport chain,* a group of enzymes and pigment molecules embedded in mitochondrial membranes (Fig. 3.7). Each member of the

Figure 3.7
The Aerobic Pathway Part 3: The Electron Transport Chain

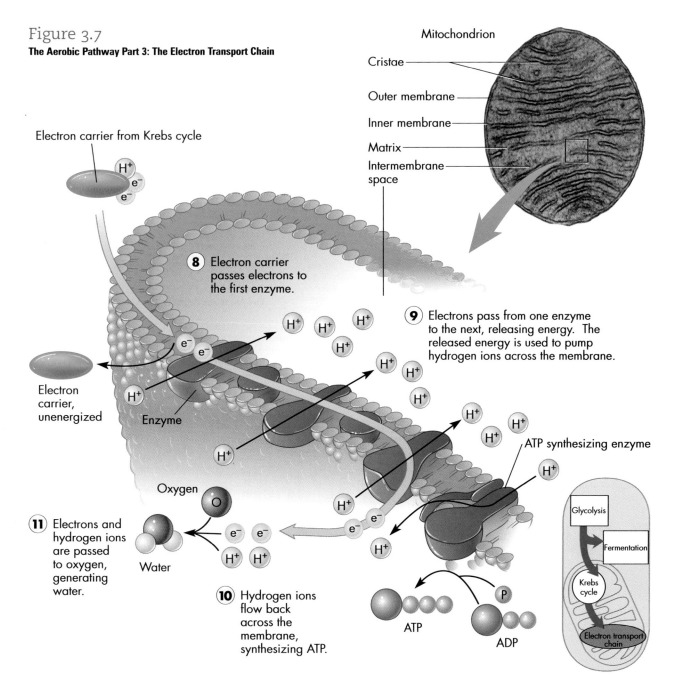

Mitochondrion
Cristae
Outer membrane
Inner membrane
Matrix
Intermembrane space

Electron carrier from Krebs cycle

8 Electron carrier passes electrons to the first enzyme.

9 Electrons pass from one enzyme to the next, releasing energy. The released energy is used to pump hydrogen ions across the membrane.

Electron carrier, unenergized

Enzyme

ATP synthesizing enzyme

Oxygen

11 Electrons and hydrogen ions are passed to oxygen, generating water.

Water

10 Hydrogen ions flow back across the membrane, synthesizing ATP.

ATP

ADP

Glycolysis
Fermentation
Krebs cycle
Electron transport chain

chain passes electrons to the next member, like a bucket brigade. During each electron transfer, the electron loses a bit of energy (like a splash of water spilling from the bucket). Particular mitochondrial enzymes use this released energy to synthesize ATP from ADP. For each initial molecule of glucose that entered glycolysis, the yield from the electron transport chain is a whopping 32 ATPs.

The electron transport chain is the stage of the aerobic pathway that actually uses the oxygen because the last electron acceptor in the chain is oxygen. As electrons are added to oxygen atoms, and hydrogen ions follow along, the hydrogen and oxygen combine to form water, H_2O. Thus, the oxygen you are breathing in as you read these sentences will be converted to water in your mitochondria as oxygen accepts electrons and aerobic respiration takes place. The legend to Figure 3.7 describes this step by step.

If oxygen is not present to accept the electrons and hydrogen ions once they have passed down the electron transport chain, the entire process quickly stops. The organism or cell, if strictly oxygen-requiring, then dies.

How Do Cells Harvest Energy Without Oxygen?

A hummingbird has a greater blood supply to its wing muscle cells than a mammal does to its wings or legs. Sometimes, though, the bird must exert itself so strenuously that its furiously beating heart still cannot deliver oxygen to the muscles as fast as they are using the gas. As a result, the hummingbird's muscle cells have to rely for short periods of time on anaerobic energy harvest with its two phases, glycolysis and fermentation (the orange arrows in Fig. 3.4).

Glycolysis

Anaerobic energy harvest or the *anaerobic pathway* begins with glycolysis, the same process that starts the aerobic pathway (Fig. 3.8). Because glycolysis doesn't vary from one pathway to the other, *all* organisms possess the enzymes of glycolysis. This universal prelude to energy metabolism leads biologists to think that glycolysis probably evolved in earth's earliest cells over 3 billion years ago, and was

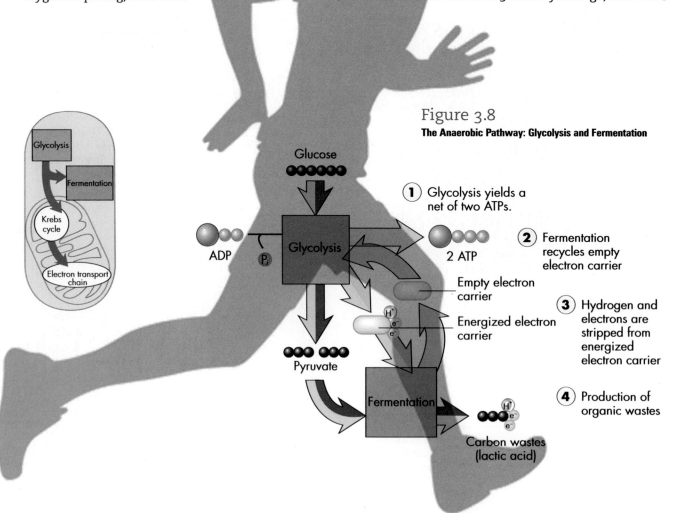

Figure 3.8

The Anaerobic Pathway: Glycolysis and Fermentation

Glycolysis

Fermentation

Krebs cycle

Electron transport chain

Glucose

ADP P_i Glycolysis

Pyruvate

Fermentation

① Glycolysis yields a net of two ATPs.

2 ATP

② Fermentation recycles empty electron carrier

Empty electron carrier

Energized electron carrier

③ Hydrogen and electrons are stripped from energized electron carrier

④ Production of organic wastes

Carbon wastes (lactic acid)

passed down to all surviving organisms. This common biochemical thread underscores the evolutionary relatedness of all life forms.

Fermentation

Recall that energized electron carriers and the 3-carbon compound pyruvate are end products of glycolysis. During the second phase of the anaerobic pathway, called *fermentation*, enzymes modify pyruvate in the absence of oxygen. The enzymes that speed the reactions of fermentation lie in the cell's cytoplasm, just like those that facilitate glycolysis. Depending on the organism, however, fermentation converts the pyruvate into various end products, such as ethanol and carbon dioxide, or lactic acid (Fig. 3.8). The intoxicating effect of wine and beer and the fragrant aroma of baking bread come from ethanol, the alcohol produced during fermentation in yeast cells. Likewise, fermentation carried on by certain bacteria growing in milk releases the lactic acid that gives some cheeses their sharp taste. Your muscle cells also produce lactic acid (or the electrically charged form called *lactate*) when you exercise anaerobically. The "burn" that you feel when you work a muscle very hard comes from the liberation of lactate.

Ironically, fermentation itself yields no ATP. The wastes—the ethanol or lactic acid—squander the energy that would be captured in ATP if the cell were using the aerobic pathway. You might wonder, then, why cells would carry out fermentation and produce toxic waste products such as ethanol and lactate? The answer is that fermentation reactions recycle the electron carrier molecule needed for glycolysis, stripping away the electrons and hydrogens from the carrier and making the carrier available for a new round of glycolysis (blue arrows, Fig. 3.8). In fermentation, it is as if the electron carrier "delivery van" dumps its load unused just so it can return and pick up a new load. Without the recycling of the energy carrier, the cell would run out of this necessary "delivery" molecule, and glycolysis would cease.

The energy yield of the anaerobic pathway may seem meager, just 2 ATPs per glucose compared to 36 for the aerobic pathway. Anaerobic metabolism, however, is crucial to the global recycling of carbon and the stability of the environment. Organic matter from dead leaves, dead microorganisms, and other sources often sinks into an environment devoid of oxygen, such as the soft layers at the bottom of lakes or oceans. If it weren't for anaerobic decomposers—organisms capable of breaking down organic matter via anaerobic metabolism—most of the world's carbon would eventually be locked up in undecomposed organic material in these oxygen-poor environments.

As a result, there would be too little carbon dioxide available as a raw material for photosynthesis, plants would be unable to generate new glucose molecules, and neither plants nor animals would survive.

> **feedback inhibition** the buildup of a metabolic product that in turn inhibits the activity of an enzyme; since this enzyme is involved in making the original product, the accumulation of the product turns off its own production

Control of Metabolism

Hummingbirds can burn carbohydrates by either the aerobic or the anaerobic pathway if their activity demands it temporarily. As we saw, they can burn fats when they are migrating nonstop, and, thanks to the Krebs cycle clearinghouse, they can also use proteins for energy. These intricacies of metabolism bring up new questions: What makes a cell start to burn its stores of lipids or proteins when glucose runs out? Then, when the supplies of glucose return, what stops the cell from burning all its lipids or proteins, literally eating itself up from the inside and destroying its cellular structures? Finally, what triggers a cell to build molecules only when they are needed?

When levels of ATP build up in a cell so high that the cell requires no more of the molecular fuel, the ATP binds to a special regulatory site on a specific enzyme that facilitates an early step in glycolysis. This binding shuts down enzyme activity. This, in turn, switches off the entire glycolytic pathway. So, when the cell already has high levels of ATP, the presence of the ATP molecule itself serves as a control to turn off its own production. When ATP levels drop, glycolysis resumes once more. This kind of metabolic regulation is called **feedback inhibition**.

Through feedback inhibition and other forms of control, the activity of a cell's metabolic enzymes is turned on or off so that the cell burns glucose when that sugar is available; it burns lipids or proteins when glucose is lacking; and it builds the appropriate biological raw materials just when they are needed for growth or maintenance activities. These control mechanisms ensure that order rather than metabolic chaos reigns within living organisms.

LO⁴ How Do We Get Energy for Exercise?

Energy for different forms of exercise comes from different parts of the metabolic pathway. Exercise physiologists have determined that three energy systems—the immediate system, the glycolytic system, and the oxidative system—supply energy to a person's muscles during exercise. The duration of physical activity and availability of oxygen dictate which system the body uses. The **immediate energy system** is instantly available for a brief explosive action, such as one bench press, one tennis serve, or one ballet leap, and the system has two components. One component is the small amount of ATP stored in muscle cells, immediately useful like the few coins you carry around in your purse or pocket.

This stored ATP, however, runs out after only half a second—barely enough time to heave a shot or return a tennis serve, let alone to trudge up a long hill. The second component of the immediate energy system is a high-energy compound called *creatine phosphate*, an amino acid–like molecule that has an energetic phosphate, like ATP. Muscle cells store creatine phosphate in larger amounts than ATP. Creatine phosphate is more like a handful of dollar bills than a few coins. When the ATP in a muscle cell is depleted, creatine phosphate transfers its phosphate to ADP; this regenerates ATP, and ATP can then fuel the muscle cell to contract and move the body. Even the cell's store of creatine phosphate, however, becomes depleted after only about a minute of strenuous work; thus, muscles must rely on more robust systems than the immediate energy system to power longer-term activities.

The **glycolytic energy system**, which depends on splitting glucose by glycolysis in the muscles, fuels activities lasting from about 1 to 3 minutes, such as an 800-m run or a 200-m swim. This storage form is more like an account at the bank than like dollars in your wallet, and it "purchases" more activity. Glycolysis going on in the muscle cell cytoplasm can cleave glucose in the absence of oxygen and generate a few ATPs. Fermentation takes the product of glycolysis a step further and makes the waste product lactic acid. Recall that there is a net yield of only two ATP molecules for each molecule of glucose from glycolysis. For this reason, the glycolytic energy system can sustain heavy exercise for only about 3 minutes, and all of it would be considered anaerobic exercise, powered by the cells' anaerobic pathway. It's also why lactic acid begins to build up in muscles in just that short amount of time and can lead to a muscle cramp or "stitch" in your side.

Activities lasting longer than about 3 minutes—a jog around the neighborhood, an aerobic dance session, or a long uphill hike—require oxygen and employ the **oxidative energy system**. This system can supply energy for activity of moderate intensity and long duration (aerobic exercise), and is like money invested in stocks and bonds that give long-term steady income. The oxidative energy system is based on cellular respiration and includes the Krebs cycle and the electron transport chain. It uses oxygen as the final electron acceptor and generates many ATP molecules per molecule of glucose burned. Clearly, anyone interested in melting away body fat should engage in aerobic (oxygen-utilizing) activities like jogging, swimming, bicycling, or strenuous hiking which rely primarily on the oxidative energy supply system and its ability to use fats as fuel.

immediate energy system
energy in the body instantly available for a brief explosive action, such as one heave by a shot-putter

glycolytic energy system
energy system based on the splitting of glucose by glycolysis in the muscles; the glycolytic system can sustain heavy exercise for a few minutes, as in a 200-m swim

oxidative energy system
the longest-sustaining energy system of the body, which relies on the Krebs cycle and electron transport chain in mitochondria and its ability to use fats as fuel; typically fuels aerobic activity

The glycolytic energy system can make ATP only from glucose or glycogen (cleaved to release glucose), but the oxidative energy system can produce energy by breaking down carbohydrates, fatty acids, and amino acids mobilized from other parts of the body and transported to the muscle cells by way of the bloodstream. The oxidative energy supply system can provide many more ATP molecules than creatine phosphate or glycolysis, but its supply rate is slower.

LO⁵ How Do Plants Trap Energy in Biological Molecules?

We've been talking so far only about how cells extract energy from biological molecules. But how did the energy get trapped in those biological molecules in the first place? It's less obvious, perhaps, but no less amazing that plants use photosynthesis to convert sunlight into chemical energy, store it in the bonds of organic molecules, and use those same molecules to build leaves, stems, flowers, and nectar as well as to fuel the plants' own energy needs and the steps of aerobic respiration taking place in all the plants' cells.

Compare, for a moment, the way you gather energy with the way a plant does it. The plant obtains its energy from the nonliving environment in the form of sunlight and inorganic raw materials, while you must get yours by eating plants or by eating other animals that ate plants. Biologists classify organisms that take in preformed nutrient molecules from the environment as **heterotrophs** (*hetero* = other + *troph* = feeder). Heterotrophs include many prokaryotes; most protists (such as protozoa); mushrooms, yeasts, and other fungi; and all animals. In contrast to heterotrophs, **autotrophs** (*auto* = self) are organisms that take energy directly from the nonliving environment and use it to synthesize their own nutrient molecules. Autotrophs include photosynthetic organisms—green plants and certain protists and prokaryotes that obtain energy from sunlight. Autotrophs also include a small group of *chemosynthetic* organisms—a few kinds of prokaryotes that extract energy from inorganic chemicals such as hydrogen gas and hydrogen sulfide with its rotten-egg smell. We can see that, ultimately, autotrophs are the source of all energy that flows through living systems, since heterotrophs obtain nutrients either from autotrophs or from heterotrophs that once consumed autotrophs.

Physical Characteristics of Light

Visible light is just a small part of the electromagnetic spectrum, which is the full range of electromagnetic radiation in the universe, from highly energetic gamma rays to very low–energy radio waves. Such radiation travels through space behaving both as particles called photons and as waves. The amount of energy in a photon determines its wavelength, the distance it travels during one complete vibration.

Photons of visible light have wavelengths in a narrow range: If the entire electromagnetic spectrum wrapped once around Earth, the visible part would be the length of your little finger. Living things can absorb and use light within the restricted wavelength range of visible light. Gamma rays are so energetic that they disrupt and destroy biological molecules they strike, while radio waves are so low in energy that they do not excite biological molecules.

heterotroph
(Gr. *heteros,* different + *trophos,* feeder) an organism, such as an animal, fungus, and most prokaryotes and protists, that takes in preformed nutrients from external sources

autotroph
(Gr. *auto,* self + *trophos,* feeder) an organism, such as a plant, that can manufacture its own food

electromagnetic spectrum
the full range of electromagnetic radiation in the universe, from highly energetic gamma rays to very low-energy radio waves

photons
a vibrating particle of light radiation that contains a specific quantity of energy

absorption spectrum
the wavelengths of light absorbed by a pigment

chlorophyll
(Gr. *chloros,* green + *phyllon,* leaf) light-trapping pigment molecules that act as electron donors during photosynthesis

carotenoids
plant pigments that absorb green, blue, and violet wavelengths and reflect red, yellow, and orange light

Chlorophyll and Other Pigments Absorb Light

Various things absorb certain colors of light and reflect others. For instance, a flower's petals are red because pigment molecules in the petal absorb light from various parts of the visible spectrum and reflect only red light. This range of absorbed light is called the **absorption spectrum**, and is unique for each pigment. The green pigment in leaves is called **chlorophyll**, and it takes part in photosynthesis as well as giving a green leaf its color.

Chlorophyll is often accompanied by colorful **carotenoids**, pigments which absorb green, blue, and violet wavelengths and reflect red, yellow, and orange light. Carotenoids are generally masked by chlorophyll and thus tend to be unnoticed in green leaves. However, they give bright and obvious color to many

chloroplast
an organelle present in algae and plant cells that contains chlorophyll and is involved in photosynthesis

stroma
in chloroplasts, the space between the inner membrane and the thylakoid membranes

thylakoid
(Gr. *thylakos*, sac + *oides*, like) a stack of flattened membranous disks containing chlorophyll and found in the chloroplasts of eukaryotic cells

nonphotosynthetic plant structures, such as roots (carrots), flowers (daffodils), fruits (tomatoes), and seeds (corn kernels). Chlorophyll absorbs all but green wavelengths of light, and carotenoids all but the red, orange, and yellow wavelengths. Functioning together in pigment complexes, chlorophylls and carotenoids can absorb most of the available energy in visible light. The importance of these pigments, of course, is not just that they absorb light, but what becomes of that captured energy.

The Chloroplast: Solar Cell and Sugar Factory

What gives a plant the ability to gather sunlight in its leaves? The photosynthetic pigments in green leaves are concentrated in layers of green cells that carry out photosynthesis (Fig. 3.9a–c). These cells contain **chloroplasts**, green organelles in which both the energy-trapping and carbon-fixing reactions of photosynthesis take place (Fig. 3.9c,d). Each leaf cell may contain about 50 chloroplasts, and each square millimeter of leaf surface may contain more than half a million of the green organelles. Chloroplasts are similar to mitochondria in several ways: Both are elon-

gated organelles with an inner and outer membrane and interior flattened sacs (see Fig. 3.7 and Fig. 3.9d); both carry out energy-related tasks in the cell; and both have their own DNA in circular chromosomes. However, while mitochondria are "powerhouses" that generate ATP, chloroplasts are both solar cells and sugar factories that capture sunlight and generate sugar-phosphates and other carbohydrates.

Chloroplast Membranes

Chloroplasts have an outer membrane and inner membrane that lie side by side and that collectively enclose a space filled with a watery solution, the **stroma** (see Fig. 3.9d). A third membrane system lies within the inner membrane and forms the **thylakoids**, a complicated network of stacked, disklike sacs, interconnected by flattened channels. Chlorophyll and other colored pigments are embedded in the thylakoid membrane and make this membrane the only part of an entire plant that is truly green. The fact that we see most leaves as green shows how incredibly abundant thylakoids are in nature. In addition to pigments, the thylakoid membrane contains members of an electron transport chain and, in some areas, many copies of an ATP-synthesizing enzyme (Fig. 3.9f).

An Overview of Photosynthesis

There is a beautiful symmetry to the metabolic processes of respiration and photosynthesis that is revealed by their nearly opposite overall equations.

Figure 3.9
Leaves and Photosynthesis

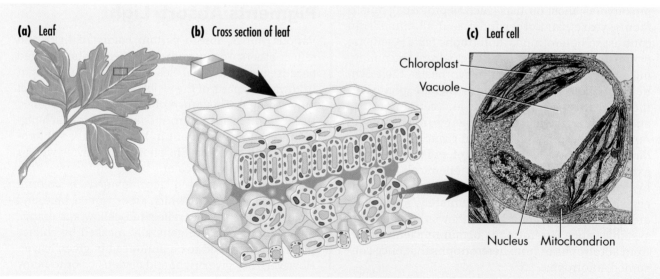

(a) Leaf

(b) Cross section of leaf

(c) Leaf cell

Chloroplast

Vacuole

Nucleus   Mitochondrion

Earlier, we saw that the aerobic cellular respiration could be summarized like this:

$$Glucose + Oxygen + ADP + Phosphate \rightarrow Carbon\ dioxide + Water + ATP$$

The process of photosynthesis is a nearly opposite equation:

$$Carbon\ dioxide + Water + Light\ energy \rightarrow Glucose + Oxygen$$

Recall that when oxygen is present, aerobic respiration in mitochondria breaks down glucose into carbon dioxide and water and releases chemical energy that becomes stored in ATP. Nearly the reverse takes place in photosynthesis: the chloroplast traps light energy, transforms it into chemical energy, and then uses that chemical energy to convert carbon dioxide and water into sugars, releasing *oxygen* as a waste product.

Clearly, living things must have both a source of energy and a means of releasing it, and for green plants and most other autotrophs, the direct energy source is sunlight. To understand photosynthesis, we'll follow the path of light striking a leaf and track the electrons whose energy level is boosted by sunlight. That pathway has two phases: a light-trapping phase and a carbon-fixing phase.

The Light-Trapping Phase of Photosynthesis

When sunlight reaches the leaf of a plant, some of the solar energy strikes chlorophyll or other colored pigment molecules in the chloroplasts and becomes trapped as it boosts electrons in the pigments to higher energy levels (Fig. 3.10a, Step ①). The electrons leave the chlorophyll and pass down an electron transport chain (Step ②). As the electrons travel down the electron transport chain, they release their energy bit by bit, and this energy is then stored in the chemical bonds of ATP and the electron carriers (Step ③). The "hole" in the chlorophyll left by the energized electrons is filled by electrons stripped from a water molecule (H_2O) (Step ④). The hydrogens from the water molecule stay in the chloroplast, but the oxygen is released to the atmosphere, where plants and animals can use it in aerobic respiration. These events make up the first phase of photosynthesis, the light-dependent reactions, also known as *energy-trapping reactions*. The reactions are driven by light energy and can take place only when light is available, and they produce oxygen, ATP, and energized electron carriers.

The Carbon-Fixing Phase of Photosynthesis

Now we move to the second part of the story. The ATP and electron carriers produced by the energy-trapping reactions supply the energy needed for the second phase of photosynthesis, a biochemical cycle called the carbon-fixing reactions (Fig. 3.10b). (These

light-dependent reactions
(also known as *energy-trapping reactions*) the first phase of photosynthesis, driven by light energy; electrons that trap the sun's energy pass the energy to high-energy carriers such as ATP where it is stored in chemical bonds

carbon-fixing reactions
(also known as *light-independent reactions* or the *Calvin-Benson cycle*) the second stage of photosynthesis in which the energy trapped and converted during the light-dependent reactions is used to combine carbon molecules into sugars

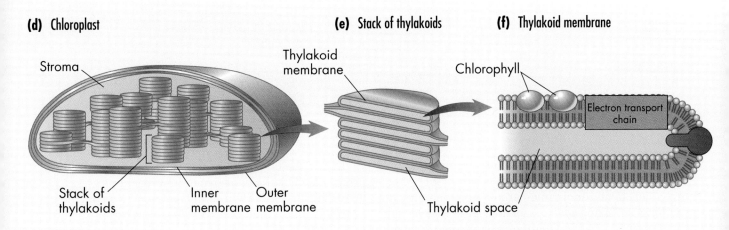

(d) Chloroplast

Stroma

Stack of thylakoids

Inner membrane

Outer membrane

(e) Stack of thylakoids

Thylakoid membrane

Thylakoid space

(f) Thylakoid membrane

Chlorophyll

Electron transport chain

Figure 3.10
The Reactions of Photosynthesis

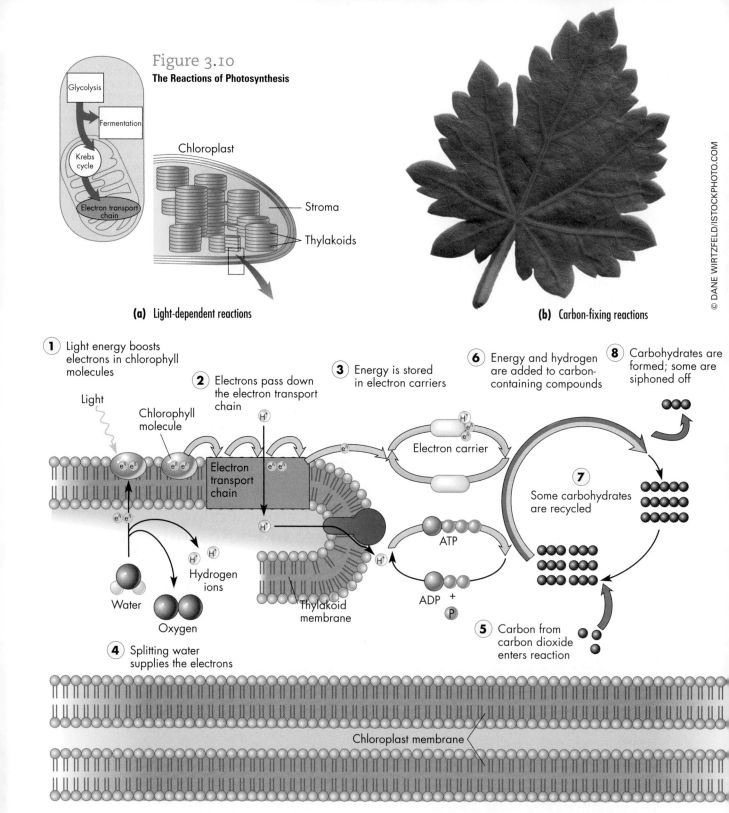

Chloroplast

Stroma

Thylakoids

Glycolysis

Fermentation

Krebs cycle

Electron transport chain

(a) Light-dependent reactions

(b) Carbon-fixing reactions

© DANE WIRTZFELD/ISTOCKPHOTO.COM

1 Light energy boosts electrons in chlorophyll molecules

2 Electrons pass down the electron transport chain

3 Energy is stored in electron carriers

6 Energy and hydrogen are added to carbon-containing compounds

8 Carbohydrates are formed; some are siphoned off

Light

Chlorophyll molecule

Electron transport chain

Electron carrier

7 Some carbohydrates are recycled

ATP

ADP + P

Hydrogen ions

Water

Oxygen

Thylakoid membrane

4 Splitting water supplies the electrons

5 Carbon from carbon dioxide enters reaction

Chloroplast membrane

are also called the *Calvin-Benson cycle* or sometimes the *light-independent reactions*.) "Carbon fixing" refers to a cell taking inorganic carbon from the air and joining it ("fixing it") to a biological molecule. The carbon-fixing reactions can go on day or night because they do not directly require light energy; they only require the energy carriers ATP and electron carriers produced by the light-dependent reactions.

During the carbon-fixing reactions, an enzyme in the stroma of the chloroplast first adds carbon dioxide from the air to a previously formed five-carbon compound, making a six-carbon compound that immediately breaks into two three-carbon compounds (Fig. 3.10b, Step 5). Then the chloroplasts transfer the energy stored in the bonds of ATP and electron carriers, and the hydrogens from the electron carriers, to the newly made three-carbon compounds (Step 6). Some of the newly formed three-carbon molecules are joined together and rearranged to regenerate the original starting molecules of the cycle (Step 7), while others can be siphoned off in energy-storing carbohydrate molecules (Step 8). Chloroplasts have to run this cycle with three carbon dioxide molecules to get out one three-carbon carbohydrate molecule. Cells can use the newly available carbohydrate to fuel the plant cell's own survival activities (and those of nonphotosynthetic plant parts such as roots) via the energy-harvesting steps of glycolysis and aerobic respiration in the plant's mitochondria. Or the plant cell can make sugar, as in flower nectar; cellulose, a structural material in cells walls, stems, leaves, and other plant parts; or starch, a form of long-term energy storage. Thanks to the formation of cellulose, we have the paper and wood we use daily. And the plant starch stored in rice, wheat, oats, potatoes, corn, and other crops are staples of the human diet.

The Global Carbon Cycle

It's hard to imagine how the metabolic pathways inside microscopic cells could possibly help perpetuate a cycle of planetary proportions. But a global carbon cycle moves vast amounts of carbon-containing compounds through the atmosphere, soil, water, and living organisms based on the carbon-fixing activities of autotrophs, the release of carbon dioxide by heterotrophs, and on geological phenomena such as erosion. You'll read more about the global carbon cycle in Chapter 15.

It is also hard to imagine that people could be altering that vast carbon cycle through their activities. But we are releasing millions of tons of extra carbon dioxide into the atmosphere each year by burning rain forests to clear new agricultural land and burning carbon-containing fossil fuels like coal and oil in factories and cars. This extra carbon dioxide causes extra heat to be trapped in the atmosphere. Scientists call this process the *greenhouse effect*. The greenhouse effect appears to be causing a slow but steady increase in average air and water temperatures called *global climate change* (also discussed in Chapter 15).

Aside from the changes in global air and water temperatures, wouldn't an increase in carbon dioxide benefit plants, since they take in the gas as a carbon source? Plant researchers have shown that they can add extra carbon dioxide to the plants growing in a controlled environment and measure an increase in the carbon-fixing reactions of photosynthesis and

Who knew?

Eating "low on the food chain" means eating more vegetables and less meat. Because energy is lost as heat every time it is converted to a different form, the amount of energy represented by a vegetarian meal is less than one composed of meat, since the loss of heat energy (entropy) must be included. The amount of energy from the sun is fixed; losing less food energy to heat by eating veggies means more energy is conserved, less land is required to feed one individual, and more vegetarians can survive than meat-eaters.

plants can grow faster. In an equivalent way, supplying more gasoline will speed up a car's engine. The problem is, some kinds of plants might respond better than others to the increased carbon dioxide, leading to imbalances as one plant species becomes overpopulated at the expense of others. If the benefit went mostly to desirable crop plants and not to the weeds that tend to choke them out, this might be a welcome outcome. Unfortunately, our limited understanding of natural ecosystems does not allow us to predict which plants would respond to heightened carbon dioxide levels and take over certain ecosystems.

Associated with the rapid increase in carbon dioxide in the atmosphere, we are experiencing an increase in global temperature as well. In fact, all of the century's warmest years have occurred in the past decade. This warming trend appears to be affecting all kinds of plant and animal populations. As Chapter 15 explains in detail, the distribution of animals is changing, along with certain disease-causing organisms. What this next century of warming will mean to populations of hummingbirds and to our own burgeoning numbers— we can only guess.

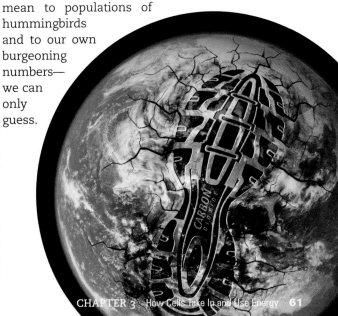

Learning Outcomes

LO 1   Understand the patterns of cell growth and cell division

LO 2   Explain mitosis and the mechanisms of cell division

LO 3   Identify what controls cell division

LO 4   Describe meiosis and the cell divisions that precede sexual reproduction

The Cell Cycle

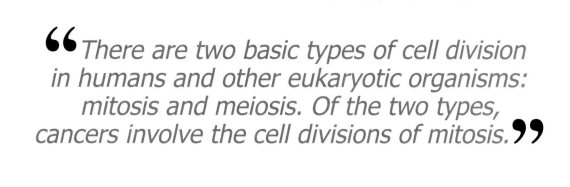

"There are two basic types of cell division in humans and other eukaryotic organisms: mitosis and meiosis. Of the two types, cancers involve the cell divisions of mitosis."

An Unavoidable Loss of Control

During the summer of 1972, 17-year-old Patricia's dermatologist found a small, pearly pink bump on her big toe and diagnosed it as a *basal cell carcinoma*. This patchy overgrowth of cells is the most common form of skin cancer—in fact, it is the most frequently diagnosed human cancer. The typical skin cancer patient, however, is middle aged or

What do you know?

Where in your body are cells dividing by mitosis? By meiosis?

older. So finding a lesion in a teenager was somewhat unusual—fair-skinned though Patricia was and susceptible to sunburns. The discovery of a second basal cell carcinoma on her temple a few weeks later was more ominous. It inspired a detailed search of her entire skin surface—and the doctor found yet more tiny, pearly cancers.

Their multiple occurrences in a girl of her age was diagnostic of a disease called *Basal Cell Nevus Syndrome (BCNS)*—a rare inherited condition that starts in adolescence and is characterized by numerous skin cancers throughout life. Today, at age 44, Patricia still sees a dermatologist every few weeks and, she says, she "can easily have 10 new carcinomas every visit." But she's accepted her situation with remarkable grace. Patricia remains hopeful that "still in my lifetime, some treatment will come up" to alleviate the disease she's been fighting for so long.

That treatment could come through the study of BCNS patients at the University of California, San Francisco—a study Patricia has been part of for years. The study's principal investigator, Ervin Epstein, is trying to find answers for the millions of people who will develop one or more basal cell carcinomas during their later years. If caught early enough, these cancers are "essentially 100 percent curable," Epstein explains. But his goal is to thoroughly understand how cells grow and divide at the level of genes, proteins, and other biological molecules. With that detailed knowledge of growth and division, he and his colleagues could possibly devise much more effective treatments and even preventative measures for skin cancers.

Patricia's long battle with skin cancer and Ervin Epstein's study of basal cell carcinoma are fitting subjects for this chapter. Here we explore the cell cycle—the stages of growth, duplication, and division in living cells. There are two basic types of cell division in humans and other eukaryotic organisms: mitosis and meiosis. *Mitosis* takes place in somatic (non-sex) cells, and *meiosis* occurs in gametes (sex cells). Of the two types, cancers involve the cell divisions of mitosis. As you explore the cell cycle, you'll see that a cancer starts when the normal controls over mitosis go haywire within a single cell. Instead of starting and stopping at appropriate times, cancerous cell division goes on and on until a mass of cells called a *tumor* results and displaces or invades other tissues.

cell cycle
the events that take place within the cell between one cell division and the next

© COMSTOCK IMAGES/GETTY IMAGES

epidermis
the outer layer of cells of an organism

dermis
the skin layer just below the epidermis or outer layer; the dermis contains tiny blood vessels, sweat glands, hair roots, and nerve endings

subcutaneous
literally below the skin; often refers to fat (adipose) cells that bind the skin to underlying organs found below the dermis layer

basal layer
the deepest layer of the epidermis, the outer layer of the skin; the basal layer contains cells that divide and replace dead skin cells; also called *germ layer*

basal cells
cells that lie in a layer just below the epidermis

The key to understanding both cancer and the normal growth and reproduction of cells and organisms lies in the intricacies of the cell cycle. That makes it one of the more important and fascinating topics in modern biology.

As we move through this chapter on the cell cycle, you'll find the answers to these questions:

☑ What are the patterns of normal cell growth and cell division?

☑ What is mitosis and what happens during cell division?

☑ What controls the timing and location of cell division?

☑ What is meiosis, the special cell divisions that precede sexual reproduction, and what happens during this process?

LO¹ Patterns of Cell Growth and Cell Division

To understand how skin cancers arise, we first need to understand normal cell growth and cell division in skin. Then we can compare these typi-cal patterns to the rare case of genetically determined BCNS in which cell growth and division patterns are abnormal and the cell cycle goes on uncontrolled.

Where and When Do Skin Cells Divide?

Your skin is your body's largest organ, and it forms a wonderful protective barrier around the muscles and other tissues. The outer skin surface layer is continu-ally abraded away by the rubbing of clothes or the scrubbing of a washcloth in the shower. How does the skin normally replace all this lost exterior mate-rial? The answer is a controlled replacement process of the outermost layers by deeper, dividing layers.

Skin consists of two main zones, a thin outer zone, or **epidermis**, and a thicker zone underneath, or **dermis**. Below the dermis is a **subcutaneous** layer, mostly fat (adipose) cells that bind the skin to under-lying organs. The dermis contains tiny blood vessels, sweat glands, hair roots, and nerve endings sensitive to heat and touch. None of these structures plays a direct role in the tumors of BCNS.

The epidermis is the skin's protective zone and it consists of several layers (Fig. 4.1). The layer near-est the dermis is a **basal layer** or dividing layer (also called the *germ layer*). Because this dividing region lies at the base of the epidermis, the cells there are sometimes called **basal cells**. This dividing layer is close to the blood in the dermis and is the only part of the epidermis that contains reproducing cells.

Figure 4.1
Where Do Cells Divide in Skin?

Epidermis cross-section

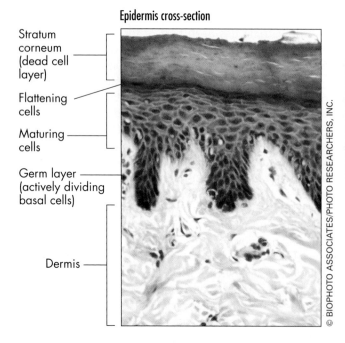

Stratum corneum (dead cell layer)

Flattening cells

Maturing cells

Germ layer (actively dividing basal cells)

Dermis

© BIOPHOTO ASSOCIATES/PHOTO RESEARCHERS, INC.

Figure 4.2
Where Do Basal Cell Skin Cancers Arise?

Section of a BCNS tumor

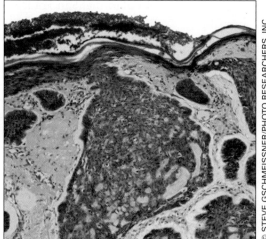

© STEVE GSCHMEISSNER/PHOTO RESEARCHERS, INC.

As these cells divide, some of them get pushed up into a layer of cell differentiation where they take on their mature characteristics. As they mature, the cells become tightly joined by cell junctions (review Fig. 2.14), they accumulate large quantities of the cytoskeletal protein keratin, and they become very flat, like miniature cookie sheets or pizza pans. As they move up further toward the body surface, their supply of nutrients becomes limited, and the cells die. The outermost portion of the epidermis is a dry layer consisting of sheet after sheet of flat, dead cells that are easily rubbed away.

To determine which cells give rise to a skin tumor, a surgeon can remove a basal cell carcinoma—say, on the palm of the hand—with a sharp instrument and then slice the cluster of cells very thinly to observe sections of it (Fig. 4.2). Comparing Figure 4.2 to the normal skin section in Figure 4.1, what do you see? You should notice a clump of cells in the dermis with the characteristics of cells that belong in the epidermis. What has happened is that basal cells from the dividing germ layer of the epidermis have divided too many times and made a mass that extends downward into the underlying dermis, an "overgrowth" process biologists call *proliferation* (an increase in cell numbers).

The Cell Cycle: Action in the Dividing Layer

The cells in the skin's dividing layer share a general strategy of cell reproduction with other living cells: they take in nutrients, increase in size, and then divide into two daughter cells. These two daughter cells may then, themselves, go through a period of growth followed by division. This alternation of growth and division is called the *cell cycle* (Fig. 4.3). During the **division phase** of the cell cycle, there is a partitioning of the cells' internal organelles, and then a dividing of the cell in two. The growth period between two division phases is called **interphase**.

As we saw in Chapter 2 (Fig. 2.10), the material inside of a cell is not a homogeneous mass like a loaf of bread that you can just slice to yield halves containing very similar materials. Cells contain various organelles in differing amounts and places. Some of these organelles, like the ribosomes, mitochondria, Golgi apparatus, and so on, are present by the thousands or millions in each cell. If the cell is just cleaved in two, each half will have sufficient numbers of these organelles to ensure smooth functioning. Some organelles, however, are present in a single copy and may be offset into one part of the cell. These organelles include the chromosomes inside the nucleus with its genetic contents and the centrioles in the cytoplasm. Special mechanisms have evolved that distribute these "singleton" organelles correctly to daughter cells.

Chromosomes

Patricia inherited her BCNS; this means her cells include the instructions for the disease in their genetic information. As we saw in Chapter 2, **chromosomes** contain a cell's hereditary information—the instructions the cell uses to construct itself—and thus the organism of which it is a part. We'll look at chromosomes in more detail in Chapter 6. The important thing, here, is that cells need an orderly distribution mechanism so that as they divide, each of the two daughter cells receives the same hereditary information and both have the same information as did the parent cell.

All organisms contain chromosomes, although the size, shape, and number of these hereditary structures differ from species to species. Eukaryotic cells have 2 or more chromosomes: a cell in a roundworm contains 4 chromosomes; the nucleus of a cell

division phase
during the cell cycle, the partitioning of the cells' internal organelles, and the dividing of the cell in two

interphase
the period between cell divisions in a cell; during this period, the cell conducts its normal activities and DNA replication takes place in preparation for the next cell division; interphase is divided into three periods: G_1, S, and G_2

chromosome
a self-duplicating body in the cell nucleus made up of DNA and proteins and containing genetic information; a human cell contains 23 pairs of chromosomes; in a prokaryote, the DNA circle that contains the cell's genetic information

Figure 4.3
Overview of the Cell Cycle

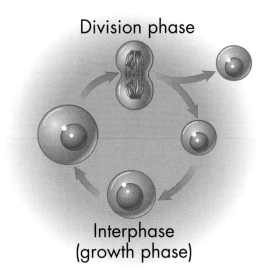

Division phase

Interphase
(growth phase)

chromatid
a daughter strand of a duplicated chromosome; duplication of a chromosome gives rise to two chromatids joined together at the centromere

replication
the copying of one DNA molecule into two identical DNA molecules

alignment
the positioning of chromosomes on the mitotic or meiotic spindle

separation
the movement of chromatids or chromosomes away from each other toward opposite poles of the dividing cell during mitosis or meiosis

sister chromatids
the two rods of a replicated chromosome

from a giant sequoia leaf contains 22; a goldfish nucleus contains 104; and the nucleus in a human skin cell has 46.

Chromosomes in the Cell Cycle

When a cell divides, each new offspring cell receives its own set of chromosomes containing an identical copy of the hereditary material. For this reason, the structure, duplication, and distribution of the chromosomes are central to the cell cycle. Chromosomes consist of protein and DNA, the long molecule that bears hereditary information. You can see chromosomes as distinct bodies by looking through a microscope, but they are visible only during a certain portion of the cell cycle, the division phase (review Fig. 4.3). At this time, the DNA is wound up into tight bundles we can see—bundles that resemble a kite string wound around a spool. The rest of the time, in interphase, the DNA is unwound and spread out, like a loose pile of kite string on the ground. It's impossible to visualize individual chromosomes in this state.

At the end of the division phase, each chromosome consists of a single long rod called a **chromatid** (Fig. 4.4b, Step ①). During interphase, the DNA in the chromosome undergoes **replication**, the copying of one DNA molecule into two identical DNA molecules (Step ②). When chromosomes become visible once again at the beginning of the division phase (Step ③), each chromosome consists of two rods (two chromatids), with each rod containing just one double-stranded DNA molecule. (Note that replication by itself does not change the number of chromosomes in a cell. Each chromosome simply doubles from one chromatid to two.) At this stage, chromosomes undergo **alignment**, aligning themselves in the middle of the cell as we will investigate shortly. Finally, in Step ④, **separation** takes place; the replicated chromosome with its two chromatids splits into two chromosomes, each with one chromatid made up of a double-stranded DNA molecule.

To summarize, the chromosome cycle involves one rod replicating to two rods during interphase, the replicated chromosome aligning in the cell, and then the two rods separating to different cells during the division phase.

Chromosome Structure

Now, let's look a bit closer at the anatomy of a chromosome. Figure 4.4a shows a sketch of a two-chromatid chromosome in the division phase of the cell cycle. You can see that each individual rod is formed by great loops of DNA complexed with protein that extend out from the axis of the condensed chromosome. In these loops, the DNA winds around proteins like string wrapped around thousands of tiny spools. Because each individual rod, or chromatid, in a chromosome contains a single extraordinarily long double-stranded DNA molecule, this packaging decreases the tangling of DNA during chromosome alignment and separation in the division phase.

The chromosomes we have just seen consist of two identical rods, called **sister chromatids**, held

Figure 4.4
Chromosome Structure and the Chromosome Cycle

(a) Sketch of a chromosome

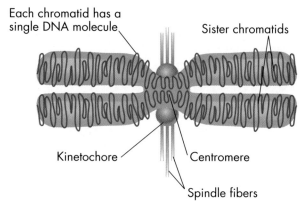

Each chromatid has a single DNA molecule

Sister chromatids

Kinetochore

Centromere

Spindle fibers

(b) The chromosome cycle

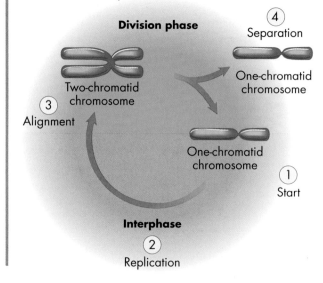

Division phase

④ Separation

Two-chromatid chromosome

③ Alignment

One-chromatid chromosome

One-chromatid chromosome

① Start

Interphase

② Replication

together at a single point, the **centromere** (Fig. 4.4a). Located at the centromere is a group of proteins called the **kinetochore**, and this structure attaches to long fibers in the cell called **spindle fibers** (Fig. 4.4a). These spindle fibers move chromosomes around, for reasons we'll see shortly. Each chromatid has just one double-stranded DNA molecule (Fig. 4.4a), and the DNA molecules in two sister chromatids are identical. As cell division progresses, the two sister chromatids separate from each other (Fig. 4.4b, Step ④). One of the sister chromatids ends up in one of the daughter cells, and the other, genetically identical chromatid ends up in the other daughter cell. Thus, immediately after division, each chromosome consists of a single chromatid with a single DNA molecule.

Interphase: The Growth Period in the Cell Cycle

Cells proliferate unchecked in basal cell carcinomas like the ones Patricia Hughes develops. Because the alternating periods of growth and division are so central to understanding this proliferation, we must continue exploring the stages of the cell cycle. Recall that the cell cycle has a division phase and a period of growth, the interphase. Biologists divide interphase into three portions called G_1, S, and G_2. G_1 and G_2 stand for *Gap 1* and *Gap 2*, because they are gaps in the cell cycle that come between the time of chromosome division and the time of chromosome replication. The S stands for *synthesis* of DNA. And biologists usually call the division phase *M*, for *mitosis* (Fig. 4.5).

Different cells require different amounts of time to pass through the entire cell cycle. Certain cells, like mature nerve cells of the brain, arise in the embryo and never divide again. In contrast, cells in your bone marrow replace worn-out blood cells by dividing every 18 hours or so. Cells that line your stomach divide in a cycle about 24 hours long. Most skin cells, even in the dividing basal layer, replicate only every week or so. A basal cell carcinoma, however, can undergo new

rounds of the cell cycle every 67 hours. Clearly, the cell cycle can accelerate (we'll discuss the reasons later).

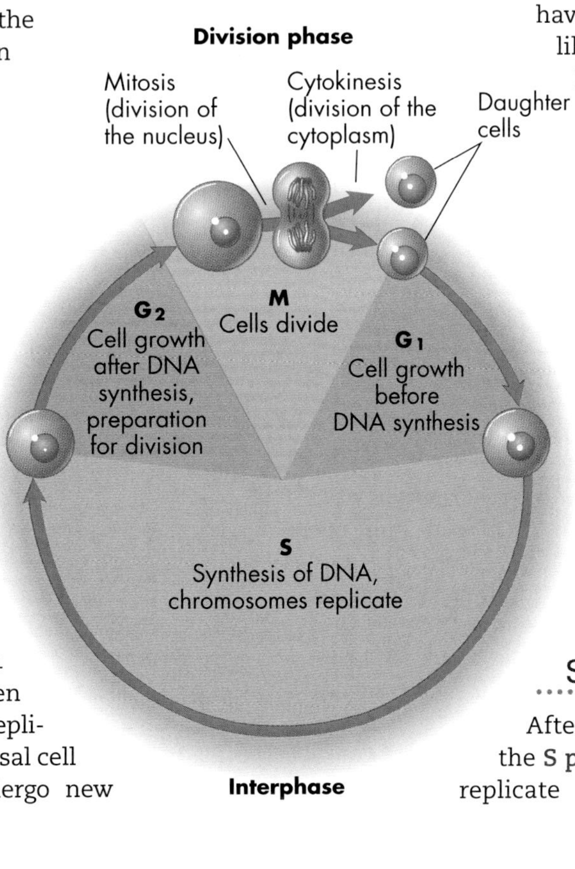

G_1: Active Growth

G_1 and G_2 are important growth phases. During the G_1 phase, cells manufacture new proteins, ribosomes, mitochondria, and other cell components in preparation for DNA synthesis and cell division. The length of the G_1 phase determines the length of the entire cell cycle. G_1 can be quite short or very long, depending on the type of cell, its role in the organism, and conditions in its environment. For example, skin cells normally have a long cell cycle and a long G_1 (a few days). That can change, however. If a wound removes some of those cells, the G_1 phase may shorten in the skin cells at the edge of the wound, speeding up growth and division and enabling the wound to heal rapidly. (Skin cancer cells have an accelerated cycle a bit like a wound that never heals.) Plants can have an analogous process. In an aspen tree, if a deer or beaver nibbles away the bark, the bark-forming cells below can enter a shortened G_1 phase, rapidly producing new bark, which protects the damaged area. Unlike in cancer cells, however, in both normal skin and tree bark the faster cell cycling stops when the wound is healed. Following G_1, eukaryotic cells enter the synthesis phase, S.

S: Synthesis of DNA

After the G_1 phase, cells enter the **S phase**, during which enzymes replicate the double-stranded DNA

centromere
the point on the chromosome where the spindle attaches and also where the two chromatids are joined

kinetochore
a group of proteins located at the centromere that attaches to long fibers called spindle fibers

spindle fibers
the cytoskeletal rods (microtubules) that move chromosomes toward the cell poles and that cause cell poles to separate during cell division

G_1 phase
the portion of the cell cycle that follows mitosis but precedes DNA synthesis

S phase
the portion of the cell cycle during which the cell synthesizes DNA

Figure 4.5

Phases of the Cell Cycle

Division phase

Mitosis (division of the nucleus)

Cytokinesis (division of the cytoplasm)

Daughter cells

G2 Cell growth after DNA synthesis, preparation for division

M Cells divide

G1 Cell growth before DNA synthesis

S Synthesis of DNA, chromosomes replicate

Interphase

G₂ phase
the portion of the cell cycle that follows DNA synthesis but precedes mitosis

M phase
the portion of the cell cycle during which the nucleus divides by mitosis and the cytoplasm divides by cytokinesis

mitosis
the process of nuclear division in which replicated chromosomes separate and form two daughter nuclei genetically identical to each other and the parent nucleus; mitosis is usually accompanied by cytokinesis (division of the cytoplasm)

cytokinesis
the process of cytoplasmic division following nuclear division

prophase
the first phase of nuclear division in mitosis or meiosis, when the chromosomes condense, the nucleolus disperses, and the spindle forms

metaphase
the period during nuclear division (mitosis) when the spindle microtubules cause the chromosomes to line up at the center of the cell

molecule in each chromosome (see Chapter 6 for details). Cells also synthesize certain proteins necessary for maintaining chromosome structure as the S phase proceeds. When the S phase ends, each chromosome consists of two identical and parallel double-stranded DNA molecules packaged into two chromatids. Every stretch of DNA in a chromosome is copied once and only once during each S phase. After copying is complete, the cell enters G₂. As you might imagine, processes occurring during S phase provide physicians with important targets for cancer therapies. Nondividing cells don't go through S, so agents that block the events of the S phase affect only dividing cells, such as Patricia's skin tumors. Such therapeutic agents include substances that mimic DNA subunits and compounds that block DNA synthesis.

G₂: Preparation for Division

During the G₂ phase, the cell continues to synthesize many proteins. If a researcher artificially blocks this synthesis, the cell fails to divide, suggesting that some proteins synthesized during G₂ promote mitosis, division of the nucleus. When all the necessary proteins have been synthesized, the cell leaves the final growth phase and begins to divide.

M: The Cell Divides

The **M phase** generally consists of two main events: **mitosis**, the division of the nuclear material, and **cytokinesis**, the division of the cytoplasm (Fig. 4.5). Both mitosis and cytokinesis are vitally important for the equitable distribution of genetic material and other cell components, so we'll talk about each one separately. But keep in mind what's at work: mechanisms to insure that a cell gives rise to identical daughter cells with the same genetic information and role in the organism. Without these carefully controlled and timed divisions, nothing would keep a toe cell from becoming a liver cell, or a skin cell from becoming a tumor.

LO² Mitosis and the Mechanisms of Cell Division

In the previous section, we've seen that cells in the lower, basal layer of the epidermis pass through the cell cycle, thereby generating new skin. If their growth is uncontrolled, the cells instead grow into basal cell carcinomas. The division phase, or M phase, is therefore a crucial part of the cell cycle. So let's see how a normal cell divides.

The Phases of Mitosis

Whether in the skin or other tissue, the mitotic dance of the chromosomes goes on continuously in a dividing cell. Biologists have named several prominent phases of mitosis to simplify its description. The events of these phases are summarized here and illustrated and explained in more detail in Figure 4.7 on pages 70–71. Recall from Figure 4.4 that chromosome replication has already occurred during the S phase, before mitosis begins.

Prophase

In **prophase** (*pro* = before), the chromosomes condense and become visible, the nucleolus (a dense organelle within the nucleus; review Fig. 2.10) disappears, and a mitotic spindle forms (Fig. 4.7a–c). The mitotic spindle is a bundle of certain filaments of the cytoskeleton (microtubules) that suspends and moves the chromosomes. In late prophase, a stage cell biologists call prometaphase (*meta* = middle), the nuclear envelope disappears, the spindle enters the nuclear region, and the spindle attaches to the chromosomes at the centromere (Fig. 4.7c). Individual chromosomes jostle back and forth, as if they were involved in a tug-of-war between the two poles.

Metaphase

In **metaphase**, the spindle microtubules align the chromosomes in the middle of the spindle, each chromosome lined up independently of the others in a single plane, called the metaphase plate, in the middle of the spindle (Fig. 4.7d). The metaphase plate is a bit like the flat surface of a grapefruit that has been sliced in half.

Anaphase

In **anaphase** (*ana* = apart, opposed), the centromeres split and the spindle microtubules separate the chromatids (now called chromosomes) and pull them toward opposite poles (Fig. 4.7e). Figure 4.8 on page 72 describes in more detail the role of the spindle in separating the chromatids during anaphase.

Telophase

In **telophase** (*telo* = goal), the chromosomes arrive at opposite poles of the cell, and the preparatory events are reversed: the nuclear envelope reappears, the spindle dissolves, and so on (Fig. 4.7f,g). Once telophase is over, the division of the cell nucleus (mitosis) is complete. Now the cell has two nuclei carrying identical sets of chromosomes. The M phase continues, however, with cytokinesis, the division of the cytoplasm (Fig. 4.7h).

"Bye Bye, Parent Cell"

There is a key difference between the replication of a cell involving mitosis and the reproduction of a person or a plant involving meiosis. When these large, complex organisms reproduce, the parent and offspring both generally continue to exist. In contrast, during cell reproduction, the parent cell (Fig. 4.7a) ceases to exist as an entity and its parts are distributed to the two offspring cells (Fig. 4.7h).

The Mitotic Spindle

Figure 4.7 shows where the chromosomes move during mitosis. It doesn't, however, reveal the mechanism that causes the chromosomes to move. This mechanism involves the **mitotic spindle**, a microscopic scaffolding of fibers made of microtubules that suspends and moves the chromosomes (Fig. 4.8). *Spindle fibers* extend from the **centrioles**, organelles consisting of two short cylinders that organize the cell's network of microtubules. Some spindle fibers attach directly to special structures (kinetochores) at the centromeres of chromosomes, and pull the two chromatids toward the poles (Fig. 4.8). Other spindle fibers overlap at the cell's center and cause the two poles to move apart from each other. Knowing how the spindle works is also important in designing anticancer drugs. The physician wants to block mitosis in tumor cells. But how?

Cytokinesis: The Cytoplasm Divides   In order for two cells to appear where there was once one, the original cell must cleave in two. Toward the end of mitosis, the cytoplasm of most plant and animal cells begins to divide by means of cytokinesis (literally, "cell movement") (Fig. 4.7f–h). In both animal and plant cells, new plasma membranes form at or near the place once occupied by the chromosomes during metaphase and separate the two nuclei into the two new cells. The details of cytokinesis vary because animal cells have a pliable outer surface, while plant cells have a rigid cell wall.

Cytokinesis in Animal Cells   Animal cells divide from the outside in, as a circle of microfilaments called a **contractile ring** pinches each cell in two. Late in mitosis, a ring of filaments containing the contractile protein, *actin*, creates a furrow in the cell surface in much the same way that a purse string tightens around the neck of a purse (Fig. 4.7g–h). The furrow deepens, and eventually squeezes the cell in two.

Cytokinesis in Plant Cells   Plant cells, with their rigid cell walls, retain their shape throughout the cell cycle, dividing from the inside out (Fig. 4.6). At the end of

anaphase
a period during nuclear division when the chromosomes move toward the poles of the cell

telophase
the final phase of nuclear division when the chromosomes are at opposite poles of the cell, the nuclear membrane and nucleolus reappear, and the spindle disappears

mitotic spindle
a weblike structure of microtubules that suspends and moves the chromosomes; formed during prophase in mitosis

centriole
pairs of short, rod-shaped organelles that organize the cytoskeletal fibers called microtubules into scaffolds; these intracellular frameworks help maintain cell shape and move chromosomes during cell division

contractile ring
the ring of cytoskeletal elements (actin filaments) that separates one cell into two during the division of the cytoplasm

Figure 4.6
Cytokinesis in Plant Cells

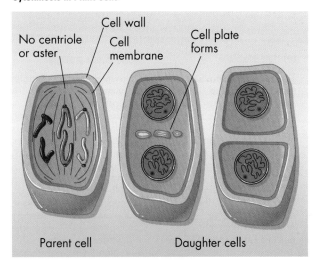

No centriole or aster   Cell wall   Cell membrane   Cell plate forms

Parent cell   Daughter cells

cell plate
in plant cells, a partition that arises during late cell division from vesicles at the center of the cell and that eventually separates the two daughter cells

mitosis, vesicles filled with cell wall precursors collect in the center of the cell. The separate vesicles gradually fuse, forming a central partition, or **cell plate**, made of cell-wall material sandwiched between plasma membranes. This fusion completes the central partition and divides the plant cell into two identical daughter cells, which remain connected. Each cell now has its own nucleus and is ready to begin interphase.

Applying Our Knowledge of Mitosis to Cancer Therapy

Patricia's multiple skin cancers result from an overgrowth of cells. In her cancer and in all cancers, a cell starts growing and dividing by means of the phases we've just explored, but then continues unchecked, forming a tumor that can displace or invade other cells and tissues. The real key to cancerous cell division is to understand how the normal control of the

cell cycle is lost, and we'll return to that shortly. In the meantime, some aspects of mitosis apply to the treatment of cancer once it arises.

The best way to treat most tumors, including BCNS lesions, is to surgically remove them. This makes sense for basal cell carcinomas because, being at the surface, they are readily accessible. Furthermore, while the masses they form crowd other cells, they do not grow especially aggressively, nor do they tend to invade and take over adjacent tissues. Once the skin tumor is removed or zapped through freezing with liquid nitrogen, it seldom returns. Certain other tumors, however, such as melanomas (pigmented skin tumors), and cancers of the breast, ovaries, and pancreas are more aggressive and invasive and often do require other methods in addition to surgery, such as chemotherapy and radiation.

Chemotherapy and the Spindle

We see in Figure 4.8 that the spindle is crucial for moving chromosomes around in mitosis. Does this open an avenue for cancer therapy? Researchers thought

Figure 4.7

Chromosome Choreography: The Stages of Mitosis in an Animal Cell

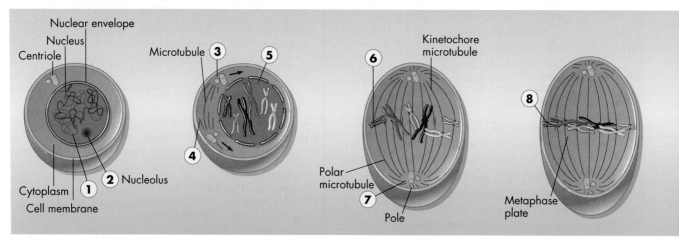

(a) Late interphase

The cell's DNA has already replicated during S in the previous interphase. As the cell enters the first part of mitosis, called *prophase,* the DNA changes from its diffuse and tangled state in interphase (1) to become more tightly packaged. Also, the nucleolus, a dense organelle within the nucleus (2), disperses.

(b) Middle prophase

In animal cells, centrioles, cylindrical groups of short microtubules, duplicate and organize spindle microtubules (3). Plant cells lack centrioles. Centrioles separate and move toward opposite ends, or poles, of the cell, spinning out the mitotic spindle (4). As the nuclear envelope disperses (5), the spindle invades the nuclear region.

(c) Late prophase

Microtubules attach to chromosomes by kinetochores (6). The chromosomes then jostle back and forth as the polar microtubules, which suspend and move the chromosomes, interact with the kinetochore microtubules, and the centrioles complete their migration to the poles (7).

(d) Metaphase

During metaphase the chromosomes become aligned on the metaphase plate (8), a plane lying halfway between each pole.

so. They reasoned that if they could block the action of the spindle, they could block cell division and hence slow cancer growth. In fact, several chemotherapy drugs now used to treat cancer attack the spindle. Taxol and related compounds, extracted from the bark of the Pacific yew tree, have proven useful in treating carcinomas of the cervix and ovary. Taxol binds to microtubules and blocks their breakdown into protein subunits. Thus, a cancerous cell gets stuck part way through mitosis and, with the spindle still in place, can't divide into new malignant daughter cells. Other drugs, like vinblastine from the periwinkle plant, stop the division of cancer cells by blocking the formation of the spindle in the first place. These chemotherapeutic drugs have powerful side effects, however, and so pharmaceutical researchers are always trying to develop new and better treatments.

Radiation Therapy

Have you known someone with cancer who received radiation therapy? During this treatment, technicians aim a radiation beam precisely at the patient's tumor and shield other parts of the patient's body from the beam. How does radiation therapy work? And why is it necessary to shield the patient's body?

Radiation can break chromosomes. If such breakage occurs in a cell that does not divide, the cell will still be able to carry on in a normal fashion because most body cells contain two copies of each chromosome. If chromosome breakage takes place in a cell that later divides—a skin cell, for example, or a tumor cell—the consequences are often quite different, and your knowledge of mitosis can help explain why. Let's say radiation breaks a chromosome and leaves a fragment that is no longer attached to a centromere. What would happen to the chromosome fragment during cell division? It might not be distributed normally to the daughter cells. This is because the centromere is the only part of the chromosome that is directly attached to spindle microtubules, which pull each chromatid to one of the cell's poles during mitosis (review Fig. 4.8b). In a case of chromosome breakage like this, one cell might end up with an extra chromosome part, while the sister cell ends up missing this chromosome part. The resulting genetic

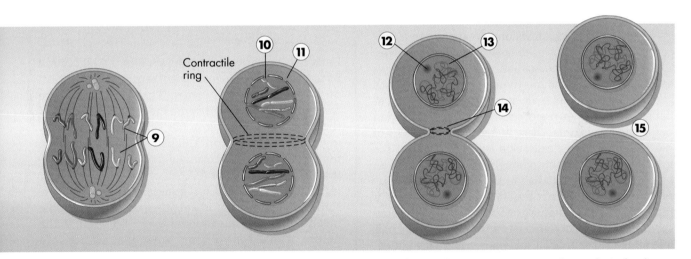

(e) Anaphase

Next, during anaphase the centromeres split, and microtubules pull sister chromatids apart, toward opposite poles (9).

(f) Early telophase

Early telophase marks the beginning of cytokinesis, the division of the cytoplasm. The daughter chromatids (now independent chromosomes) arrive at each pole (10), and the nuclear membrane re-forms around the chromosomes (11).

(g) Late telophase

As telophase progresses, the nucleolus reappears (12), the spindle dissolves, and the chromosomes reel out again into a tangled mass of DNA and protein (13). In addition, in late telophase in animal cells, a contractile ring tightens around the cell's midline where the metaphase plate had been, creating a furrow (14).

(h) Completion of cytokinesis

After the completion of nuclear division, daughter cells finally separate in cytokinesis (15).

Figure 4.8
What Moves the Chromosomes?

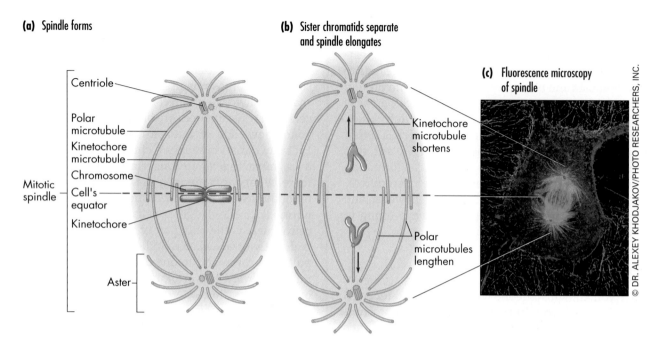

(a) Spindle forms

Centriole
Polar microtubule
Kinetochore microtubule
Chromosome
Cell's equator
Kinetochore
Mitotic spindle
Aster

(b) Sister chromatids separate and spindle elongates

Kinetochore microtubule shortens
Polar microtubules lengthen

(c) Fluorescence microscopy of spindle

© DR. ALEXEY KHODJAKOV/PHOTO RESEARCHERS, INC.

imbalance can alter the cell's information and lead to its death.

The most rapid cell division taking place in a cancer patient often involves the cancer cells themselves. Therefore, well-aimed radiation therapy damages and kills those cells more than it hurts the patient's surrounding cells. Like all humans, however, cancer patients have other rapidly dividing cells in addition to the cancerous cells. These include the precursors of red and white blood cells, skin cells, and cells of the intestinal lining. Not surprisingly, these cell types can be damaged during radiation therapy, and their disruption explains some of the short-term side effects of radiation therapy: anemia (too few red blood cells), susceptibility to infection (too few white blood cells), hair loss (damaged skin cells), and nausea (damaged intestinal cells). Ironically, long-term side effects include an increased risk of cancer, since, as we say, radiation can cause genetic mutations and these can lead to the uncontrolled divisions in a tumor. The disruption of rapidly dividing cell types also explains the destructive, often lethal effects of exposure to high levels of radiation from a hydrogen bomb or an accident at a nuclear power plant. So-called radiation sickness is like a severe set of symptoms from radiation therapy. These facts about mitosis underscore the devastating consequences nuclear war or nuclear accidents could have for people and most other life forms on Earth. They also highlight the restorative powers of mitosis, which keep most of us healthy most of the time.

LO³ What Controls Cell Division?

Let's return, now, to Patricia's Basal Cell Nevus Syndrome (BCNS) and the frequent formation of basal cell carcinomas. The growth of these tumors is evidence that some mechanism is missing that would normally stop her skin cells from dividing so rapidly and continuously. Some mechanism may be broken that normally acts like a car's brake to reduce the speed of the cell cycle. Or perhaps her cells have an "accelerator" that is working overtime. Normal cells in the skin and other tissues have some means of regulating the cell cycle. So what is the nature of that control? And what goes wrong with it in BCNS?

Stem Cells and Growth Control

Think, for a minute, about cell division in the skin. Normally after a basal cell in the dividing layer of the skin undergoes mitosis, then one of the daughter cells stops cycling and matures into a cell of the outermost layer of the skin (Fig. 4.9a). Although the process is entirely healthy, this cell is, in effect, on a suicide mission—it's "born to die," since it will never divide again and will eventually expire and flake off. The other daughter, however, can continue to divide. Cells with the ability to continue dividing are called stem cells and their progeny can behave in two ways, with one daughter maturing into a differentiated cell type and the other retaining the ability to divide.

How do stem cells in the dividing cell layer "know" when they should divide? Here's a simple thought experiment: If you were to scrape off the upper layer of the epidermis in a small patch of skin, the dividing layer below it would somehow "recognize" the thinness. More cells in that dividing basal layer (or germ layer) would then leave the G_I phase of the cell cycle, enter S, and eventually complete a division. When the epidermis becomes thick enough once more, the basal layer "senses" this, too, and slows its rate of cell division.

Now, in a basal cell carcinoma, the signal to divide is somehow turned on but the signal to slow or cease dividing never comes, or if it does, it goes undetected. One possibility is that cells produce too much of the signal to divide; as a result, at any given time, more of the stem cells would undergo division than is needed to replace sloughed off skin. Here's another possibility: The daughter cell that should mature into an epidermal cell doesn't and instead, it too continues to divide (Fig. 4.9b). This is part of the overall question: What tells a cell to divide or stop dividing? Let's look at some possibilities for what is most likely happening.

The Molecular Basis of Basal Cell Carcinoma

People like Patricia have inherited genetic factors that predispose skin cells to form basal cell carcinomas. If she were to have children, about half of them would be likely to be affected with the condition (and Chapter 5 explains why). By investigating the inheritance of the disease gene in many families, Dr. Erwin Epstein and colleagues at the University of California at San Francisco were able, in 1996, to isolate the specific gene that is disrupted in BCNS. They were astonished at what they found. The gene turned out to be closely related to a gene already isolated from a fruit fly, *Drosophila melanogaster*. The gene is called *patched*, because fly embryos with the defective gene have abnormal little patches of hair-like structures in their skin. Epstein's group found that human families with BCNS had mutations in the human *patched* gene in all of their cells. They also found that people with individual, spontaneous basal cell carcinomas due to sun exposure and not inheritance often had mutations in the *patched* gene, but only in the cells of their skin tumor, not in *all* of their skin cells. It was clear that the *patched* gene normally functions in some way to prevent the growth of basal cell carcinomas and that mutations of the gene allow skin tumors to form.

By studying flies, workers had shown that the *patched* gene causes a certain protein to appear on the surface of cells. That protein, in turn, is necessary for the cell to interpret signals coming from the outside of the cell that stimulate cell division. The basic idea is that a substance in the cell's environment, often a protein called a **growth factor** made by a nearby cell, can act as a signaling protein telling other cells to divide. In flies, researchers showed that *patched* is the receptor for the signaling protein. In humans, the specific signaling protein is called sonic hedgehog because it is made by the *sonic hedgehog* gene. (This odd name comes from a mutant fly that, in this case, has prickly skin, making it look like a hedgehog.)

How Growth Factors Act

Still looking, then, at what instructs a cell to divide or stop dividing, let's see how growth factors might work. At the site of a cut or other wound, growth factors such as the human sonic hedgehog protein, may be released from dying cells (Fig. 4.10a, Step ①). The factors could diffuse locally, and bind to a **receptor**, a protein that chemically recognizes the specific growth factor. Receptors may be embedded in the membranes of nearby cells (Step ②). The binding

Figure 4.9
Stem Cells and Skin Cancer

(a) Normal cell growth   **(b)** Basal cell carcinoma

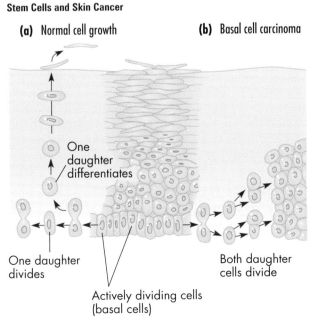

One daughter differentiates

One daughter divides

Actively dividing cells (basal cells)

Both daughter cells divide

meiosis
the type of cell division that occurs during gamete formation; the diploid parent cell divides twice, giving rise to four cells, each of which is haploid

sexual reproduction
a type of reproduction in which new individuals arise from the mating of two parents

gamete
(Gr., wife) a specialized sex cell, such as an ovum (egg) or sperm, that is haploid; a male gamete (sperm) and a female gamete (ovum) fuse and give rise to a diploid zygote, which develops into a new individual

of a growth factor from the wounded cell to the receptor of a nearby cell then stimulates an interior cascade of signals (Step ③). Some of those internal signals include *cyclins*, proteins whose levels rise and fall at different parts of the cell cycle and cause the cell to move from one phase to the next. The net result of this signaling (Step ④) is that the cells lining the wound are stimulated to divide. After enough cell division in the neighboring cell, the tear in the skin eventually fills in with new cells, growth factor levels fall, and the rate of cell division slows down.

Dr. Epstein's work showed that BCNS cells have a defective *patched* gene (Fig. 4.10b). This mutated gene makes an altered receptor that acts as if it is bound to the sonic hedgehog even when that signaling molecule is absent. Even without the sonic hedgehog "signal," the mutant patched protein stimulates the cascade of internal signals telling the cell to divide. This causes the cells in BCNS sites like those on Patricia's face and arms to enter S phase and divide inappropriately. Further investigations of this pathway in BCNS cells may eventually allow Dr. Epstein to understand exactly why and how basal cells start dividing in a skin cancer but never stop. This, in turn, could lead to treatments for BCNS as well as for the more common basal cell carcinomas that some people get later in life from too much exposure to sunlight.

Sonic hedgehog protein signal →
Patched receptor → Turned-on cell division

Cancer as a Disease of Altered DNA

Recent evidence indicates that most cancers are related to changes in a cell's DNA. Numerous studies have shown that many substances in the environment, including ultraviolet light, industrial chemicals, radiation, the tar in cigarettes, and certain viruses, cause such changes in DNA structure. Some DNA changes can affect either growth factors or receptors for growth factors on the cell's plasma membrane, as Dr. Epstein found for BCNS. Surprisingly, some cancer cells may produce *both* the growth factor to turn on cell division *as well as* its specific receptor; the result is cells that are constantly stimulating themselves to divide. There is still much uncertainty about the causes of cancer, but it is clear that the answers will be found in the regulation of the cell cycle, and the stages of growth, division, and rest. In the meantime, it's wise to avoid the most common environmental hazards associated with cancers, such as ultraviolet light and cigarette smoke.

LO⁴ Meiosis: The Special Cell Divisions That Precede Sexual Reproduction

If a BCNS patient like Patricia has children, there is a 50–50 chance that each child will inherit the disease of multiple skin cancers. Yet consider a teenager playing in the sun who experiences an ultraviolet light-induced change in the DNA of the *patched* gene in a cell on, say, the nose. This change or mutation could then lead to basal cell carcinoma arising on that person's nose. But this individual would *not* pass on to his or her children an increased likelihood of having either a single basal cell carcinoma or the multiple reoccurrences of BCNS. How can this be? What's the difference in their response? The answer revolves around the special cell population from which sex cells arise and the special type of cell division that produces them: meiosis.

Sexual Reproduction: Offspring from Fused Gametes

In **sexual reproduction**, parents (usually two, but sometimes one) generate specialized sex cells called gametes (Fig. 4.11). When gametes from two individuals (usually one male and one female) fuse during

Figure 4.10

Growth Factor Control, Normal Cell Division, and Cancer

(a) Growth control in a normal cell

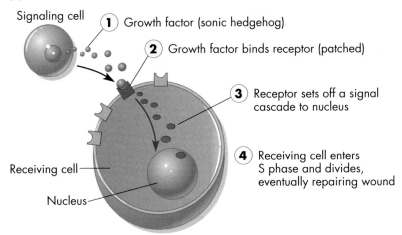

Signaling cell

1 Growth factor (sonic hedgehog)

2 Growth factor binds receptor (patched)

3 Receptor sets off a signal cascade to nucleus

4 Receiving cell enters S phase and divides, eventually repairing wound

Receiving cell

Nucleus

(b) Several ways to get faulty growth control in a cancer cell

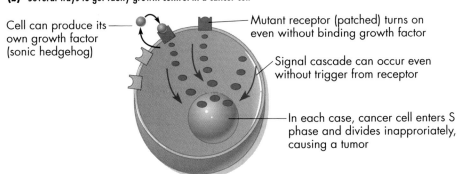

Cell can produce its own growth factor (sonic hedgehog)

Mutant receptor (patched) turns on even without binding growth factor

Signal cascade can occur even without trigger from receptor

In each case, cancer cell enters S phase and divides inapproriately, causing a tumor

---

fertilization
the fusion of two haploid gamete nuclei (egg and sperm), which forms a diploid zygote

egg
the haploid female gamete

sperm
the haploid male gamete

gonad
an animal reproductive organ that generates gametes; testes and ovaries

ovary
egg-producing organ

testis
(pl. testes) the male reproductive organ that produces sperm and sex hormones

zygote
(Gr. *zygotos,* paired together) the diploid cell that results from the fusion of an egg and a sperm cell; a zygote may either form a line of diploid cells by a series of mitotic cell divisions or undergo meiosis and develop into haploid cells

germ cell
a sperm cell or ovum (egg cell) or their precursors; the haploid gametes produced by individuals that fuse to form a new individual

---

fertilization, they set into motion the life of a new individual.

Most of us are familiar with sexual reproduction and the human life cycle. As with most plants and animals, the human female's gametes are large cells that are incapable of spontaneous movement called eggs, while the male gametes are small motile cells called sperm, which can move or be carried from the male to the egg (Fig. 4.11a). Eggs and sperm are usually produced in specialized organs. In flowering plants, they are produced by structures in the flowers; in animals, gametes are made by special organs called gonads. The female gonad is the ovary, which produces eggs, and the male gonad is the testis, which produces sperm.

In many complex organisms, including human beings and ginkgo trees, each individual produces just one kind of gamete, either egg or sperm. However, in pear trees, earthworms, and a number of other species, each adult individual can produce both types of gametes.

The fusion of egg and sperm, or fertilization, results in a single cell called the zygote (Fig. 4.11b).

In the zygote, the hereditary information from both parents unites, creating a genetically unique combination of genes and chromosomes. The single-celled zygote undergoes *development,* usually a period of rapid mitosis and cellular specialization during which the new cells emerge and take on their specific roles in the organism (Fig. 4.11c). As a result of development, an immature form emerges, continues to grow, and eventually changes into a mature adult.

Germ Cells and Somatic Cells

Early in animal development, a group of cells called germ cells is set aside. Germ cells are like the stem cells we discussed earlier; they retain the potential to divide to produce more germ cells, or to differentiate into gametes (eggs or sperm), and to migrate to the developing gonad during development (Fig. 4.11d). Animal eggs have a particular group of proteins that become separated into certain cells as the egg divides by mitosis (Fig. 4.11c). Whichever cells

somatic cell
(Gr. *soma,* body) A cell in an animal that is not a germ cell

receive these proteins develop into germ cells. The cells that don't receive these proteins become the rest of the body's cells in the muscles, brain, nose, and so on. These special proteins are called germ cell determinants, because they determine whether embryonic cells will become germ cells.

Figure 4.11
A Human Life Cycle

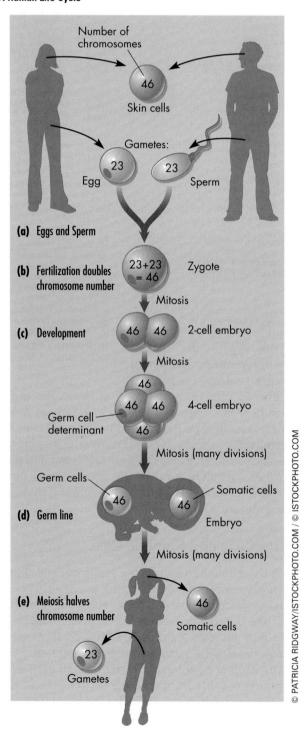

Number of chromosomes

46 — Skin cells

Gametes:

23 — Egg

23 — Sperm

(a) Eggs and Sperm

(b) Fertilization doubles chromosome number — 23+23 = 46 — Zygote

Mitosis

(c) Development — 46 46 — 2-cell embryo

Mitosis

46 46 46 46 — 4-cell embryo

Germ cell determinant

Mitosis (many divisions)

Germ cells — 46   46 — Somatic cells

(d) Germ line — Embryo

Mitosis (many divisions)

(e) Meiosis halves chromosome number — 46 — Somatic cells

23 — Gametes

© PATRICIA RIDGWAY/ISTOCKPHOTO.COM / © ISTOCKPHOTO.COM

Germ cell determinants form a continuous cell lineage extending back to your mother, her mother, and so on back in time. The normal body cells, or **somatic cells**, of a multicellular animal can't form egg and sperm, and these somatic cells eventually die. If, however, an organism's egg or sperm cells unite with those of another individual of the same species, then in a sense, that germ cell lineage lives on in the offspring even though the somatic cells die.

Now let's return to the question of how a BCNS patient might pass on the condition to offspring. In the case of BCNS, the disease gene is in every body cell, including the germ cells (Fig. 4.11). It is therefore passed into the eggs or sperm and can be inherited. In a sunbathing teenager who develops a basal cell carcinoma, however, the diseased copy of the *patched* gene brought about by solar radiation occurs only in one or more somatic cells (in this case, skin cells on the nose) and not in the germ cells, because the teenager did not inherit the genes for skin cancer. Therefore, the mutation could be passed on to the progeny of that one skin cell, but not to the person's future offspring.

An organism's life cycle comes full circle when its germ cells undergo the special type of cell division called meiosis. This division decreases the number of chromosomes present in germ cells by half, from 46 to 23 in the case of humans (Fig. 4.11e). The resulting cells can then become egg or sperm and lead to a new generation.

Meiosis: Halving the Chromosome Number

Why would an organism need a special type of cell division before producing gametes? Each of your somatic cells has 46 chromosomes. Let's say you produced gametes that had 46 chromosomes. How many chromosomes would your children's somatic cells have? Without a special mechanism, your child would get 46 chromosomes from you and another 46 from your mate, giving a total of 92. The next generation would have 184 and so on. Clearly this doesn't happen because each human baby has 46 chromosomes just like each parent. So what prevents the doubling of chromosomes in each generation?

The special type of cell division, meiosis, prohibits this runaway increase in chromosome number. Meiosis ensures that gametes contain half as many chromosomes as normal body cells (Fig. 4.12). In other words, each sperm or egg cell you make has 23 chromosomes, not 46. And the fusion of gametes at fertilization restores the original parental chromosome number, 46.

Figure 4.12
Haploid and Diploid Cells

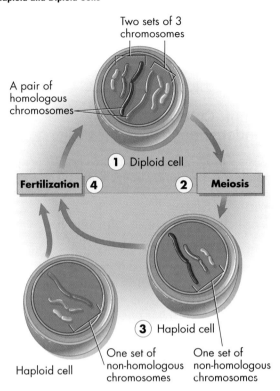

Two sets of 3 chromosomes

A pair of homologous chromosomes

① Diploid cell

Fertilization ④ ⟷ **②** **Meiosis**

③ Haploid cell

Haploid cell

One set of non-homologous chromosomes

One set of non-homologous chromosomes

Meiosis (literally, to make smaller) produces gametes or, in some species, such as mushrooms and ferns, other specialized reproductive cells called *spores*, whose chromosome number is half that of other body cells (see Fig. 4.13i on page 79).

In terms of chromosome number, fertilization and meiosis play opposite roles in a life cycle involving sexual reproduction. Fertilization *doubles* the chromosome number, while meiosis divides it in *half*. As we will see later in the chapter, meiosis also increases genetic variation, which is a precondition for evolution.

Chromosome Sets

Before we can investigate how meiosis reduces the number of chromosomes, we must understand how many sets of chromosomes each cell contains at different phases of the life cycle. As we have seen, the body cells of each species have a characteristic number of chromosomes: human beings have 46, chimpanzees 48, houseflies 12, onion plants 16, roundworms 4. What do all these chromosome numbers have in common? They are all even numbers. This is because in the body cells of most eukaryotes, *chromosomes are present in pairs*. A pair of chromosomes that have similar size, shape, and usually gene

order are called homologous chromosomes (*hom* = alike).

A human skin cell contains 23 pairs of homologous chromosomes, for a total of 46 chromosomes. One member of each pair came from the individual's mother, the other member of each pair came from the individual's father. Thus, a skin cell has two *sets* of chromosomes: a maternal set of 23 and a paternal set of 23. A cell such as this that has two sets of chromosomes is called a diploid cell (*di* = two). A cell that has just one set of chromosomes, one copy of each homologous pair, is called a haploid cell. Human gametes are examples of haploid cells.

Follow through the steps of Figure 4.12 to see these principles at work in an organism with just three pairs of chromosomes in each diploid cell.

The Cell Divisions of Meiosis

Because you've already explored the divisions of mitosis, you are in a good position to understand the variations that give rise to meiosis. Keep in mind that:

- Only somatic cells such as skin cells undergo mitosis and that the process leads to cell replacement and to growth and repair.

- Only germ cells like those in the gonads undergo meiosis and lead to the production of gametes and the possibility of future generations.

- The result of a meiotic division is to reduce the number of chromosomes by half, changing a diploid stem cell into haploid cells that can become gametes.

The first point to notice about meiosis is that the change from diploid to haploid chromosome number involves two sequential cell divisions called meiosis I and meiosis II. The chromosomes are duplicated before meiosis I, and then they divide. No duplication occurs before the second division, so when the cells divide in meiosis II, four haploid cells are produced. As in mitosis, chromosome *replication, alignment,* and *separation* are central concepts. Figure 4.13 charts chromosome movements during meiosis.

homologous chromosomes
chromosomes that pair up and separate during meiosis and generally have the same size, shape, and genetic information; one member of each pair of homologous chromosomes comes from the mother and the other comes from the father

diploid
a cell that contains two copies of each type of chromosome in its nucleus (except, perhaps, sex chromosomes)

haploid
having only one copy of a chromosome set; a human haploid cell has 23 chromosomes

meiosis I
the first division of meiosis, during which the number of chromosomes in a diploid cell is reduced from a diploid set of duplicated chromosomes to a haploid set of duplicated chromosomes

meiosis II
the second division of meiosis, during which a haploid cell with duplicated chromosomes divides to form two haploid cells with unduplicated chromosomes

Replication: The Interphase Before Meiosis I

Let's return to our organism with three chromosomes in a haploid set, one long, one medium sized, and one short. As Figure 4.12 showed, the germ cell from which this haploid cell arose is initially diploid, and so it has two long, two medium, and two short chromosomes. Each of the two chromosomes make a homologous pair (Fig. 4.13a).

We start with the cell just after its parent cell has divided (for example, the lower cell in Fig. 4.7f, with two sets of one-chromatid chromosomes). At this stage of meiosis, our cell is in the G_I phase of the cell cycle (Fig. 4.13a). This germ cell leaves G_I and enters S phase, and replicates each chromatid. Now, after replication, each chromosome has two chromatids (Fig. 4.13b).

Alignment: Homologous Chromosomes Pair in Meiosis I

As meiosis I begins, homologous chromosomes pair, lining up very close together: the two long chromosomes next to each other, the two short ones next to each other, and so on (Fig. 4.13c). In fact, homologous chromosomes pair so closely together that they exchange genetic material, as we'll see later.

As meiosis I progresses, the paired homologous chromosomes align in the center of the cell, moved by the spindle fibers (Fig. 4.13d). The order of nonhomologous chromosomes on the spindle, however, is random.

Separation: Homologous Chromosomes Separate from Each Other in Meiosis I

As meiosis I continues, homologous chromosomes separate from each other (Fig. 4.13e). When the nucleus divides and cytokinesis is completed after meiosis I, the two resulting cells now have the haploid content of chromosomes (Fig. 4.13f). Look at the figure to confirm that. Note that each cell in Figure 4.13f has three chromosomes: one long, one medium, and one short; these two cells, therefore, are haploid: Meiosis I has reduced the chromosome number from diploid to haploid. Notice, however, that each chromosome is a two-chromatid chromosome, not a one-chromatid chromosome as at the end of a mitotic division. Meiosis II takes care of that problem.

Replication: Chromosomes Do Not Replicate Between Meiosis I and II

After meiosis I, an interphase follows that is special in that it involves no DNA synthesis or chromosome replication. At the beginning of meiosis II, then, each cell still has a haploid set of two-chromatid chromosomes (Fig. 4.13f).

Alignment: Chromosomes Align Independently in Meiosis II

As meiosis II progresses, the chromosomes line up on the spindle independently of each other (Fig. 4.13g).

Separation: Sister Chromatids Separate in Meiosis II

Meiosis II then follows like a normal mitotic division, and the sister chromatids separate to opposite poles of the cell (Fig. 4.13h). The result, after cytokinesis (Fig. 4.13i), is now four cells, each of which is haploid and each of which has one set of one-chromatid chromosomes.

Compare, now, the parental cell and the daughter cells of one complete meiotic division. While the parental cell had two sets of one-chromatid chromosomes (Fig. 4.13a), the daughter cells—four of them from the two successive divisions of meiosis—each have one set of one-chromatid chromosomes (Fig. 4.13i). Depending on the adult's sex, those cells can develop into either sperm or eggs.

The Fate of the Haploid Products of Meiosis

The four haploid products of meiosis can have different fates in different species or in males and females of the same species. For example in the human female, only one of the four products becomes the egg; that cell keeps nearly all of the cytoplasm. The other three cells are called polar bodies and eventually die. Geneticists sometimes use polar bodies during genetic tests because from them, they can determine the genes in the egg cell. In the human male, each of the four haploid products will become a sperm.

Meiosis Contributes to the Origin of Genetic Variation

Meiosis plays a large role in the genetic differences that exist in a group of brothers and sisters because during meiosis, there is a reshuffling of the maternal and paternal chromosomes. This reshuffling is called genetic recombination, and it occurs in two ways: crossing over and independent assortment.

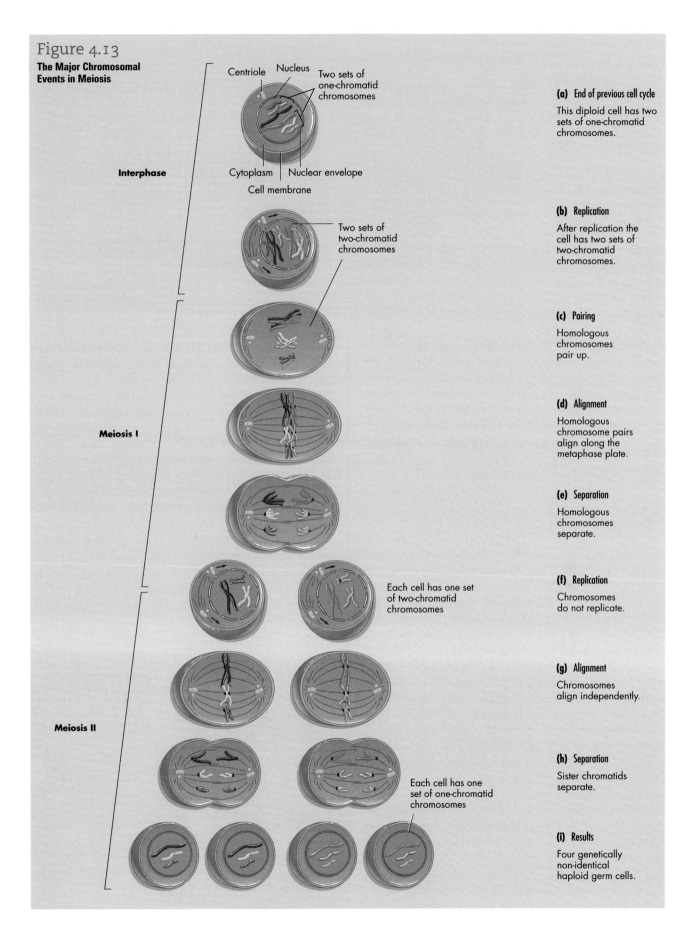

Figure 4.13
The Major Chromosomal Events in Meiosis

Centriole — Nucleus — Two sets of one-chromatid chromosomes

Cytoplasm — Nuclear envelope

Cell membrane

Interphase

(a) End of previous cell cycle
This diploid cell has two sets of one-chromatid chromosomes.

Two sets of two-chromatid chromosomes

(b) Replication
After replication the cell has two sets of two-chromatid chromosomes.

(c) Pairing
Homologous chromosomes pair up.

Meiosis I

(d) Alignment
Homologous chromosome pairs align along the metaphase plate.

(e) Separation
Homologous chromosomes separate.

Each cell has one set of two-chromatid chromosomes

(f) Replication
Chromosomes do not replicate.

(g) Alignment
Chromosomes align independently.

Meiosis II

(h) Separation
Sister chromatids separate.

Each cell has one set of one-chromatid chromosomes

(i) Results
Four genetically non-identical haploid germ cells.

independent assortment
the random distribution of genes located on different chromosomes to the gametes; Mendel's second law, the principle of independent assortment

Crossing Over: Homologous Chromosomes Exchange Parts

Crossing over occurs during meiosis I, when homologous chromosomes pair (Fig. 4.14a). While the chromosomes are paired, en-zymes can break the DNA molecule in each homologue, switch corresponding regions of each chromosome (the actual crossing over), and then attach them to the new chromosome (Fig. 4.14b). After meiosis II, some of the individual haploid cells will contain recombinants; that is, they will contain chromosomes of mixed ancestry, as the red and blue colors in Figure 4.14 indicate. Note that in Fig. 4.14c, just one crossover event makes each haploid cell genetically unique.

Independent Assortment: Chromosome Pairs Align Randomly

A second mechanism also contributes to genetic variety after meiosis and requires no chromosome breaks. It is called independent assortment, a property based on the fact that nonhomologous chromosomes align independently during meiosis I (review Fig. 4.13d). The chromosomes in Figure 4.15a are arranged with all of the paternal copies of the chromosomes oriented toward the same pole of the cell. Because of this alignment, each of the haploid products of meiosis will contain either all paternal copies or all maternal copies. Another possible arrangement is shown in Figure 4.15b, with one of the paternal chromosome copies oriented toward one pole and the other toward the opposite pole. With this arrangement, each meiotic product will be recombinant, with one paternal and one maternal chromosome.

Take a moment to look at the set of eight gam-etes in Figure 4.15a and b. Count how many different types of gametes have formed. Each gamete pictured has a haploid set of chromosomes (one short and one long). But there are four combinations present based on the parental origin: (1) both paternal, (2) both maternal, (3) long maternal and short pater-

Figure 4.14
Genetic Recombination through Crossing Over

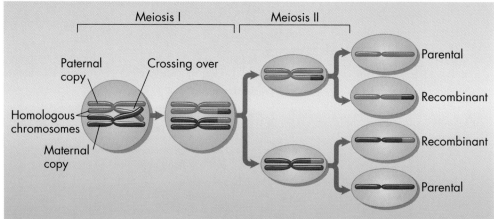

(a) Cross-over   **(b)** Regions exchanged   **(c)** Products of meiosis

nal, and (4) long paternal and short maternal. These four combinations differ not only from each other, but also from the diploid parent cells.

The independent assortment of chromosomes during meiosis can be compared to choosing from the menu of a restaurant where there are two choices for each course. Each course represents a chromosome, and the two choices—chicken or fish, rice or potatoes, apple pie or chocolate cake, and so on—represent the two homologous copies of each chromosome. Just as the potential number of different meals depends on the number of courses, the potential number of unique genetic combinations in the gametes depends on the number of chromosomes. From a menu with 3 courses and 2 choices per course, you could make up eight ($= 2 \times 2 \times 2$) different meals. For each chromosome added, you'd have to multiply again by 2. So for a human being, that number would be 2^{23}, or

Figure 4.15

Genetic Recombination through Independent Assortment

(a) One possible chromosome arrangement

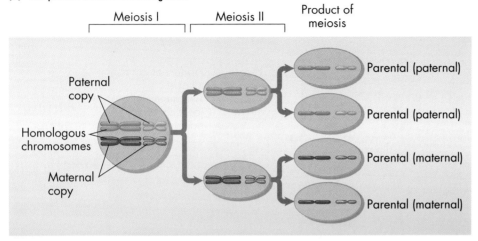

Meiosis I | Meiosis II | Product of meiosis

Paternal copy
Homologous chromosomes
Maternal copy

Parental (paternal)
Parental (paternal)
Parental (maternal)
Parental (maternal)

(b) Another possible chromosome arrangement

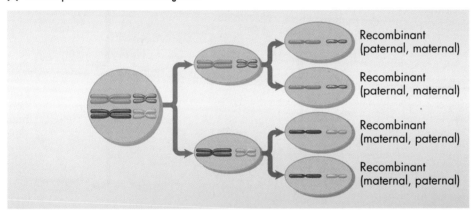

Recombinant (paternal, maternal)
Recombinant (paternal, maternal)
Recombinant (maternal, paternal)
Recombinant (maternal, paternal)

a potential of 8 million different chromosome combinations of eggs or sperm in the nuclei. Because crossing over (review Figure 4.14) adds even more new combinations, the number of actual possible types of gametes made by a single person is astronomical. Finally, the random combination of maternal and paternal chromosomes in the zygote at fertilization further increases the number of genetic combinations.

The incredible genetic diversity that results from genetic recombination helps explain why an organism is highly unlikely to produce two genetically identical gametes, and why, in turn, all other organisms resulting from sexual reproduction may resemble their parents but are never exactly like either parent.

Mitosis and Meiosis Compared

The details of mitosis and meiosis are relatively easy to confuse, so it's worth one last comparison of the two (see Figure 4.16).

Mitosis occurs only in somatic cells and allows for the growth of the organism and repair of its parts. Mitosis accomplishes two things:

1. Reproduction of cells.
2. Equal distribution of DNA to each new daughter cell.

Meiosis occurs only in germ cells and can result in the production of gametes that can take part in sexual reproduction. Meiosis accomplishes three things:

1. By reducing the chromosome number from diploid to haploid, meiosis prevents an increase in chromosome number that otherwise would occur at fertilization.
2. Crossing over during meiosis permits new combinations of maternal and paternal hereditary traits.
3. Independent assortment allows for the further random combination of maternal and paternal chromosomes.

Figure 4.16
Mitosis and Meiosis Compared

(a) Mitosis

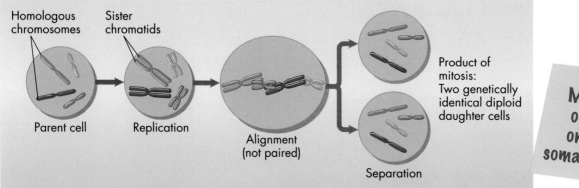

Homologous chromosomes

Sister chromatids

Parent cell

Replication

Alignment (not paired)

Separation

Product of mitosis: Two genetically identical diploid daughter cells

Mitosis occurs only in somatic cells

(b) Meiosis

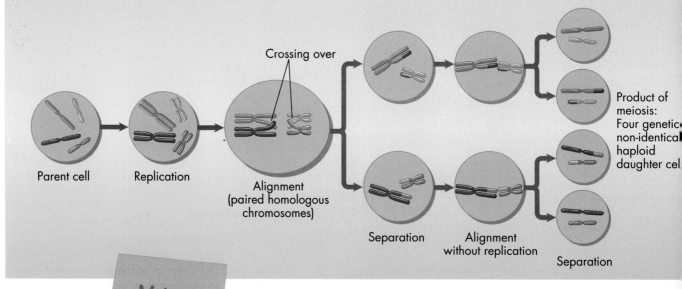

Crossing over

Parent cell

Replication

Alignment (paired homologous chromosomes)

Separation

Alignment without replication

Separation

Product of meiosis: Four genetic non-identical haploid daughter cel

Meiosis occurs only in germ cells

Who knew?

Somatic cells divide by *mitosis* for growth and replacement throughout the body. Cells divide by *meiosis* only for the production of gametes (eggs and sperm); these cells are found only in the gonads (ovaries and testes).

The podcasts are the best thing in the world! If one week I don't have enough time to read the chapter for the lesson, it is so easy to listen to it on my way to University on the train, so I can at least have a basic knowledge of that chapter before the lecture, and I can catch up with my reading later.

– Sandra DeWitt, Student at University of Notre Dame Fremantle, Australia

LIFE was designed for students just like you – busy people who want choices, flexibility, and multiple learning options.

LIFE delivers concise, focused information in a fresh and contemporary format. And... **LIFE** gives you a variety of online learning materials designed with you in mind.

At **4ltrpress.cengage.com/life,** you'll find electronic resources such as **animations, visual reviews, flash cards,** and **interactive quizzes** for each chapter.

These resources will help supplement your understanding of core biology concepts in a format that fits your busy lifestyle. Visit **4ltrpress.cengage.com/life** to learn more about the multiple resources available to help you succeed!

Patterns *of*
Inheritance

Learning Outcomes

LO[1] Understand the universal principles of heredity

LO[2] List the rules that govern the inheritance of a single trait

LO[3] Explain how geneticists analyze human inheritance patterns

LO[4] List the rules governing how organisms inherit multiple traits

LO[5] Explain how sex influences the inheritance of traits

LO[6] Identify how genetics is changing our world

> **"** *140 years ago, most observers thought each individual's traits resulted from a blending of their parents' traits.* **"**

A Devastatingly Common Illness

With one affected child in every 3,000 births, cystic fibrosis (CF) is the most common lethal inherited illness among Caucasians. It causes a constellation of breathing, digestion, and other medical problems, and until recently an affected child born was unlikely to survive past his or her teens.

What do you know?

Can you tell an organism's genotype by its phenotype?

Cystic fibrosis is essentially a disease of clogged ducts. A child who inherits one mutated cystic fibrosis gene from each parent will produce a faulty version of a protein. The protein is involved in salt and water movement across cell membranes, and being defective, it prevents normal fluid transport. The walls of the ducts and the protective coatings they secrete tend to dry out, creating a thick, sticky mucus layer. This, in turn, clogs narrow passageways and ducts in the lungs, stomach, pancreas, sweat glands, and reproductive organs. Because of this, an individual who inherits cystic fibrosis usually has difficulty breathing. He or she repeatedly contracts dangerous bacterial infections in the lungs and suffers stomachaches and a diarrhea-like condition due to poor absorption of fats in the diet. Most also exude a salty secretion on the skin. And affected males are almost always sterile because of blocked ducts leading from the testes.

Our goal in this chapter is to help you understand inheritance patterns like these—patterns that determine who will display lethal disease symptoms and who won't. Inheritance patterns underlie each of our thousands of traits—eye color, hair color, height, and so on—and those of all other living organisms. The science of genetics explores the nature of genes and how they are organized on chromosomes; how genes govern our appearance, physical functioning, and even behavior; and how medical researchers can manipulate genes to treat diseases like cystic fibrosis.

As you explore Chapter 5, you'll find the answers to these questions:

- ☑ How did a 19th-century monk discover the universal principles of heredity?
- ☑ What rules govern the way organisms inherit individual traits?
- ☑ How do geneticists analyze inheritance patterns in people?
- ☑ What rules govern the way organisms inherit several traits at the same time?
- ☑ How does our sex influence how we inherit traits?
- ☑ How is the study of genetics changing the way we predict and treat diseases?

genetics
the study of genes and inheritance

LO¹ How Did Scientists Discover the Universal Principles of Heredity?

To help potential parents calculate the risk of having a child with cystic fibrosis, geneticists apply the universal laws of heredity, the principles that govern how traits are passed from parents to offspring. These rules have a long and interesting history. They were discovered by a European monk named Gregor Mendel, who first made his discoveries public in 1865. Even today, in the 21st century, it is easiest to understand these rules of heredity if we learn how Mendel himself discovered them.

In Mendel's day, 140 years ago, most observers thought each individual's traits resulted from a blending of their parents' traits. Looking at organisms in nature, it is not hard to see why people believed that offspring were intermediates between their parents. Consider, for example, two monkey flower plants whose flowers have petals of vastly different sizes. Let's say we mated plants with these different flower shapes—one with long petals to one with short petals. The result would be a hybrid: the offspring of two individuals with differing forms of a given trait. In this case, the hybrid's flowers had petals intermediate in length between those of the two parents. Such observations made people think that the hereditary "stuff" of a mother and father was liquid and would *blend* to produce the characteristics found in the offspring, just as cream mixes with dark-brown coffee to produce the beige-colored café au lait. This idea became known as the blending model of heredity.

While Mendel was at the University of Vienna, he learned that all matter is made up of discrete atoms and molecules. He wondered if heredity could also be governed by "particles" that retain their identity from generation to generation. He put his new particulate model of heredity to the test in a long-term study involving pea plants, controlled matings between them, and careful tabulations of the kinds of offspring each cross produced.

© DAVID CROCKETT/ISTOCKPHOTO.COM

Genetics in the Abbey

The blending hypothesis predicted that, like café au lait, each hereditary factor would be permanently diluted in the hybrid. Mendel's particulate model, however, predicted that each hereditary factor would remain unchanged in a hybrid, like dark-brown and cream-colored marbles mixed in a bag. Mendel's key insight was that he could disprove one of these two models not by looking at the hybrid itself—the first generation of the mating—but by checking the *offspring* of hybrids—the second generation. If the original parental forms reappeared in the second generation, this would show that the hereditary factors had passed through the hybrids unchanged and remained as some kind of intact particles. If, however, the original forms *failed* to reappear in the hybrid's offspring, then the factors would appear to have been blended.

Mendel chose common garden pea plants as his test subject because peas have several advantages. From seed stores he could purchase strains of pea plants that showed clear alternative forms for single traits, such as stem length or flower color. For example, long-stem plants versus short-stem, or purple flowers versus white. By selecting strains that differed in only one trait such as height or flower color, he could study inheritance of one feature unconfused by all other variations. In addition, Mendel could also easily control which pea plant mated with which other pea plant. A pea flower normally self-fertilizes or mates

Figure 5.1

Mendel's Evidence for a Nonblending (Particulate) Model of Heredity

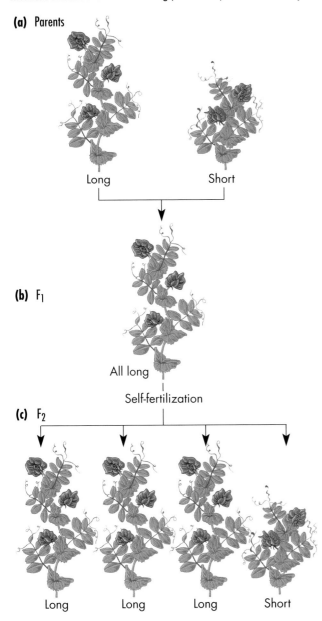

(a) Parents

Long   Short

(b) F₁

All long

Self-fertilization

(c) F₂

Long   Long   Long   Short

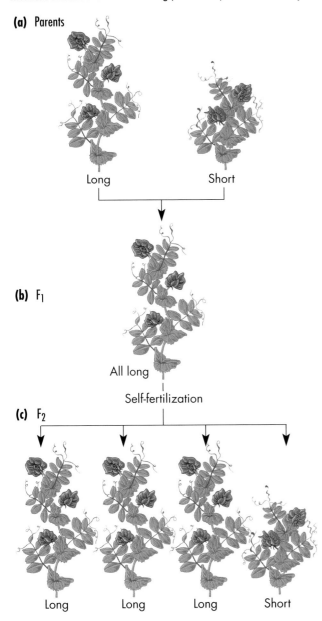

© ISTOCKPHOTO.COM

With his clearly stated hypotheses and well-chosen experimental system, Mendel was now ready to perform the scientific tests that would lead to the rules of heredity, rules that medical doctors can still apply more than a century later to patients.

Mendel Disproves the Blending Model

In one of Mendel's first crosses, he planted seeds from long-stem and short-stem plants early one spring and let them grow into the parental (P₁) generation (Fig. 5.1a). Later that spring, when the parental plants had flowered, Mendel cross-fertilized long-stemmed plants with pollen from the short-stemmed plants. In the summer, when the pods became swollen with plump peas, he collected the seeds. These seeds would produce the next generation, called the first filial (F₁) generation, meaning the first generation in the line of descent. Planted in the spring of the second year, the F₁ seeds of the long-stem/short-stem cross all grew into plants with stems just as long as the original long-stemmed parent (Fig. 5.1b). Mendel repeated this type of experiment for other traits—flower color (purple vs. white), seed shape (round vs. wrinkled), and so on—and he found that in each case, only one alternative of each trait appeared in the F₁ hybrid generation. It was as if one of the traits had totally disappeared. The trait that appears in the F₁ hybrid (such as long stems in peas) is said to be **dominant**, while the trait that does not show in the hybrid (such as short stems in peas) is referred to as **recessive**.

Now came the crucial part of the experiment. What happened to the recessive characteristic in the hybrid? Did it blend with the dominant characteristic? Did it disappear completely and forever? Or did it remain intact but hidden in the F₁ generation? To find out, Mendel allowed the long-stemmed F₁ hybrid plants to self-fertilize, and the next spring he planted the seeds of the **second filial (F₂) generation**. When the second generation of pea plants grew up,

with itself. But Mendel **cross-fertilized** plants. From a purple flower, for example, he could simply clip off the organ that produces pollen, the sources of the sperm, and dust the egg-containing organ of that flower with pollen from another plant (for example, a white flower). From the seeds of this cross fertilization or "cross," Mendel could grow a new generation of pea plants and watch to see which traits were expressed.

cross-fertilize
to deliberately cross two organisms; in plants, to transfer pollen from one self-fertilizing flower to another

parental (P₁) generation
in Mendelian genetics, the individuals that give rise to the first filial (F₁) generation

first filial (F₁) generation
in Mendelian genetics, the first generation in the line of descent

dominant
in genetics, an allele or corresponding phenotypic trait that is expressed in the heterozygote (in other words, that shows in the hybrid)

recessive
an allele or corresponding phenotypic trait that is hidden by a dominant allele in a heterozygote

second filial (F₂) generation
in Mendelian genetics, the second generation in the line of descent

most of them had long stems, but significantly, some plants had short stems. Again, there were no stems of intermediate length (Fig. 5.1c). The reappearance of plants with stems just as short as the stems of the original short-stemmed parents, and the absence of any intermediates were the results predicted by the particulate model of heredity and dramatic disproof of the blending model of heredity.

LO^2 What Rules Govern the Inheritance of a Single Trait?

Being a careful and inquisitive person, Mendel was not satisfied with just saying that "some" of the F_2 plants had short stems and therefore the blending hypothesis was wrong. He wanted to understand what he saw. So he counted the plants and by analyzing the numbers, was able to infer the mechanisms that hid the short-stemmed trait in the F_1 and its reappearance in the F_2.

The good monk found that 787 of the F_2 plants he counted had long stems and 277 had short stems. These numbers showed a 787:277 ratio or approximately 3:1 ratio of long-stemmed to short-stemmed plants in the F_2 generation. (A perfect 3:1 ratio for 1064 plants would be 798:266, not much different from the 787:277 he actually observed.) It turns out that the results of Mendel's observations for pea stem length apply to many traits in eukaryotic organisms. The general finding is that with two clear alternative traits such as long versus short stems, purple versus yellow seeds, or presence of cystic fibrosis versus absence of the disease, the hybrid (the F_1 generation) shows only one trait, the dominant one. The mating of two hybrids (the F_2 generation) produces offspring in which three quarters show the trait that appears in the hybrid (the dominant trait), while one quarter show the trait that is hidden in the hybrid (the recessive trait). How can we understand the mechanism that causes such a result to occur?

Genes and Alleles

Mendel reasoned that because short stems reappeared in the F_2 plants, the hereditary factor that causes short stems had to be an individual unit, like a particle, and not like a liquid that could be mixed with another liquid of a different color. Modern geneticists call this particulate factor a *gene* (see Chapter 1). While Mendel did not use that term, we will use it in the following discussion for clarity.

A gene influences a specific trait in an organism, such as the length of a pea stem, the color of a corn kernel, or the presence or absence of a hereditary disease like cystic fibrosis. The gene is not the trait itself. Instead it is a factor that causes the organism to develop a specific trait.

Mendel's insight was remarkable. Even though he had no knowledge of DNA or genes, he reasoned that hereditary "particles" must come in different forms. Nearly a century later, molecular researchers would show that genes do, in fact, have different forms, which are now called alleles. An allele (AL-eel) is an alternative form of a gene. In pea plants, the gene for stem length has two alleles, one causing long stems and one causing short stems. Likewise, modern geneticists know that one allele of the cystic fibrosis gene causes the disease, while another allele (alternative form) of the same gene is necessary for the normal functioning of the airways and other ducts.

Geneticists have also known for a half-century that a gene is a portion of a DNA molecule in a chromosome (Fig. 5.2 and Table 5.1). Although an individual chromosome may contain thousands of genes controlling hundreds of different traits, each chromosome will have just one allele for any individual gene. Because eukaryotic cells contain pairs of homologous chromosomes (review Fig. 4.13), each individual pea plant or person generally has two alleles for each gene, which may be the same or different.

Dominant and Recessive Alleles

Mendel realized that the reappearance of short-stemmed plants in the F_2 generation meant that the short-stem allele was present but invisible in the F_1 hybrids. If the short-stem allele had not been present

Figure 5.2

Genes, Alleles, and Chromosomes

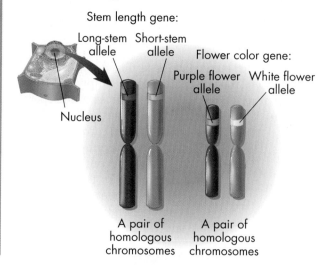

Stem length gene:

Long-stem allele   Short-stem allele

Flower color gene:

Purple flower allele   White flower allele

Nucleus

A pair of homologous chromosomes

A pair of homologous chromosomes

Table 5.1
Principles of Heredity

1. A hereditary trait is governed by a gene.
2. Genes reside on chromosomes and are specific sequences of DNA in all cells, but they are RNA in some viruses.
3. A gene for each trait can exist in two or more alternative forms called alleles. An individual's alleles, interacting with the environment, determine its external appearance, biochemical functioning, and behavior.
4. Most higher organisms have two copies of each gene in body cells (they are diploid). Gametes (eggs or sperm), however, have only one copy of each gene (they are haploid).
5. Homologous chromosomes are two chromosomes that are similar in size, shape, and genetic content.
6. A homozygote has two identical alleles of a gene; a heterozygote has two different alleles of a gene.
7. An individual's physical makeup (the way it looks and functions) is its phenotype; an organism's genetic makeup is its genotype.
8. In a heterozygote, generally only one of the two alleles shows in the phenotype, while the other allele is hidden. The allele that shows is the dominant allele, and the hidden allele is the recessive allele.
9. Pairs of alleles separate, or segregate, before egg and sperm formation, so each gamete has a single copy of each gene. At fertilization, sperm and egg combine randomly with respect to the alleles they contain, and the resulting zygote in general has two copies of all genes.
10. Genes on different chromosomes assort independently of each other into gametes.
11. Linked genes lie on the same chromosome and tend to be packaged into gametes together.

in the hybrid, it could not have been passed on to the F_2 offspring. Because the hybrids showed the long-stem trait, Mendel knew that the long-stem allele was also present in the hybrid. So Mendel concluded that a hybrid plant contains two copies, or alleles, of each gene, one visible and one invisible.

The allele whose trait shows in a hybrid is said to be *dominant*. The allele that is overshadowed each time it is paired with a dominant allele is said to be *recessive*. The long-stem allele of the stem length gene in peas was dominant to the recessive short-stem allele. Can you guess which allele is dominant and which is recessive for cystic fibrosis?

In his work with pea plants, Mendel reasoned that because each hybrid plant has two alleles of each gene, each pure-breeding parent plant must also have two copies of each gene. (A pure-breeding organism always produces offspring with traits identical to its own.) In the case of the hybrid plant, the two alleles are different, one dominant and one recessive. But in the case of the pure-breeding parents, both alleles are identical, either both dominant or both recessive.

Genotype and Phenotype

Although the long-stemmed F_1 hybrid plants Mendel studied looked just like the long-stemmed pure-breeding plants of the parental generation, they were genetically different. Today, we refer to an organism's physical characteristics—stem length or airway functioning, for example—as its **phenotype**. We call the organism's specific alleles or genetic makeup its **genotype**. In the case of a long-stemmed phenotype, there are two possible genotypes. Some long-stemmed plants could have two identical dominant long-stem alleles, but other long-stemmed plants could have two different alleles, the visible dominant long-stem allele and the hidden recessive short-stem allele (Fig. 5.3a,b). Geneticists often indicate dominant alleles with uppercase (capital) letters and recessive alleles with lowercase letters. We can represent with L the dominant long-stem allele for stem length, and with l the recessive short-stem allele. In the case of long-stemmed plants, then, the genotype would be either *LL* or *Ll*. Organisms with two different types of alleles for a given trait are said to be **heterozygous** for that trait (Fig. 5.3b). Pure-breeding organisms, with a pair of identical alleles for a given trait, are **homozygous** for that trait (Fig. 5.3a,c). A heterozygous individual is called a **heterozygote**, and a homozygous individual is called a **homozygote**. Again, geneticists following in Mendel's footsteps learned that pure-breeding long-stemmed and short-stemmed parents are homozygotes, while their hybrid offspring are heterozygotes.

Mendel's Segregation Principle

Mendel concluded that each individual has two copies of each factor (each gene)—two copies of the stem length gene and two copies of the flower color gene. Where did these two copies come from? Mendel suggested that each individual receives one allele from its mother and the other from its father for each of its many traits. Thus, the two alleles possessed by a

phenotype
the physical appearance of an organism controlled by its genes interacting with the environment

genotype
the genetic makeup of an individual

heterozygous
(Gr. *heteros,* different + *zygotos,* pair) Having two different alleles for a specific trait

homozygous
having two identical alleles for a specific trait

heterozygote
an organism with two different alleles for a given trait

homozygote
an organism with two identical alleles for a given trait

law of segregation Mendel's first law, or principle, states that sexually reproducing diploid organisms have two alleles for each gene, and that during the gamete formation these two alleles separate from each other so that the resulting gametes have only one allele of each gene

parent must separate, or *segregate*, from each other so that only one allele of each gene goes into each egg and only one allele of each gene goes into each sperm. Recall from Chapter 4 that a cell with just one copy (allele) of each gene is said to be haploid and a cell with two copies (alleles) of each gene is diploid. Eggs and sperm are haploid, but all other cells in a human being and nearly all other cells in a pea plant are diploid.

If we generalize from Mendel's pea experiments, we can define his law of segregation this way: Sexually reproducing diploid organisms have two copies of each gene, which segregate from each other during meiosis without blending or being altered. When gametes form, they each contain only one copy of each gene.

> "A cell with just one copy (allele) of each gene is said to be haploid, and a cell with two copies (alleles) of each gene is diploid."

Genetic Symbols and Punnett Squares

The segregation principle is probably easiest to understand using the upper and lowercase symbols *L* and *l* for the alleles of the stem length gene (Fig. 5.4). The heterozygous F_1 generation is then designated as *Ll*.

During meiosis in the *Ll* heterozygote, the alleles separate. As a result, half the gametes end up with the capital *L* allele and the other half with the lowercase *l* allele (Fig. 5.4b). Mendel pointed out that to get the 3:1 phenotypic ratio, eggs and sperm can come together totally at random with

Figure 5.3
Phenotype Versus Genotype

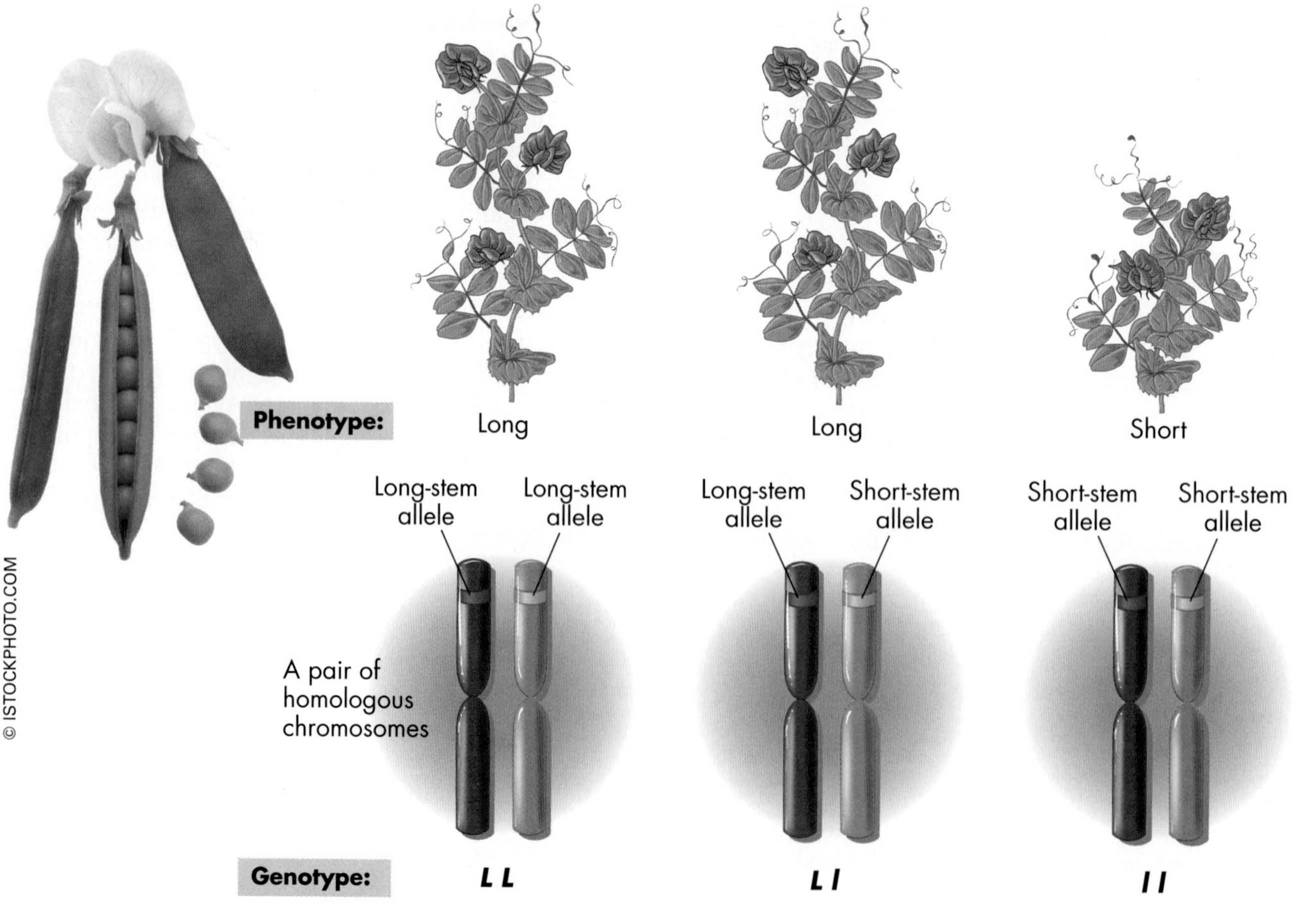

(a) Homozygous dominant (two matching dominant alleles)
(b) Heterozygous (nonmatching alleles)
(c) Homozygous recessive (two matching recessive alleles)
Phenotype:
Long
Long
Short
Long-stem allele
Long-stem allele
Long-stem allele
Short-stem allele
Short-stem allele
Short-stem allele
A pair of homologous chromosomes
Genotype:
L L
L l
l l
© ISTOCKPHOTO.COM

respect to the allele they carry (Fig. 5.4c). In other words, an egg cell with an l allele is just as likely to be fertilized by a sperm cell with an l allele as it is to be fertilized by a sperm carrying an L allele.

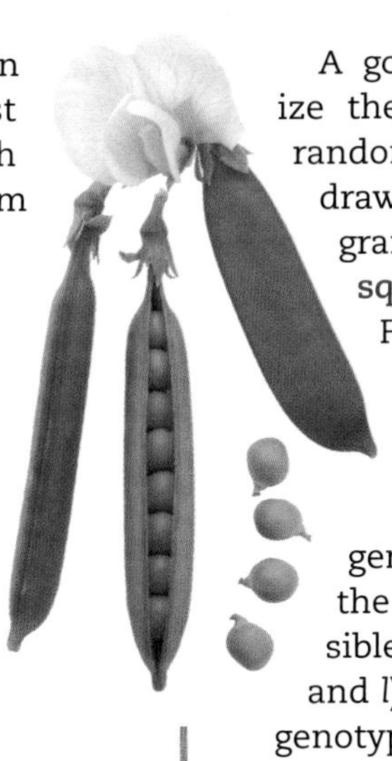

Figure 5.4
Meiosis and Mendel's Principle of Segregation

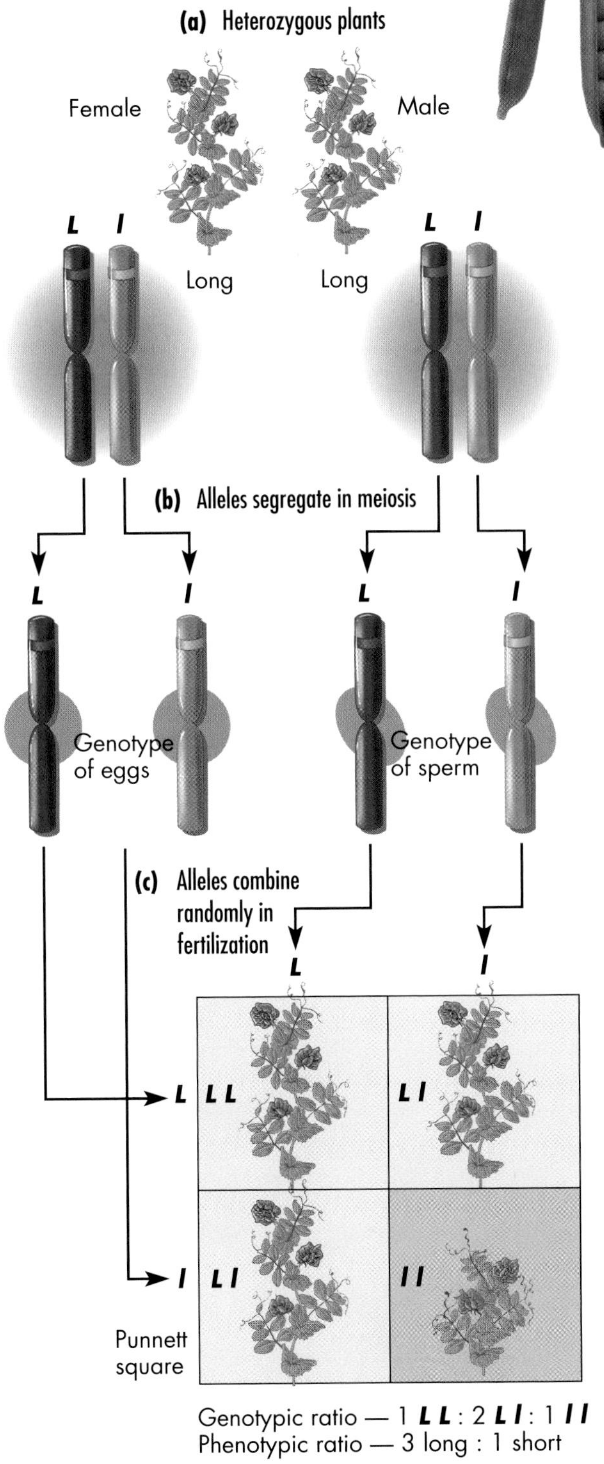

(a) Heterozygous plants

Female   Male

L   l   L   l
Long   Long

(b) Alleles segregate in meiosis

L   l   L   l

Genotype of eggs   Genotype of sperm

(c) Alleles combine randomly in fertilization

L   l

	L	l
L	LL	Ll
l	Ll	ll

Punnett square

Genotypic ratio — 1 **LL** : 2 **Ll** : 1 **ll**
Phenotypic ratio — 3 long : 1 short

A good way to visualize the consequences of random fertilization is to draw an organized diagram called a **Punnett square**, as shown in Figure 5.4c. To construct a Punnett square for the mating of two heterozygous pea plants, draw a large square made up of four smaller squares. Along the top of the large square, write the two possible genotypes of the pollen (L and l) and along the left side of the square, write the two possible genotypes of the eggs (also in this case L and l). Then in the four empty boxes, fill in the genotypes of the offspring that result from the fertilization of each egg type with each pollen type.

Fig. 5.4c shows four F$_2$ genotypes: LL, Ll, lL, and ll. Because the order of alleles is not important, Ll and lL are equivalent; thus, there are really only 3 genotypes, found in the ratio 1 LL to 2 Ll to 1 ll. If we look at the physical characteristics of the plants themselves, however, we find that the 1:2:1 genotypic ratio produces a 3:1 phenotypic ratio (3 long stem to 1 short stem). The reason is that the single LL genotype and both Ll genotypes have the same long-stem phenotype, because L is dominant to l. Recall that this 3:1 ratio is very close to what Mendel observed in his experiment (787:277).

Punnett square
in genetics, a diagrammatic way of presenting the results of random fertilization from a mating

Genetics and Probabilities

Mendel's segregation principle predicts a 3:1 phenotypic ratio in the offspring from a mating of two heterozygotes. But he actually found 2.84:1 for the mating we discussed, and 3.15:1 and 2.96:1 for other similar matings involving different traits. Why don't the figures come out to exactly 3:1? The answer is that the principles of genetics rely on the laws of chance and probability.

You can demonstrate the probability of obtaining the 3:1 relationship by tossing two different coins simultaneously. Let a penny represent sperm from a pollen grain, and let a nickel represent an egg. The head of each coin represents the dominant allele, and the tail represents the recessive allele. Note that each coin has an equal number of dominant and recessive alleles, just like the population of gametes from a heterozygote.

To model fertilization, flip both coins at the same time and record whether they land heads up or tails up. If both are heads, the genotype is homozygous dominant; if both are tails, the genotype is homozygous recessive; and if one coin is heads and the other is tails, the "offspring" will be heterozygous. Flip the pair of coins 20 times. How many times would you expect each of the three possible outcomes? Did you obtain exactly what you would expect? If not, how can you explain the discrepancy?

What would be the probable result if you tossed the coins many more times than 20, say, 1,064 times, as Mendel did when he was experimenting with pea stem length? Like the toss of a coin, the combination of alleles in fertilization is governed by the laws of chance. In a low number of trials, as you conducted, the results may differ substantially from those predicted for random tossing, but as the number of trials increases, the results will come closer to the mathematically predicted values. This principle is especially important when doing human genetics because of small family size, as we will see in the next section.

LO^3 How Do Geneticists Analyze Human Inheritance Patterns?

How can we apply Mendel's principles of heredity to the problem of how likely a set of parents is to have children with cystic fibrosis?

Homo sapiens: An Inconvenient Experimental Animal

Even with Mendel's principles in mind, humans are uniquely difficult subjects for a geneticist to study. First of all, geneticists aren't matchmakers and can't convince people to choose mates and produce offspring just to satisfy their curiosity. Investigators must search for existing subjects and matings that happen to express traits of interest. In addition, there is never a true F_2 generation available for study because brothers and sisters rarely mate. Beyond that, individual human families are too small for statistical analysis; couples rarely produce more than ten children, and usually produce fewer than three. Finally, the human life cycle is too long. It could take an entire career to follow the traits in two human generations. So scientists and physicians rely heavily on collecting and analyzing family histories.

Pedigrees: Family Genetic Histories

A major method in human genetics is to follow the inheritance of a

trait through all the members of a family. Geneticists search out families with particular genetic traits, and then interview family members, check their medical records, and collect samples of blood or other tissues from as many family members as possible. From such records, the investigator draws up pedigrees, orderly diagrams that show family relationships, birth order, gender, phenotype, and, when possible, the genotype of each family member.

To see how a family pedigree works, let's consider the family tree of a family with the cystic fibrosis trait (Fig. 5.5). In a pedigree, each generation occupies a separate horizontal row, with the ancestors at the top and more recent generations below. Males are indicated by squares and females by circles. Symbols for people affected with the trait are filled in (red, in this case). Geneticists designate each generation with a Roman numeral (I, II, etc.) and each individual with an Arabic number (1, 2, etc.) from left to right. For example, the matriarch of the family, a woman born in 1859, is I1, and her two daughters are II2 and II3. The boy and girl VI1 and VI2 are the only family members with cystic fibrosis. As in many pedigrees, this one arranges a group of brothers and sisters in order from oldest (left) to youngest (right).

Another convention is that a horizontal line joins two parents, and the offspring are attached to the line below. Parents II1 and II2, for example, produced two daughters and two sons, individuals III2 to III5. Geneticists sometimes omit from a pedigree parents who are unrelated and unaffected. They also tend to show consanguineous marriages (unions between blood relatives) with double horizontal lines like the ones in Figure 5.5.

Figure 5.5
Pedigree for a Family with Cystic Fibrosis

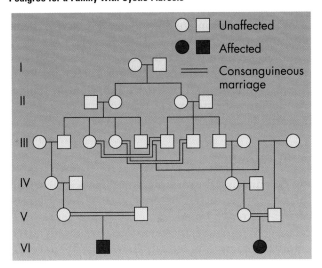

Is Cystic Fibrosis Inherited as a Recessive or Dominant Trait?

A pedigree can look rather formidable, with its marching rows of grandparents, aunts, brothers, and sisters. Nevertheless, the rules for analyzing a pedigree follow Mendel's principles. Let's analyze our hypothetical family's pedigree more closely. By doing this, we can determine whether cystic fibrosis shows a pattern of dominant or recessive inheritance.

The pedigree (Fig. 5.5) shows that several of the siblings in the family lacked the cystic fibrosis trait; neither parent showed the trait, either. Let's represent the cystic fibrosis gene by CF, with CF^- representing the disease allele and CF^+ the healthy allele. Because our affected female VI2 has cystic fibrosis, she must have at least one CF^- allele and must have inherited it from one of her parents. That shows that at least one of the parents must carry at least one CF^- allele. Since neither parent shows the trait, we can conclude that each parent has at least one CF^+ allele, and that at least one parent is a heterozygote with one CF^+ allele and one CF^- allele. Because both parents are healthy, we must conclude that a person with the heterozygous genotype has a healthy phenotype. We saw earlier that in a heterozygote, the dominant allele shows. Therefore, the CF^+ (healthy) allele must be dominant to the CF^- (disease) allele. In other words, the allele that causes cystic fibrosis must be recessive and the genotype of VI2 is $CF^- CF^-$. To generalize this argument: If an offspring inherits a condition but neither parent shows the condition, the trait is usually recessive.

Because the disease allele of the cystic fibrosis gene is recessive, affected people must have two copies of the disease allele. One of those copies must have come from the dad, and the other from the mom. Since both parents passed on the disease allele but do *not* show its effects, they must be heterozygotes, or carriers. In carriers, the dominant normal allele masks the recessive allele, which is mutant (the result of a mutation).

It turns out that many human genetic diseases are inherited as recessive traits like cystic fibrosis. Some, however, are inherited as dominants. Let's look at some of each.

How Alleles Interact

Experimenting in his quiet abbey garden, Mendel showed that each gene—for plant height, flower color, and so on—has two alleles, which are either dominant or recessive. Life, however, is not always so simple, as later geneticists found with more sophisticated experiments. The alleles of some genes fail to fall clearly into either the dominant or recessive category, and some genes have many more than two alleles.

Incomplete Dominance

In 1905, a young African American experiencing pains in his joints and abdomen, chronic fatigue, and shortness of breath consulted a Chicago physician. A blood test showed that the man had too few red blood cells (a condition called *anemia*) and that many of his blood cells were shaped like crescents, or sickles, instead of the normal disks (Fig. 5.6a). Studies revealed sickle-shaped blood cells to be fragile and easily destroyed. This condition is called *sickle-cell anemia*, and it's the most commonly inherited lethal disease among African Americans.

A condition related to sickle-cell anemia is called *sickle-cell trait*. In people with sickle-cell trait, red blood cells form a sickle shape when deprived of oxygen in a test tube—a condition that fails to induce sickling in normal red blood cells. People with sickle-cell trait are normal except when exposed to extreme conditions, such as high altitude or severe physical exertion. For example, several men with sickle-cell trait living in low-altitude cities suffered severe spleen pain within two days of arrival in a part of Colorado with high altitudes. Sickle-cell trait is

carrier
[1] in genetics, a heterozygous individual not expressing a recessive trait but capable of passing it on to her or his offspring; [2] in biochemistry, a substance, often a protein, that transports another substance

mutant
the allele that results from a mutation; also used to refer to the organism containing such a mutation

sickle-cell anemia
a genetic condition inherited as a recessive mutation in a hemoglobin gene and characterized by pains in joints and abdomen, chronic fatigue, and shortness of breath

thus intermediate in severity between full-blown sickle-cell anemia and normal health. What is its genetic basis?

Figure 5.6b shows a pedigree for sickle-cell anemia in a family from Jamaica. Notice that each person with sickle-cell anemia has two parents who both display sickle-cell trait. By examining a large number of families with sickle-cell anemia, geneticists have found that the mating of two people with sickle-cell trait produces offspring in a 1:2:1 ratio with 1/4 showing full blown sickle-cell anemia, 1/2 showing sickle-cell trait, and 1/4 showing neither condition. The Punnett square in Figure 5.6c reveals the origin of this 1:2:1 phenotypic ratio. Sickle-cell anemia displays incomplete dominance: the phenotype of heterozygotes—in this case individuals with sickle-cell trait—is intermediate between

the homozygous dominant and the homozygous recessive conditions. In incomplete dominance, the phenotypic and genotypic ratios are the same. The principle of incomplete dominance can help explain why early observers devised the incorrect blending hypothesis of inheritance (review LO1). Several genes act together to control petal length in monkey flowers, for example, and these are inherited in typical Mendelian fashion—except that their alleles display incomplete dominance.

Codominance

We just discussed incomplete dominance, in which the phenotype of the heterozygote is intermediate between the two homozygotes. Another variation is called **codominance**, in which the phenotype of the heterozygote simultaneously shows *both* phenotypes. A familiar example of codominance is the blood-type gene called *ABO* (Fig. 5.7a). For this gene, allele A causes a certain carbohydrate molecule called type A to appear on the surface of red blood cells, and a

Figure 5.6

Sickle-Cell Anemia: A Pattern of Incomplete Dominance

(a) Sickle cells

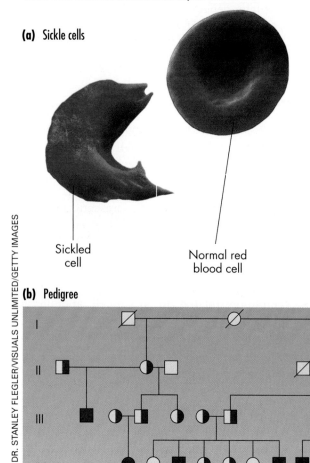

Sickled cell

Normal red blood cell

(c) Punnett square

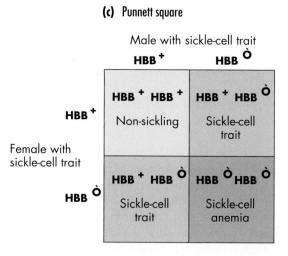

Male with sickle-cell trait

	HBB$^+$	HBB$^{\dot{O}}$
HBB$^+$	HBB$^+$ HBB$^+$ — Non-sickling	HBB$^+$ HBB$^{\dot{O}}$ — Sickle-cell trait
HBB$^{\dot{O}}$	HBB$^+$ HBB$^{\dot{O}}$ — Sickle-cell trait	HBB$^{\dot{O}}$ HBB$^{\dot{O}}$ — Sickle-cell anemia

Female with sickle-cell trait

(b) Pedigree

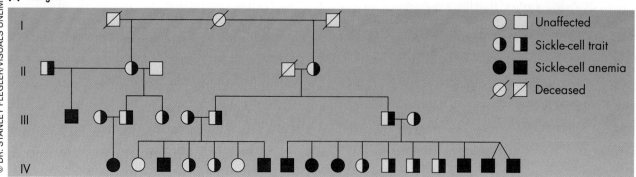

○ □ Unaffected
◑ ◐ Sickle-cell trait
● ■ Sickle-cell anemia
⊘ ⊠ Deceased

© DR. STANLEY FLEGLER/VISUALS UNLIMITED/GETTY IMAGES

Figure 5.7

Blood Groups, Incomplete Dominance, and Multiple Alleles

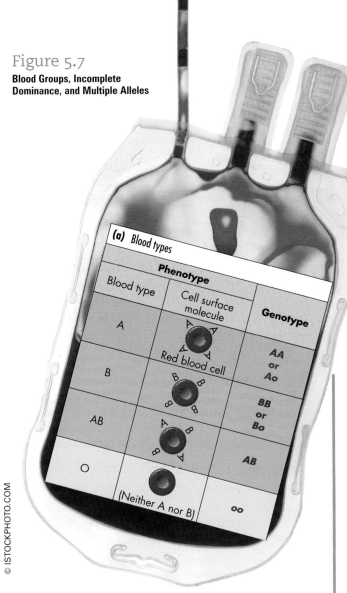

(a) *Blood types*

Blood type	Phenotype	Genotype
	Cell surface molecule	
A	Red blood cell	AA or Ao
B		BB or Bo
AB		AB
O	(Neither A nor B)	oo

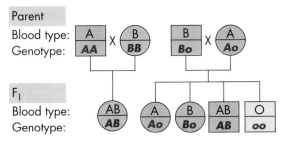

(b) Family studies

Parent					
Blood type:	A	X	B	B	X	A
Genotype:	AA		BB	Bo		Ao

F₁

Blood type:	AB	A	B	AB	O
Genotype:	AB	Ao	Bo	AB	oo

person with this allele may have blood type A. Allele B causes a different carbohydrate molecule called type B, to appear on the surface of red blood cells, and produces blood type B. Someone who has two A alleles has only the A molecule, and a person with two B alleles has only the B molecule. But a heterozygote with one A allele and one B allele has both A and B molecules on the surface of red blood cells. That person has blood type AB, a codominant phenotype.

Students are sometimes confused by the difference between codominance and incomplete domi-nance. In codominance, *both* alleles are fully expressed in the heterozygote, while in incomplete dominance, the phenotype is interme-diate. AB blood type is not intermediate between A and B: it is fully A *and* B. But people with sickle-cell trait are nearly normal in phenotype, becoming ill only under extreme circumstances, and thus incomplete dominance is at work.

Multiple Alleles

If your blood type is O, not A, B, or AB, then you are a good example of another genetic concept: some genes have more than two alleles, and the human ABO blood group gene is an example. In addition to the two codominant alleles A and B, the ABO gene has a third allele that is fully recessive to both A and B. This recessive allele is called o. A person with two doses of o has neither the A nor B molecular marker and has blood type O. Because o is recessive, an Ao heterozygote has blood type A, and a Bo heterozygote has blood type B. Although there are three alleles of the ABO gene found in the human population, no one person can have all three at once, because each child gets only *one* allele of each gene from each par-ent, for a total of two copies of each gene. Figure 5.7b shows some pedigrees for the ABO gene.

The ABO gene has three alleles, but some genes have even more than that, and this is important to patients with severe cystic fibrosis who have received transplanted organs. Because the effects of cystic fibrosis on the lungs and airways can be life-threatening, hundreds of cystic fibrosis patients have received transplanted lungs as a treatment of last resort. Unfortunately, as you have probably read in newspapers or magazines, tissue transplants from unrelated people are likely to be rejected, and the reason hinges on multiple alleles.

The **major histocompatibility complex (MHC)** is a group of genes that encode certain proteins on cell surfaces. These substances serve as identifica-tion markers that help the body distinguish its own

major histocom-patibility complex (MHC)
a complex of proteins that are specific for each individual and are the factors that cause the body to reject trans-planted tissues; their main function is to aid in communication among immune cells

> In codominance, *both* alleles are *fully* expressed in the heterozygote, while in incomplete dominance, the phenotype is intermediate.

© ISTOCKPHOTO.COM

parental type
an offspring having the characteristics of one of the parents

recombinant type
an offspring in which characteristics of the parents are combined in new ways

independent assortment
Mendel's second law, or principle; the random distribution of genes located on different chromosomes to the gametes

cells from foreign substances like bacteria, viruses, or parasites that might otherwise successfully invade the body and cause disease. Because there are several genes in the MHC, and because each gene has many alleles, it is highly unlikely that two unrelated persons will have precisely the same combination of alleles. That is why a person with kidney or liver disease or lung damage from cystic fibrosis must often wait a long time before being matched with a suitable donor. If there are too many allelic differences between the tissues of donor and recipient, the immune system cells of the recipient will kill the cells of the donated organ. Even with immunosuppressant drugs that help stop tissue rejection, the multiple alleles for tissue types constitute a major obstacle to many life-saving transplants.

LO⁴ What Are the Rules Governing How Organisms Inherit Multiple Traits?

So far, we have discussed single genes and their alleles, whether for flower color or cystic fibrosis. But organisms have thousands of genes. A single-celled yeast has about 6,000 genes, a soil-living roundworm has about 19,000, and you have about 40,000. What happens when a geneticist studying the cross between two individuals focuses on more than one gene at the same time in the same cross?

Formation of Gametes

Suppose a female is homozygous for the cystic fibrosis trait and has two recessive alleles: CF^-CF^-. She also has blood type A and is homozygous dominant for this blood type, with the genotype AA. Suppose a male is heterozygous $CF^+ CF^-$, and he is homozygous recessive for blood type O, with genotype oo. Suppose they decided to have a child and produced a son who is simultaneously heterozygous for cystic fibrosis $CF^+ CF^-$ and has blood type A with the genotype Ao (one dominant A allele, one recessive o allele of the ABO blood group gene). This son's genotype for the two traits would then be $CF^+ CF^-$ Ao.

When their son grows up and begins to generate gametes, what types would he make? Recall that Mendel's principle of segregation says that each gam-

ete gets one copy of each gene, and so each gamete must have one copy of the cystic fibrosis gene and one copy of the blood type gene. Mendel's principle further suggests that half of the sperm cells would get a CF^- allele and the other half a CF^+ allele. Likewise, half of the sperm would get an A blood type allele and the other half an o allele. So the son's sperm could be of four types:

But in what proportions will these four types of gametes actually form? Would the sperm possess only the parent's original genotypes, CF^- A and CF^+ o? Geneticists call these **parental types** because they are like the original parents. Or would some of the sperm also possess the new combinations CF^- o and CF^+ A? Geneticists call these types the **recombinant types** (see Chapter 4), because they are "recombined" and not present in the original parents.

In working with peas, Mendel found that alleles of different genes move independently into the gametes, a process he called **independent assortment**. What it means is that the segregation of a particular allele pair into separate gametes is independent of other allele pairs. As a result, all four types of gametes (such as those we just showed for cystic fibrosis and blood type) are equally likely, each occurring one quarter of the time.

One way to visualize this is to use the following diagram:

Cystic fibrosis alleles	ABO alleles	gametes
1/2 CF^-	1/2 A	1/4 CF^- A
	1/2 o	1/4 CF^- o
1/2 CF^+	1/2 A	1/4 CF^+ A
	1/2 o	1/4 CF^+ o

This diagram shows the essential features of Mendel's principle of independent assortment. For genes that are inherited independently of each other, half of the gametes from an individual that is doubly heterozygous are of the parental type (CF^-A and CF^+o) and half are of the recombinant type (CF^-o and CF^+A).

Recall that Mendel always took his experiments through an F_2 generation. So let's consider what would happen if the theoretical son we've been discussing married a woman with exactly his same genotype for cystic fibrosis and blood type ($CF^+ CF^-$ Ao). Furthermore, since this is hypothetical, let's say that this couple had hundreds of children so we can

Figure 5.8

Independent Assortment in Pea Plants and People

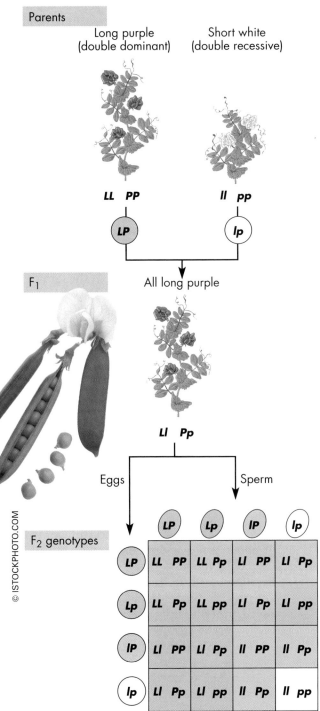

Parents

Long purple
(double dominant)   Short white
(double recessive)

LL PP   **ll pp**

LP   **lp**

All long purple

F_1

Ll Pp

Eggs   Sperm

F_2 genotypes

	LP	**Lp**	**lP**	**lp**
LP	LL PP	LL Pp	Ll PP	Ll Pp
Lp	LL Pp	LL pp	Ll Pp	Ll pp
lP	Ll PP	Ll Pp	ll PP	ll Pp
lp	Ll Pp	Ll pp	ll Pp	ll pp

F_2 phenotypes

9	Long purple (dominant – dominant)
3	Long white (dominant – recessive)
3	Short purple (recessive – dominant)
1	Short white (recessive – recessive)

16 TOTAL

obtain statistically meaningful results. What genotypes would the children have and in what proportions? Mendel carried out similar crosses, which he called **dihybrid crosses** (that is, crosses following two traits), with pea plants. He followed both long and short stems and purple and white flowers (represented by these alleles *LL, Ll, ll* and *PP, Pp, pp*). Figure 5.8 shows the results in the offspring, and we can see that the phenotypic ratio is 9:3:3:1. We can apply Mendel's results to the human situation as well and get the same 9:3:3:1 ratio. What we would see is 9 double dominant showing both the healthy (noncystic fibrosis) phenotype and the A blood type, 3 with the recessive cystic fibrosis phenotype but the dominant A blood type, 3 with the dominant noncystic fibrosis phenotype but the recessive O blood type, and 1 double recessive with both the cystic fibrosis phenotype and the O blood type. (Note that 9 + 3 + 3 + 1 adds up to 16, which is the number of squares in the 4 × 4 Punnett Square in Figure 5.8.)

In summary, Mendel's second principle shows that different hereditary factors segregate into gametes independently of each other. As a consequence of independent assortment, we see the 9:3:3:1 ratio in the F_2 generation.

Genes Are Located on Chromosomes

There are several parallels between the inheritance of genes and the distribution of chromosomes during meiosis:

1. Two copies of each gene and two copies of each chromosome exist in each body cell.
2. Pairs of alleles and pairs of homologous chromosomes both segregate during gamete formation.
3. Genes for different traits and nonhomologous chromosomes both assort independently when egg and sperm are formed.

These facts suggest that genes are physically linked to chromosomes. To test that possibility, early investigators had to locate individual chromosomes and show that when an organism inherits that chromosome, a specific trait is always transmitted with it. That became possible by investigating sex chromosomes.

> **dihybrid cross**
> a mating between two individuals in which the investigation follows the inheritance of only two traits

> **9:3:3:1 ratio**
> the ratio of phenotypes found in the offspring of two individuals, both of whom are heterozygous for two traits whose alleles assort independently

autosome
a chromosome other than a sex chromosome

sex chromosomes
pairs of chromosomes where the members of the pair are dissimilar in different sexes and are involved in sex determination, such as the X and Y chromosomes

X chromosome
the sex chromosome found in two doses in female mammals, fruit flies, and many other species

Y chromosome
the sex chromosome found in a single dose in male mammals, fruit flies, and many other species

mutation
any heritable change in the base sequence of an organism's DNA

LO⁵ How Does Sex Influence the Inheritance of Traits?

The pedigree we looked at earlier for cystic fibrosis show about the same number of affected males as affected females. Many other genetic conditions, however, such as *color blindness* (the inability to see specific colors) and *hemophilia* (inability to form a blood clot) are much more prevalent in males than in females. By investigating traits influenced by sex, early 20th-century geneticists were able to show that genes are indeed located on chromosomes.

Sex Chromosomes

Have you ever wondered why there are roughly as many boy babies as girl babies (the actual ratio is about 106 boys to 100 girls)? A *karyotype* or arrayed set of chromosome photographs reveals why (Fig. 5.9). For 22 of our 23 chromosome pairs, both members are identical in size and shape. For the 23rd

chromosome pair, however, males and females differ. Chromosome pairs in which both chromosomes look the same in both sexes are autosomes, while chromosome pairs with dissimilar members in males and females are sex chromosomes. Humans have 22 pairs of autosomes and one pair of sex chromosomes. Females have two identical sex chromosomes, called X chromosomes, and males have one X chromosome and another, often smaller chromosome called a Y chromosome. Although sex chromosomes are common in animals, they are rarely found in plants, fungi, or protists.

The way sex chromosomes become distributed during meiosis explains the appearance of about equal numbers of males and females. An *XY* male is like the heterozygous parent, and an *XX* female is like the homozygous parent (see Fig. 5.10). In the male, the X and Y segregate during meiosis, and as a result, one half of the sperm contain a Y chromosome and one half an X chromosome. In the female, the two X chromosomes segregate during meiosis; as a result, each egg contains one X chromosome. If the X and Y sperm randomly fertilize a group of eggs, then half of the zygotes formed will be male (*XY*) and half female (*XX*). Note that a male's single X chromosome must be inherited from his mother. Because males and females have different chromosomes, we know that at least one trait—sex—is regulated by chromosomes. But are there any others?

Sex-Linked Traits

In 1910, Thomas Hunt Morgan and his associates at Columbia University began a series of experiments that would change genetics forever. Morgan wanted to find out about genes and chromosomes but did not have Mendel's monastic patience, so he chose the fast-breeding fruit fly, *Drosophila melanogaster*. No bigger than an "l" in this sentence, fruit flies are easy to raise and breed, and in just 12 days, an egg becomes a reproductive adult ready to produce hundreds of offspring.

One day, as Morgan observed fruit flies under the microscope, he noticed a fly with white eyes instead of the usual red. A mutation—a permanent change in the genetic material—had altered a gene for eye color from the normal red-eye allele (symbolized by fly geneticists as *w⁺*) to the mutant white-eye allele (*w*).

From a series of crosses like the one shown in Figure 5.10, Morgan realized that the gene for eye color is carried on the X

Figure 5.9

A Karyotype: A Set of Human Chromosomes

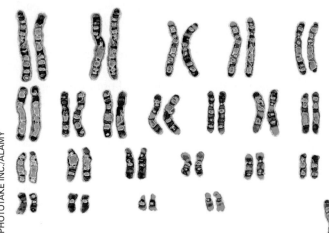

© PHOTOTAKE INC./ALAMY

chromosome. That gene is therefore a sex-linked gene, or more specifically, an *X-linked* gene.

Other genes were found on the fly X chromosome, including *yellow* body and *singed* bristles. After

studying such genes, Morgan and his coworkers drew an important conclusion: The Y chromosome, being considerably smaller, carries no allele of the gene for eye color or for most of the other X-linked genes. From this series of experiments, Morgan drew three important conclusions:

X-linked
characteristic of a heritable trait that occurs on the X chromosome

1. genes are located on chromosomes,
2. each chromosome carries many different genes, and
3. genes on the X chromosome have a distinct pattern of inheritance.

Chromosomes and Sex Determination

The historic experiments with sex chromosomes in fruit flies showed that the expression of male and female characteristics depends on chromosomes. They did not show, however, how sex determination works. Consider this: In flies as well as in people, *XX* individuals are females and *XY* individuals are male. But in both cases, males differ from females in two factors: the presence or absence of a Y, and the number of X chromosomes. Which is more important? To answer, geneticists have studied individuals with unusual numbers of sex chromosomes. Before reading on, look at the data in Table 5.2 to see if Y or X chromosomes are more important for flies. Then do the same for humans.

By analyzing the data in the table, you can see that any fly with at least two X chromosomes is a female, regardless of how many Y chromosomes she has. What about humans? Did your analysis of the table show that people with a Y chromosome

Figure 5.10
Fly Eyes and Sex-Linked Inheritance

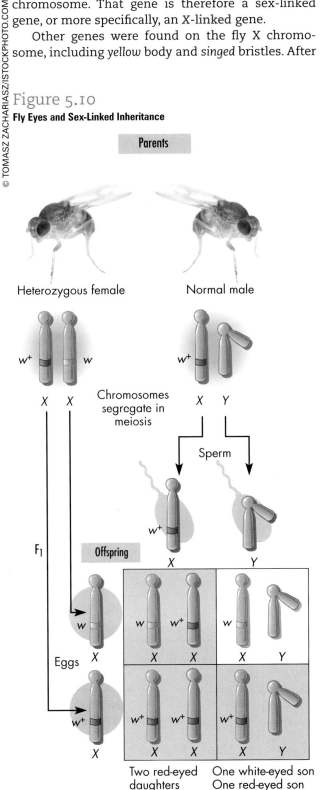

Parents

Heterozygous female · Normal male

w^+ · w · w^+

X X · X Y

Chromosomes segregate in meiosis

Sperm

w^+

X · Y

F_1 · **Offspring**

Eggs

w · X
w^+ · X

w · w^+ · w
X · X · X Y

w^+ · w^+ · w^+
X · X · X Y

Two red-eyed daughters · One white-eyed son One red-eyed son

Table 5.2
Chromosomes and Sex Differentiation

CHROMOSOME CONSTITUTION	FRUIT FLY SEX	HUMAN SEX
X	Male	Female (Turner syndrome)
Y	Lethal	Lethal
XY	Male	Male
XX	Female	Female
XXY	Female	Male (Klinefelter syndrome)
XYY	Male	Male
XXX	Female	Female
XXXY	Female	Male

develop as males, regardless of the number of X chromosomes? Good! This fact indicates that there must be a genetic factor on the human Y chromosome that is essential for producing the male phenotype. Geneticists have isolated that gene, and named it SRY, for "sex-determining region, Y chromosome." They still don't know yet exactly how it works, but in some way, SRY turns on some or all of the genes that stimulate the male phenotype and suppresses those leading to the female phenotype.

More evidence of human sex determination comes from the Turner and Klinefelter syndromes. A person with one X and no Y chromosome (XO) is a sterile female with Turner syndrome. About 1 in 2,200 newborns show this condition, characterized by folds of skin along the neck, a low hairline at the nape of the neck, a shield-shaped chest, and later in life, failure to develop adult sexual characteristics at puberty. About 1 newborn male in 1,000 has two X chromosomes and one Y chromosome (XXY), a condition called Klinefelter syndrome. Affected people develop as sterile males with small testes, long legs and arms, and somewhat diminished verbal skills, although their IQ scores are near normal. Most men with Klinefelter syndrome manage well in society, and many are unaware of their chromosomal abnormality until they marry and are unable to father a child.

Y-Linked Genes

We said earlier that the human Y chromosome was small, and you can see that on Figure 5.9. The Y actually contains only about 20 genes, in contrast to about 1000 on the X chromosome. A few Y chromosome genes have copies on the X chromosome, but most do not. Most of those 20 Y-chromosome genes are expressed only in the testes, where they are probably responsible for male fertility. Many sterile men who come to fertility clinics have mutations in a Y-linked gene. These mutations probably arose in a single sperm cell in the sterile man's dad, because a man whose Y chromosome carries a sterile mutation will have no offspring. If a Y-linked gene had a phenotype other than sterility, then an affected man would pass the trait to all of his sons and none of his daughters.

© ISTOCKPHOTO.COM

X Chromosome Inactivation

A person can get along quite well with only one X chromosome even though the absence of two copies of any other chromosome causes death before or shortly after birth. What's so special about the X? The answer is, no matter how many X chromosomes are present, *both sexes have only a single functional copy of it*. At the stage when a female human embryo (or other mammal) consists of only about a thousand cells, one of the X chromosomes in each of her cells becomes genetically inactive—it no longer reads out any genetic information. Hence, the genes on that inactivated chromosome can have no effect on the phenotype. After one of the X chromosomes in a female embryonic cell becomes inactive, all of the millions of daughter cells derived from it will have the same inactive X. Thus, a female mammal is a mosaic of cells containing active X chromosomes of maternal or paternal origin. You can see this mosaicism in the patches of black and orange fur in a calico cat.

In a female with two Xs (the typical number), a geneticist can see the inactive X chromosome in cells scraped from the inside of the mouth as a small, dark spot on the edge of a nucleus. XY males, who have no inactive X, lack this dark spot in the nucleus. For several Olympic games before 1992, officials relied on this procedure as a test to certify the "femininity" of female athletes, regardless of the other sex chromosomes.

LO6 How Is Genetics Changing Our World?

The majority of cystic fibrosis patients are now surviving into midlife, although there has been a leveling off of life expectancy over the last few years. To move beyond the environmental remedies now available (diet, airway clearing therapies, and antibiotics), new therapies are needed to extend patients' lives further. To this end, researchers are mapping genes, learning what the genes do in healthy and diseased cells, and working on molecular solutions. The history of gene mapping helps explain the pivotal importance of this technique.

Gene Mapping

Gene mapping, the assignment of genes to specific locations or loci (singular *locus*) along a chromosome, was developed in fruit flies, like so many other genetic principles. Recall that Thomas Hunt Morgan used flies to show that a single chromosome can carry many genes—that is, to show genetic linkage. In 1913, an enterprising undergraduate in Morgan's genetics laboratory, Alfred Sturtevant, showed that genes lie in a straight line along a chromosome and that simple mating experiments can map the genes—that is, reveal their order and relative distance from each other.

Gene Mapping and the Human Genome Project

In 1985, Dr. Francis Collins of the University of Michigan used gene mapping information to identify all the base pairs in the cystic fibrosis gene *CFTR*, and how it works. Today Dr. Collins heads the Human Genome Project at the National Institutes of Health. The goal of the project was the complete sequencing of the human genome, that is, the precise order of As, Ts, Gs and Cs for all 23 human chromosomes. This would be the ultimate gene map, revealing the position of every human gene.

By the year 2000, the sequencing of the entire human genome, all 3 billion nucleotides, was completed. Biologists were amazed to learn that humans have far fewer genes than they had previously thought. For instance, chromosome 22 has just 545 genes and chromosome 21 has just 225 genes. This suggests that we humans have just 40,000 genes, rather than the 100,000 to 140,000 genes they once predicted. This is truly amazing when you consider that a nematode worm has 19,000 genes and a fruit fly has 14,000 genes. How can humans have only two to three times as many genes as worms and flies? The answer may lie with the escalating ways genes can interact as their numbers increase, but a full understanding awaits further research.

Sequencing the human genome is important because researchers will have a far easier time now identifying the structure and activity of disease-related genes. As a result, they'll be better able to design new drugs to treat debilitating conditions. Knowing the sequence may also help geneticists determine why different people respond differently to therapies for serious diseases.

Isolating Disease Genes

Knowing a gene's nucleotide sequence can help reveal its function. By isolating and then analyzing the cystic fibrosis gene, for example, researchers showed that it causes cell membranes to make a particular protein, which causes aberrant ion transport in the ducts of the lungs, pancreas, sweat glands, and other organs leading to sticky mucus build up. This discovery gave patients and their doctors hope that we would someday have a cure for this fatal genetic disease.

The mapping and detection of diseases has another important application: revealing unaffected carriers (heterozygotes) of the disease. Mutations change DNA structure, and this fact can be used to help detect carrier status. If two people who are carriers know their status as heterozygotes for a disease gene, they can learn (often with the help of a genetic counselor) what the chance would be of passing the disease to their own child. After conception, physicians test early-stage fetuses for genetic diseases, including the most common forms of cystic fibrosis.

Treating Genetic Disease

To researchers, doctors, and patients, developing adequate treatments for genetic diseases is an urgent problem; living with a disease and making reproductive and other decisions are very real, day-to-day issues. The future of genetic research, based on Mendel's principles of heredity, is sure to be fascinating, powerful, and with any luck, life-extending.

---

gene mapping
the assignment of genes to specific locations along a chromosome

locus (pl. loci)
the location of a gene on a chromosome

linkage
alleles of two genes located so close to each other on the same chromosome that they fail to assort independently

Human Genome Project
the research effort to sequence the entire set of human genes and to understand their functions

---

Who knew?

You can't always tell genotype by looking at phenotype. For dominant characteristics, the homozygous genotype and heterozygous genotype are phenotypically indistinguishable. For example, if B (black fur) is dominant to b (white fur), both BB and Bb will exhibit black fur.

© KEVIN CURTIS/PHOTO RESEARCHERS, INC.

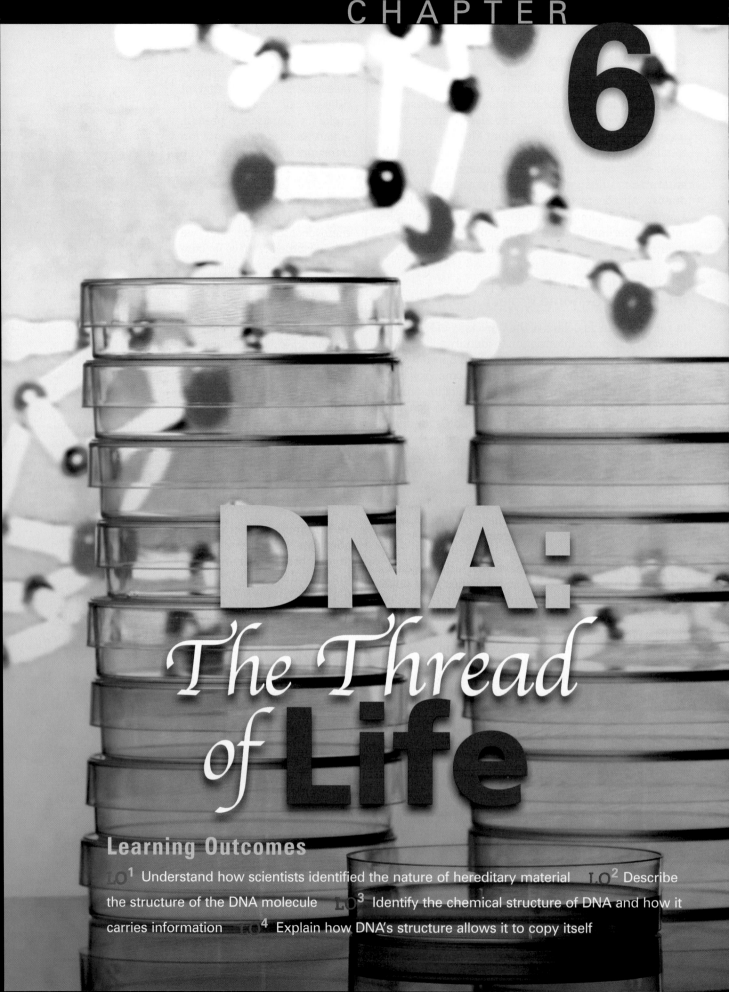

DNA:
The Thread
of **Life**

Learning Outcomes

LO¹ Understand how scientists identified the nature of hereditary material   **LO²** Describe the structure of the DNA molecule   **LO³** Identify the chemical structure of DNA and how it carries information   **LO⁴** Explain how DNA's structure allows it to copy itself

> ❝*We knew that you can get only about one-tenth as much DNA from an animal hair root as from a human hair.*❞

A Cat, A Crime, An Identity

One day in October 1994, a 32-year-old mother of five named Shirley went out on an errand and failed to return to her home on Prince Edward Island, Canada. Within days, the Canadian police found her car abandoned in the woods and splattered with blood, soon identified as Shirley's. Toward the end of October, soldiers on a military maneuver found a man's leather jacket hidden in underbrush and also spotted with Shirley's blood. In May 1995, a fisherman spotted an earthen mound in the woods and dug up Shirley's decomposing body.

What do you know?

Why was the structure of DNA so important that researchers raced to find a model?

The detective in charge of what was now a murder investigation began amassing evidence. The chief suspect was Douglas, Shirley's estranged husband, who had been released from prison not long before Shirley disappeared. Did the discarded jacket belong to Douglas? The crime lab found no blood, human hairs, saliva, or other traces that could have linked the clothing to the suspect. They did, however, find 27 white cat hairs in the jacket's lining, and since his release from prison, Douglas had been living with his parents and their white cat Snowball! The detective arrested the suspect and contacted the U.S. National Institutes of Health in Frederick, Maryland. Through the Internet, the detective had learned that a laboratory group at NIH had for years been studying the DNA of felines—cheetahs, tigers, pumas, ocelots, and domestic cats. If anyone could tie the cat hairs to Douglas it was this team of scientists.

The analysis fell to Dr. Marilyn Menotti. Among the cat hairs, she found four with roots, each one made up of several skin cells and each cell containing DNA in its cell nucleus. "We knew," says Menotti, that you can get "only about one-tenth as much DNA from an animal hair root as from a human hair." So the task was to carefully extract the minute quantities of DNA, amplify it with a special copying procedure, and then identify its unique "fingerprint."

After months of testing and retesting, the team confirmed that the DNA from the hair root in the jacket's bloody lining matched Snowball's DNA exactly and would be unlikely to turn up by chance even in millions of domestic cats of the genotypes on the island. Dr. Menotti testified before the Supreme Court of Prince Edward Island in 1996. The lab work was careful and irrefutable. And the jury, convinced that the cat hairs were Snowball's and the jacket had been worn by Douglas, convicted the defendant of murder.

In this chapter, you'll find a story within a story. Inside the case history of cat hairs and a murder trial, you'll see the race to discover the famous **double-helix** shape of DNA.

double helix
the term used to describe the physical structure of DNA, which resembles a ladder twisted along its long axis

You'll also see how that shape explained the molecule's information coding and copying. Along the way, you'll find answers to these specific questions:

☑ How did scientists identify the nature of hereditary material?

☑ How is DNA like a twisted ladder?

☑ What is the exact chemical structure of DNA and how does it carry information?

☑ How does that structure allow DNA to copy itself?

LO¹ Identifying the Hereditary Material

The DNA that Dr. Menotti extracted from one of Snowball's hairs contained the animal's hereditary instructions. Along with environmental factors, it determined Snowball's unique combination of body size; hair color, texture, and length; eye color; disposition; and hundreds of other traits both obvious and subtle, morphological and biochemical. As in all living organisms, the cat's DNA contained its *genes*, the very same hereditary "factors" Mendel discovered over 150 years ago (see Chapter 5). At that time, however, Mendel had no idea what these hereditary factors might be made of or how they might work. The first step toward our present knowledge of genes was the insight that genes occur in chromosomes. Biologists were able to determine in the 1930s that chromosomes in eukaryotes contain mainly protein, RNA, and DNA. They presumed that one of those substances had to make up the genes carrying genetic information. But which one?

In the 1940s, some geneticists argued that only proteins were versatile enough molecules to carry the com-

> Clearly, 20 amino acids can form many more combinations—and hence carry much more information—than 4 bases, just as you can form more words from an alphabet of 20 letters than from an alphabet of 4 letters.

plex information in genes. These biologists pointed out that proteins are constructed from 20 different subunits (amino acids), while DNA has only four subunits (nucleotides): the nucleotide bases adenine (A), thymine (T), guanine (G), and cytosine (C). Clearly, 20 amino acids can form many more combinations—and hence carry much more information—than 4 bases, just as you can form more words from an alphabet of 20 letters than from an alphabet of 4 letters. In the mid-20th century, geneticists devised tests to determine whether genes are made of protein or nucleic acid, and these experiments led to a biological revolution.

Evidence for DNA: Bacterial Transformation

In 1928, British researcher Frederick Griffith had two strains of pneumococcus bacteria, one that grew into smooth colonies in the lab and could cause a lethal infection if injected into a mouse, and another that grew into rough colonies and did not cause mice to die when injected. Griffith injected mice simultaneously with live cells from the nonlethal bacterial strain *and* with cells from of the disease-causing strain that had been killed with heat. These dually injected mice died. The formerly nonlethal bacteria had somehow acquired the ability to cause lethal pneumonia from the heat-killed cells. As a control, Griffith injected mice with only the heat-killed lethal strain and found that the mice survived. (Why is that control procedure important?) The "transformed" cells—formerly nonlethal bacteria exposed to the lethal strain—could pass the lethal trait to their daughter cells during cell division.

In 1944, Oswald Avery in New York sought to determine which chemical component was carrying hereditary information from the lethal bacteria to the nonlethal strain. To do so, he extracted the carbohydrates, proteins, and DNA from the lethal strain (Fig. 6.1a,c), incubated the nonlethal bacteria (Fig. 6.1b,d) with the various chemicals from the lethal strain, and checked to see which substance would transform the nonlethal cells (Fig. 6.1e). They observed that the nonlethal bacteria treated with either carbohydrate or protein remained nonlethal (Fig. 6.1c–f). In contrast, the nonlethal bacteria treated with DNA from the lethal cells picked up the ability to cause pneumonia in mice and passed that trait to their progeny (Fig. 6.1c–f). They concluded that DNA contains the genes for physical and bio-chemical traits, in this case, the genetic information for the ability to cause fatal pneumonia in mice. Researchers have a word for the transfer of an inherited trait by the uptake of DNA: **transformation**. This process is responsible for the transfer of genes for resistance to antibiotics from one bacterium to another and is a serious problem in modern medicine (see Chapter 9).

Confirmation That Genes Are Made of DNA

The transformation experiments showed that DNA can carry the information for one trait in one species. But what about other traits in other organisms? In 1952, Alfred D. Hershey and Martha Chase got an answer by experimenting with viruses that infect and reproduce in bacteria (Fig. 6.2). We'll refer to them as bacterial viruses, but their official biological name is **bacteriophages** (literally "bacteria eaters"; also called simply **phages**).

They chose to use bacterial viruses for several reasons. First, these viruses are easy and inexpensive to maintain. Second, they can produce new viruses rapidly by injecting a part of themselves into a host cell, which then spawns 100 or so exact copies of the original virus about 25 minutes later. Third, and most important, bacterial viruses consist simply of a core of DNA surrounded by a protein coat. This

transformation
the process of transferring an inherited trait by incorporating a piece of foreign DNA into a prokaryotic or eukaryotic cell

bacteriophage (or phage)
"bacteria eater"; a virus that infects bacterial cells

Figure 6.1

The Chemical Composition of Genes

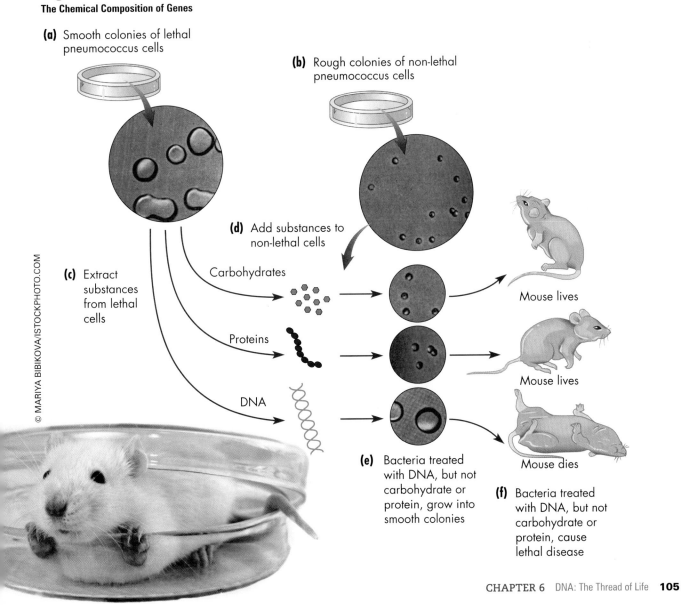

(a) Smooth colonies of lethal pneumococcus cells

(b) Rough colonies of non-lethal pneumococcus cells

(c) Extract substances from lethal cells

(d) Add substances to non-lethal cells

Carbohydrates

Proteins

DNA

Mouse lives

Mouse lives

Mouse dies

(e) Bacteria treated with DNA, but not carbohydrate or protein, grow into smooth colonies

(f) Bacteria treated with DNA, but not carbohydrate or protein, cause lethal disease

© MARIYA BIBIKOVA/ISTOCKPHOTO.COM

Figure 6.2

Life Cycle of a Bacterial Virus

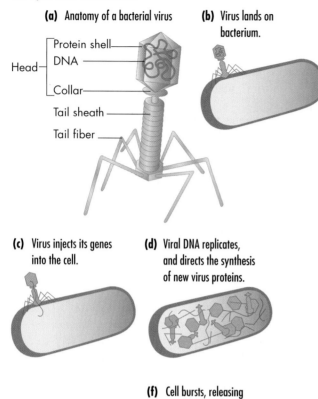

(a) Anatomy of a bacterial virus

Head
- Protein shell
- DNA
- Collar

Tail sheath

Tail fiber

(b) Virus lands on bacterium.

(c) Virus injects its genes into the cell.

(d) Viral DNA replicates, and directs the synthesis of new virus proteins.

(e) Virus particles assemble.

(f) Cell bursts, releasing new virus particles.

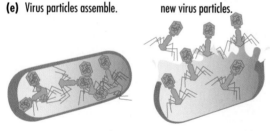

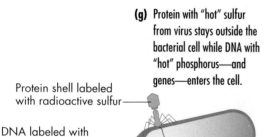

(g) Protein with "hot" sulfur from virus stays outside the bacterial cell while DNA with "hot" phosphorus—and genes—enters the cell.

Protein shell labeled with radioactive sulfur

DNA labeled with radioactive phosphorus

gave Hershey and Chase a clear shot at showing which component contains genes and is responsible for heredity. If only protein from the virus entered the host cell, then protein must be the hereditary material. But if only DNA from the virus entered the bacterial cell, DNA must be the molecule containing the genes. (What would you conclude if both substances entered the host cell? What if neither entered?) Hershey and Chase knew that:

1. proteins contain sulfur but do not contain phosphorus, and
2. DNA contains phosphorus but no sulfur. (Review protein and nucleic acid structure in Chapter 2.)

They labeled the proteins and DNA with radioactive isotopes of sulfur and phosphorus, respectively, which give off detectable signals. By tracing these chemicals, Hersey and Chase were able to determine whether protein (bearing radioactive sulfur) or DNA (bearing radioactive phosphorus) entered the host cell and altered that recipient's genetic activity. The results showed that after infection, "hot" phosphorus was on the inside of the infected cell, and "hot" sulfur was on the outside (Fig. 6.2g). This demonstrated that DNA had entered the cell while protein did not, and that the DNA encoded new phage particles that eventually killed the cell. The researchers concluded that DNA, not protein, was responsible for directing the genetic activity of the virus.

With these experiments, the researchers showed that DNA is definitely the hereditary material in a virus and a bacterium. But what about in more complex species? Research by others confirmed that even in complicated organisms, the answer is still DNA. (In a few viruses, including the virus that causes AIDS [see Chapter 2], genes can be made of RNA.)

These historic experiments changed our concept of the gene from Mendel's abstract hereditary "particle" to a tangible chemical that biologists could see and manipulate. Nowadays, molecular biologists such as Marilyn Menotti break open cells, separate the DNA from the proteins, add ice-cold ethanol to the DNA, and put it in the freezer. A few hours later, a stringy white precipitate a bit like cotton fibers sits at the bottom of a test tube (see photo p. 111)—pure DNA, pure genes.

Learning that genes are made of DNA was a huge step. But to be able to use DNA for sophisticated analyses such as identifying an individual cat from a couple dozen hairs, a researcher needs to know the precise structure of the hereditary molecule.

LO² DNA: The Twisted Ladder

Both a cat and the mice it preys upon have genes encoded in molecules of DNA. DNA can replicate so perfectly that the offspring of two Siamese cats will have the same creamy fur and dark colored "points" on the nose, ears, feet, and tail. DNA can still contain enough variation, however, so that a Siamese cat looks and acts different from Snowball, a tiger, or a mouse. The variability inherent in DNA is the basis of natural selection—the key to how organisms evolve—as well as the explanation for life's wonderful variety. This leaves us with an interesting puzzle, however. How does the structure of DNA account for both the *unity* of life—the shared traits and common descent of living things—and also its stunning *diversity*?

In the early 1950s, James D. Watson, an American postdoctoral fellow, and Francis H.C. Crick, a British researcher, met in Cambridge, England, and began their quest to understand the structure of DNA. They knew that American biochemist Linus Pauling, who had already done his Nobel Prize–winning work on the nature of the chemical bond, was also researching DNA structure, and they wanted to beat this outstanding scientist to the finish line. Watson and Crick also knew from published experiments that DNA is a linear molecule; that is, it is a very long thread.

Watson and Crick knew two additional facts: that DNA is a chain of nucleotides (see Fig. 6.3b on the next page), and what those nucleotides are. Recall that each nucleotide consists of three parts—a sugar, a phosphate, and a portion called a base. Because of the shape of the sugar portion of the molecule, the nucleotide has a front and a rear end, like a car. The carbon atoms in the sugar are labeled $1'$ (pronounced "one prime"), $2'$, $3'$, $4'$, and $5'$. At the rear end of the "car" is a "trailer hitch," the phosphate group, attached to the $5'$ carbon of the sugar (labeled in Fig. 6.3b). The sugar portion acts like the car's chassis, and the base like the car's interior compartment. At the front is the "grill," representing the $3'$ carbon. Watson and Crick also knew that DNA has nucleotides of four types (see Fig. 6.3b), identical except for the bases they contain. These are the adenine (A), cytosine (C), guanine (G), or thymine (T) we encountered in Chapters 2 and 5.

Geneticists often describe a section of DNA by the *sequence* of bases in the chain. For example, a 22-nucleotide portion of a single-stranded DNA chain might have bases in the sequence AGGAAAA TGAAGTCAAGAAAATGG. As we will see later, this specific 22-base sequence played a role in helping to convict Douglas of killing Shirley.

But first, back to Watson and Crick. From the work of Erwin Chargaff, the team knew another significant detail about DNA: in any molecule of a cell's DNA, the bases A and T appear in equal amounts, and the bases C and G also exist in equal amounts. Watson and Crick were anxious to build a model of the DNA molecule that accounted for this peculiar regularity. But they couldn't do it until a last piece of information came from the British biophysicist Rosalind Franklin,

who was working in the laboratory at King's College in London. Franklin took some particularly good images of DNA in an attempt to see how the four subunits—A, T, G, and C—were arranged. She made the images using **x-ray diffraction**, a process in which a beam of x-rays passes through a crystalline fiber made of many parallel strands of pure DNA. Within the DNA fiber, similar structures repeat, like the pattern of tiles on a floor. When x-rays pass through these repeated structures, the x-rays bend, just as light rays bend when they pass from air into water, causing a twig sticking out of a pond surface to appear bent. This bending results in spots cast on photographic film (Fig. 6.3d). By analyzing patterns of spots, biophysicists can map the relative positions of atoms in a molecule.

When Watson and Crick saw the x-ray photos, they noticed a certain symmetry, suggesting that the molecule might consist of *two* connected strands of DNA. The pictures further suggested that DNA was most likely a **helix**, a structure similar to a spiral staircase. Each loop of the helix consisted of ten nucleotides. Now the young researchers had to find out how the bases and sugar-phosphate backbones were arranged in three-dimensional space. They hoped that knowing the structure would also reveal how the molecule replicates itself and stores genetic information.

Excited by Rosalind Franklin's stunning data, Watson and Crick chose a model-building approach to testing their hypotheses about the helical structure. They arranged and rearranged pieces of Tinker Toy–like sticks and balls into various combinations to see which arrangement of basic components might best reproduce the evidence from Franklin's x-ray data. After building one incorrect structure after another, Watson and Crick were finally able to visualize the possible molecular structure. The structure was a *double helix*, which resembles a twisted ladder. By combining their intuition, tinkering, and knowledge from pre-existing research, Watson and Crick arrived at the structure of DNA before any other researchers. In 1953, Watson and Crick published their findings on the structure of DNA in a two-page report in the international journal *Nature*. In a classic understatement, they wrote that it had "not escaped our notice" that the model immediately suggested ways in which DNA could fulfill its two major biological functions: replicating itself and storing information.

A, C, G, T (adenine, cytosine, guanine, thymine)
the four types of nucleotides contained in DNA; they are identical except for the bases they contain

x-ray diffraction
a process in which a beam of x-rays is passed through a crystalline material to help determine its three-dimensional structure

helix
a structure similar to a spiral staircase; DNA is a double helix

The model's simplicity, plus its enormous power to explain observations of nature, led to its rapid acceptance by the scientific world.

In 1962, Watson, Crick, and Wilkins were awarded the Nobel Prize for their assessment of the structure of DNA. Franklin had died four years earlier of breast cancer at the age of 37, and most observers agree that she had played a crucial, but underappreciated, role in the elucidation of the structure of DNA.

LO³ The Structure of DNA

What are the detailed features of the structure of DNA that explain its function?

1. A DNA molecule is composed of two nucleotide chains (Fig. 6.4a).
2. These two chains are oriented in opposite directions, like the northbound and southbound

Figure 6.3
Elucidating the Structure of DNA

(a) Watson and Crick and the DNA model

(c) Rosalind Franklin

(d) An x-ray diffraction image of DNA

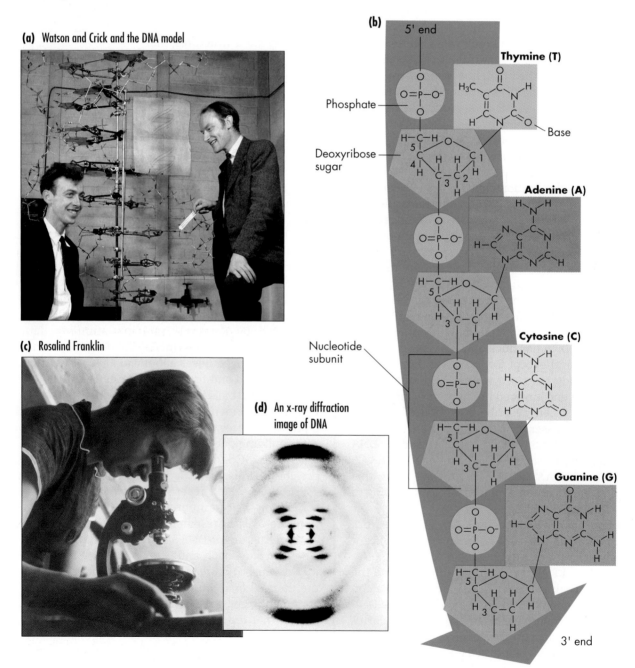

lanes of a highway (Fig. 6.4b). All the nucleotide "cars" in each opposing lane of the highway face in the same direction, with the 3′ sugar leading forward and the 5′ phosphate trailer hitch behind (review Fig. 6.3b). To emphasize the opposite orientation of the two strands, geneticists refer to them as "antiparallel."

3. The two sugar-phosphate chains form the outside of the molecule and are the uprights of the twisted ladder (Fig. 6.4c). In contrast, the bases attached to the backbones face inward, connecting in the middle like the rungs of a ladder (Fig. 6.4d).

4. The bases A and T pair with each other, and the C and G bases also pair; that is, A is complementary to T, and C is complemen-

tary to G—the two fit together like adjacent puzzle pieces (Fig. 6.4e). Bases are held together by hydrogen bonds (Fig. 6.4e), hydrogen atoms shared between an A and a T base or a C and a G base.

This **complementary base pairing** by hydrogen bonds is significant in three ways:

> **complementary base pairing**
> in nucleic acids, the hydrogen bonding of adenine with thymine or uracil, and guanine with cytosine; it holds two strands of DNA together and holds different parts of RNA molecules in specific shapes, and is fundamental to genetic replication, expression, and recombination

- First, it provides the force that holds two single strands of DNA together into a double-stranded molecule. Because hydrogen bonds are relatively weak, however, they are easily broken by temperatures of 60°C or so.

- Second, complementary base pairing by hydrogen bonds explains Erwin Chargaff's finding (see p. 107) that cellular DNA always has equal amounts of A and T and equal amounts of C and G: Whenever one strand has a T, the other has an A, and so on. Knowing the rules of base pairing, you should be able to finish writing out the sequence complementary to the 22 bases shown here:

5′ A G G A A A A T G A A G T C A A G A A A A T G G 3′

3′ T C C T _ _ _ _ _ _ _ _ _ _ _ _ _ _ _ _ _ _ _ 5′

- Third, complementary base pairing is important for DNA's major biological activities: replication and information storage .

5. A final feature of DNA structure is that the two strands of the DNA molecule twist together to form the double helix (Fig. 6.4f). This twist is important to at least two of DNA's features. It's crucial to the regulation of DNA expression, since specific proteins bind in the grooves of the double helix and control which genes a cell will use. And it's also crucial to DNA replication since a cell's DNA must unwind like the fibers of a rope and allow matching up of complementary base pairs. Figure 6.4g points out the parts of a nucleotide: a sugar, a base, and a phosphate.

Packaging DNA in Chromosomes

There are very few cells in the follicle of a cat hair. As a result, Dr. Menotti had to use micromethods to purify the DNA from those few cells and separate it from lipids, carbohydrates, and proteins in the hair root. Prying DNA away from proteins is especially difficult because the two kinds of biological molecules are intimately associated in chromosomes.

Figure 6.4
The Structure of Double-Stranded DNA

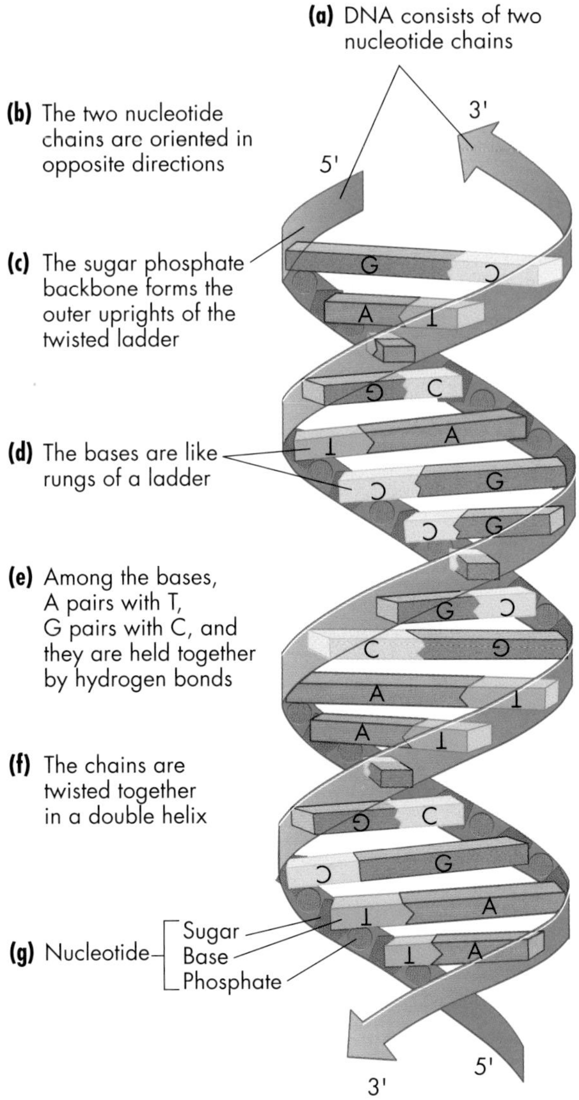

(a) DNA consists of two nucleotide chains

(b) The two nucleotide chains are oriented in opposite directions

(c) The sugar phosphate backbone forms the outer uprights of the twisted ladder

(d) The bases are like rungs of a ladder

(e) Among the bases, A pairs with T, G pairs with C, and they are held together by hydrogen bonds

(f) The chains are twisted together in a double helix

(g) Nucleotide — Sugar, Base, Phosphate

DNA's major biological activities: replication and information storage

histone
protein in the nucleus around which DNA molecules of the chromosomes wind, allowing extremely long DNA molecules to be packed into a cell's nucleus

nucleosome
the basic packaging unit of eukaryotic chromosomes; a histone wrapped with two loops of DNA

chromatin
the substance of a chromosome

In the nucleus of a cat's cells and those of most other eukaryotes, each chromosome consists of a single, long, tightly wound DNA molecule. In the fruit fly, for example, the actual length of the DNA molecule from the largest of the fly's 4 chromosomes is more than an inch long—about 12 times as long as the fly itself! Despite the molecule's length, each of the fly's millions of cells contains two copies of this chromosome, as well as pairs of the other three chromosomes. Likewise, a cat has 19 chromosomes, each even longer than a fruit fly's. How do cells package such a huge genetic molecule into a structure as small as a chromosome?

The enormous length of DNA in a eukaryotic cell can't just be wadded up haphazardly. If it were, the separation of DNA molecules during cell division would be as difficult as unraveling two tangled

kite strings. What happens instead is that DNA, like a proper kite string, is wound in an orderly way (Fig. 6.5). Specifically, DNA is wound around spools of proteins called histones (see Fig. 6.5d). A single spool consisting of several histone molecules wrapped with two loops of DNA (140 base pairs long) is called a nucleosome (Fig. 6.5d). Adjacent nucleosomes pack closely together to form a larger coil, somewhat like a coiled telephone cord. This cord, in turn, is looped and packaged with scaffolding proteins into chromatin, the combined proteins and genetic material that constitute the substance of chromosomes.

Compare this understanding about DNA packing in chromosomes with what you already know about chromosome activity in mitosis. Recall that during the interphase portion of mitosis, individual chromosomes are invisible (review Figs. 4.5 and 4.7). This is because in interphase, the spools of DNA and protein are not packed closely together, allowing the DNA to spread diffusely in the nucleus. In contrast, during prophase (review Fig. 4.7), the spools compact together as shown in Fig. 6.5d, leading ultimately to a visible chromosome (Fig. 6.5b).

Figure 6.5
DNA Is Packaged into Chromosomes

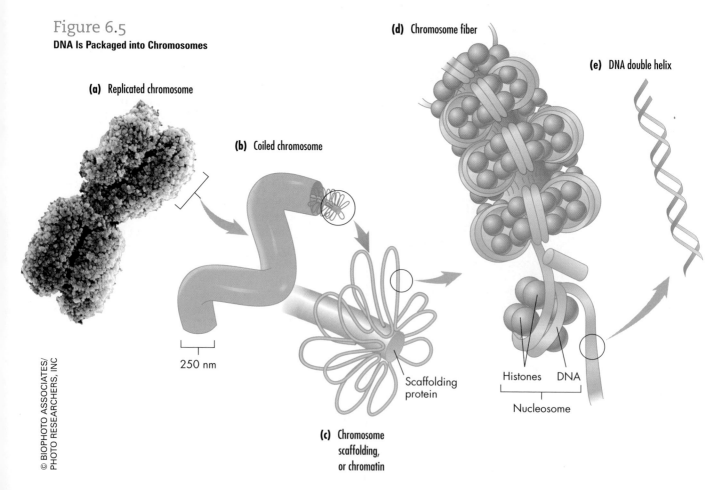

(a) Replicated chromosome

(b) Coiled chromosome

250 nm

(c) Chromosome scaffolding, or chromatin

Scaffolding protein

(d) Chromosome fiber

(e) DNA double helix

Histones   DNA

Nucleosome

© BIOPHOTO ASSOCIATES/ PHOTO RESEARCHERS, INC

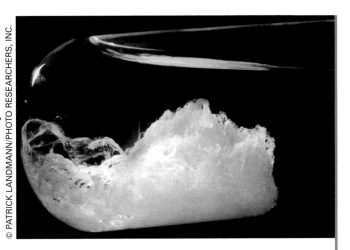

The orderly packaging of DNA around proteins prevents massive DNA tangles during cell division. A molecular biologist like Marilyn Menotti studying DNA separates the genetic molecule from these protein spools by using special solvents that destroy the structure of proteins but leave DNA intact. After this, Menotti's next step was to make millions of copies of certain regions of Snowball's chromosomes so she could investigate their genetic properties, identify the cat hairs, and eventually help solve the mystery of who killed Shirley.

LO⁴ DNA Replication

As we've seen, the amount of DNA in a single hair follicle is very small. Because there is a single DNA molecule in each chromosome, any individual cat, for example, will have only two copies of any gene. (Recall from Chapter 5 that a gene is a unit of inheritance and is specifically a portion of a DNA molecule encoding an RNA and usually a polypeptide chain.) One copy of the gene on the DNA is inherited from the mother and the other copy on the DNA is inherited from the father. Recall that only four cat hairs in Douglas's coat had root cells attached. To get enough DNA to work with, therefore, Menotti had to make many copies of specific regions of DNA by using a test tube version of the normal method of DNA replication. Let's first examine the ways in which cells copy DNA and why that's important. Then we can see how Menotti harnessed the process of DNA replication to help solve the murder case.

Let's start by placing the biochemical process of DNA replication into the familiar context of the cell cycle. We saw in Chapter 4 that cells cycle through a period of growth (interphase) and a period of division (M phase) (see Fig. 4.5). Interphase, remember, has three parts: In G_I, cells have one double-stranded copy of each nuclear DNA molecule; in the S phase, DNA rep-

licates; as a result, in G_2, there are two double-stranded copies of each DNA molecule. Finally, in mitosis, those two DNA copies separate into the two nuclei of the daughter cells. Let's now focus on the events of the S phase, the copying of DNA.

polymerization
the joining together of newly paired bases, creating a DNA strand identical to the original double helix strand of DNA

DNA polymerase
the enzyme that catalyzes the polymerization of DNA strands

Steps in Replication

The replication of DNA occurs in the cell nucleus (see Chapter 4) and follows directly from the principle of complementary base pairing. It can be divided into three steps: (1) strand separation, (2) complementary base pairing, and (3) joining. Keep in mind that before the S (synthesis) phase of the cell cycle, DNA is present in the double helix form (Fig. 6.6).

1. *Separation.* For replication to begin, the two strands of the double helix must first unwind and then strands must separate from each other (Fig. 6.6, Step ①). In cells, the unwinding and separation of the strands are catalyzed by enzymes that help break the "rungs" of the ladder. Those rungs, remember, are the bases on each strand that are bound together by weak hydrogen bonds. In the test tube, Marilyn Menotti and her colleagues used heat to "melt" the hydrogen bonds. After that, for a short time, the separated base pairs are unpaired.

2. *Complementary base pairing.* The unpaired bases form new hydrogen bonds with free nucleotides (As, Ts, Gs, Cs) that happen to diffuse into the area (Fig. 6.6, Step ②). An A base on one DNA strand pairs only with a free T base (complete with its sugar-phosphate backbone), and an attached C pairs only with a free G. Likewise, attached Ts bond only to free As, and attached Gs bond only to free Cs. Thus, the sequence of bases in the original strand specifies the same sequence in the new strand according to the rules of complementary pairing.

3. *Joining.* The joining together of the newly paired bases creates a new strand that is complementary to the parent strand, forming two new double helices that are identical to the original double helix (Fig. 6.6, Step ③). The joining, or **polymerization**, of the new double helices is catalyzed by an enzyme called **DNA polymerase**. This enzyme joins the phosphate group (the trailer hitch in our car analogy) of one nucleotide to the "grill" of the previous nucleotide.

Semiconservative Replication

The three steps of DNA replication—strand separation, base pairing, and joining—occur over and over again along the length of the DNA molecule and produce two double-stranded DNA molecules identical to the parental molecule. Each new DNA has a base sequence identical to the base sequence of the original. You can see in Figure 6.6 that each of the two daughter DNA molecules has one strand intact from the original parent, while the other strand is completely new. Because only one of the two strands

in the daughter molecule is inherited intact—or conserved—from the parent molecule, this type of replication is called **semiconservative replication**. Apparently, all living creatures share this mode of DNA replication. Semiconservative copying of DNA is very different from, say, copying a piece of paper on a photocopy machine. The machine produces a totally new copy but conserves the original fully intact. In contrast, during DNA replication, the original molecule ceases to exist, but one half of it becomes part of one offspring molecule and the other half becomes part of the other offspring molecule.

Accuracy of DNA Replication

It is a wonder that DNA molecules are ever copied correctly, considering the immense length of DNA

Figure 6.6

An Overview of DNA Replication

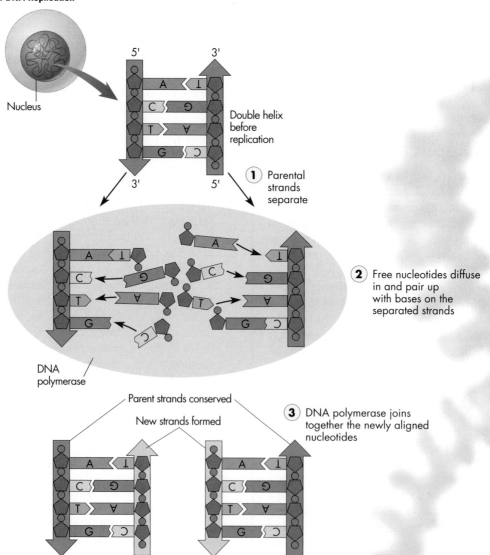

Nucleus

5' 3'
A T
C G
T A
G C

Double helix before replication

3' 5'

(1) Parental strands separate

A T
C G
T A
G C

DNA polymerase

(2) Free nucleotides diffuse in and pair up with bases on the separated strands

Parent strands conserved

New strands formed

(3) DNA polymerase joins together the newly aligned nucleotides

A T
C G
T A
G C

A T
C G
T A
G C

molecules and the complexities of the unwinding, separation, base pairing, and polymerization required for semiconservative replication. Nevertheless, DNA synthesis is very accurate: an error is made only about once in every 10⁹ bases. Since there are approximately 3 billion base pairs in the human genome, this still provides enough genetic variation for natural selection to take place. For many organisms, survival requires extreme accuracy of DNA replication. For example, the human genome (the total of all the genes in a single haploid egg or sperm cell) contains about 3×10^9 base pairs. On average, then, each egg or sperm will have about three new errors. If the rate were much higher, the genetic information would be so altered that the new organism resulting from fertilization could not function. Cells have enzymes that search out and correct genetic errors. Some errors will go undetected and can be harmful, even lethal. But some are not harmful and ultimately provide the genetic variability that fuels evolution.

The Principles of DNA Replication Applied to a Murder Case

Dr. Marilyn Menotti used the principles of DNA structure and replication to positively identify the cat whose hairs clung to the lining of the discarded leather jacket alongside droplets of Shirley's blood. The genetic "fingerprinting" process depends on two principles we've discussed in this chapter, the principle of base order along the DNA molecule and the process of DNA replication.

Base Order and Individual Identity

At thousands of places along the DNA of many species, the two nucleotides C and A are repeated over and over: CACACACACA. The opposite DNA strand, of course, has the sequence TGTGTGTGTG, which is the complementary sequence in the opposite orientation. For convenience, however, we'll talk about the sequence of just one strand, because given that ordering of base pairs, one can figure out the sequence of the other strand by applying the rules of base pairing.

Cats have 19 pairs of chromosomes. In comparison, we humans have 23 pairs, fruit flies have 4 pairs, and corn plants have 10 pairs. Studying Snowball the cat's DNA, Menotti found an important spot along the DNA from one of the two copies of chromosome B3. She called this locus, this region of 115 base pairs, "FCA88" and it had the following sequence of bases: AGG AAAATGAAGTCAAGAAAATGGCTTAATCCAAAGTCA CACAGTACTTAATGTGTGTGTGTGTGTTTGTGTG TGTGTGTGTGTGTATGTGTGTAACGGGAA AAAGAAAA.

Note that the sequence "TG" appears over and over again in this portion of the chromosome. Also notice that we've printed the sequence of just one of the two strands of the DNA double helix. What would the repeated portions "read" on the other strand? If you said, "CA" repeated over and over, you're right!

Dr. Menotti carefully studied the repeated sequences in this FCA88 position on the chromosome. Areas of repeated base sequences are also called **genetic markers** because different numbers of repeats tend to occur in different individuals and this can serve as a specific recognizable section of the DNA that adds to the unique identity. Next, she found 28 copies of the TG repeat on one copy of chromosome number B3 and 25 copies of the TG repeat on the other copy of chromosome B3 from the hair root cell DNA left on the bloody jacket. (The differences are understandable if you consider that each individual has two copies of each chromosome, one from the mother and one from the father.) Once she saw this "fingerprint" in the DNA from the cat hairs on the bloody jacket, Menotti could determine that it matched the number of TG repeats at this locus for the cat Snowball. She also had to test other cats on Prince Edward Island to see if this fingerprint was common or truly unique.

Menotti examined DNA from 19 cats who lived on Prince Edward Island but were unrelated to Snowball, as well as another 9 cats from around the United States. As we just saw, Snowball's DNA had precisely 28 copies of the TG repeat at the FCA88 locus on copy 1 of chromosome B3 and 25 copies of the TG repeat at the FCA88 locus on copy 2 of chromosome B3. The researcher found that an unrelated cat—say, a Siamese cat living on Prince Edward Island—might have as few as 12 or as many as 29 TGs in a row at position FCA88 on chromosome B3. Only a few cats on the island had the same combination of 28 and 25 TG repeats at locus FCA88 as found in the DNA from the cat hairs taken into evidence. By studying repeated base sequences at nine more loci along the DNA retrieved from the cats as well as from the leather jacket, Menotti came up with a set of sequences absolutely individual to one single cat. With it, she could rule out 219,999,999 of every 220 million cats living on Prince Edward Island. (This is a theoretical number, of course, since only a few thousand cats actually live there). She could also rule out 69,999,999 out of every 70 million cats on the U.S./Canadian mainland. This virtually guaranteed that the hairs in the discarded jacket came from the one

Who knew?

Once DNA was known to be the carrier of hereditary information, knowledge of its structure was needed to understand how it could account for both the unity of life (the heritability) and the diversity of life (the enormous amount of variation). Only by understanding the structure of DNA could scientists explain both how DNA is replicated and how it directs the activities of cells that lead to the formation of differences between and within species. To be known for making such an important and fundamental discovery was a valuable "prize" for many researchers.

cat, Snowball, who lived with Douglas and his parents.

Our cat hair case study has demonstrated DNA's capacity for identifying individuals with unique "fingerprints" of repeated sequences at different loci along the chromosomes. But the significance of DNA's elegant double helix structure goes far beyond genetic fingerprints, important as they are to the medical and legal systems. DNA's structure—two twisted strands of nucleotides, oriented in opposite directions—explains its ability to replicate with amazing accuracy as the strands separate and enzymes synthesize two daughter molecules, each a complementary copy of the parent strand. DNA structure also explains the way the "thread of life" controls an organism's physical make up and abilities. Living things, of course, are made up of cells, and it is the collective form and function of those cells that determines the entire organism's appearance, its physical and chemical properties, and its day-to-day behaviors. In our next chapter, we'll see how the blueprints for form and function inscribed in DNA are actually decoded into proteins and cellular activities, and how molecular geneticists have learned to manipulate these blueprints for medicine, agriculture, and industry.

It's easy to read, it outlines important topics, and it's relevant. Thanks for the good stuff on the website, I think it will **really help with tests**.

– Thomas Scholtes, Student at University of Maryland, College Park

REVIEW

HE DID

LIFE puts a multitude of study aids at your fingertips. After reading the chapters, check out these resources for further help:

- **Chapter in Review cards**, found in the back of your book, include all learning outcomes, definitions, and visual summaries for each chapter.

- **Online printable flash cards** give you three additional ways to check your comprehension of key biology concepts.

Other great ways to help you study include **animations, visual reviews,** and **interactive quizzes.**.

You can find it all at **4ltrpress.cengage.com/life**.

The Mechanisms of Evolution

Learning Outcomes

LO[1] Understand the emergence of evolutionary thought

LO[2] Describe the evidence for evolution

LO[3] Identify pathways of evolutionary change

LO[4] Explain genetic variation

LO[5] Understand how genetic variation occurs

LO[6] Identify agents of evolution

LO[7] Understand natural selection

LO[8] Explain how new species arise

> **"** *Species that exist today are not ancestors to other currently living species; the ancestral species are long extinct.* **"**

Resistance on the Rise

To Wayne Chedwick *Staphylococcus aureus*—a common bacterium—*is* an unseen enemy that robbed him of his livelihood, his ability to walk, and parts of his feet. In any college lecture hall, movie theater, or ballpark, up to 10 percent of the crowd will have "staph" populations living harmlessly in their noses and throats. But S. *aureus* can quickly turn against people—regular carriers and others—and cause boils, ulcerated wounds, bone infections, even blood poisoning. Mr. Chedwick has had them all.

His doctors prescribed various antibiotics, of course. But the *Staphylococcus* strain colonizing Wayne's foot bones can't be killed by most of the usual antibiotics. The reason? The strain he contracted has, over time, acquired genes for drug resistance: it has evolved new and dangerous genetic traits.

What do you know?

Why is extinction the likely fate of any species?

At the Federal Centers for Disease Control and Prevention in Atlanta, Dr. Fred Tenover has been carefully tracking these new cases of antibiotic resistance and considers them "worrisome" and potentially "a major threat." Each year, says Tenover, 2 to 3 million people pick up an infection while in the hospital. Over 70 percent of these "are resistant to at least one antibiotic," he explains, and the infections claim 90,000 lives annually.

These cases of near and total antibiotic resistance have profound medical implications, conjuring a world where simple infections take lives as they often did before penicillin became widely available in the 1940s. But the cases have obvious biological significance, as well. They are modern examples of evolution by natural selection, our subject in this chapter.

By exploring this chapter, you'll see how natural selection brings about antibiotic resistance, but also how it engenders Earth's stunning diversity of plant and animal life. You'll encounter Charles Darwin and Alfred Russell Wallace once again, as we did in Chapter 1. You'll see the patterns of evolution that established the dinosaurs and Ice Age mammals. And you'll see how natural selection brings about new species, eliminates poorly adapted ones, and helps outfit organisms with successful survival tools such as genes for resisting antibiotics. Along the way, you'll find the answers to these questions:

- ☑ How did naturalists develop the concept of evolution?
- ☑ What is the evidence for evolution?
- ☑ What are the various patterns of evolutionary change?
- ☑ How does genetic variation arise?
- ☑ What principles govern the inheritance of genetic variation in populations?
- ☑ What are the mechanisms of evolution and how do they work?
- ☑ How does natural selection fit populations to their environments?
- ☑ What are species and how do they originate?

LO¹ Emergence of Evolution as a Concept

An explanation for how such antibiotic resistance evolves in bacteria helps us understand evolution, or changes in gene frequencies in a population over time. But does evolution operate the same way in other organisms? And how does evolution account for the tremendous diversity of life? There are millions of kinds of insects, hundreds of thousands of kinds of plants, and so on. Did evolution produce them all and if so, how?

Until the end of the 18th and beginning of the 19th centuries, most naturalists believed that each species had been created separately and had remained unchanged from their creation to the current day. They thought, for example, that striped bass and sparrows were created at the beginning of the world and have remained exactly the same ever since.

About this same time, however, scientific exploration of the natural world was already uncovering facts that contradicted the notion of a single creation event and unchanging species. If all types of organisms were created at a single place and at a single point in time, then *why were there different groups of organisms in Earth's different regions?* If all organisms were created at one time, then *why would ancient extinct organisms be different from modern living species?* If each species had been created individually and never changed, then *how could the same basic bone plan be the best design for swimming* and *flying* and *fine manipulation?* Faced with such puzzles, a few naturalists began to suggest that populations of organisms might have changed, or evolved, over time.

Lamarck: An Early Proponent of Evolutionary Change

French naturalist Jean Baptiste Lamarck (1744–1829) was the first writer to attract much attention to the idea that species (including humans) are descended from other species. Lamarck also attributed this change to natural laws, not to miracles, and proposed a hypothetical mechanism for how this change could come about.

Lamarck suggested two main points. First, he proposed that the physical needs of an animal determine how its body will develop. Second, Lamarck proposed that changes in organ size caused by use or disuse would be inherited. For example, the longer neck a giraffe acquired through stretching

to reach leaves to eat would be passed on to its offspring. Later biologists called Lamarck's hypothesis the inheritance of acquired characteristics.

Biologists in the mid-1800s did not yet understand cellular mechanisms of heredity. But two English naturalists, Charles Darwin and Alfred Russell Wallace, were able to make detailed observations in various parts of the globe and devise a remarkable and elegant explanation for how living things evolve.

Voyages of Discovery

Darwin and Wallace lived in a time when many areas of science were advancing quickly. One area of excitement was the growing conviction that the natural world is in a constant state of change. Fossils discovered in the late 1700s and early 1800s convinced many scientists that the forms of plants and animals had changed, or evolved, over time. One active fossil hunter from the era, Mary Anning, discovered the first plesiosaur, an extinct marine reptile, as well as many other fossils that contributed to the debates over evolution. Geologists of that same period also found evidence of physical evolution that contradicted Biblical timetables established for creation. They documented mountain building, erosion, and volcanic eruptions to prove that our planet must be millions, not thousands, of years old and must be undergoing slow but continuous change.

It was in this diverse social and scientific context that Darwin and Wallace independently observed unfamiliar organisms on their travels, and—unaware of each other's ideas—drew nearly identical conclusions about how the mechanisms of evolution might occur.

Darwin was passionately interested in natural history. He became the ship's naturalist for Captain Fitzroy of the HMS *Beagle* on a five-year voyage (1831–1836) to map the coastline of South America. At stops during the voyage, Darwin explored South American jungles, plains, and mountains. A seminal stop on the trip was the Galápagos, a cluster

© KEN BROWN/ISTOCKPHOTO.COM

of black volcanic islands west of Ecuador inhabited by a small but unique set of plants and animals. Darwin was impressed by the variable shapes and colors the members of a single species could show, and he wondered how such variety could have arisen. He returned to England with notebooks full of sketches and observations, convinced that the living plants and animals he observed could illuminate the origin of species. Alfred Russell Wallace had also sailed to South America to collect plants, insects, and other natural specimens. Like Darwin, he had noticed on his travels the striking variations among populations of individual species. Also like Darwin, Wallace had devised a theory of evolution by natural selection to explain what he saw.

By 1858, Wallace had published several papers containing portions of a theory of evolution that included natural selection, the notion of changes over time from a common ancestor, and the idea of survival of the fittest. Then the following year, Darwin released his monumental and well-documented book, *On the Origin of Species by Means of Natural Selection*.

Darwin and Wallace left the world a priceless legacy with their two key ideas: (1) descent with modification—the notion that all organisms are descended with changes from common ancestors; and (2) natural selection, the increased survival and reproduction of individuals better adapted to the environment.

Descent with Modification

Darwin thought of evolution as a branching tree with the more recently evolved organisms at the tips of the outer branches and the more ancient or extinct species at the base and on lower branches. This contrasts sharply with the form predicted by Lamarck or by advocates of creation. It also contradicts the still widespread but wrong idea that evolution is a ladder from "lower forms," like worms and fish, to "higher forms," like birds, dogs, and humans. Species that exist today are *not* ancestors to other currently living species; the ancestral species are long extinct. The biggest conceptual advance Darwin and Wallace put forward was the *mechanism* for how descent with modification could occur.

Evolution by Natural Selection

Darwin's and Wallace's experiences in then-remote regions such as South America and the Galápagos Islands convinced them that evolution had occurred. But Darwin returned to England still puzzling over some mechanism that could cause evolution. He eventually put together two indisputable facts based on observations, and drew a far-reaching conclusion:

Fact 1. Individuals in a population vary in many ways, and some of these variations can be inherited.

Fact 2. Populations can produce many more offspring than the environment's food, space, and other assets can possibly support. This causes individuals within the same population to compete with each other for limited resources.

Darwin's Conclusion. Individuals whose hereditary traits allow them to cope more efficiently with the local environment are more likely to survive and produce offspring than individuals without those traits. As a result, certain inherited traits become more common in a population over many generations.

descent with modification
the notion that all organisms are descended with changes from common ancestors

natural selection
the increased survival and reproduction of individuals better adapted to the environment

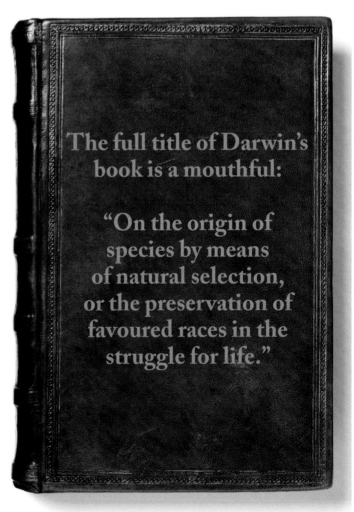

The full title of Darwin's book is a mouthful:

"On the origin of species by means of natural selection, or the preservation of favoured races in the struggle for life."

© JOE CICAK/ISTOCKPHOTO.COM

fossils
traces or remains of a living thing from a previous geologic time

sedimentary rock
layer upon layer of sand and dirt accumulated over thousands or millions of years and eventually forming rock layers that sometimes entomb fossilized organisms from different eras

Darwin (and later Wallace) used the term "natural selection" to describe the pressure exerted by environmental factors. Their term also applied to the greater reproductive success displayed by better-adapted individuals. Both chose this term because nature "selects" the favorable traits that are passed on to the next generation. The favorable traits, or *adaptations,* include body parts, behaviors, and physiological processes that enable an organism to survive in its current environment. Favorable traits are modified or maintained as a result of natural selection because they improve an organism's chance of surviving and reproducing successfully. Biologists now accept the principle of natural selection as a main mechanism behind evolution in nature.

People sometimes get confused, thinking that natural selection *causes* the variations within a population. However, short necks, long necks, antibiotic resistance, and other traits already exist in populations as a result of mutations or, sometimes in bacteria, of picking up foreign genes (transformation). Natural selection simply results in the best-competing individuals: those with the traits best adapted to current environmental conditions survive and produce more offspring in the next generation.

Later in the chapter, we'll return to a more detailed explanation of how natural selection favors certain genes. First, though, let's examine some of the evidence for evolution by natural selection amassed by Darwin, Wallace, and biologists after them.

> Natural selection simply results in the best-competing individuals: those with the traits best-adapted to current environmental conditions survive and produce more offspring in the next generation.

LO² Evidence for Evolution

Evolution has such tremendous power to explain so many different aspects of biology that most biologists accept it as a fact. Researchers have found supporting evidence for evolution in the fossil record, in the anatomy of plants and animals, in molecular genetics, and in the geographical distribution of organisms.

The Fossil Record

Fossils are traces or remains of living things from a previous geologic time. Fossils give scientists tangible evidence of what past organisms looked like, and when and where they lived. A fossil can be nothing more than the trail, preserved in rock, of an animal that once slithered across the muddy bottom of some ancient lake or sea. Other fossils preserve leaf prints, footprints, casts, outlines, or sometimes even soft body parts in rock after the perishable organic matter is removed and replaced with minerals. The most familiar fossils, however, form from hard, decay-resistant structures such as shells, bones, and teeth.

Fossils and Sedimentary Rock

Although some fossils turn up in ice, peat bogs, or tar pits, fossil hunters find most fossils in sedimentary rock, which forms as layer upon layer of sand and dirt accumulated over thousands or millions of years. Newer layers press down on older ones, until pressure and heat cement the dirt, clay, and/or sand particles together, gradually changing them into rock.

Paleontologists discovered one of the richest fossil beds in North America in the Badlands region near the border of North and South Dakota, and learned from it priceless lessons about the evolutionary process (Fig. 9.1). Today, the Badlands region contains grasslands, high plateaus, and rock outcroppings. About 70 million years ago, however, the area lay beneath a shallow sea. The warm, expansive waters were densely populated by ammonites, extinct shelled relatives of squids and octopuses. By about 30 million years ago, the seas had retreated, and huge rhinoceros-like animals, the titanotheres, roamed the land. A few million years after that, a three-toed, knee-high ancestor of the horse, named *Mesohippus,* grazed where the larger titanotheres had roamed. Finally, fossils reveal that sheeplike oreodonts became abundant by about 25 million years ago. Paleontologists found each type of fossil at a particular level, suggesting that each of the different kinds of animals lived during a well-defined period.

If organisms evolved over immense time spans, then paleontologists ought to be able to find fossils intermediate in form between major groups of today's organisms (Fig. 9.2). And indeed they have. A famous example involves the 150-million-year-old crow-sized *Archaeopteryx.* This animal looked like a small dinosaur in nearly all respects, but it had feathers like a bird (Fig. 9.2c). A recently discovered series of fossils from China shows animals very similar to the velociraptors from the movie *Jurassic Park.*

Figure 9.1
Layers in Time

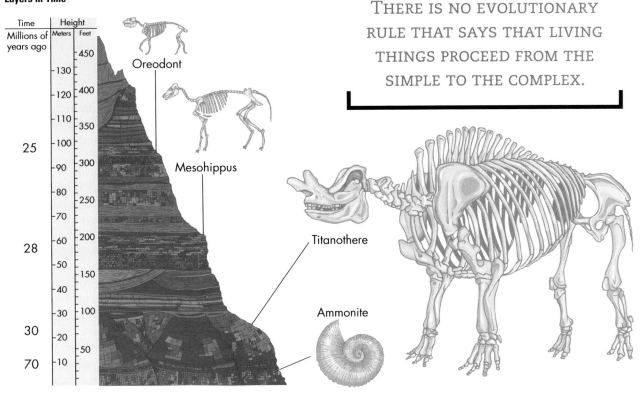

The tip of the animal's tail, however, was shaped like the feather-supporting tail stump in today's birds. Based on the similarities between birds and dinosaurs, some paleontologists now classify birds as a type of living dinosaur!

Fossil evidence supports evolution in several ways:

- Different organisms lived at different times.

- Past organisms were different from today's living organisms.

- Fossils in adjacent rock layers are more similar to each other than to fossils in distant layers.

- Many intermediate forms like *Archaeopteryx* have surfaced.

- In general, older rocks contain simpler forms, and younger rocks contain more complex ones.

As we saw before, though, there is no evolutionary rule that says that living things proceed from the simple to the complex. Instead, species have proceeded from being well-suited to their environments to being better suited—or else disappearing.

Evidence from Comparative Anatomy

If evolution occurs by descent with modification, that is, inheritance with changes, then one would predict the anatomy of living species to resemble that of extinct relatives, but with changes. And that is just what biologists see by studying two types of anatomical evidence: homologous structures and vestigial organs.

Homology: Organs with Similar Origins

Similar structures on different organisms help support the argument for descent with modification. Think, for a moment, about the forelimbs of various mammals and the functions they allow: human hands can deftly manipulate keyboards, surgical tools, paintbrushes; a cheetah's front legs help it run 116 kilometers (72 miles) per hour for short sprints; a whale's flippers allow it to dive powerfully and gracefully; a bat's wings enable it to fly. As different as they are, each type of limb is made up of the same skeletal elements (Fig. 9.3).

Fossil evidence supports the hypothesis that the varied forelimbs of mammals arose from the forelegs of ancestral five-fingered amphibians and became modified by natural selection in ways that facilitated different tasks. The idea that this same set of bones—one in the upper part of the limb, two in the lower part, and five digits—are the very best arrangement for manipulation *and* running *and* swimming *and* flying seems unreasonable to most anatomists. Elements (such as legs, flippers, and wings) in different species that derive from a single

homologous elements
elements (such as a leg, flipper, or wing) in different species that derive from a single element in a common ancestor

vestigial organ
a rudimentary structure with no apparent utility but bearing a strong resemblance to structures in probable ancestors

element in the last common ancestor of those species are called homologous (*homo* = same) elements. Homologous organs can have different functions but similar genetic blueprints, and can be constructed in much the same way in the embryos of different species.

Figure 9.2
Fossil Intermediates

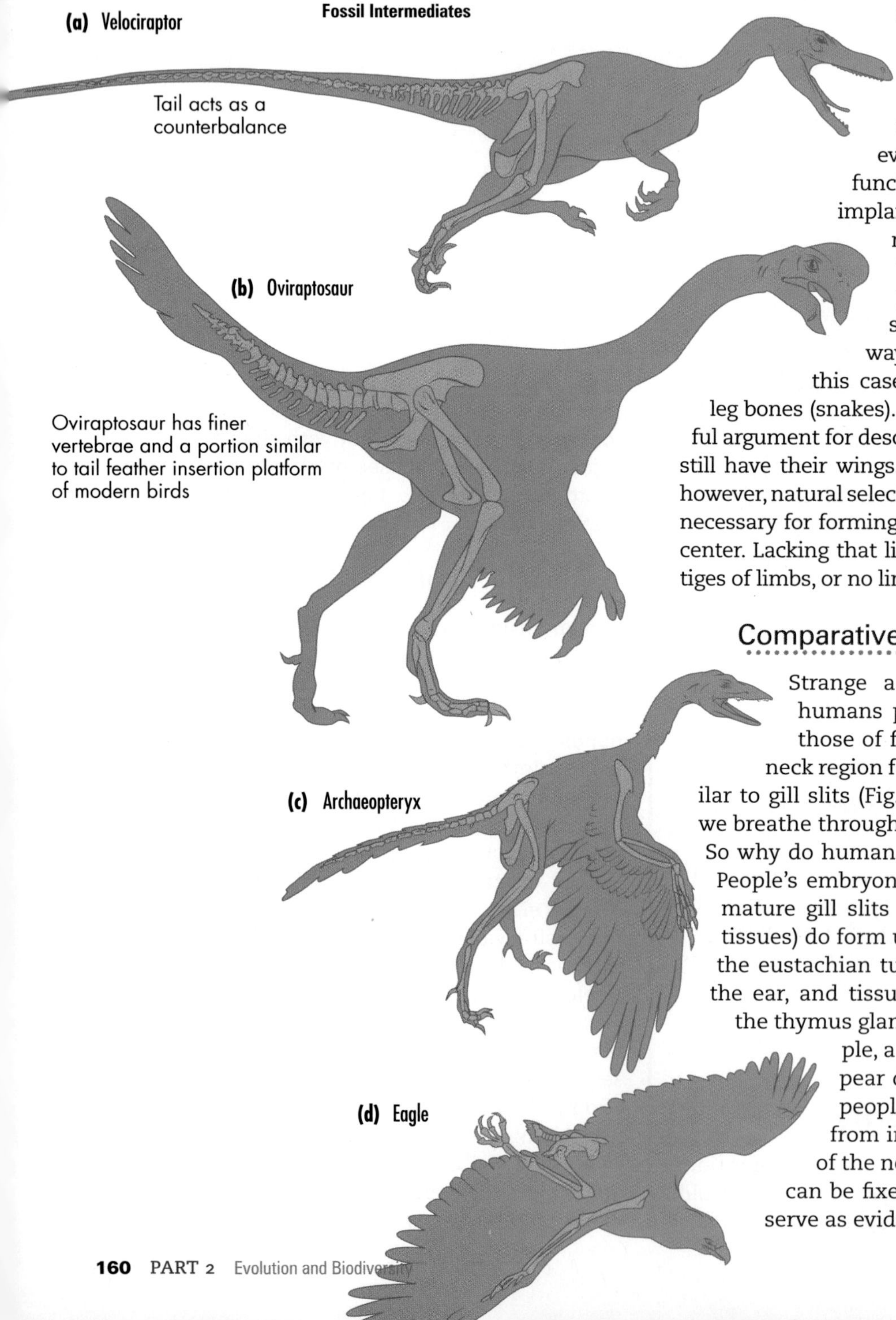

(a) Velociraptor

Tail acts as a counterbalance

(b) Oviraptosaur

Oviraptosaur has finer vertebrae and a portion similar to tail feather insertion platform of modern birds

(c) Archaeopteryx

(d) Eagle

Vestigial Organs

What does your appendix have in common with your wisdom teeth and with a snake's hipbones? The answer is they're all vestigial organs (veh-STIHJ-uhl; Latin *vestigium* = footprint, trace): or rudimentary structures with no apparent use in the organism, but strongly resembling useful structures in probable ancestors. You may have lost both your appendix and wisdom teeth because these structures can be worse than useless if they become infected or impacted. We humans also have the vertebrae (spinal bones) for a tail and for muscles that can wiggle our ears, despite their uselessness today for our survival. In the same way, python snakes have vestigial hipbones and thighbones, even though the bones no longer function. Curiously, a snake embryo implanted with a chick limb bud starts making signals to build legs. This shows that as different as pythons are from chickens, they still share developmental pathways for homologous organs, in this case, wings (chickens) and useless leg bones (snakes). This type of sharing is a powerful argument for descent with modification. Chickens still have their wings. In snakes and their ancestors, however, natural selection has removed alleles of genes necessary for forming the limb bud, with its signaling center. Lacking that limb bud, snakes make only vestiges of limbs, or no limbs at all.

Comparative Embryology

Strange as it seems, as embryos, we humans pass through stages similar to those of fish embryos, during which our neck region forms grooves and pouches similar to gill slits (Fig. 9.4a,b). Like most vertebrates, we breathe through lungs, not gill slits (as fish do). So why do human embryos form these pouches? People's embryonic neck pouches don't become mature gill slits but they (along with adjacent tissues) do form useful organs: one pouch forms the eustachian tube leading from the mouth to the ear, and tissue between the pouches forms the thymus gland and the tonsils. In some people, a pouch fails to change or disappear during development, and these people are born with a tube leading from inside the mouth to the outside of the neck like a fish. This abnormality can be fixed surgically and does, at least, serve as evidence of evolution.

Figure 9.3

Comparative Anatomy Supports Descent with Modification

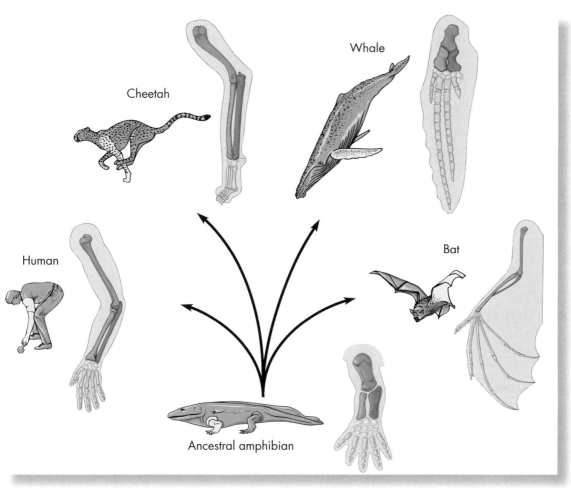

Whale

Cheetah

Human

Bat

Ancestral amphibian

Figure 9.4

Comparative Embryology, Gills Slits, and Descent

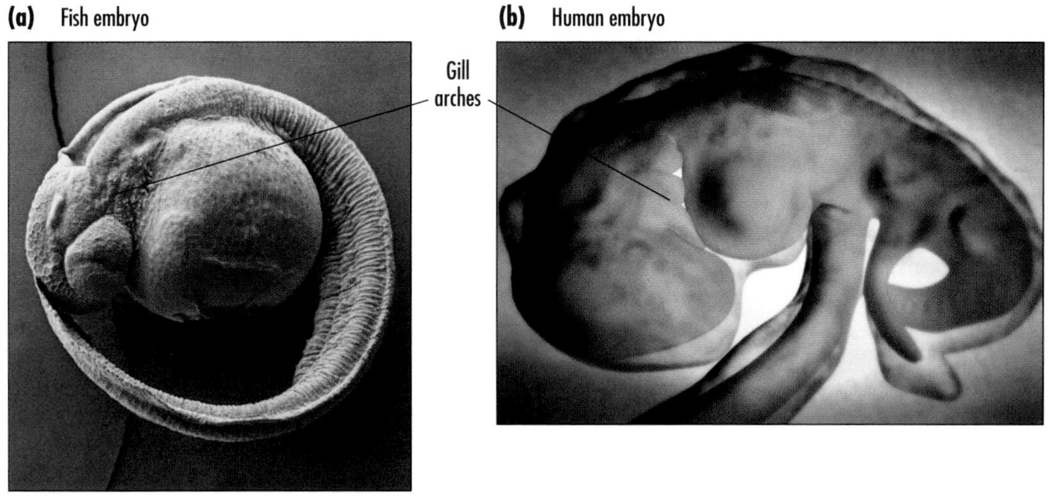

(a) Fish embryo

(b) Human embryo

Gill arches

Evolutionary theory can easily explain why all vertebrate embryos look similar to fish embryos for a while, right down to the pouches. The last common ancestor of humans and ray-finned fish (such as bluegill or bass) lived 450 million years ago, and the embryos of this ancestor developed gill pouches like today's human and fish embryos. In the lineage giving rise to humans, changes in gene frequencies driven by natural selection caused the pouches and nearby tissues to develop into the eustachian tube, thymus, and tonsils. In fish, natural selection modified the same embryological structures into efficient oxygen-gathering gills. Embryology therefore supplies evidence that organisms often inherit features that originated in ancient ancestors but became genetically modified over time.

Evidence from Molecules

If all life evolved from a common ancestor that underwent gradual genetic changes, then all living organisms today should share basic features at the molecular level. In fact, all organisms have the same four bases in DNA, the same 20 amino acids in proteins, virtually the same genetic code, and so on. By comparing the same protein or the same gene in dozens of different species, molecular geneticists can construct molecular family trees. On such a molecular tree, they would place two very similar proteins or genes on branches diverging from each other more recently, and two less similar proteins or genes on branches that diverged longer ago. Biologists then assume that the organisms from which the genes or proteins came share the same evolutionary relationships as the molecules on the tree.

Molecular family trees powerfully support evolution because totally independent molecular and fossil data show common patterns of relationships between living and extinct species. Biologists have even been able to isolate DNA from some fossils. For example, researchers have extracted DNA from 30-million-year-old termites trapped in amber, the fossilized sap of ancient conifer trees. The DNA from the fossil termites was very similar to DNA from living termites that share the same physical features, and very different from DNA in living termites with radically different physical features. These results are exactly what evolutionary biologists expected to find—that ancient species are more similar to some of today's species and less similar to others.

Evidence from Biogeography

When Darwin and Wallace sailed separately to foreign lands, their first clue about evolution was biogeography, or the geographic distribution of organisms. In the Galápagos Islands, for example, Darwin was astonished by the unusual plants and animals he saw: finches using cactus spines to pry insect larvae out of dead wood; gigantic tortoises that varied in form from island to island; iguanas that swam in the sea and fed on algae instead of living exclusively on dry land. He saw no frogs or salamanders, however, and the only native mammals he observed were a few bats and one type of mouse.

Darwin compared these Galápagos organisms to the plants and animals he had seen while visiting the Cape Verde Islands off the coast of Africa. Even though the two island groups had similar climates, sizes, and the same dark volcanic soil, their organisms were of totally different species, genera, and taxonomic families. Rather than being related to *each other's* fauna and flora, each island's organisms were more closely related to those inhabiting the nearest *mainland*. Ironically, though, those mainland areas were very different from the neighboring islands in climate, soil, and other ecological details. So why were the island animals more closely related to those of the mainland than those on other similar islands?

Most 19th-century naturalists accepted the idea of special creation, and would explain the distribution of organisms by suggesting that each individual island had its own individual creation event related somehow to the creation event on the nearest mainland. But why would that creation event have discriminated against frogs, salamanders, and most mammals in a place like the Galápagos? Darwin thought it unlikely that creation overlooked amphibians. Instead, it seemed much more likely to him that the Galápagos harbored only organisms that had flown, swam, or rafted over from the nearest continental shore on floating vegetation to the newly forming volcanic islands. Encountering no competition on the young islands, these "colonists" could then diverge into new species as they adapted to different island environments through natural selection. Like Wallace, Darwin had begun his travels believing that every species was created in its special place, but saw evidence in biogeography that argued against it and the notion of unchanging species.

Throughout his travels in the Galápagos and Cape Verde Islands, Darwin also noted the powerful influence of the environment. For example, in both places, species of plants that grew as low, green herbs on the mainland had close relatives on the islands that were woody and treelike. He saw examples of unrelated organisms, as well, displaying similar characteristics in response to common environmental conditions. Australia, South America, and Africa, for instance, all have large, flightless birds with heavy bodies and long necks: the emu, the rhea, and the ostrich, respectively (Fig. 9.5). Why wouldn't the ostrich ever be created in South America, Darwin wondered? Why would an open grassland environment in Africa produce an ostrich but in South American a rhea and in Australia an emu? Why would three types of flightless birds have been created when surely one would have sufficed for the different continental grasslands? Darwin suggested that descent with modification led to the different species on the different continents, with similar physical and behavioral adaptations resulting from similar selection pressures.

LO³ Pathways of Descent

We've seen all sorts of evidence for evolution from fields as different as paleontology, anatomy, embryology, genetics, and biogeography. Now we need to focus on *how* it supports the principles of evolution. This section focuses on how evolutionary change takes place over time. What are the patterns of evolutionary change? How fast do organisms evolve? And how do extinctions affect evolution? The answers will help us understand the many pathways of descent over time.

Figure 9.5
Big Birds and Biogeography

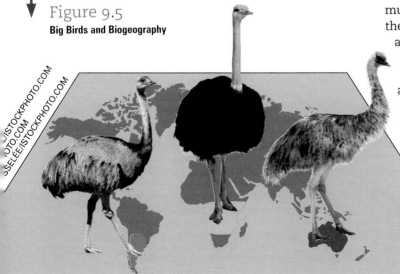

Patterns of Evolution

The *Staphylococcus* bacteria infecting Wayne Chedwick's feet could have become resistant to antibiotics in several small steps as mutations accumulated or in one jump if the cells acquired genes for antibiotic resistance from other bacteria. In multicellular organisms, evolution can also take place at different rates and can follow a number of converging, diverging, or radiating patterns.

Gradual Evolutionary Change

One species can gradually change into a new species as genetic differences accumulate in a population slowly over many generations (Fig. 9.6a). A certain genus (*Globoratalia*) of marine protists called *foraminifera* is a good example. From about 10 million to 5.6 million years ago, the chalky shells secreted by these saltwater species changed very little in shape. Gradually, over the next 0.6 million years, they underwent rather rapid change in size and shape into what experts consider a new species, which remains alive and nearly unchanged in today's Indian Ocean.

In a bacterium like *Staphylococcus*, gradual change can occur as a species is exposed to a low level of antibiotic, and a random mutation results in an altered gene. This mutation could change a gene that, for example, encodes an enzyme that helps digest a compound related in structure to penicillin. Now altered slightly, the enzyme can slowly digest the antibiotic, too, allowing the cell to resist low (but not high) concentrations of the antibiotic. This mutated cell will divide and leave more daughter cells. In time, another mutation in the same gene might occur that enables the enzyme to digest the antibiotic even more rapidly, and thus allow the cell to resist higher and higher doses of the antibiotic. Eventually, the accumulating population of daughter cells could be classified as a different strain. If similar change happens in many different proteins, the cells might be classified as a new species.

Divergent Evolution

Sometimes, a single population splits into two or more populations and the isolated populations start to accumulate genetic differences gradually. This is divergent evolution. Millions of years ago, before the Colorado River cut a mile-deep gash through what is now the high plateau of northern Arizona, a single species of squirrel occupied the area. As the gash deepened into the Grand Canyon, it became an uncrossable barrier and the squirrels were divided into two separate populations. Genetic changes accumulated and the two squirrel populations diverged into two separate species that have inhabited opposite rims of the Grand Canyon ever since (Fig. 9.6b).

Adaptive Radiation

Sometimes several populations of a single species diverge simultaneously into a variety of species (Fig. 9.6c). This process, adaptive radiation, may take place when one ancestral species invades new territories that allow it to exploit a variety of environments and different ways of life. Hawaiian honeycreepers are a good example. One ancestral species of the colorful birds colonized the Hawaiian Islands and radiated into about 20 different species, each adapted to survive on different foods.

Convergent Evolution

Two or more dissimilar and distantly related lineages can evolve in ways that make the organisms resemble each other superficially the way the streamlined bodies of sharks and porpoises do (Fig. 9.6d). A good example of this process, convergent evolution, involves the squirrel-like sugar gliders of Australian forests and the flying squirrels of Europe, Asia, and North America. Both kinds of animals soar through forests on thin folds of skin that extend along both sides of

the body from wrist to ankle. Like all of Australia's original mammals, sugar gliders are marsupials that grow in the mother's pouch (marsupium), while flying squirrels are placental mammals. These two lineages diverged more than 150 million years ago.

Geologists agree that the Australian continent separated from the rest of Earth's continents more than 50 million years ago, and had few, if any, placental mammals at the time of the separation. Without competition from placental mammals, Australian marsupials radiated into a great number of species, many of which look and act like placental mammals on other continents that inhabit similar environments. In this case, sugar gliders resemble flying squirrels closely in ways associated with the gliding life style, but their most recent common ancestor lived over 150 million years ago. Convergent evolution can also happen when different bacterial species inhabit "environments" (including hospital patients) with high concentrations of antibiotics. The different bacteria—say, different staphylococcal and streptococcal species—can independently undergo mutations that allow them to survive one or more of the drugs. Thus they can converge, independently, on an antibiotic-resistant phenotype such as the ability to survive methicillin or vancomycin.

The Tempo of Evolution

How fast do old species converge, diverge, or radiate into new ones? One idea suggests that all lines change at about the same constant rate over time. More recent analyses, however, imply that structural changes often occur in fits and starts.

Phyletic Gradualism

Traditionally, evolutionary biologists thought that after a population splits into two, natural selection

Figure 9.6
Patterns of Descent in Evolution

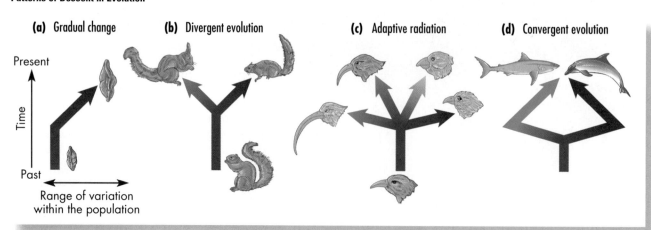

(a) Gradual change   **(b)** Divergent evolution   **(c)** Adaptive radiation   **(d)** Convergent evolution

Present

Time

Past

Range of variation within the population

and random genetic changes would cause the new subgroups to diverge from each other at about equal and constant rates. In this model, termed phyletic gradualism, the giraffe's short-necked ancestor would have slowly acquired giraffelike qualities as genetic changes gradually accumulated.

Punctuated Equilibrium

Starting in the 1970s, some evolutionary biologists pointed out that if new species usually form gradually, then the fossil record should show numerous intermediate species. This certainly does occur, but paleontologists often find surprisingly little evidence of continually, gradually transforming lineages with a complete series of intermediate forms. Instead, fossils often reveal that species exist for millions of years with little change and that very rarely these long periods of equilibrium are interrupted, or "punctuated," by great phenotypic changes, resulting in new species.

The punctuated equilibrium model has three main tenets:

1. Changes in body form evolve rapidly in geologic time.

2. During speciation (the formation of a new species), changes in body form occur almost exclusively in small populations, and new species that result are quite different from their ancestral species.

3. After the burst of change that brings about speciation, species keep basically the same form until they become extinct, perhaps millions of years later.

Models Compared

The family trees for the okapi and giraffe can help you compare the two hypotheses. Phyletic gradualism predicts that the lines eventually becoming okapis and giraffes began to diverge slowly (Fig. 9.7a). Gradually, changes accumulated that eventually prevented the two groups from interbreeding, thus making two separate species. Changes continued to accumulate gradually in both species until the okapi and giraffe emerged as we know them. In contrast, punctuated equilibrium predicts that offshoots of the initial evolutionary line split off repeatedly (Fig. 9.7b). These split-offs took place as small, isolated populations splintered from the main group, underwent bursts of evolutionary change, and then maintained new features for long periods (usually) before the line died out.

In fact, it seems quite likely that evolution proceeds in *both* ways. Evolution may often take place when a small

phyletic gradualism
the concept that morphological changes occur gradually during evolution and are not always associated with speciation; distinct from punctuated equilibrium

punctuated equilibrium
the theory that morphological changes evolve rapidly in geologic time; in small populations, the resulting new species are distinct from the ancestral form; after speciation, species retain much the same form until extinction; distinct from phyletic gradualism

speciation
the emergence of a new species; speciation is thought to occur mainly as a result of populations becoming geographically isolated from each other and evolving in different directions

Figure 9.7
Okapis and Giraffes: Two Models of Descent

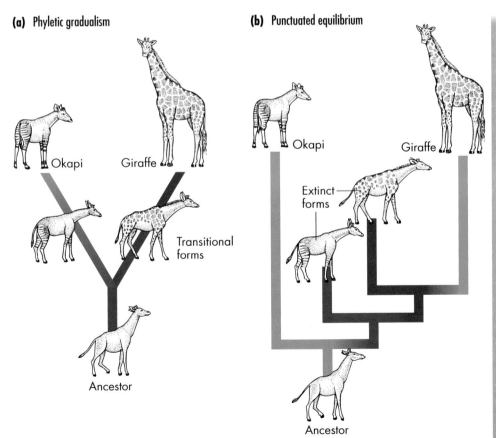

(a) Phyletic gradualism

Okapi Giraffe

Transitional forms

Ancestor

(b) Punctuated equilibrium

Okapi Giraffe

Extinct forms

Ancestor

population becomes isolated geographically or reproductively from other members of its species. Gradually, over many generations (but nonetheless a very short stretch of geologic time), the isolated population accumulates genetic changes. Once enough change has occurred and the new species is fitted to its environment, the species may stay essentially the same for millions of years.

Whether evolution is slow and gradual or fast and punctuated in any particular case, the fundamental raw material giving rise to the change is the same: genetic variation.

LO⁴ Genetic Variation: The Raw Material of Evolution

In the 1930s and 1940s, biologists began to combine evolutionary theory with genetics in the so-called **synthetic theory of evolution**. It suggests that:

(1) Gene mutations occur in reproductive cells at high enough frequencies to impact evolution.

(2) Gene mutations occur in random directions unrelated to the organism's survival needs in its environment.

(3) Natural selection acts on the genetic diversity brought about by such random mutations.

To understand how modern biologists see evolution, we need to understand how genetic variation occurs in the first place and how it is maintained in a population.

Sources of Genetic Variation

Mutations, new base pair sequences, and new combinations of genes (all of which we encountered in previous chapters) can lead to the varied genetic raw material that evolution acts upon.

Single-Gene Mutation

Mistakes or alterations in the DNA sequence of a single gene can (but don't always) alter how that gene functions (Fig. 9.8a). Some of these so-called *single-gene mutations* are neutral mutations: they leave the gene's function basically intact and neither harm nor help the organism. Other mutations produce favorable effects that benefit the organism. Many mutations, however, are either harmful or lethal; they reduce, modify, or destroy the function of a gene necessary for survival.

New Genes with New Functions

Mutation can alter old genes. But how do new genes arise with new functions? One way is through gene duplication. Sometimes, a chance error in DNA replication or recombination creates two identical copies of a gene, and mutation in one or both of these copies can change their nucleotide sequences such that one gene maintains the original gene function while the other acquires a related, new function (Fig. 9.8c).

Recombination

Mutation can create new versions (new alleles) of old genes. The process of *genetic recombination,* the shuffling of existing genetic material, can rearrange those alleles further (Fig. 9.8b). Recombination might bring together advantageous alleles of different genes into the same cell.

It is important to keep in mind that recombination merely shuffles existing alleles into new combinations but keeps the frequency the same (in the absence of selection), while mutation can change the frequency (commonness) of alleles in a population's gene pool (all the genes in a population at any given time) by changing one allele into another.

How Much Genetic Variation Exists?

At the end of the 20th century, geneticists for the first time compared corresponding large portions of a chimpanzee and a human chromosome to see how different and variable our DNA sequences are. Using as subjects 30 chimpanzees and 69 humans who represented all the world's major language groups, geneticists found that, on average, any 2 chimpanzees differed at about 13 places in the stretch of 10,000 base pairs, while any 2 humans differed only at about 3.7 places. These results show two things. First, there is a high rate of genetic variation within a species. For example, you differ from an unrelated person by about a million base pairs over your entire

Figure 9.8
The Sources of Genetic Variation

(a) Single-gene mutation

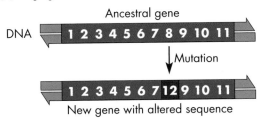

(b) Recombination

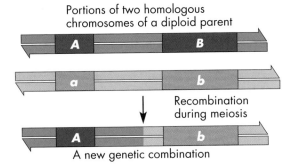

(c) Duplication and divergence

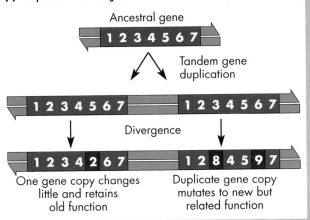

This genetic uniformity may someday propel cheetahs toward extinction. Because each individual is so similar genetically, a single new virus, for example, to which all cheetahs were vulnerable could wipe out their entire population. Furthermore, because genetic variation is required for evolution to occur, cheetahs have much less chance for evolutionary change than organisms with abundant genetic diversity.

Hardy-Weinberg principle
in population genetics, the idea that in the absence of any outside forces, the frequency of each allele and the frequency of genotypes in a population will not change over generations

Hardy-Weinberg equilibrium
a proposed state wherein a population, in the absence of external pressure, has both stable allele and stable genotype frequencies over many generations

LO⁵ How Is Genetic Variation Inherited in Populations?

For a century, biologists have called the mathematical model describing how genes behave in populations the **Hardy-Weinberg principle**, in honor of G.H. Hardy and of E. Weinberg, scientists who discovered the principle independently.

Biologists say that a population is in **Hardy-Weinberg equilibrium** when, in the absence of external pressure, it has both stable allele frequencies and stable genotype frequencies over many generations. (Appendix C presents simple equations that allow the analysis of any ratios in the starting population.)

Hardy-Weinberg Equilibrium

In the absence of outside influence, the frequencies of alleles do not change over the generations, and the frequencies of different genotypes do not change after the first generation.

How Do Biologists Use the Hardy-Weinberg Principle?

Using the Hardy-Weinberg principle, a biologist can predict allele frequencies in populations, and, in turn, can determine whether or not a population is evolving. The allele frequencies stay the same, and hence the population won't evolve, as long as it is free of outside influences. These "outside influences" are obviously important and a key to evolution. So what are they?

Five conditions must hold in order for allele and genotype frequencies to remain constant over many generations:

(1) no mutation,

(2) no migration into or out of the population,

genome. This amount of genetic variation is probably enough to provide the material for natural selection. Second, different species can harbor different amounts of genetic variation. Chimpanzees are about four times as variable as humans. Assuming equal mutation rates, this might reflect a more ancient origin of the chimpanzee populations than of the human populations.

Some animals have very little genetic variation. For example, cheetahs, the handsomely spotted cats of the African savannah that are the world's fastest runners, have less genetic variation than most other mammals, about 100 times less than humans do.

gene flow
the incorporation into a population's gene pool of genes from one or more other populations through migration of individuals

genetic drift
unpredictable changes in allele frequency occurring in a population due to the small size of that population

(3) large population size,

(4) random mating, and

(5) no natural selection at work.

How likely is it that all five conditions will be met and that allele frequencies in a population will remain unchanged (nonevolving) generation after generation? Zero. Populations in nature *do* evolve, and allele frequencies do change within populations over time. The Hardy-Weinberg principle is useful only as a theoretical standard—an unchanging baseline—to compare against real populations in real environments that have outside influences.

LO⁶ The Agents of Evolution

Although the Hardy-Weinberg equations only apply to sexually reproducing diploid eukaryotes, the basic logic is similar for a population of *Staphylococcus* bacteria lurking on your skin, in your throat, or deep in your nasal cavities. These cells can have plenty of genetic variation and the potential to show many different traits, but that variation doesn't work alone to bring about change in a population of cells evolving toward antibiotic resistance. First something has to *act* on the genetic raw materials, the heritable variation. That something can be any of the outside factors we just saw—*mutation, migration, chance in small population size, nonrandom mating,* or *selection.* Working alone or together, these can alter allele frequencies and upset the Hardy-Weinberg equilibrium. Let's see how.

Mutation as an Agent of Evolution

By changing an original allele into a new one, mutation can alter allele frequencies in a population. The main importance of mutation to evolution, however, is not tiny changes in allele frequencies. Instead, it is the new phenotype that the new mutation may cause, and how natural selection acts on it.

Gene Flow: Migration and Alleles

When organisms migrate from one population to another one nearby, they may take alleles away from the first group and introduce them into the second.

Biologists call this change in allele frequencies due to migration in or out gene flow.

Archaeologists have applied the gene flow concept to a mystery of human history. Several decades ago, archaeologists began to dig up a certain type of decorated beaker at widely separated sites in Europe and the Middle East where humans lived about 9,000 years ago. It seems that ancient peoples originally made the vessels in the Middle East. Over several thousand years, however, their production and use spread across Europe. Archaeologists wondered what exactly spread: Was it simply the knowledge of how to make and decorate this new pottery? Or did the Middle Eastern potters themselves migrate slowly across the continent? To answer this question, human geneticists sampled allele frequencies for 95 genes in various populations now living across Europe. They found gradients of allele frequencies as one travels from southeast to northwest. These gradients suggest that the potters themselves migrated towards the northwest, intermarrying with the local populations as they went. A single holdout tribe, the Basques living at the border of what is now Spain and France, resisted intermarrying with the migrating Middle Easterners. Today they alone display the language and genetic makeup of the prehistoric, premigration Europeans!

Gene flow is especially important in the evolution of bacterial antibiotic resistance. Many antibiotic resistance genes are present on the small circles of DNA called plasmids. These DNA circles can escape from one species of bacterium infecting a hospital patient, for example, then encounter another bacterial population in a dirty hospital drain and enter a second species by the process of transformation (Chapter 6). If another patient or staff member touches a towel, glass, or bedpan from that sink, he or she could pick up the second type of bacterium now carrying a plasmid bearing the antibiotic resistance genes. These genes, in effect, will have entered a new population and changed allele frequencies. As we've seen, they could also endanger people's lives.

Genetic Changes Due to Chance

Genetic drift is a term that refers to changes in allele frequencies that happen by chance and can't be predicted. Drift occurs most dramatically in small populations. Two types of genetic drift are the bottleneck effect and the founder effect. Let's look at each one.

Bottleneck Effect

Genetic drift can affect real-world organisms through a mechanism called a *population bottleneck.* Before we define it formally, let's consider the cheetah again.

Until about 10,000 years ago, cheetahs had a large population inhabiting all of Africa and the Middle East, and stretching into Asia. About ten millennia ago, however, the population apparently crashed due to disease, drought, or overhunting by humans, leaving only a few thousand of the beautiful felines. Since then, cheetah populations have rebounded but genetic diversity remains low (despite the few mutations that have accumulated since the crash) because all of the living cheetahs derive from the same few survivors. Biologists call a situation like this, in which a large population is slashed and then recovers from a few survivors, a **population bottleneck**. They call the reduced genetic diversity based on the few surviving original alleles the **bottleneck effect**. If the chance survivors have allele combinations that leave them susceptible to certain diseases, then the population's long-term future can be in doubt. Elephant seals are another example of the bottleneck effect. Hunted to near extinction in the late 1800s, a remaining population of just 20 animals has now recovered to tens of thousands, but their genetic diversity is extremely limited.

Founder Effect

Another type of genetic drift stems from the long-term isolation of a population founded by a few individuals. This kind of genetic drift is called a **founder effect**, because a few individuals split off from a large population and founded a new, isolated one. Nevertheless, both populations continue to exist. Because the small group of "founders" bears such a small fraction of the larger population's alleles, it may be a skewed sample, genetically speaking.

Nonrandom Mating

A population's mating tendencies—who mates with whom—can alter the ratio of heterozygotes and homozygotes. One type of nonrandom mating occurs when relatives are more likely to mate with each other than with unrelated individuals, a situation we call **inbreeding**. In many species, one member tends to mate with another that was born nearby, for example, frogs born in the same pond or people living in the same valley. Chances are good, therefore, that the two are related to some degree and have more identical alleles than nonrelatives. As a result, homozygotes become more common and heterozygotes become less common than expected by chance. If these individuals are homozygous for deleterious recessive alleles, then the population will have many more individuals that are less fit than in a normally breeding population, a situation called **inbreeding depression**. (In heterozygotes, these alleles would remain hidden by the dominant alleles.)

LO⁷ Natural Selection Revisited

How do populations become better adapted to their environments? Natural selection can alter a species' evolutionary trajectory in at least three different ways. In **directional selection**, a population shifts toward one extreme form of a trait (Fig. 9.9a). In the last 4 million years, for example, cheetahs have become half their former size, presumably because natural selection favored alleles that constantly pushed cheetah weight downward.

A second mode of natural selection is called **stabilizing selection**, because it results in individuals with intermediate phenotypes, as extreme forms are less successful at surviving and reproducing (Fig. 9.9b).

population bottleneck
a situation arising when only a small number of individuals of a population survive and reproduce; therefore only a small percentage of the original gene pool remains

bottleneck effect
the reduced genetic diversity that results from a drastic drop in a population's size

founder effect
in evolutionary biology, the principle that individuals founding a new colony carry only a fraction of the total gene pool present in the parent population

inbreeding
nonrandom mating that occurs when relatives mate with each other rather than with unrelated individuals

inbreeding depression
a situation of weakened genetic viability that occurs when a population has many more individuals that are less fit than in a normally breeding population

directional selection
a type of natural selection in which an extreme form of a character is favored over all other forms

stabilizing selection
a mode of natural selection that results in individuals with intermediate phenotypes; under these selection pressures, extreme forms are less successful at surviving and reproducing

We'll be back.

The third mode of natural selection acts opposite to stabilizing selection. In **disruptive selection**, two extreme phenotypes become *more* frequent in a population (Fig. 9.9c). For example, a butterfly species that tastes good to birds might mimic in coloration other butterfly species that are distasteful to birds. Some of the good-tasting mimics occur in a blue form, and others in an orange form. Mimics of either foul-tasting model are likely to escape being eaten. In contrast, intermediate forms mimic neither of the bad-tasting species and are more likely to be eaten by predators. This has caused alleles for the intermediate phenotype to decrease in frequency over time.

All five agents of evolution we've been exploring—mutation, migration, genetic drift, nonrandom mating, and selection—can nudge a population away from Hardy-Weinberg equilibrium.

LO⁸ How Do New Species Originate?

According to modern evolutionary theory, a *species* is a group of populations that interbreed with each other in nature and produce healthy and fertile offspring. New species arise when one group of organisms becomes **reproductively isolated** from another—it fails to generate fertile progeny with other true species. But what isolates species in the first place?

Reproductive isolating mechanisms are biological features that keep the members of species A from successfully breeding with the members of species B. Some reproductive isolating mechanisms act before fertilization and others act after fertilization.

Looking at isolating mechanisms that act before fertilization, some are behavioral. For example, dozens of frog species can live in the same area, but one species will mate only in ponds, one species only in running water, and a third species only in shallow puddles.

Other mechanisms that act before fertilization can be mechanical or chemical. For example, sometimes one species' sperm can't fertilize another species' eggs because a specific chemical surrounds the egg and allows binding only by sperm from the same species.

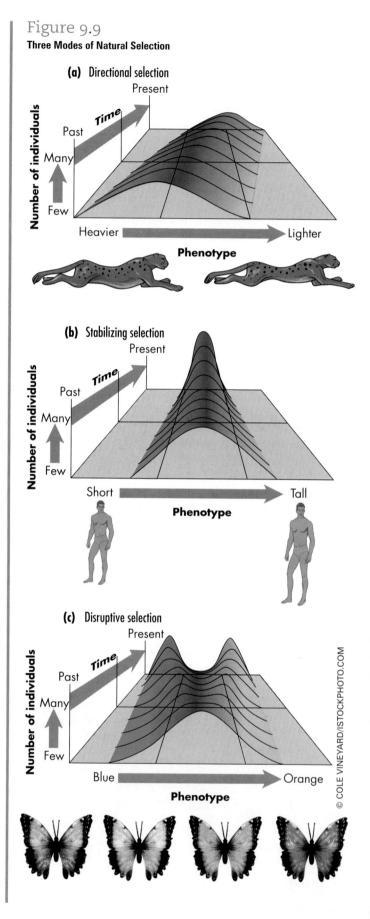

Figure 9.9
Three Modes of Natural Selection

(a) Directional selection

(b) Stabilizing selection

(c) Disruptive selection

© COLE VINEYARD/ISTOCKPHOTO.COM

Looking at reproductive isolating mechanisms that operate after fertilization, sometimes different species mate and offspring result, but they die or are themselves infertile. Many American frogs, for instance, can interbreed, but genetic differences between the species lead to abnormal zygotes and tadpoles that do not grow to adulthood. In contrast, the mules that result from the mating of a male donkey with a female horse are very hardy hybrids, noted for strength and endurance. They usually don't produce offspring with other mules, horses, or donkeys, however, because chromosomes can't pair normally during meiosis. This prevents a flow of genes between donkeys and horses, and keeps the species separate.

How, then, do reproductive isolating mechanisms arise and lead to new species?

The Origin of New Species

Most biologists believe that many species arise after populations are split apart geographically and then evolve based on the reproductive isolating mechanisms we just discussed.

A physical barrier, such as a river, a desert, or different zones of vegetation can separate populations of a single species and prevent gene flow between them. The split populations grow more and more distinct from each other as mutation, genetic drift, and adaptation cause different sets of characteristics to accumulate. Eventually, the differences are great enough to prevent matings even if the two populations come into contact again later. This mechanism is called *geographical speciation,* or **allopatric speciation** (*allo* = different + *patra*

= native land) (Fig. 9.10). If the isolated populations are small, the founder effect can come into play and so can punctuated equilibrium, because in the small, separated populations, the pace of evolution can speed up for a while before stable species emerge.

It's easy to see how species can evolve where populations are totally separate (allopatric). But species can evolve even without any geographical barriers separating the populations. This is called **sympatric speciation** (*sym* = same + *patra* = native land). In plants living in the same geographic region, new species can sometimes arise in a single generation based on **polyploidy**, an increase in the number of chromosome sets in a cell. A genus of wildflowers called *Clarkia* provides a good example of polyploidy. Geneticists discovered that one species, *Clarkia concinna,* has seven pairs of chromosomes in a diploid set, while *Clarkia virgata* has five pairs in a diploid set. If these two species mate, the hybrid progeny gets seven haploid chromosomes from one parent and five from the other. The hybrid is sterile because the two different sets of chromosomes don't pair and move correctly during meiosis. At some time in the past, however, a **tetraploid** hybrid plant

allopatric speciation
the divergence of new species as a result of geographical separation of populations of the same original species

sympatric speciation
a situation in which a population diverges into two species after a genetic, behavioral, or ecological barrier to gene flow arises between subgroups of the population inhabiting the same region

polyploidy
an increase in the number of chromosome sets in a cell

tetraploid
the condition of having four sets of chromosomes

Figure 9.10
Geographical Barriers and Allopatric Speciation

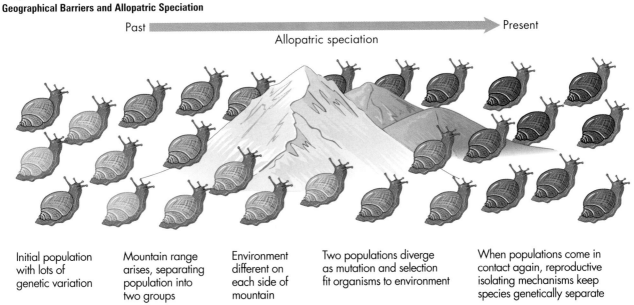

Past → Present
Allopatric speciation

| Initial population with lots of genetic variation | Mountain range arises, separating population into two groups | Environment different on each side of mountain | Two populations diverge as mutation and selection fit organisms to environment | When populations come in contact again, reproductive isolating mechanisms keep species genetically separate |

arose in which the chromosome count had doubled from 12 (7 + 5) to 24. Every chromosome in the new tetraploid hybrid, *Clarkia pulchella*, had a partner, so meiosis could occur normally. The species can't produce fertile hybrids with either diploid species *C. concinna* or *C. virgata*, but it can fertilize itself and produce new seeds. In this case, a new species was formed in one step within one original population without a geographical barrier. Sympatric speciation is relatively common in plants, and has contributed to the development of wheat, cotton, and some of our other important crops.

Evolutionary Pathways of Antibiotic Resistance

As we've explored evolution in this chapter, we've seen how natural selection can bring about new species and even higher orders of organisms. We've seen that the heavy use of antibiotics in hospitals, for example, can act as an agent of natural selection, "choosing" as parents of the next generation potentially dangerous cells that can't be killed. What, then, does our exploration of evolution suggest for dealing with the life-threatening problem of antibiotic-resistant bacteria?

Researchers have shown that under normal conditions (an environment free of antibiotics), antibiotic-resistant bacteria are poor competitors. They're actually at a disadvantage when they're *not* challenged with antibiotics because normal bacterial cells can outcompete them. In many cases, they'll die out, just like cavefish with fully developed eyes. What's the evolutionary implication here? It's this: one logical way to fight resistance is to cut the load of antibiotics in our everyday environments. By some estimates, half of all prescribed antibiotics are unnecessary, and medical consumers need to cut back on their demands. Farmers also use large amounts of antibiotics to stimulate the growth of farm animals and to protect fruit trees from bacterial diseases.

Mutations occur in any given gene about 1 in every 100,000 to 1,000,000 times the gene replicates. In a bacterial population of 1,000,000 cells, therefore, between 1 and 10 of them might have a mutation in an antibiotic resistance gene. If bacterial populations are kept smaller through vigilant hygiene, it is that much less likely that a mutation will arise.

For patients like Wayne Chedwick, with serious bone infections that threaten to destroy toes and feet, effective antibiotics are a lifeline. Researchers continue to develop new drugs for which resistance has not yet evolved. Unfortunately, bacteria will eventually evolve resistance to any new antibiotics; we can only slow that process by using the principles of natural selection to our own advantage.

> "
> Half of all prescribed antibiotics are unnecessary, and medical consumers need to cut back on their demands.
> "

Ecology
of Populations
and Communities

Learning Outcomes

LO¹ Understand the distribution and interaction of organisms in an environment

LO² Identify the limiting factors that influence a population's location

LO³ Identify the limiting factors that influence a population's size

LO⁴ Identify long-term human population trends and predict future population growth

LO⁵ Identify the relationships among organisms in a community in terms of how they make a living

LO⁶ Categorize interactions between species

LO⁷ Examine how communities change over time

"The tenets of ecology are crucial to human survival."

Crashes and Clashes

Until the mid-20th century, no one worried about sustaining or endangering fish populations. In the wide continental shelf system called the Georges Bank offshore from Cape Cod and the coast of Maine, upwelling nutrients have always supported an enormous population of fish. By "trawling," or dragging nets across the sea floor, fishers were able to catch thousands of pounds of fish at a time. Most of the fish species produce hundreds of thousands of eggs and larvae each year, so the fish populations could recover fairly quickly.

What do you know?

Explain the difference between a yellowtail flounder's habitat and its niche.

In the 1960s, huge foreign fishing vessels started trawling on Georges Bank alongside smaller American boats and harvesting millions of metric tons of fish annually. After years of such enormous catches, some of the fish populations started dwindling—an indication that overfishing was damaging the area's natural ecological balance.

In 1976, the United States extended its territorial limit to 200 miles off shore and the "factory ships" left. In their wake, the American fishing fleet grew, by then with technological improvements such as electronic navigation and satellite weather data to help crew members find large aggregations of target fish such as Atlantic cod or yellowtail flounder. This fleet growth was also spurred by the skyrocketing demand for fish among health-conscious American consumers.

In the early 1990s, once again overfishing took a drastic toll and fish stocks plummeted to record low levels. For a number of fish stocks, at least half or three quarters of the fish in a population was removed every year.

Now management programs limit the access of commercial fishers. They have closed areas in certain seasons, regulated net and mesh sizes, restricted numbers of fishing permits, and limited each day's catch per boat. As a result, stocks of fish are recovering—some quickly, some slowly. The challenge now is in allowing an increased access to those fish without repeating the mistakes of the past.

The subjects of fishing, overfishing, and wildlife conservation in New England waters make an ideal case history for this chapter. Our topic here is the ecology of populations and communities, that is, the study of how groups of organisms are distributed in a particular area at a particular time and how they interact with other species coexisting in the same locale. As we explore population and community ecology, you'll discover the answers to these questions:

- ☑ At what level do organisms interact in ecology?
- ☑ What limits where a species lives?
- ☑ What factors limit population size?
- ☑ How do species interact in communities?

ecology of populations and communities
the study of how groups of organisms are distributed in a particular area at a particular time and how they interact with other species coexisting in the same locale

© ROGER BULL/ISTOCKPHOTO.COM

LO¹ Ecology: Levels of Interaction

A fisher's livelihood depends on knowing about the habits of fish: Where do yellowtail flounder or other crop fish live in the oceans? What times of year are best to harvest them? At what depths do they feed? What do they eat? In short, he or she needs as much information as possible to locate and catch the fish efficiently. As you read in Chapter 1, the science of ecology studies the distribution and abundance of organisms and how organisms interact with each other and the nonliving environment. The tenets of ecology are crucial to human survival. That's because our food, our shelter, the quality of our water, and even fundamental factors such as the air we breathe, the temperature of Earth's surface, and, to some degree, its climate depend on where organisms live and how they interact.

A key word in the definition of ecology is *interact*. Organisms interact with other living things and with the nonliving physical surroundings. For a yellowtail flounder, the living environment includes the worms and other small invertebrates it eats, the blackback and witch flounder that competes with it for food, the mackerel that prey on the larval yellowtail, and the roundworms that parasitize and weaken its body. The physical environment includes the temperature, salinity, and depth of the water; whether the bottom is sandy, rocky, or muddy; and the annual cycle of storms and ocean upwellings.

So numerous are each organism's interactions with other living things and the physical environment that biologists organize their study of ecology into a hierarchy of four levels: populations, communities, ecosystems, and the biosphere.

- A *population* is a group of interacting individuals of the same species that inhabit a defined geographical area.

- A *community* consists of two or more populations of different species occupying the same geographical area.

- An *ecosystem* consists of a community of living things interacting with the physical factors of their environment.

- The *biosphere* consists of all our planet's ecosystems and thus is the portion of Earth that contains living species. The biosphere includes the atmosphere, the oceans, and the soil in which living things are found, as well as global phenomena, such as climate patterns, wind currents, and nutrient cycles that affect living things.

This chapter and the next examine ecological interactions at increasingly higher levels of organization. We begin by discussing the factors that influence a population's location and size in time and space. Then we turn to community ecology and discuss how living organisms interact with each other.

LO² What Limits Where a Species Lives?

Few species are scattered evenly throughout the world; they exist, instead, only in certain spots and are absent entirely from other places. What limits where an organism lives on a global scale and in individual locales?

Limits to Global Distribution

Understanding why an organism's range extends to one part of the world but not to another is important to people when those organisms serve as food or materials, or when they cause disease in people, domestic animals, or crop plants. In general, three conditions limit the places where a specific organism might be found: physical factors, interactions with other species, and geographical barriers.

Physical Factors

Organisms may be absent from an area because the region lacks the proper sunlight, water, temperature, mineral nutrients, or any one of a host of physical or chemical requirements.

Interactions with Other Species

Other species may block survival and limit a population's distribution. If certain species are already firmly established in an area, they may prevent the incursion of new species by monopolizing food supplies or acting as predators or parasites.

Geographical Barriers

A species may be absent from an area because a geographical barrier blocks access. Seas, deserts, and mountain ranges can be so wide or high that an organism cannot crawl, swim, fly, or float across the barrier. For example, bird fanciers from Europe artificially bridged a geographic gap in 1890, when about 80 starlings were introduced into New York City's Central Park. Now millions of the speckled birds chatter throughout America's cities and countrysides. Only their inability to cross the Atlantic had previously stopped their dispersal to North America (Fig. 14.1).

LO³ What Factors Limit Population Size?

One goal of researchers working with the Fishing Management Council in New England is to maintain populations of yellowtail floun-

Figure 14.1

Crossing the Atlantic Barrier Allowed Starlings to Spread throughout North America

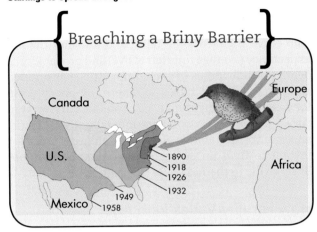

{ Breaching a Briny Barrier }

Canada

Europe

U.S.

Africa

1890
1918
1926
1932

Mexico 1949
1958

der and other crop fish at optimal levels so the Georges Bank area can sustain a healthy population of the animals. One measure of the population of yellowtail flounder is the weight of fish caught per year. Take a quick look at Figure 14.2. What happened to the yellowtail flounder population between 1962 and 1996? What happened to the populations of skates and spiny dogfish, a type of small shark? Researchers wanted to learn what factors caused this dramatic crash of the yellowtail population, how it might relate to the increase in skates and spiny dogfish, and how to restore populations to their original state to maintain a stable yield of fish.

Figure 14.2

The Population Crash of Yellowtail Flounder

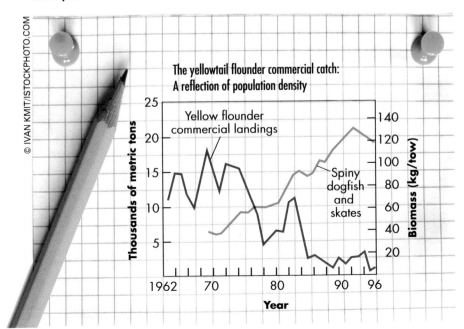

The yellowtail flounder commercial catch: A reflection of population density

Yellow flounder commercial landings

Spiny dogfish and skates

Thousands of metric tons

Biomass (kg/tow)

© IVAN KMIT/ISTOCKPHOTO.COM

1962 70 80 90 96

Year

This practical side of ecology is concerned with a population's *density*, the number of individuals in a certain amount of space, for example, the number of metric tons of fish caught per year on Georges Bank. When reporting density, it is often helpful to take into account the species' habitat—that yellowtail flounder on Georges Bank may occupy only the sandy bottoms or that in a certain field a particular species of butterfly might cluster mainly around yellow sulfur flowers. Human populations illustrate quite well the effect of clustering. The density of Earth's population averaged over the whole planet is less than one person per square kilometer (two per square mile). Most people live near ocean coasts, riverbanks, and lake shores, making local densities in those areas much higher than the average.

zero population growth
in a population, the number of individuals gained is exactly equal to the number lost

Factors Affecting Population Size

Curious biologists want to understand both how population density changes over time and the factors that cause it to change. Population size may change when individuals enter or leave the population. Clearly, if more members enter than leave, the population will grow, but if more individuals leave than enter, the population will shrink. Individuals can enter a population by either birth or immigration, and members can leave a population by either death or emigration. If the number of individuals gained is exactly equal to the number lost, then the population shows zero population growth. For people, an average of 2.1 children per couple results in zero population growth.

Let's look now at how populations change as individuals leave a population by death or join a population by birth. We will assume that the effects of immigration and emigration remain constant and equal in the populations we are studying.

How Survival Varies with Age

Death and birth clearly affect population size. For many species, the likelihood that an individual will die depends on its age. For a yellowtail flounder, the chances that it will die

survivorship curve
a plot of the data representing the proportion of a population that survives to a certain age

late-loss survivorship curve
a plot of survivorship data indicating that an organism's life expectancy decreases with each passing year

early-loss survivorship curve
a plot of survivorship data indicating that most individuals in a population die young

life expectancy
the maximum probable age an individual will reach

as a newly hatched larval fish is very high, but after an individual becomes an adult, the likelihood of dying is much smaller. This is reflected in a survivorship curve, a plot of data representing the proportion of a population that survives to a certain age (Fig. 14.3). Look first at the human survivorship curve. The chances that a 90-year-old person will live for 1 more year are much slimmer than the chances that a 20-year-old will live for 1 additional year. In contrast, yellowtail flounder die mostly in the first month or two after hatching as they drift in the open ocean and become prey to mackerel, herring, and shrimplike krill. Once they settle on the bottom

and become adults, it is less likely that a yellowtail will die in each passing month. The human follows a late-loss survivorship curve, whereas the flounder follows an early-loss survivorship curve.

A table of numbers used to generate a survivorship curve is called a life table, and it shows the life expectancy (average time left to live) and probability of death for individuals of each different age. Insurance companies use life tables to determine policy costs for customers of different ages. From the survivorship curve in Figure 14.3, you can understand why insurance companies charge an 80-year-old man more for insurance than an 80-year-old woman: He is more likely to die in the next year than she is.

How Fertility Varies with Age

Survivorship curves help predict how many individuals of each age class will leave a population through death. The major force that counteracts death is the birth of new individuals. Birth rates, like death rates,

Figure 14.3
Survivorship Curves

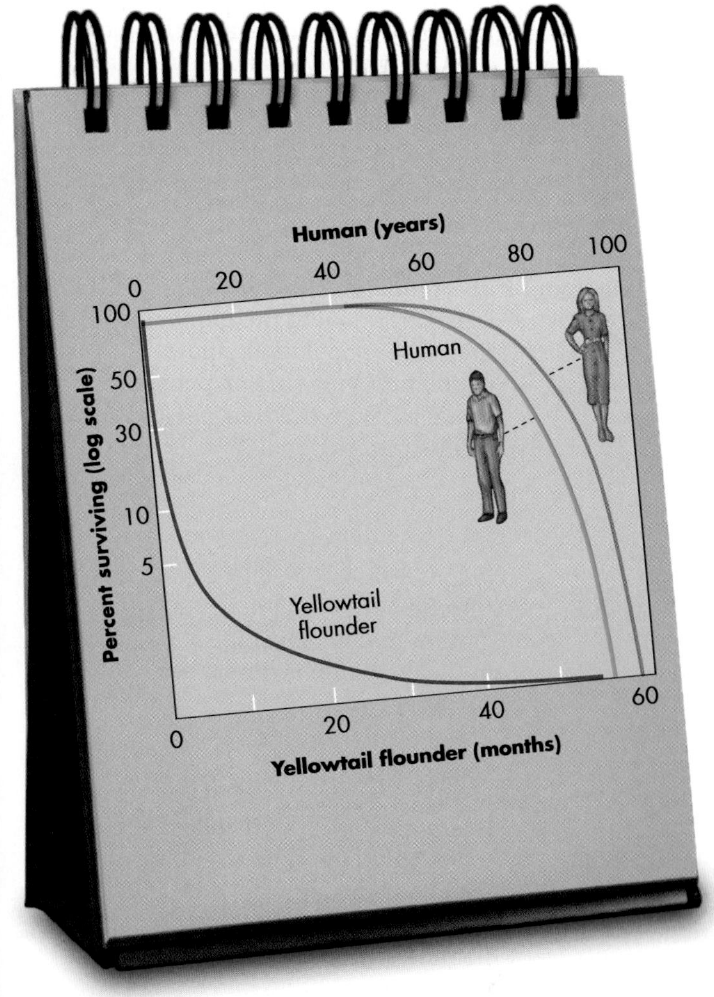

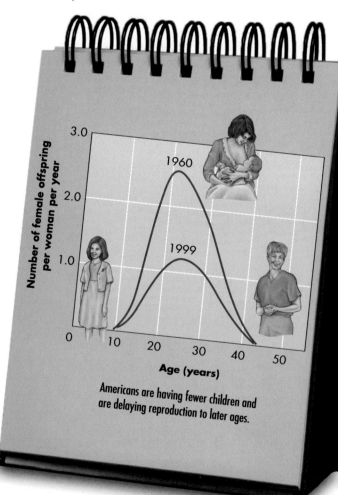

Figure 14.4
Human Fertility Curve

Americans are having fewer children and are delaying reproduction to later ages.

depend on age, and this fact is revealed by fertility curves, graphs of reproduction rate versus the age of female population members. (Since only females bear young, ecologists often view populations as females giving rise to more females.)

The human fertility graph in Figure 14.4 shows that American women younger than 20 or older than 30 are less likely to reproduce. Note the difference in the curves for 1960 and 1999. Fertility curves are significant because with them and with a knowledge of a population's age structure, one can predict future population growth. For example, a population with a high proportion of 20- to 30-year-old women is going to grow much more rapidly than a population with few women in these prime childbearing years. Data show that about 12 out of every 100 American women between the ages of 20 and 25 will have a baby girl in any given year.

How Populations Grow

Birth rates and death rates are frequently the major factors influencing changes in population size. By combining the two (but discounting immigration and emigration), population ecologists can make a model for how populations grow. Given plenty of nutrients, space, shelter, water, benign weather, and the absence of predators or disease, every population will expand infinitely, because all organisms have a high innate reproductive capacity under ideal conditions. The capacity for reproduction under idealized conditions, or biotic potential, is amazing.

Rapid population growth is easier to visualize when plotted on graphs such as those in Figure 14.5. Let's say that individuals of a long-lived mouse species grow to reproductive age in one year and that, ignoring males, a population initially consists of ten female mice that each produce on average one female offspring per year. At the end of the first year, the population will include 20 female mice (the 10 mothers and each of their daughters). If each of those has 1 more female per year, there will be 40 female mice at the end of 2 years, 80 after 3 years, and so on. The explosive increase results in a J-shaped curve representing exponential growth.

What factors do you think might affect the shape of the J-shaped curve of Figure 14.5? It turns out that there are two factors: (1) the reproductive rate per individual and (2) the initial population size. If the reproductive rate per individual increases to two female offspring per female mouse rather than one each year, the population would grow much faster. Ecologists represent the reproductive rate per individual by the symbol *r*. For human populations, the reproductive rate per individual can vary widely. Women are capable of having about 30 children each, but they rarely reach that grand potential.

While the reproductive rate per individual is an important factor in the contour of the J-shaped curve, the size of the initial

fertility curve
generally, a graph that plots reproduction rate versus the age of female population members

biotic potential
an organism's capacity for reproduction under ideal conditions of growth and survival

J-shaped curve
a plot of population growth with an upsweeping curve that represents exponential growth

exponential growth
growth of a population without any constraints; hence, the population will grow at an ever-increasing rate

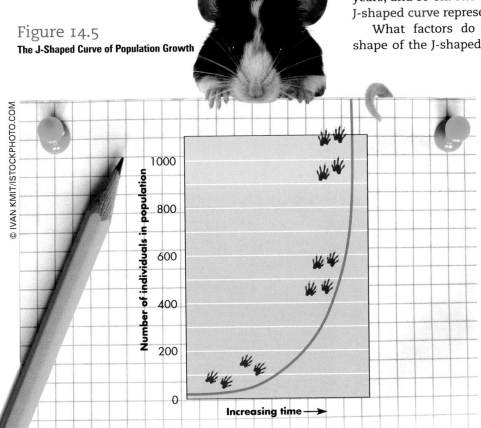

Figure 14.5
The J-Shaped Curve of Population Growth

Number of individuals in population: 1000, 800, 600, 400, 200, 0

Increasing time →

© IVAN KMIT/ISTOCKPHOTO.COM

© EMILIA STASIAK/ISTOCKPHOTO.COM / © ROBERT ADRIAN HILLMAN/ISTOCKPHOTO.COM

population is also important. If there are only five female mice in the initial population instead of ten, as in the first example, and each produces one female offspring per year, then only five more will be added by the end of the first year rather than ten. This is why small populations add fewer individuals per year than larger ones, all other factors being the same.

Under the artificially ideal conditions we've discussed so far, any population would follow the J-shaped curve of exponential growth if the birth rate exceeded the death rate by even a small amount. Fortunately, real organisms in natural situations do not follow the J-shaped exponential growth pattern—at least not for long. Organisms in nature cannot sustain limitless growth at the full force of their reproductive potential because food supplies and living space are finite. Hence, our planet is not covered with elephants neck-deep in flounders. The realities of supply and demand explain this curb on population growth despite the organism's reproductive capabilities.

Limited Resources Limit Growth

The J-shaped curve gives ecologists an idealized standard against which to measure growth in real populations. A classic case of growth in a real population was that of sheep on the island of Tasmania, south of Australia, in the early 19th century (Fig. 14.6). When English immigrants first introduced sheep to the new environment, resources were abundant and the sheep population expanded nearly exponentially for a couple of decades, following a J-shaped curve during this time. As the density of sheep on the island rose, competition for limited resources increased, and by 1830, each sheep had a smaller share of food and living space. As a result, each individual was less likely to survive and more likely to die, and each had a smaller chance of reproducing. After 1850, the total growth rate decreased, and the population size fluctuated around a mean of about 1.6 million sheep.

As Figure 14.6 shows, the graph representing population growth began like a J-shaped curve, but then flattened into an S-shaped curve representing logistic growth, a situation in which a large population grows more slowly than a small population would in the same area. The density at which a growing population levels off—1.6 million sheep on Tasmania in the preceding example—is called the carrying capacity (ecologists abbreviate this with the letter K). Carrying capacity is the number of individuals an environment can support for a prolonged period of time. At the carrying capacity, individuals are using all of the resources available to them.

Carrying capacity is not a constant number for each species and environment. You can tell that by looking at the fluctuations around the carrying capacity for the sheep shown in Figure 14.6. Because environments change with the season, with alterations in weather

Figure 14.6

Sheep on Tasmania: The Growth of Real Populations Often Follows an S-Shaped Curve

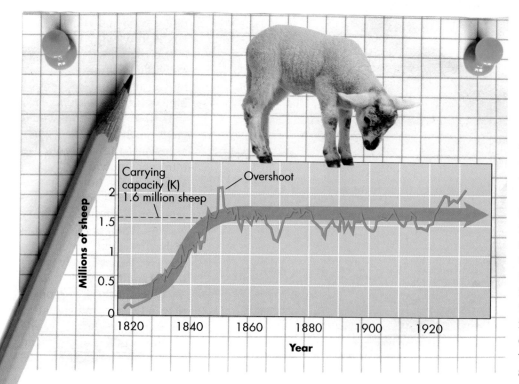

patterns, and with changes of species composition within the community, we should think of carrying capacity as a range of densities toward which populations tend to move from initial densities that can be higher or lower.

Population Crashes

While population growth often slows and reaches a plateau, as it did with sheep in Tasmania, in some species there can be a bust following the boom: a rapid decline following a period of intense population growth. The growth of reindeer introduced onto an island off the southwest coast of Alaska represents a frequently observed pattern (Fig. 14.7). From an initial population of 25 animals in 1891, the herd grew to about 2,000 reindeer in 1938 and then crashed to 8 animals by 1950. The crash can be readily explained on the basis of carrying capacity. When the reindeer were first introduced, lichens and other food sources were plentiful, having accumulated for centuries without predation. Thus, the island's carrying capacity was high. After the reindeer ate the accumulated food, however, new food would appear only as the remaining lichens regrew slowly during each short summer growing season. This change in carrying capacity of that environment is what caused the reindeer population to crash.

How the Environment Limits Growth

The limited growth of real populations is due to such factors as limited food supplies, limited living space, and interactions with other organisms.

The Role of Population Density

Some limits to population growth depend on how dense a population is, and others do not. For instance, in a sparsely populated colony of prairie dogs, the incidence of flea-transmitted bubonic plague is also low. But when the prairie dogs are densely packed, outbreaks of plague often wipe out entire populations. Competition among members of the same species for limited resources is another way density can regulate population size. For example, all the squirrels in a given forest might compete for the same nut crop.

Some factors limit population expansion regardless of population density. A harsh winter, for example, might kill 25 percent of a deer population regardless of population density. In practice, it can be difficult to separate the effects of population density from other factors, and this interaction leads many ecologists to look at whether the mechanism that limits population growth originates outside or inside the population.

Figure 14.7
Overexploiting Limited Resources Can Lead to a Population Crash

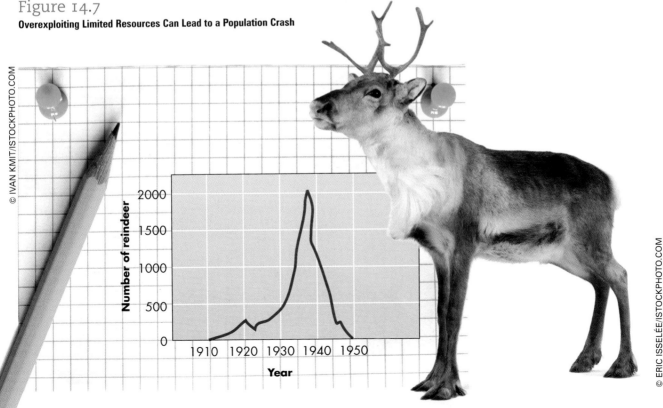

Extrinsic or Intrinsic Population-Regulating Mechanisms

Extrinsic population-regulating mechanisms originate outside the population and include living factors, such as food supplies, natural enemies, and disease-causing organisms, as well as physical factors, such as weather, shelter, pollution, and habitat loss. In contrast to extrinsic factors that limit population size, intrinsic factors originate within an organism's anatomy, physiology, or behavior. For example, crowded conditions and depletion of resources can cause many marsupials, such as kangaroos and koalas, to absorb their own developing embryos; this intrinsic response lowers the rate of population growth.

Competition

The most important intrinsic population-regulating mechanism is competition among members of the same species for resources that they require but are available in limited supply. The effects of competition among members of a species depend on population density. As the population grows and resources diminish, competition for food and space becomes intense. In a coastal tidepool, for example, where a population of barnacles grows on a rock, other barnacles cannot occupy that same spot, even if food is present in abundance.

While extrinsic and intrinsic factors in the environment limit the growth of all species, they result in populations following either a roughly S-shaped curve or a boom-and-crash curve. Let's look at the factors that dictate which shape growth curve a population follows in nature.

Population Growth and Strategies for Survival

To survive, reproduce, and thus make a genetic contribution to the future, individuals must allocate their limited energy supplies. A fast-growing organism that expends most of its energy enlarging its body may have little energy left over for reproducing. Conversely, an individual that expends a huge amount of energy attracting a mate or producing thousands of eggs may have little energy remaining for day-to-day survival activities. The way an organism allocates its energy is its life history strategy.

To see how different life history strategies work, let's contrast the life history strategy of a dandelion and a rhinoceros. A dandelion reproduces rapidly, based on fast embryonic development and the production of large numbers of small seeds containing few stored nutrients. Dandelions experience an early-loss type of survivorship: most of the light, windborne seeds die shortly after germination. Because of these traits, they can quickly fill a newly plowed field before winter comes or the corn grows and shades them out. Our expression "to grow like a weed" reflects this type of life history strategy.

In contrast, a rhinoceros reproduces only after about 5 years of age, and the development of its embryo (usually single) is very slow (gestation takes about 15 months). Although rhinoceroses have only one calf at a time, the newborns are huge—the weight of an average male college student. Once born, the new individual survives for about 40 years, thus rhinoceroses experience a late-loss type of survivorship. Rhinoceroses are quickly approaching extinction because people slaughter them for their nasal horns. Some people have a superstition that the powdered horn can act as an aphrodisiac, and they are willing to pay more for the material than for gold, ounce for

ounce. Knowing the life strategy of a rhinoceros, you can appreciate how hard it is for their populations to become reestablished once decimated.

Many species have some elements of each strategy and can't be easily pigeon-holed. Which strategy—if either—do you think people follow? Let's look in more detail at the human population.

LO⁴ The Human Population

Are humans governed by ecological rules? Or have we somehow moved beyond booms, crashes, and growth curves? The answers involve a look at human history, long-term population trends, and some predictions for our future population growth.

Trends in Human Population Growth

You can see in Figure 14.8 the three historical phases of human population growth, and our current staggering rate of population growth.

Hunting and Gathering Phase

Until about 10,000 years ago, the human population grew slowly as people existed by hunting animals, catching fish, and gathering roots and fruits from nature. The worldwide population was probably about 10 million by 8000 B.C. During this early phase, the human life history strategy emphasized slow embryonic development, long lives, large bodies, few offspring, extended parental care, and highly specialized brains that help us compete for resources with cunning efficiency.

Agricultural Phase

Population growth accelerated during a second phase of human history, beginning about 10,000 years ago, when people started planting and tending crops and domesticating animals in the Agricultural Revolution. The shift to agriculture was rapid and worldwide, perhaps because people can transmit their culture, or ways of living, to others. As agricultural techniques spread and improved between about 8000 B.C. and 1750 A.D., world population increased from 10 million to about 800 million. Because agriculture uses some resources more efficiently, its practice increases the environment's carrying capacity for humans.

Industrial Phase

A third phase of growth began in 18th-century England with the Industrial Revolution. Inventions such as the steam engine triggered vast changes that transformed a populace living mainly as farmers and craftspeople into a population working mainly in factories and living in crowded cities. In the next 250 years, much of the world would follow this pattern of industrialization and social upheaval. A farmer with a steam engine attached to a tractor could accomplish the work of dozens of people in a single day and thus increase food production. A steam-driven train or ship could rapidly distribute food and other necessities of life, and thus blunt the impact of local famine.

In recent times, the rise in human population has been staggering. While it took from the beginning of life until 1950 for the first 2.5 billion people to accumulate on Earth, it took just 40 years—a blink of evolutionary time—for a second 2.5 billion to be added. At current growth rates, by 2025 an additional 5 billion *more* people will join the planet's current population of over 6 billion. How old will you be when the 11 billion figure is reached? What might life be like when there are twice as many people as there are today?

As you look at the graph of human population growth, the towering ascension should unnerve you: It is the familiar J-shaped pattern of exponential growth, much like that of the island reindeer just

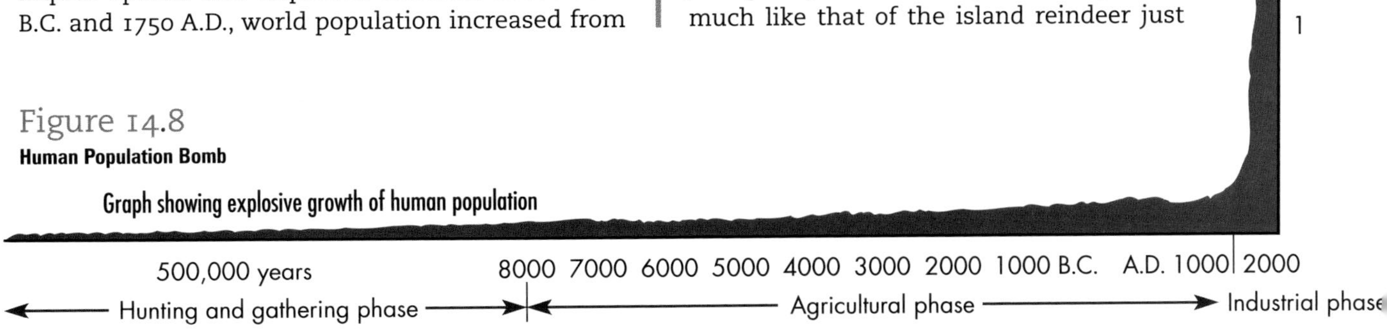

Agricultural Revolution the transition of a group of people from an often nomadic hunter-gatherer way of life to a usually more settled life dependent on raising crops, such as wheat or corn, and on livestock; it was under way in the Middle East by 8000 years ago

Industrial Revolution the replacement of hand tools with power-driven machines (like the steam engine) and the concentration of industry in factories beginning in England in the late 18th century

Figure 14.8
Human Population Bomb

Graph showing explosive growth of human population

500,000 years

◄──── Hunting and gathering phase ────►

8000 7000 6000 5000 4000 3000 2000 1000 B.C.   A.D. 1000 2000

◄──────── Agricultural phase ────────► Industrial phase

Billions of people: 1 2 3 4 5 6

demographic transition
a changing pattern from a high birth rate and high death rate to a low birth rate and low death rate

age structure
the number of individuals in each age group of a given population

before they overexploited their environment and suffered a population crash. By analyzing the causes of our own population boom, ecologists hope to learn how humans can avert a crash in the future.

Change in Human Population Size

How did the agricultural and industrial revolutions quicken the pace of the human population explosion? Did the invention of agriculture *allow* human populations to increase, or were people *forced* to invent agricultural practices to help support population densities that were already exceeding the carrying capacity of the land? Many observers believe the latter and suggest that population growth has been a constant feature of the human experience, continually forcing people to adopt new strategies for increasing the amount of food their land could produce. Carrying capacity, however, cannot be increased forever; the productivity of the land must, at some point, be reached and exceeded.

Birth Rates and Death Rates

To understand the causes of human population increase, particularly the tremendous surge after the Industrial Revolution, we must recall that the population growth rate equals the birth rate minus the death rate. Prior to 1775, the birth rate in developed countries like those of northern Europe was slightly higher than the death rate, and so the population enlarged at a low rate (Fig. 14.9, Step ①). After 1775, as industry expanded, people enjoyed improved nutrition, better personal and public hygiene, protection of water supplies, and the reduction of communicable diseases such as smallpox. These innovations caused a gradual decline in the death rate (Step ②). While the death rate began to decline in 1775, the birth rate did not start to drop in developed countries until about a hundred years later. Consequently, each year many more people were born than died, and this caused an increase in the rate of population growth. By the last decade of the 20th century, both the birth rates and death rates in industrialized nations had dropped to all-time lows, and the gap between them had once again narrowed (Fig. 14.9, Step ③). For example, Japan in 1999 had a birth rate of 9.5 per thousand, and a death rate of 7.3 per thousand, giving a low growth rate. A changing pattern from high birth rate and high death rate to low birth

rate and low death rate is called the demographic transition (Fig. 14.9, Step ④).

Growth Rates and Age Structure

A sure sign of a population's growth rate is its age structure: the number of individuals in each age group (Fig. 14.10).

The age structure of a growing Swedish population in 1900—a time when the death rate had already declined substantially but the birth rate had yet to fall—shows a high percentage of people in the younger age classes (Fig. 14.10a). This results in a pyramid-shaped age distribution.

By 1977, the Swedish birth rate had dropped close to the death rate, and each age class was only slightly smaller than the younger one below it (Fig. 14.10b). This results in a bullet-shaped age profile with almost

Figure 14.9

The Difference between Birth Rate and Death Rate Detonates the Population Bomb

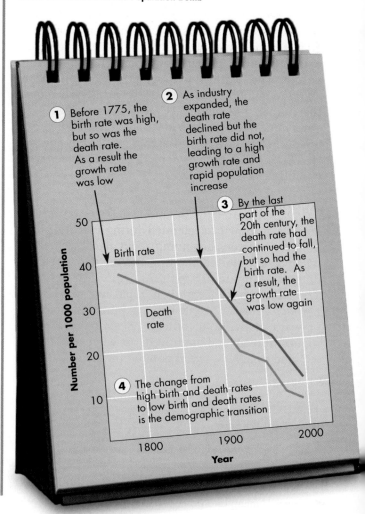

① Before 1775, the birth rate was high, but so was the death rate. As a result the growth rate was low

② As industry expanded, the death rate declined but the birth rate did not, leading to a high growth rate and rapid population increase

③ By the last part of the 20th century, the death rate had continued to fall, but so had the birth rate. As a result, the growth rate was low again

④ The change from high birth and death rates to low birth and death rates is the demographic transition

no difference in the size of age classes until the end of the human life span (the point of the bullet).

Age structure is significant because it helps predict a population's growth potential. A pyramid-shaped population with many young people, like the African nation of Uganda in 2002, will grow rapidly (Fig. 14.10d–e). In contrast, a bullet-shaped population, like Sweden in 1977, will be stable or decline. With a look at data graphed this way, you can infer the kinds of social services needed by different populations: schools for pyramid-shaped populations, and health-care facilities for the elderly and pension plans for bullet-shaped ones.

LO⁵ Where Do Organisms Live and How Do They Make a Living?

The rapidly increasing human population makes it imperative to successfully manage resources such as the fish populations in Georges Bank. Ecologists need to understand not only how fish populations have changed over time, including the disastrous drops that have occurred, but also where the organisms live and how they react with other organisms—their prey, predators, and competitors. These assemblies of different species in a particular area at a particular time are called *communities*.

Habitat and Niche

To understand the intricate web of relationships among organisms in a community, we must discover where the organisms live and how they make a living. The physical place in the environment where an organism resides is its habitat. A habitat is like an organism's address or home.

Whereas a species' physical home is its habitat, its functional role in the community is its niche. The niche is analogous to the organism's job—how it gets its supply of energy and materials. A niche is what an organism does in and for a biological community.

> **habitat**
> the physical place within a species' range where an organism actually lives
>
> **niche**
> the role, function, or position of an organism in a biological community

> By 2050, Sweden's population will likely be top-heavy with older people because Swedes are having smaller families.

Figure 14.10

Age Structure Diagrams Reveal Potential for Population Growth

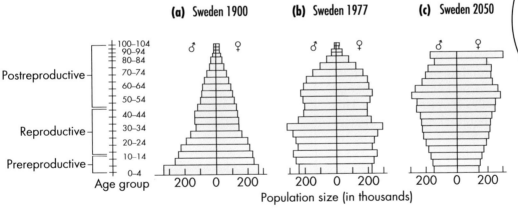

(a) Sweden 1900   **(b)** Sweden 1977   **(c)** Sweden 2050

Postreproductive / Reproductive / Prereproductive — Age group — Population size (in thousands)

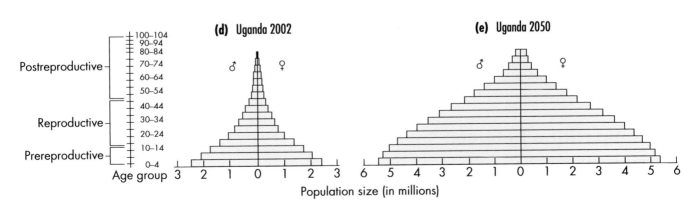

(d) Uganda 2002   **(e)** Uganda 2050

Postreproductive / Reproductive / Prereproductive — Age group — Population size (in millions)

Limits to Niches

The niche an organism actually occupies is often restricted by other organisms. For example, consider a warbler's niche in the forests of Cape Cod (Fig. 14.11a). The bird has the potential to eat insects wherever they occur in trees, at any height and at any distance from the trunk. The bird might also nest any time in June or July. The potential range of all biotic and abiotic conditions under which an organism can thrive is called its fundamental niche. If a warbler could catch insects any place in the tree, it would be operating in its fundamental niche for prey location.

A warbler in eastern forests cannot obtain insects just anywhere, however, because several species compete for food, and each species performs a slightly different role in the community. The different species obtain insects at different heights in the trees, at different distances from the trunk, and their heavy eating comes at slightly different times during the year, depending on when they nest. The myrtle warbler, for instance, eats insects at the base of trees, the bay-breasted warbler specializes in insects in middle branches, and the Cape May warbler seeks insects at the outer edges of the top branches (Fig. 14.11b). Thus, other community residents may force a warbler species from its broader fundamental niche into its narrower realized niche, the part of the fundamental niche that a species actually occupies in nature. This kind of niche restriction is rather common. Species interactions like these can be a major factor in defining a species' distribution and abundance.

LO⁶ How Species Interact

Ecologists have categorized interactions between species into four general types. In (1) competition and (2) predation, one or both of the species suffer. In (3) mutualism and (4) commensalism, neither species is harmed by the interaction. Let's investigate each of these types of species interactions.

Competition between Species

There are never enough good things to go around— sunny spots in which to germinate and put down roots, sheltered places to build nests, or marine

Figure 14.11
Niche: An Organism's Role in the Community

(a) A warbler in its fundamental niche might find food at any height in the tree, any distance from the trunk, or nest at any time in June or July

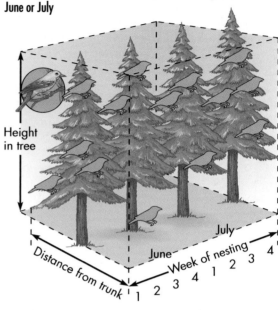

(b) A warbler in its realized niche might be restricted to finding food at certain positions in the tree, and nesting in just a couple of weeks of summer

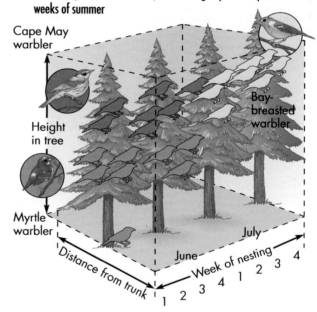

worms of a particular size to consume. Because of such restrictions, two different species often compete for the same limited resource, and this interaction restrains the abundance of both species. The key feature of interspecific competition, the use of the same resources by two different species, is that one or both competitors have a negative effect on the other's survival or reproduction.

A Model for Species Competition

To see how competition works, imagine populations of yellowtail flounder and witch flounder. If only one species inhabits a region of the Georges Bank, then, in the absence of fishers, that species would increase in numbers until competition between the species' own members limited the population size, as we saw earlier with the Tasmanian sheep. But if both yellowtail and witch flounder inhabit the same area, any individual fish will compete against not only members of its own species, but against individuals from the other species as well. The outcome will depend on the relative strengths of the interspecific and intraspecific competitions.

If a high density of one species (for instance, yellowtail flounder) affects the growth of the other species (witch flounder) more than it affects its own growth, then the first (yellowtail) will eliminate the second (witch flounder). A situation like this, where one species excludes another through competition, is called competitive exclusion. In another possible interaction, competition can affect each species' own population growth more than it affects the other species. In this case, the two species could end up coexisting. As a final possibility, each species may slow the growth of the other equally. In this case, the species with the biggest population to start with would take over the community.

Natural Causes of Competitive Exclusion

Laboratory and field experiments with organisms as different as Paramecium, beetles, field mice, and aquatic plants typically show that competition does take place and that it can result in either competitive exclusion or in species coexisting.

For example, the Caribbean island of St. Martin has two lizard species that are slightly different in size but eat the same kinds of insects. To find out whether the two species actually compete with each other, researchers fenced off large squares of land that contained individuals of the smaller species, the larger species, or both. They found that where both species coexisted, members of the larger species had less food in their stomachs, grew more slowly, laid fewer eggs, and were forced to perch higher in the bushes than when that species lived alone in an enclosure. Studies like these proved that strong competition does exist in natural populations and that the presence of one species can limit another species to its realized (rather than fundamental) niche.

While competition often limits population size in both interacting species, the second major type of community interaction, predation, is beneficial for one species but harmful to the other.

Predation

Animals that kill and eat other animals are predators, their food is prey, and the act of procurement and consumption is predation. Here we focus on how predation affects the population size of both prey and predator on a short time scale, and how hunter and hunted evolve strategies to outwit each other on a longer evolutionary time scale.

competitive exclusion
a situation in which one species eliminates another through competition

predator
an organism, usually an animal, that obtains its food by eating other living organisms

prey
living organisms that are food for other organisms

predation
the act of procurement and consumption of prey by predators

Do Predator Populations Control Cycles of Prey Populations or Vice Versa?

Many populations of predator and prey rise and fall in cycles like the ripples in a pond. For example, wild populations of the snowshoe hare and lynx periodically rise and fall in phase on about a 10-year cycle. The hare populations occasionally boom when vegetation is abundant and crash when food becomes scarce. When hare populations rise, lynx also increase and devour more of their prey.

In other cases, predators can be the driving force behind the population swings of their prey. To test the effect of predators on populations of pine bark beetles, researchers enclosed some trees with predator-proof cages, while nearby uncaged trees served as controls. They found that populations protected from predation grew better than those exposed to predators. They concluded that predators can indeed help drive the cycles of population growth.

Populations of predator and prey may grow or shrink over the short term, but over the long term, genetic changes can influence the evolutionary balance between hunter and hunted.

The Coevolution of Predator and Prey

Predator-prey interactions lead to a grand coevolutionary race, with predators evolving more efficient ways to catch prey, and prey evolving better ways to escape.

Predators need a way to catch their food, and the two main options are pursuit and ambush. Predators that pursue their prey are selected for speed and often for intelligence as well. Carnivores store information about the prey's escape strategies and make quick choices while in pursuit. In keeping with evolutionary pressures, vertebrate predators generally have larger brains in proportion to their body size than the prey they catch.

camouflage
body shapes, colors, or patterns that enable an organism to blend in with its environment and remain concealed from danger

chemical warfare
a defense strategy of prey species in which these organisms produce distasteful oils or other toxic substances that kill or harm predators

mimicry
the evolution of similar appearance in two or more species, which often gives one or all protection; for example, a nonpoisonous species may evolve protection from predators by its similarity to a poisonous model

parasite
a type of predator that obtains benefits at the expense of another organism, its host; a parasite is usually smaller than its host, lives in close physical association with it, and generally saps its host's strength rather than killing it outright

Some predators ambush their prey. A familiar example is the frog that zaps flying insects by snapping out a sticky tongue. Certain mantis insects ambush their prey by hiding in the open with a camouflaged, plantlike appearance (Fig. 14.12). Those mantises that carry genes for resemblance to the plants they inhabit can be nearly invisible to prey and are thus more effective at ambushing their food and surviving to reproduce than mantises without those genes.

Despite the stealth, athleticism, and cunning of predators, prey species have evolved some remarkably devious tricks—in addition to speed—that help them avoid being eaten. One defense strategy is camouflage: the use of shapes, colors, or behaviors that enable organisms to blend in with their backgrounds and decrease the risk of predation. Many insects have evolved shapes that look like twigs, flowers, or leaves, complete with phony leaf veins (Fig. 14.12). Still other insects, and a few amphibians, escape detection by resembling bird excrement on leaves. Behavior plays a role, too; when a flounder nestles to the bottom, it will flap a bit to cover itself with sand. Some flounders can even change their colors to match the color of the bottom on which they rest (Fig. 14.12).

Chemical warfare is another defense strategy. Eucalyptus and creosote bushes, for example, produce distasteful oils or toxic substances that kill or harm herbivores. People sometimes plant oleanders as decorative shrubs because they resist insect pests, but the leaves are so poisonous that chewing a few can kill a child. Animals are not without their own arsenals: Toads, stinkbugs, and bombardier beetles produce highly offensive chemicals that repel attackers. Poisonous prey species often evolve brightly colored patterns, enabling the experienced predator to recognize and avoid them. This is called *warning coloration*. The brilliantly colored but poisonous strawberry frogs of South America have evolved this strategy.

Mimicry

Many nonpoisonous prey species masquerade as poisonous species; this is one form of the process called mimicry, wherein one species resembles another. Mimicry could arise in the following way. Individuals of a nonpoisonous butterfly species that by chance contain alleles causing them to resemble the poisonous species even slightly may occasionally escape predation if a hungry animal mistakes them for the poisonous species. A selective pressure like this could, over time, allow the nonpoisonous species to accumulate more and more alleles for resemblance to the poisonous neighbor.

Parasites: The Intimate Predators

Parasites are insidious kinds of predators; they are usually smaller than their hosts, often live in close physical association with individual victims, and generally just sap their strength rather than kill them

Figure 14.12
A Natural Arms Race: The Coevolution of Predator and Prey

Praying Mantis

Moth

Flounder

outright. Ectoparasites, like fleas, ticks, and leeches, live on the host's exterior, while endoparasites, like tapeworms, liver flukes, and some protozoa, inhabit internal organs or the bloodstream. In a special type of parasitic interaction, certain insects develop inside the body of another insect and inevitably kill it.

Commensalism and Mutualism

The community relationships we have discussed so far—competition and predation—have involved harm to at least one of the species. Sometimes, however, neither species is harmed by their interactions. In commensalism, one species benefits from the alliance, while the other is neither harmed nor helped, whereas in mutualism, both species are helped.

Commensalism

Commensalism is common in tropical rain forests, and the most easily observed examples are the epiphytes, or air plants, that grow on the surfaces of other plants. Using the tree merely as a base of attachment, epiphytes take no nourishment from the host and usually do no harm. Other commensal relationships include birds that nest in trees, algae that grow harmlessly on a turtle's shell, and the small fish that live among the stinging tentacles of sea anemones—unharmed and safe from predators.

Mutualism

In a mutualistic interaction, both species benefit. An example involves the yucca plant that grows in hot, dry regions of the western United States. The yucca plant has a mutualistic relationship with the yucca moth. The moth lays its eggs in the ovary at the base of a yucca flower and then pollinates the flower. Moths depend on the plant for food and reproduction; the plant depends on the moth for pollination. In this relationship, both species benefit: the yucca moth gets a high-energy nectar reward and the plant becomes pollinated. If one species becomes extinct, likely so will the other.

LO⁷ Organization of Communities

The interactions we have considered—competition, predation, commensalism, and mutualism—affect not just pairs of species, but entire communities consisting of tens to hundreds of species. Communities consist of some species that happened to immigrate into the area and can survive under the available physical conditions, and some

species that will grow only if other species are also present. It is a goal of ecologists to learn how the addition or subtraction of a species affects the whole community in the short and long term.

Communities Change over Time

Occasionally, a cataclysm will strip an area of its original vegetation, as can happen after a volcanic explosion or fire, or even after a farmer clears a field. Left to nature, however, a regular progression of communities will regrow at the site in a process called succession.

Soon after a region is denuded, a variety of species begin to colonize the bare ground. These species make up a pioneer community, and they modify environmental conditions, such as soil quality, at the site. Conditions produced by the activities of the pioneer community determine which additional species can establish themselves in the area and form a transition community. Changes are rapid at first, as more and more species join the transition community. Eventually, a particular community of plants and animals becomes relatively stable, and changes take place more slowly over time. Such an assemblage is often called a climax community, but most ecologists today recognize that change is constantly occurring even in old communities, driven by such environmental variables as hurricanes, floods, and fires, as well as global climatic changes.

Species Diversity in Communities

The total number of species found in a community is its species richness. In most communities, there are few common species but many rare types of organisms. For example, ecologists captured a group of almost 7,000 moths and identified individuals of 197 different species in one local area. One quarter of the moths belonged to a single species and another quarter belonged to just five other species. The

commensalism
a relationship between two species in which one species benefits and the other suffers no apparent harm

mutualism
a symbiotic relationship between two species in which both species benefit

succession
the process through which a regular progression of communities will regrow at a particular site

pioneer community
the species that are first to colonize a habitat after a disturbance such as fire, plowing, or logging

transition community
a community of organisms that establish themselves at a particular site based upon conditions produced by the activities of the pioneer community

climax community
the most stable community in a habitat and one that tends to persist in the absence of a disturbance

species richness
the total number of species in a community

remaining half of the moths fell into 191 species—some represented by just one or two individuals.

What factors allow a region to have large numbers of rare species? Both *latitude* (north-south position) and *isolation* (peninsulas, island chains, or other out-of-the-way locales) influence species richness. Some communities in tropical latitudes, for example, have about 600 types of land birds, while an area of similar size in the arctic tundra may have only 20 to 30 species of land birds (Fig. 14.13).

A single hectare of mainland tropical forest can have 300 different species of trees and tens of thousands of insect species; on a peninsula, however the species richness is diminished. This is because in an isolated area, the many rare species can easily become extinct and their replacement from the mainland is unlikely due to isolation. Species richness on island chains is limited in such specific ways that ecologists are now applying the principles of island ecology to the design of nature preserves, which are, in fact, islands within a sea of human development.

Figure 14.13

Latitude and Isolation Affect Species Richness

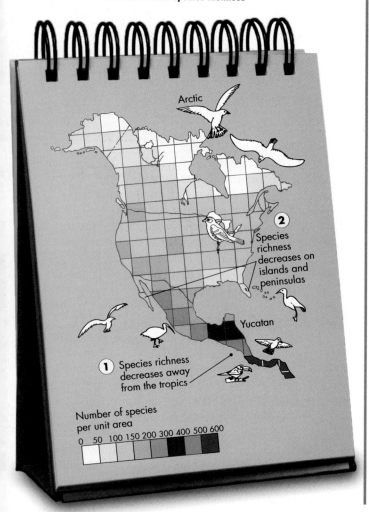

Arctic

2 Species richness decreases on islands and peninsulas

Yucatan

1 Species richness decreases away from the tropics

Number of species per unit area

0   50   100 150 200 300 400 500 600

The more resources available in an area—water and solar energy, for instance—the greater the species richness the area can support. Competition and predation also influence species richness. High competition forces smaller niches, and a community can accommodate more species.

Predation can also increase species richness. For example, a sea star preys on barnacles, snails, clams, and mussels. When experimenters removed the sea star, diversity dropped because the mussel population increased and crowded out the other invertebrates. By eating young mussels, the sea star reduces competition for space and so preserves higher species richness. Species like this predatory sea star, whose activities determine community structure, are called *keystone species.*

Species Diversity and Community Stability

Species richness is dwindling all over the globe. The loss of tropical forest ecosystems is one familiar example, and the cutting of old-growth (virgin) forests in the Pacific Northwest is another. Until recently there was little actual data on how species richness affects the health of an ecosystem. The diversity-stability hypothesis suggests that because the species in a community encompass many different traits, a diverse community is more likely to contain at least some species that can survive environmental disturbances such as drought, fire, hailstorms, or overfishing.

In one of the first tests of this hypothesis, researchers measured the amount of living plant material in plots of grassland. These plots contained differing numbers of species, from undisturbed native prairies with more than 20 species per plot to abandoned farmers' fields with less than 10 species per plot. The results showed that the species-rich plots were four times more productive in drought years, and they recovered more quickly than species-poor plots. These results were predicted by the diversity-stability hypothesis; they suggest that a community's ability to resist adverse environmental conditions increases with species richness. The long-term stability of communities may thus depend on the biodiversity of their many interrelating species. These results for grasslands help underscore the urgency of pleas to conserve that biodiversity.

The Future of Species Richness

Perhaps the greatest challenge in the world today is the immense increase in human population and its disastrous disturbance of Earth's biological communities. The collapse of the fishery off the coast of Cape

Cod is an example. But in the species-rich communities of tropical latitudes, human population pressure is threatening the destruction of entire ecosystems. Tropical peoples have traditionally cleared land for agriculture by burning the forest, planting crops for a few years, and then moving on when the soil becomes depleted of nutrients. With enough time, the process of ecological succession can repair these small wounds. Now, however, the J-shaped curve of the human population results in vast areas of the rain forest going up in smoke to provide farmland for crops and pastureland on which to graze cattle for export to developed nations. These fires are so huge and so common that they are clearly visible on satellite photos from space. Many ecologists fear that the plant and animal communities of the tropics may not be able to recover from such extreme disturbances and that early in the 21st century, no tropical rain forests will remain intact. Still worse, many fear that this disruption may cause a distressingly large percentage of all living species to become extinct in our lifetimes.

Ecologists consider it an urgent research priority to learn what makes communities resilient and how they may (or may not) be able to persist in the face of human encroachment. We must solve this problem if our most diverse and interesting communities are to survive through the 21st century.

Who knew?

The yellowtail's habitat is *where* it lives (fingerlings in open water, and adults on the sandy bottoms of the Georges Bank); its niche is *how* it lives (as a bottom predator, eating marine invertebrates).

Nearly two-thirds of deforestation in the Amazon rain forest results from cattle ranches and soybean cultivation; a small proportion results from small-scale agriculture.

Satellite image of Borneo shows smoke from fires started by slash-and-burn agriculture.

Venezuelan children watch as a portion of the tropical rain forest is burned to clear land for cattle grazing.

biomes, 291–295
climatic regions, 289–290
defined, 13, 264, 289
global material cycles,
286–289
global warming, 199–200, 281,
297–298
ozone hole, 298
sustainability, 298–299
biotic potential, 267
bipedalism, 257, 258
birds, 253–254, 260
birth, 152
birth control, 141
birth rates, 265–268, 272
bivalves, 242
blastocysts, 148–150
blastula, 147
blending model of heredity, 86,
87–88
blood clots, 117, 127
blood type, 94–95
blood-filled cavity, 241–242
blubber, 255
bony fishes, 251
bottleneck effect, 168–169
Brachiopoda, 242
brain
in humans, 52, 258–259
in primates, 257–258
brown algae, 205–206
bryophytes, 220–221
buffers, 26, AppA
bulbourethral glands, 139

C
Calvin-Benson cycle, 60
Cambrian explosion, 183
camouflage, 276
cancer. *See also* cell cycle
basal cell carcinoma, 63, 67,
72–74
carcinogens, 129
DNA alteration and, 74
growth controls and growth
factor, 72–74
therapy for, 70–72
capsaicins, 209, 219
Capsicum, 209–210
capsid, 200
carbohydrates, 27–28
carbon 14 (^{14}C), 21–22
carbon backbones, 26–27
carbon compounds, 26–27
carbon cycle, 61, 288–289
carbon dioxide, 297, 298
carbon isotopes, 21–22
carbonaceous chondrites,
177–178
carbon-fixing reactions, 59–61

carcinogens, 129
carotenoids, 57–58
carpels, 226
carrageenan, 203
carriers, 93
carrying capacity, 268–269, 272
cartilaginous fishes, 250–251
castes, 245
catalysts, 47, 179
cDNA (complementary DNA),
134–135
cell cycle
action of the dividing layer, 65
cancer therapy and mitosis,
70–72
chromosome number and
meiosis, 76–77
chromosomes in, 65–67
defined, 63
division of skin cells, 64–65
embryonic development, cell
division in, 147
genetic recombination in
meiosis, 78–81
growth controls, 72–74
interphase, 67–68
meiosis, cell divisions of, 77–78
mitosis, phases of, 68–70
mitosis and meiosis compared,
81–82
sexual reproduction and, 74–76
cell division. *See* cell cycle
cell plate, 70
cell theory, 31–32
cell walls
defined, 40
of fungi, 211–212
of plants, 218
in prokaryotic cells, 198
cells
in Cnidarians, 237
defined, 30
discovery of, 30–31
entropy and, 45
eukaryotic vs. prokaryotic,
32–33
evolution of first cells, 179–182
HIV as threat to, 19
import-export and size of, 31
parts of, and HIV infection,
33–40
prokaryotic structure, 197–198
viruses vs., 31–32
cellular respiration, 44, 51. *See
also* aerobic pathway
cellular slime mold, 202
cellulose, 28
Cenozoic Era, 183–186, 254
centipedes, 244
centrioles, 39, 69

centromere, 66–67
cephalization, 240
Cephalochordata, 248, 249
cephalopods, 242
cephalothorax, 243
cervix, 142
chance and genetic drift, 168–169
chaparral, 294
Chargaff, Erwin, 107
Chase, Martha, 105–106
Chedwick, Wayne, 155, 163
chemical bonds, 22–23
chemical energy, 45
chemical reactions, 45–46
chemical warfare, 276
chemoautotrophs, 181–182,
198–199
chemosynthetic organisms, 57
chemotherapy, 70–71
chile peppers, 209–210, 222, 228
Chilopoda, 244
chimpanzees, 258
chitin, 28, 211
chlamydia, 200
Chlamydomonas, 218
chlorofluorocarbons (CFCs), 297,
298
chlorophyll, 57–58
chlorophyta, 206, 217–218
chloroplasts
defined, 58
evolution of, 182–183, 218
photosynthesis and, 58
as plastids, 40
choanocytes, 236
choanoflagellates, 206, 233
Chordata
Cephalochordata, 250
characteristics of, 246–248
Urochordata, 248–250
Vertebrata, 249–255
chorion, 150
chorionic villus sampling, 150
chromatids, 66–67, 78
chromatin, 110
Chromista, 205
chromosomal mutation, 127
chromosomes
in cell cycle, 65–67
defined, 65
genes linked to, 97, 104
homologous, 77, 78, 80
independent assortment of,
80–81
meiosis and number of, 76–77
packaged into DNA, 109–111
sets of, 77
sex chromosomes, 98–100
sex determination and, 99–100
structure of, 66–67

cilia, 39
ciliates, 205
circulatory system, open, 242
clades, 188
cladistics, 188
classes, 10
classification of living things. *See*
taxonomy
cleavage, 147
climate, 289
climates, regional, 289–290
climax communities, 277
clones, 133
cloning, 133, 134–135
Cnidaria, 236–237
cocci, 198
codominance, 94–95
codons, 123, 125–127
coelacanths, 251
coelom, 238
coevolution, 228
cohesion, AppA
collagen, 40
Collins, Francis, 101
color blindness, 98
commensalism, 277
communities
commensalism and mutualism,
277
defined, 13, 264, 273
diversity-stability hypothesis,
278
habitat and niche, 273–274
interspecific competition,
274–275
species richness, 277–279
succession in, 277
comparative anatomy, 157–162
competition
interspecific, 274–275
as population-regulating
mechanism, 270
predation, 275–277
competitive exclusion, 275
complementary base pairing, 109,
111, 120
complementary DNA (cDNA),
134–135
complex carbohydrates, 27–28
compounds, hydrophylic and
hydrophobic, 25
coniferous forests, 294–295
conifers, 226
conjugation, 199
conservation, law of, 44–45
contraceptives, 141, 142
contractile ring, 69
controls in scientific method, 15
convergent evolution, 164
coral reefs, 297

corpus luteum, 141, 144, 145
Cosmic Background Explorer
    (COBE), 176
covalent bonds, 23
creatine phosphate, 56
creation, special, 162
Crenarachaeota, 200
Crick, Francis H.C., 107–108, 124
cristae, 51
crop rotation, 287
cross-fertilization, 87
crossing over, 80
cross-pollination, 228
crustaceans, 244
ctenophores, 237
cuticles, 226
cyanobacteria (glue-green algae),
    200
cycads, 226
cyclins, 74
cystic fibrosis (CF), 85, 88, 93,
    95–97, 100, 101
cytokinesis, 69–70
cytoplasm, 31, 37, 50
cytosine (C), 107. *See also* DNA
    (deoxyribonucleic acid)
cytoskeletons, 39, 182

D

Dalton, John, 20
dandelions, 270
Darwin, Charles, 12, 156–158,
    162–163
daughter cells, 65, 70, 72–73, 147
DDT, 286
death rates, 265–268, 272
decomposers, 213
demographic transition, 272
deoxyribonucleic acid. *See* DNA
derived traits, 188
dermis, 64–65
descent with modification, 157
deserts, 293
detritivores, 283
detritus, 231, 283
deuterostomes, 238, 245–246
development
    defined, 8–9, 137
    embryonic, 145–148, 151–152,
        233, 237–238
    growth, 148, 152–153
    human, 148–152
    maturation and aging, 152–153
Devonian period, 250–251
diatomaceous earth, 205
diatoms, 205
dicots, 227
diffusion, 35
dihybrid crosses, 97
dikaryon, 214

dinoflagellates, 204
dinosaurs, 253
diploid cells, 77, 145
diplomonads, 202
Diplopoda, 244
directional selection, 169
disaccharides, 27
disassembly, 125
disordered loops, 28
disruptive selection, 170
divergent evolution, 163–164
diversity-stability hypothesis, 278
division phase of the cell cycle, 65
divisions, 10, 216
DNA (deoxyribonucleic acid)
    bacteriophage experiments,
        105–106
    cancer and, 74
    cDNA, 134–135
    in cell cycle, 66
    chromosome structure and,
        66–67
    defined, 30
    double helix model, discovery
        of, 106–108
    genetic fingerprinting, 113–114
    heredity and, 9
    HIV and, 30, 35
    information flow and, 37
    murder case example, 103–104,
        109–110, 111, 113–114
    recombinant DNA technology,
        131–135
    replication of, 111–114, 121
    repressors and, 130
    RNA contrasted with, 119
    structure of, 108–111
    synthesis of, 67–68
    testing evolutionary hypotheses
        with, 260
    transcription, 118–121
    transformation experiments,
        104–105
DNA ligase, 133
DNA polymerase, 111, 129
domains, 10, 186, 189–190
dominant traits, 87, 88–89, 93–94
double helix, 103, 107–108. *See
    also* DNA (deoxyribonucleic
    acid)
Drosophila melanogaster, 98–99
drug farming ("pharming"), 117
dung beetles, 231, 243, 244

E

E. coli bacteria, 129–130, 197
early-loss survivorship curves,
    266, 270
Earth, formation of, 176
Ecdysozoa, 239, 242–245
embryonic development
    animals patterns of, 233

Echinodermata, 245
ecology
    aquatic ecosystems, 295–297
    biomes, 291–295
    climatic regions, 289–290
    commensalism, 277
    competition, interspecific,
        274–275
    defined, 13
    energy flow and material
        cycling, 282–284
    energy flow through
        ecosystems, 284–286
    fish populations, 263, 264–265,
        273
    global material cycles,
        286–289
    global warming, 199–200, 281,
        297–298
    habitat and niche, 273–274
    human population, 271–273
    interaction levels, 264
    limits to global distribution, 264
    limits to population size,
        264–271
    mutualism, 277
    ozone hole, 298
    predation, 275–277, 278
    science of, 264
    species richness, 277–279
    succession, 277
    sustainability, 298–299
ecosystems, defined, 13, 264. *See
    also* ecology
ectoderm, 147
ectoparasites, 277
eggs
    aminote, 252–253
    in cell theory, 32
    defined, 75
    in fertilization, 138, 144–145
    of gymnosperms, 225
    production and pathways of,
        141–143
    shelled, 225, 254
    size and structure of, 144
ejaculation, 139, 140–141
electromagnetic spectrum, 57
electron carriers, 50, 55
electron transport chain, 49,
    53–54
electronic microscopes (EMs),
    AppB
electrons, 20, 21, 22
elements, 20
elongation, 125
embryology, comparative,
    160–162

four stages of, 147–148
    frog, 145–147
    human, 151–152
    protostomes vs.
        deuterostomes, 237–238
embryos, 142, 218
endocytosis, 35
endoderm, 147
endometrium, 143
endoparasites, 277
endoplasmic reticulum (ER),
    37–39
endoskeletons, 245
endospores, 199
endosymbiont hypothesis, 182, 202
end-Permian extinction, 183
energetics, 43
energy
    aerobic pathway, 49, 50–54
    anaerobic pathway, 50, 54–55
    as characteristic of life, 5–8
    defined, 44
    ecosystem energy flow,
        282–286
    for exercise, 55–57
    feedback inhibition, 55
    hummingbirds and, 43, 44, 49
    law of energy conservation,
        44–45
    law of inefficient energy
        changes, 45
    plants and photosynthesis,
        57–61
    potential and kinetic, 44
energy allocation, 270
energy budgets, 284–285
energy flow, 45–49
energy pyramids, 285–286
energy shells, 21
energy-absorbing reactions, 45–46
energy-releasing reactions, 45–46
energy-trapping reactions, 59
entropy, 45
environment, characteristics of life
    related to, 13
enzymes
    activation energy and, 47–48
    beta-galactosidase, 130
    as catalysts, 47
    in cristae, 51
    defined, 47
    DNA ligase, 133
    DNA polymerase, 111, 129
    induced fit model of enzyme
        action, 48–49
    in Krebs cycle, 52
    mutations repaired by, 129
    protease, 41
    restriction enzymes, 133
    reverse transcriptase, 30, 134

RNA polymerase, 120
enzyme-substrate complex, 48
epidermis, 64–65, 236
epididymis, 139
Epstein, Ervin, 63, 73, 74
equilibrium, punctuated,
    165–166
ER (endoplasmic reticulum),
    37–39
erection, 140
estrogen, 143, 144
estuaries, 296
ethanol, 55
euglenoids, 202
Eukarya domain, 11, 189–190
eukaryotes, 32, 131, 203–206
eukaryotic cells
    chromosomes in, 65–66
    defined, 32
    evolution of, 182–183
    size of, 33
Eumycota (true fungi), 211
Euryarchaeota, 200
eustachian tube, 248
eutrophication, 288
evolution
    adaptive radiation, 164
    agents of, 168–169
    animal evolution innovations,
        232–233, 236–237
    animal origins, 233
    animal phyla, evolutionary
        relationships among,
        233–234
    animals, evolutionary
        relationships among, 233
    antibiotic resistance and, 155,
        163, 168, 171–172
    biogeography evidence for,
        162–163
    as characteristic of life, 9–13
    of chordates, 246–255
    classification of living things,
        9–11
    coevolution, 228, 275–276
    comparative anatomy evidence
        for, 157–162
    convergent, 164
    defined, 9
    directional selection, 169
    disruptive selection, 170
    divergent, 163–164
    of dung beetles, 231
    emergence of concept of,
        156–158
    fossil evidence for, 156–157
    genetic variation, 166–167
    gradual evolutionary change,
        163
    of humans, 258–260

molecular evidence for, 162
of multicellular protistans,
    202–203
phyletic gradualism, 164–166
of plants, 220–221
punctuated equilibrium,
    165–166
of seeds, 224
speciation, 165, 170–172
stabilizing selection, 169
synthetic theory of, 166
exocytosis, 35
exercise, energy for, 55–57
exons, 121
exoskeletons, 243
experimentation, 15, 92
exponential growth, 267–268,
    271–272
extinctions, 183, 192–193, 253
extracellular matrix, 39–40
extremophiles, 199
extrinsic population-regulating
    mechanisms, 270

F

F_1 and F_2 hybrids, 87–89
facilitated diffusion, 35
fallopian tubes, 141–142
family, 10, 186
family pedigrees, 92–93
family trees, molecular, 162
fats, 29
fat-soluble molecules, 35
feathers, 254
feedback inhibition, 55
female reproductive system,
    141–145
fermentation, 49, 55, 56
ferns, 223–224
fertility curves, 266–267
fertilization
    cross-fertilization, 87
    female reproductive system
        and, 142
    fused gametes, 74–75
    gonads in, 139
    mating and, 138
    by pollination, 228
    process of, 144–145
    in reptiles, 253
    self-fertilization, 86–87
    in vitro, 137
fertilization membrane, 145
fetal development, 150
fetal membranes, 150
fetus, defined, 142
filter feeders, 242
first filial (F_1) hybrids, 87–89
fish populations, 263, 264–265, 273
fishes, ancient, 249–251

flagellum, 39
flatworms, 239–240
flight, 254
flowering plants (angiosperms or
    Anthophyta), 221, 222, 224,
    226–229, 255
flowers, 221, 226–227, 228
follicles, 141
follicle-stimulating hormone (FSH),
    141, 144, 150
follicular cells, 141
food chains, 283, 285
food webs, 283–284
foraminfer, 163
foraminiferans, 204–205
forests
    coniferous, 294–295
    logging of, 295
    temperate, 294
    tropical dry forests, 292
    tropical rain forests, 291–292
fossils, 9, 15, 156–157, 177
founder effect, 169
four-chambered heart, 254
Franklin, Rosalind, 107, 108
freshwater ecosystems, 295, 296
frog development, 145–147
fronds, 206, 224
fruit, 226
fruiting bodies, 202, 212
FSH (follicle-stimulating hormone),
    141, 144, 150
functional groups, 27
fundamental niches, 274
fungi
    body plan of, 211–212
    defined, 210–211
    divisions of, 216
    as heterotrophs, 212–213
    medical mycology, 216
    plant roots and, 214–215
    protists closely related to, 206
    reproduction of, 213–214
Fungi kingdom, 11, 190
fur, 255
fusion, sexual or nuclear, 214

G

G_1 phase, 67, 78
G_2 phase, 68, 78
Galápagos Islands, 156–157, 162
gametes, 74, 96–97
gametophytes, 218, 219–220, 225
gastropods, 242
gastrulation, 147
gene flow, 168
gene mapping, 101
gene phylogenies, 189
genes. *See also* genetics and
    inheritance

alleles and, 88–89
linked to chromosomes, 97,
    104
protein structure specified by,
    118
regulation of, 129–131
genetic clock hypotheses, 153
genetic code, 125–127
genetic disease
    cystic fibrosis, 85, 88, 93,
        95–97, 100, 101
    isolating the gene, 101
    treatment of, 101
genetic drift, 168–169
genetic engineering, 117,
    131–135
genetic fingerprinting, 113–114
genetic markers, 113
genetic recombination, 78, 80,
    166
genetic variation, 166–168
genetics and inheritance
    chance and genetic drift,
        168–169
    chromosomes, genes linked to,
        97, 104
    defined, 85
    family pedigrees, 92–93
    gene mapping and genetic
        disease, 101
    genes and alleles, 88–89
    genetic symbols and Punnett
        squares, 90–91
    inheritance of acquired
        characteristics, 156
    interaction of alleles, 93–96
    Mendel's experiments and
        models, 86–90
    molecular evidence for
        evolution, 162
    multiple traits, 96–97
    probabilities and, 91–92
    segregation principle, 89–90
    sex, influence of, 98–100
    universal principles of, 86–88,
        89
genotype. *See also* genetics and
    inheritance
    defined, 89
genus (genera), 10, 186
geographical barriers, 264
geographical speciation, 170
geologic eras, 183–186
germ cell determinants, 76
germ cells, 75–76
germ layer, 64
gill slits, 248
gills, 241
ginkgo, 226
giraffe, 165

global carbon cycle, 61, 288–289
global nitrogen cycle, 287
global phosphorus cycle, 287–288
global warming, 199–200, 281, 297–298
global water cycle, 287
glucose, 52
glue-green algae (cyanobacteria), 200
glycogen, 27–28
glycolysis
  in aerobic pathway, 49, 50
  in anaerobic pathway, 54–55
  exercise and, 56
glycolytic energy system, 56, 57
gnetophytes, 226
goats, 117, 134–135
Goldberg, Daniel, 195
Golgi apparatus, 38
gonads, 75, 139
gorillas, 258
gradual evolutionary change, 163
gradualism, phyletic, 164–166
gram-negative organisms, 198
gram-positive organisms, 198, 200
Gram's stain, 198
grasslands, 293, 299
great apes, 258
green algae, 206, 217–218
greenhouse effect, 281
greenhouse gases, 199–200, 297–298
Griffith, Frederick, 104
gross primary productivity, 284
growth factors, 73–74
growth of populations. *See* population ecology
guanine (G), 107. *See also* DNA (deoxyribonucleic acid)
Gulf Stream, 290
gymnosperms, 221, 222, 224–226

H

habitats, 273
Haleakala silversword, 175, 193
half-life, 22
halophiles, 200
hand dexterity, 257
haploid cells, 77, 213–214
haploid products of meiosis, 78
Haplorhini, 255, 256
Hardy-Weinberg equilibrium, 167
Hardy-Weinberg principle, 167–168, AppC
hCG (human chorionic gonadotropin), 150
heart, four-chambered, 254
heat, 45, 48
helix, 107. *See also* DNA

(deoxyribonucleic acid); double helix
Hemichordata, 245–246
hemophilia, 98
heredity, 9. *See also* genetics and inheritance
hermaphrodites, 138
Hershey, Alfred D., 105–106
heterotrophs, 57, 181, 198
heterotrophy, 282
heterozyotes
  codominance and, 94
  defined, 89
  inbreeding and, 169
  incomplete dominance and, 94
hierarchy of life, 13
Hippocrates, 207
Hirudinea, 241
histones, 110
HIV (human immune deficiency virus)
  amino acids and, 29
  cell parts and infection by, 33–40
  cycle of infection, completion of, 40–41
  defined, 19, 20
  hydrogen bonds and, 23
  import-export problem and, 31
  lipids and, 29, 35
  as nonliving particle, 20, 31
  nucleic acids and, 30, 35
  threat of, 19
HMS *Beagle*, 156–157
holdfasts, 206
homeothermic, 254
hominoids, 256
Homo erectus, 260
Homo habilis, 259
Homo neanderthalensis, 260
Homo sapiens, 92, 255, 260
homologous chromosomes, 77, 78, 80
homologous elements, 157–158
homologous traits, 188
homozygotes
  codominance and, 94
  defined, 89
  inbreeding and, 169
  incomplete dominance and, 94
Hooke, Robert, 30
horsetails, 223–224
human chorionic gonadotropin (hCG), 150
human evolution, 258–260
Human Genome Project, 101
human immune deficiency virus. *See* HIV
human life cycle, 76
hummingbirds, 43, 44, 49
hunting and gathering, 271

hybrids, 86–88
hydrogen bonds, 23, 133, AppA
hydrogen ions, 25–26, AppA
hydrophilic compounds, 25
hydrophobic compounds, 25
hydroxyl group (OH), 27
hyphae, 206, 211, 212
hypotheses, 14–15

I

ice caps, polar, 295
immediate energy system, 56
implantation, 150
import-export problem, 31
in vitro fertilization, 137
inbreeding, 169
inbreeding depression, 169
incomplete dominance, 93–94
independent assortment, 80–81, 96
induced fit model of enzyme action, 48–49
Industrial Revolution, 271
inefficient energy changes, law of, 45
infant care in primates, 258
infertility, 137, 153
inheritance of acquired characteristics, 156
inherited traits. *See* genetics and inheritance
initiation, 125
inorganic molecules, 26
insecticides, 286
insects, 244–245
intercellular junctions, 39–40
intermediates, 50
interphase, 65, 67–68
interspecific competition, 274–275
interstitial cells, 139
intertidal zone, 296
intrinsic population-regulating mechanisms, 270
introns, 121
ionic bonds, 23
ions, 22
iron in seawater, 182
isotopes, 21–22

J

Jacob, François, 130–131
jawed fishes, 250
jawless fishes, 250
joints, 243
J-shaped curve, 267–268, 271–272, 279

K

kelps, 205
kinetic energy, 44
kinetochore, 67

kinetoplastids, 202
kingdoms, 10, 186, 200
kit fox, 12
Klinefelter syndrome, 100
Korarchaea, 200
Krebs cycle, 49, 51–53

L

labia major, 143
labia minor, 143
labor, 152
lactation, 152
lactic acid, 55
lactose, 130
lakes, freshwater, 296
Lamarck, Jean Baptiste, 156
lamp shells, 242
lampreys, 250
lancelets, 249
larvaceans, 249
larvae, 244–245
late-loss survivorship curves, 266, 270–271
law of energy conservation, 44–45
law of inefficient energy changes, 45
law of segregation, 89–90
leeches, 241
legumes, 287
LH (luteinizing hormone), 141, 144, 150
lichens, 215
life, characteristics of, 3–5
  energy-related, 5–8
  environment-related, 13
  evolution-related, 9–13
  reproduction-related, 8–9
life expectancy, 266
life history strategies, 270–271
life on Mars. *See* Mars meteorite and search for life
life, origins of. *See* origins of life
light-dependent reactions, 59
light-independent reactions, 59–61
light microscopes, AppB
lignin, 223
linkage, genetic, 101
Linnaeus, Carolus, 186
lipids, 29, 35
lobe-finned fishes, 251
locus (loci), 101
logging, 295
logistic growth, 268
lophophores, 239
Lophotrochozoans, 239
lungfishes, 251
lungs, 251, 254
luteinizing hormone (LH), 141, 144, 150
lycopods, 224
lysosomes, 39

protostomes, 238, 239–242
pseudocoelom, 243
pseudopodia, 202
pterosaurs, 253
puberty, 141, 153
punctuated equilibrium, 165–166
Punnett squares, 91, AppC
pupa stage, 244
pyramids of biomass, 286
pyramids of energy, 285–286
pyruvate, 50, 51–52, 55

Q

quaking aspens, 227

R

radial body plan, 236
radial symmetry, 236–237
radiation therapy, 71–72
radiolarians, 205
radula, 241
rain, 287, 289–290
rain forests, 291–292
ray-finned fishes, 251
reactants, 45
reading frames, 127
realized niches, 274
receptors, 73–74
recessive traits
    alleles and, 88–89, 95–96
    cystic fibrosis, 93
    defined, 87
recombinant DNA technology,
    131–135
recombinant types, 96
recombination and mutation, 166
red algae (rhyodophyta), 202–203
red blood cells, 93–94
red tides, 204
reindeer, 269
replication
    in cell cycle, 66
    defined, 66
    of DNA, 111–114, 121
    in meiosis, 78
    origins of life and self-
        replication, 179
    recombinant DNA and, 133
    semiconservative, 112
repressors, 130
reproduction. See also
    development; meiosis;
    mitosis
    asexual, 8, 138, 213
    as characteristic of life, 8
    defined, 8
    female reproductive system,
        141–145
    germ cells and somatic cells,
        75–76

infertility, 137, 153
male reproductive system,
    139–141
    in mammals, 255
    mating and fertilization, 138
    offspring from fused gametes,
        74–75
    of plants, 218, 219, 221,
        224–225
    primary and secondary sex
        characteristics, 138–139
    in prokaryotes, 199
    in reptiles, 252–253
reproductive isolating
    mechanisms, 170–171
reproductive medicine, 137
reptiles, 252–253, 260
respiration. See cellular respiration
responsiveness, 7–8
restriction enzymes, 133
reverse transcriptase, 30, 134
rhinoceros, 270–271
rhizoids, 221
rhizomes, 224
rhyodophyta (red algae), 202–203
ribbon worms, 240
ribosomal RNA (rRNA), 123–124,
    189
ribosomes, 37, 123–125
ribozymes, 179
rickettsias, 200
RNA polymerase, 120
RNA (ribonucleic acid)
    defined, 30
    DNA contrasted with, 119
    HIV and, 30, 35
    information flow and, 37
    mRNA, 122, 130
    rRNA, 123–124, 189
    self-replicating, 179, 180
    transcription, 118–121
    translation, 118
    tRNA, 122–123
    viroids, 201
Robichaux, Robert, 175
roundworms, 242–243
rRNA (ribosomal RNA), 123–124,
    189
Ruckelshaus, William, 298

S

S phase, 67–68, 78, 111
saprobes, 198, 213
savanna, 13, 292–293
scanning electron microscope,
    AppB
scientific method, 14–15
scientific reasoning, 14
scolex, 240
scrotum, 139
sea squirts, 248–249

seasons, 289
second filial (F_2) generation, 87–89
secondary consumers, 283
secondary metabolites, 219
secondary sexual characteristics,
    138–139
sedimentary rock, 158
seed-forming vascular plants, 221
seedless vascular plants, 221,
    223–224
seeds, 224, 225, 226
segmented worms, 241
segregation principle, 89–90
selection. See natural selection
self-copying molecules, 179
self-fertilization, 86–87
self-pollination, 228
self-replicating systems, 179
semen, 139
semiconservative replication, 112
seminiferous tubules, 139
senescence, 153
separation, 66, 78
Sertoli cells, 139
sessile, 234
sex chromosomes, 98–100
sex determination, 99–100
sex-linked traits, 98–99
sexual characteristics
    female reproductive system,
        141–145
    hormonal similarities between
        male and female, 144
    male reproductive system,
        139–141
    primary and secondary,
        138–139
sexual fusion, 214
sexual reproduction, 74-75. See
    also reproduction
    defined, 8, 74
    germ cells and somatic cells,
        75–76
    mating and fertilization, 138
    in plants, 218, 221
    sexual characteristics,
        138–144
shared, derived traits, 188
sheep on Tasmania, 268
sickle-cell anemia, 93–94
silverswords, 175, 187, 189, 193
simple carbohydrates, 27
single-gene mutations, 127–129,
    166
siphons, 242
sister chromatids, 66–67, 78
skin cancer (basal cell carcinoma),
    63, 67, 72–74
slime molds, 202
smooth ER, 38–39
social insects, 245

soft-bodied animals, 183
solutes, 25
solvents, 25
somatic cells, 76
somites, 147
sonic hedgehog, 73, 74
special creation, 162
speciation, 165, 170–172
species
    in binomial nomenclature, 186
    defined, 10, 170, 186
    formation of, 165, 170–172
species richness, 277–279
sperm
    in cell theory, 32
    defined, 75
    delivery of, 139
    in fertilization, 144–145
    production of, 139
    size and structure of, 144
sperm count, 140–141
spermatogenic cells, 139
spicules, 236
spiders, 244
spina bifida, 148
spinal chords, 246, 248
spindle fibers, 67, 69
spinnerets, 244
spirilla, 198
spirochetes, 200
sponges, 234–236
spores, 213, 216
sporophytes, 218, 219–220, 225
SRY (sex-determined region, Y
    chromosome), 100
S-shaped curve, 268
stability of communities, 278
stabilizing selection, 169 .
stamen, 226
Staphylococcus, 155, 163, 168
starch, 27
start codons, 125, 127
stem cells, 72–73
steppes, 293
stereoscopic vision, 257
steroids, 29
sticky ends, 133, 135
stigma, 202
stinging capsules, 237
stipes, 206
stomata, 223
strand separation, 111, 119
stream ecosystems, 296
Strepsirhini, 255
stroma, 58
Sturtevant, Alfred, 101
subcutaneous layer, 64
substrates, 48
succession, 277
sugar gliders, 163
surface-to-volume ratio, 31

survivorship curves, 265–266
sustainability, 298–299
symbionts, 198
symbiosis, 214–215
sympatric speciation, 170
synthetic theory of evolution, 166

T

tails, 248
tarsiers, 256
taxol, 71
taxonomy
    binomial nomenclature, 10, 186
    categories of, 186
    cladistics, 188
    criteria for classification, 187
    evolution and, 9–11
    importance of, 193
    molecular phylogenies, 188
    tree of life, 188–189
teeth, 258
teleosts, 251
telophase, 69
temperate forests, 294
temperate grasslands, 293
Tenover, Fred, 155
termination, 125
tertiary consumers, 283
testes, 75, 139
testosterone, 139, 141
thecodonts, 253
theories, 16
therapsids, 253
thermophiles, 200
thermotoga, 200
thorax, 243
thumbs, opposable, 257
thylakoids, 58
thymine (T), 107. *See also* DNA
    (deoxyribonucleic acid)
tide pools, 296
tissues

defined, 7
    layers, development of, 233,
        236–237, 240
    origin of, 232–233
toolmaking, 258, 259
torsion, 242
trade winds, 290
transcription, 118–121
transduction, 199
transfer RNA (tRNA), 122–123
transformation
    bacterial, 104–105
    in cloning, 134
    defined, 105
    in prokaryotes, 199
transgenic animals, 135
transition communities, 277
transition state, 47–48
translation
    defined, 118
    gene mutations, 127–129
    genetic code and, 125–127
    protein synthesis, 124–125
    types of RNA, 121–124
transmission electron microscope
    (TEM), AppB
transpiration, 287
tree of life, 189–190. *See also*
    taxonomy
trichocysts, 205
tRNA (transfer RNA), 122–123
trochophore, 239
trophic levels, 282–283
tropical dry forests, 292
tropical rain forests, 291–292
true slime mold, 202
true stems, 224
trypanosomes, 202
tundra, 295
tunicates, 248–249
Turner syndrome, 100
twins, identical, 9

U

Ulva, 218
uniformity of nature, 14
unity of life, 11, 114
upright posture, 257
urethra, 139
Urochordata, 248–249
uterus, 142, 143–144

V

vacuoles, 40
vagina, 142–143
vas deferens, 139
vascular plants, 221–224
vascular system, 220
vasectomy, 139
vectors, 133
veldt, 293
vertebral column, 246, 250
Vertebrata (vertebrates), 249
    amphibians, 251–252
    birds, 253–254
    defined, 246, 248
    fishes, 249–251
    mammals, 254–255
    reptiles, 252–253
vestigial organs, 160
Viagra, 140
vibrios, 198
Viking mission, 7
villi, 150
viroids, 201
viruses, 31–32, 200–201. *See
    also* HIV (human immune
    deficiency virus)
visceral mass, 241
vision in primates, 257

W

walking, 251, 257
Wallace, Alfred Russell, 12,
    156–158, 162

warning coloration, 276
water
    aquatic ecosystems, 295–297
    on Mars, 7
    metabolism and, 7
    physical and chemical
        properties of, 23–26,
        295–296, AppA
water currents, 290
water cycle, 287
water molds, 206
water vascular system, 245
water-soluble molecules, 35
Watson, James D., 107–108, 124
waxes, 29
wear-and-tear hypotheses, 153
weather, 289
white blood cells, 37–38
witch flounder, 275

X

X chromosome inactivation, 100
X chromosomes, 98–100
X-linked genes, 98–99
x-ray diffraction, 107

Y

Y chromosomes, 98–100
yeasts, 211
yellowtail flounder, 264–265, 275
Y-linked genes, 100

Z

zero population growth, 265
zoologists, 233
zoology, 239
zygotes, 75, 145

" Overall, I enjoy the textbook and feel that **you have made it as easy as possible to succeed in this course by providing numerous study aids online.** "

– Ben Larkins, Student at Middle Tennessee State University

GET ONLINE

HE DID

Discover your **LIFE** online experience at **4ltrpress.cengage.com/life**.

You'll find everything you need to succeed in your class.

- Interactive Quizzes
- Printable and Online Flash Cards
- Animations
- Visual Reviews
- And more

4ltrpress.cengage.com/life

Chapter in Review

2

AIDS (acquired immune deficiency syndrome)
a partial or total loss of immune function based on infection by the human immune deficiency virus (HIV)

HIV (human immune deficiency virus)
the causative agent in acquired immune deficiency syndrome (AIDS)

element
a pure substance that cannot be broken down into simpler substances by chemical means

atom
(Gr. *atomos*, indivisible) the smallest particle into which an element can be broken down and still retain the properties of that element

molecule
a cluster of two or more atoms held together by specific chemical bonds

proton
a positively charged subatomic particle found in the nucleus of an atom

neutron
(L. *neuter*, either) a subatomic particle without any electrical charge found in the nucleus of an atom

electron
a negatively charged subatomic particle that orbits the nucleus of an atom; the negative charge of an electron is equal in magnitude to the proton's positive charge, but the electron has a much smaller mass

atomic nucleus
the central core of an atom, containing protons and neutrons

energy shells
energy levels occupied by electrons in orbit around an atomic nucleus; each shell can contain a maximum number of electrons, for example, two electrons for the first shell, eight for the second

isotopes
an alternative form of an element having the same atomic number but a different atomic mass due to the different number of neutrons present in the nucleus

half-life
the length of time it takes for half of the total amount of radioactivity in an isotope to decay; as a result of such decay, for example, the concentration of carbon-14 relative to carbon-12 decreases; half of the carbon-14 will decay in 5,730 years; this is the half-life

ion
an atom that has gained or lost one or more electrons, thereby attaining a positive or negative electrical charge

chemical bond
an attractive force that keeps atoms together in a molecule

covalent bond
(L. *co*, together + *volere*, sharing) a form of molecular bonding characterized by the sharing of a pair of electrons between atoms

nonpolar
having a symmetrical distribution of electrical charge; i.e., a nonpolar molecule like most lipids will not dissolve readily in water

Introduction Just momentary contact with the human immune deficiency virus (HIV) and a human can contract acquired immune deficiency syndrome, or AIDS. Reviewing HIV serves as a good introduction to the molecules of life, to the structure of the cell, and to the differences between living cells and nonliving virus particles.

LO1 **What Is HIV?** HIV is a nonliving particle that infects human cells. It is made up of the same groups of biological molecules in all living things: carbohydrates, lipids, proteins, and nucleic acids, but it lacks metabolism and responsiveness, and it cannot reproduce independently. HIV has an inner sphere of protein, the matrix, and within the matrix, a capsid containing enzymes.

LO2 **What Are Atoms?** Pure substances that can't be broken down further into different chemical constituents are elements, 89 of which occur in nature. The elements hydrogen, oxygen, and carbon make up 98 percent of most animal and plant bodies. Elements are composed of identical particles or atoms, whereas molecules are combinations of two or more atoms. Atomic structure and the unique number of particles in the atoms of each element give atoms their physical and chemical properties and in turn give elements their characteristics. Isotopes of the same element are atoms with the same number of protons but different numbers of neutrons. Carbon-dating is based on isotopes of carbon. In ions, electron numbers vary, so the whole atom has a positive or negative charge. The strengths of acids are based on the levels of hydrogen ions.

Figure 2.1
Models of an Atom

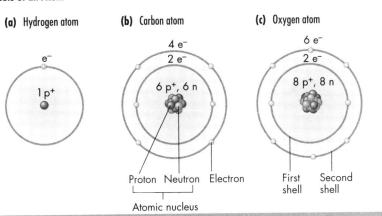

(a) Hydrogen atom **(b)** Carbon atom **(c)** Oxygen atom

e⁻

$1 p^+$

$4 e^-$
$2 e^-$
$6 p^+, 6 n$

$6 e^-$
$2 e^-$
$8 p^+, 8 n$

Proton Neutron Electron
Atomic nucleus

First shell Second shell

LO3 **How Do Atoms Form Molecules?** The atoms in molecules are linked by chemical bonds. Atoms share electron pairs in covalent bonds. When a molecule has an equal sharing of charge at both ends, it's called *nonpolar;* when the sharing is unequal, as in the water molecule, it's called *polar.* Polar molecules can form hydrogen bonds, such as occur in the ice lattice. Salt (NaCl) has ionic bonds, or the attraction between oppositely charged ions. This follows the transfer of electrons between atoms rather than the sharing of electrons.

LO4 **What Makes Water Special for Life?** Water's tendency to form hydrogen bonds allows the molecules to stick to each other, to soil, to glass, and to other substances and explains how water can "climb" inside plants. Water tends to "break down" into H and OH ions, and this contributes to forming an acid or a base, which are measured on the pH scale.

LO5 **What Are Biological Molecules?** The human body is 18 percent carbon by weight; a tree, 50 percent carbon. Carbon can form covalent bonds with up to four

polar
having an asymmetrical distribution of electrical charge; i.e., a polar molecule like glucose will dissolve readily in water

hydrogen bond
a type of weak molecular bond in which a partially negatively charged atom (oxygen or nitrogen) bonds with the partial positive charge on a hydrogen atom when the hydrogen atom is already participating in a covalent bond

ionic bond
a type of molecular bond formed between ions of opposite charge

solvent
a substance capable of dissolving other molecules

solute
a substance that has been dissolved in a solvent

hydrophilic
compounds that dissolve readily in water, such as salt

hydrophobic
compounds that do not dissolve readily in water, such as oil

acid
a proton donor; any substance that gives off hydrogen ions when dissolved in water, causing an increase in the concentration of hydrogen ions; acidity is measured on a pH scale, with acids having a pH less than 7; the opposite of a base

base
any substance that accepts hydrogen ions when dissolved in water; basic solutions have a pH greater than 7

pH scale
a logarithmic scale that measures hydrogen ion concentration; acids range from pH 1 to 7, water is neutral at a pH of 7, and bases range from pH 7 to 14

buffer
a substance that resists changes in pH when acids or bases are added to a chemical solution

biological molecules
molecules derived from living systems; the four major types are carbohydrates, lipids, proteins, and nucleic acids

organic
molecules that are based on carbon and contain hydrogen

inorganic
molecules that are not based on carbon

functional group
a group of atoms that confers specific behavior to the (usually larger) molecules to which they are attached

monosaccharide
a simple sugar that cannot be decomposed into smaller sugar molecules; the most common forms are the hexoses, six-carbon sugars such as glucose, and the pentoses, five-carbon sugars such as ribose

disaccharide
a type of carbohydrate composed of two linked simple sugars

polysaccharide
a carbohydrate made up of many simple sugars linked together; glycogen and cellulose are examples of polysaccharides

For further review, exercises, practice quizzes, and more, log into the LIFE Web site at 4ltrpress.cengage.com/life.

atoms, and can form chains and rings. Carbon-containing or organic molecules often contain functional groups that lend special properties to the molecules and help explain why the large biological molecules form and act as they do.

Figure 2.7

The Overall Shape of a Protein and Amino Acids

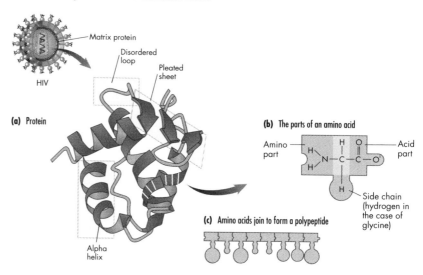

(a) Protein

(b) The parts of an amino acid

(c) Amino acids join to form a polypeptide

LO6 **Living Cells versus Nonliving HIV** Robert Hooke first saw a cell more than 300 years ago. Cells contain organelles that carry out specialized functions. The small size of cells insures a beneficial surface-to-volume ratio and adequate speed of import and export. The 18th-century cell theory set out the basic roles and properties of cells. Eukaryotic cells contain DNA in a distinct nucleus, whereas prokaryotic cells have DNA loose in one region of the cell.

Figure 2.9

Prokaryotic Cells and Eukaryotic Cells Compared

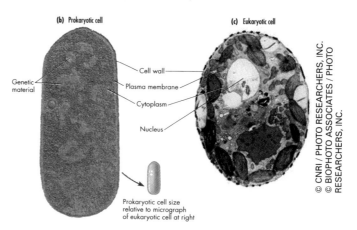

(b) Prokaryotic cell

(c) Eukaryotic cell

© CNRI / PHOTO RESEARCHERS, INC.
© BIOPHOTO ASSOCIATES / PHOTO RESEARCHERS, INC.

LO7 **Cell Parts and HIV Sabotage** The flexible outer plasma membrane acts as a boundary separating the cell's contents from the surrounding environment. This membrane is often studded with proteins and carbohydrates and HIV uses these to enter the cell. Cells are selectively permeable, allowing nutrients, wastes, and viruses to pass through by diffusion and/or osmosis, but barring most other substances.

The nucleus is roughly spherical and contains genetic information. It is bounded by a nuclear envelope perforated by nuclear pores, through which molecules can pass. DNA is packed into microscopic structures called *chromosomes*. Information flows from DNA to RNA to protein. Nucleoli in the nucleus form one type of RNA. The cytoplasm is a semifluid ground substance acting as a pool of raw materials and containing a number of organelles.

Chapter in Review

2

starch
a polysaccharide composed of long chains of glucose subunits; the principal energy source of plants

glycogen
a polysaccharide made up of branched chains of glucose; an energy-storing molecule in animals, found mainly in the liver and muscles

cellulose
(L. *cellula,* little cell) the chief constituent of the cell wall in green plants, some algae, and a few other organisms; cellulose is an insoluble polysaccharide composed of straight chains of glucose molecules

chitin
a complex nitrogen-containing polysaccharide that forms the cell walls of certain fungi, the major component of the exoskeleton of insects and some other arthropods, and the cuticle of some other invertebrates

alpha-helix
one possible shape of amino acids in a protein that resembles a spiral staircase

pleated sheet
secondary protein structure in which hydrogen bonds link two parts of a protein into a shape like a corrugated sheet

disordered loop
regions of a less specific but constant shape that link other parts of a protein

amino acid
a molecule consisting of an amino group (NH_2) and an acid group (COOH); the 20 amino acids are the basic building blocks of proteins

peptide bond
a bond joining two amino acids in a protein

polypeptide
(Gr. *polys,* many + *peptin,* to digest) amino acids joined together by peptide bonds into long chains; a protein consists of one or more polypeptides

fat
an energy storage molecule that contains a glycerol bonded to three fatty acids; fats in the liquid state are known as oils

wax
a sticky, solid, waterproof lipid that forms the comb of bees and waterproofing of plant leaves

steroid
(Gr. *stereos,* solid + L. *oi,* having the form of + *oleum,* oil) a major class of lipids based on a 4-carbon-atom ring system and often a hydrocarbon tail; cholesterol and sex hormones are steroids

nucleic acid
a polymer of nucleotides, e.g., DNA and RNA

RNA (ribonucleic acid)
a nucleic acid similar to DNA except that it is generally single-stranded and contains the sugar ribose and the base uracil replaces thymine

Figure 2.10

Generalized Animal and Plant Cells

(a) Animal cell

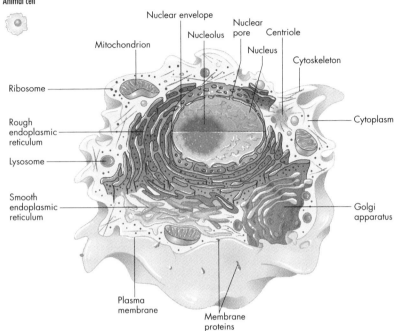

(b) Plant cell

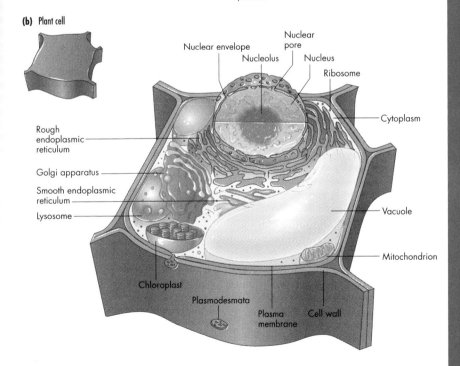

LO8 The HIV Infective Cycle HIV works its way into the cell through a receptor and helper; its viral RNA is copied into DNA; this DNA enters the nucleus and integrates into the cell's own chromosomes; the cell starts making viral proteins; these are

DNA (deoxyribonucleic acid)
the twisting, ladderlike molecule that stores genetic information in cells and transmits it during reproduction; DNA consists of two very long strands of alternating sugar and phosphate groups that form a double helix; each "rung" of the ladder is a base (either adenine, guanine, cytosine, or thymine) that extends from the sugar and bonds with a base from the other strand; genes are made of DNA

reverse transcriptase
the enzyme that facilitates "reverse" transcription of RNA to DNA

cell theory
the biological doctrine stating that all living things are composed of cells; cells are the basic living units within organisms; the chemical reactions of life occur within cells, and all cells arise from pre-existing cells

eukaryotic cell
a cell whose DNA is enclosed in a nucleus and associated with proteins; contains membrane-bound organelles

prokaryotic cell
a cell in which the DNA is loose in the cell; eubacterial and archaebacterial cells are prokaryotic; prokaryotic cells generally have no internal membranous organelles and evolved earlier than eukaryotic cells

prokaryote
an organism made up of a prokaryotic cell

eukaryote
an organism made up of one or more eukaryotic cells

diffusion
(L. *diffundere,* to pour out) the tendency of a substance to move from an area of high concentration to an area of low concentration

facilitated diffusion
a type of transport in which a protein helps a substance pass across a cell membrane down its concentration gradient without energy expenditure by the cell

active transport
movement of substances against a concentration gradient requiring the expenditure of energy by the cell

phagocytosis
the type of endocytosis through which a cell takes in food particles

phagocyte
a specialized scavenger cell that devours debris

endocytosis
the process by which a cell membrane invaginates and forms a pocket around a cluster of molecules; this pocket pinches off and forms a vesicle that transports the molecules into the cell

exocytosis
the process by which substances are moved out of a cell by cytoplasmic vesicles that merge with the plasma membrane

nucleus
the membrane-enclosed region of a eukaryotic cell that contains the cell's DNA

ribosome
a structure in the cell that provides a site for protein synthesis; ribosomes may lie freely in the cell or attach to the membranes of the endoplasmic reticulum

For further review, exercises, practice quizzes, and more, log into the LIFE Web site at 4ltrpress.cengage.com/life.

transported to the cell surface as new viral particles; they bulge out and bud off from the cell membrane; and the particles finally move toward new cells to infect.

Figure 2.15
The Infective Cycle of HIV

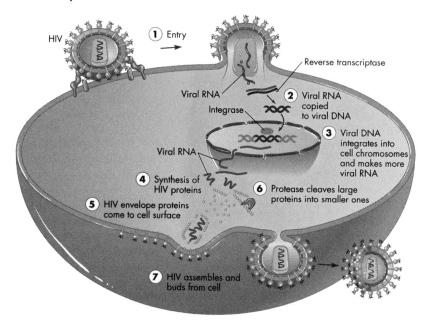

endoplasmic reticulum (ER)
a system of membranous tubes, channels, and sacs that forms compartments within the cytoplasm of eukaryotic cells; functions in lipid synthesis and in the manufacture of proteins destined for secretion from the cell

Golgi apparatus
in eukaryotic cells, a collection of flat sacs that process proteins for export from the cell or for shunting to different parts of the cell

smooth ER
the part of the endoplasmic reticulum folded into smooth sheets and tubules, containing no ribosomes; synthesizes lipids and detoxifies poisons

lysosome
spherical membrane-bound vesicles within the cell containing digestive (hydrolytic) enzymes that are released when the lysosome is ruptured; important in recycling worn-out mitochondria and other cell debris

cytoskeleton
found in the cells of eukaryotes, an internal framework of microtubules, microfilaments, and intermediate filaments that supports and moves the cell and its organelles

centriole
pairs of short, rod-shaped organelles that organize the cytoskeletal fibers called *microtubules* into scaffolds; these intracellular frameworks help maintain cell shape and move chromosomes during cell division

mitochondrion (pl. mitochondria)
organelle in eukaryotic cells that provides energy that fuels the cell's activities; mitochondria are the sites of oxidative respiration; almost all of the ATP of nonphotosynthetic eukaryotic cells is produced in the mitochondria

flagellum (pl. flagella)
long whiplike organelle protruding from the surface of the cell that either propels the cell, acting as a locomotory device, or moves fluids past the cell, becoming a feeding apparatus

extracellular matrix
a meshwork of secreted molecules that act as a scaffold and a glue that anchors cells within multicellular organisms

plastid
an organelle found in plants and some protozoa that harvests solar energy and produces or stores carbohydrates or pigments

vacuole
large fluid-filled sac inside cells surrounded by a single membrane; in plant cells, it is important for maintaining cell shape

cell wall
a fairly rigid structure that encloses some protists, and all prokaryotic, fungal, and plant cells

plasmodesmata
specialized junctions between plant cells that facilitate cell-to-cell communication

Chapter in Review

energetics
the study of energy intake, processing, and expenditure

photosynthesis
the metabolic process in which solar energy is trapped and converted to chemical energy (ATP), which in turn is used in the manufacture of sugars from carbon dioxide and water

cellular respiration
the harvest of energy from sugar molecules in the presence of oxygen

energy
the power to perform chemical, mechanical, electrical, or heat-related work

potential energy
energy that is stored and available to do work

kinetic energy
the energy possessed by a moving object

heat
the random motion of atoms and molecules

entropy
a measure of disorder or randomness in a system

chemical reaction
the making or breaking of chemical bonds between atoms or molecules

reactant
the starting substance in a chemical reaction

product
a substance that results from a chemical reaction

energy-releasing reactions
reactions that proceed spontaneously or need a starting "push" but eventually release energy

energy-absorbing reactions
reactions that will not proceed spontaneously and do not give off heat

metabolic pathway
the chain of enzyme-catalyzed chemical reactions that converts energy and constructs needed biological molecules in cells and in which the product of one reaction serves as the starting substance for the next

ATP (adenosine triphosphate)
a molecule consisting of adenine, ribose sugar, and three phosphate groups; ATP can transfer energy from one molecule to another; ATP hydrolyzes to form ADP, releasing energy in the process

ADP (adenosine diphosphate)
an energy molecule related to ATP but having only two phosphate groups instead of three

AMP (adenosine monophosphate)
an energy molecule related to ATP but having only one phosphate group instead of two (ADP) or three (ATP)

enzyme
a protein that facilitates chemical reactions by lowering the required activation energy but is not itself permanently altered in the process; also called a *biological catalyst*

catalyst
a substance that speeds up the rate of a chemical reaction by lowering the activation energy without itself being permanently changed or used up during the reaction

Introduction For their size and weight, hummingbirds have the highest rate of energy use among animals with backbones. Studying them and the flowers they feed on helps us understand energetics: universal energy principles; how energy is transferred in the cell; and pathways for energy harvest and storage in living organisms.

LO¹ Universal Energy Laws and Cellular Energy Energy flowing from the sun is trapped via photosynthesis in the chemical bonds of sugar molecules. A hummingbird sips sugar concentrated in flower nectar, and the bird's cells break down the sugar molecules in the presence of oxygen, releasing stored chemical energy; this process is called *cellular respiration*. Energy transformations in cells are inefficient, and energy is lost as heat with every step; thus it takes many pounds of sugary nectar to make and maintain a few ounces of hummingbird tissue. Throughout the universe, energy can be transformed from one state to another, but the conversion is always inefficient and heat is produced.

LO² Energy Flow in Living Things In chemical reactions, chemical bonds break and reform and atoms become rearranged into new molecules. The starting substances are reactants; the new substances are products. Some reactions release energy and are spontaneous; some won't proceed unless they absorb additional energy. The power for energy-absorbing reactions in the cell comes from energy-releasing reactions, and these two kinds are linked in chains of reactions called *metabolic pathways.* ATP is the most common energy-carrying molecule in the cell. ADP and AMP are forms that carry less energy. Enzymes are proteins that function as biological catalysts; they facilitate and speed chemical reactions in the cell. Enzymes bring molecules together with enough energy to reach the transition state and cross the energy barrier called the *activation energy.* Enzymes have a deep groove or pocket, the active site where chemical reactants or substrates fit, forming an enzyme-substrate complex. Together, all the enzyme-catalyzed reactions and other reactions in the cell constitute metabolism.

LO³ Energy Harvest Metabolic pathways in the cell break down nutrient molecules and make energy available for sustaining life. When oxygen is present, energy is harvested through an aerobic pathway (also called *cellular respiration*), which begins with the breakdown of glucose or glycolysis and continues with the Krebs cycle. During this reaction series, six-carbon glucose molecules are dismantled, CO_2 is released, some energy is stored in ATP, and some in the electron carriers. During the final phase, the electron transport chain, electrons captured during the Krebs cycle are joined with oxygen and water by moving down a chain of enzymes and pigment molecules located in the mitochondrion's inner membrane or cristae. A large number of ATP molecules form and move into a compartment of the mitochondrial matrix, enclosed by the mitochondrion's inner membrane.

When oxygen is absent, energy is harvested through an anaerobic pathway that begins with glycolysis and ends with fermentation. Energy metabolism is controlled by processes such as feedback inhibition. The accumulation of ATP, for example, can build up, and this feeds back and inhibits further production.

Figure 3.4
An Overview of Energy Harvest

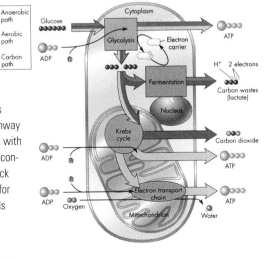

LO⁴ Energy for Exercise During exercise, the muscles get quick energy through the immediate energy system, longer-

transition state
in a chemical reaction, the intermediate springlike state between reactant and product

activation energy
the minimum amount of energy that molecules must have in order to undergo a chemical reaction

active site
a groove or a pocket on an enzyme's surface to which reactants bind; this binding lowers the activation energy required for a particular chemical reaction; thus, the enzyme speeds the reaction

substrate
a reactant in an enzyme-catalyzed reaction; fits into the active site of an enzyme

enzyme-substrate complex
in an enzymatic reaction, the unit formed by the binding of the substrate to the active site on the enzyme

metabolism
(Gr. *metabole,* to change) the sum of all the chemical reactions that take place within the body; includes photosynthesis, respiration, digestion, and the synthesis of organic molecules

aerobic pathway
energy harvest in the presence of oxygen; also called *cellular respiration*

anaerobic pathway
the series of metabolic reactions that results in energy harvest in the absence of oxygen

glycolysis
the initial splitting of a glucose molecule into two molecules of pyruvate, resulting in the release of energy in the form of two ATP molecules; the series of reactions does not require the presence of oxygen to occur

Krebs cycle
the second stage of aerobic respiration, in which a two-carbon fragment is completely broken down into carbon dioxide and large amounts of energy are transferred to electron carriers; occurs in the mitochondrial matrix

electron transport chain
the third stage in aerobic respiration, in which electrons are passed down a series of molecules, gradually releasing energy that is harvested in the form of ATP

fermentation
extraction of energy from carbohydrates in the absence of oxygen, generally producing lactic acid or ethanol and CO_2 as byproducts

electron carriers
molecules that transfer electrons from one chemical reaction to another

crista (pl. cristae)
a fold or folds formed by the inner membrane of a mitochondrion

matrix
in HIV and many other viruses, a sphere of protein inside the envelope and outside the capsid; in a mitochondrion, the area enclosed by the inner membrane

feedback inhibition
the buildup of a metabolic product that in turn inhibits the activity of an enzyme; since this enzyme is involved in making the original product, the accumulation of the product turns off its own production

term energy through the glycolytic energy system, and energy for sustained activity through the oxidative energy system.

LO5 Plants Trap and Convert Light Energy to Sugars Heterotrophs must take in preformed nutrient molecules, while autotrophs can make their own nutrient molecules through photosynthesis or, in a few cases, other chemical processes. Photosynthesis begins after photons of light leave the sun and reach Earth's surface. The green pigments called *chlorophyll* and yellow/red/orange pigments called *carotenoids* absorb different parts of the color spectrum of light. Plants have green organelles called *chloroplasts,* which contain chlorophyll in the membranes of thylakoids surrounded by the stroma, a space filled with a watery solution. The light-dependent or energy-trapping reactions as well as the carbon-fixing reactions (also called the *Calvin-Benson cycle* or *light-independent reactions*) of photosynthesis both take place in chloroplasts.

Figure 3.10
The Reactions of Photosynthesis

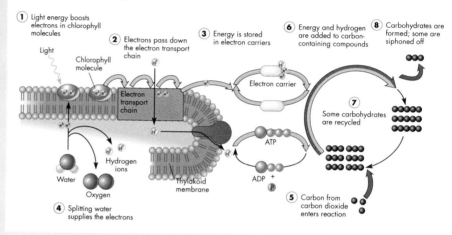

① Light energy boosts electrons in chlorophyll molecules

② Electrons pass down the electron transport chain

③ Energy is stored in electron carriers

④ Splitting water supplies the electrons

⑤ Carbon from carbon dioxide enters reaction

⑥ Energy and hydrogen are added to carbon-containing compounds

⑦ Some carbohydrates are recycled

⑧ Carbohydrates are formed; some are siphoned off

Light
Chlorophyll molecule
Electron transport chain
Electron carrier
ATP
ADP + P
Water
Hydrogen ions
Oxygen
Thylakoid membrane

immediate energy system
energy in the body instantly available for a brief explosive action, such as one heave by a shot-putter

glycolytic energy system
energy system based on the splitting of glucose by glycolysis in the muscles; the glycolytic system can sustain heavy exercise for a few minutes, as in a 200-m swim

oxidative energy system
the longest-sustaining energy system of the body that relies on the Krebs cycle and electron transport chain in mitochondria and its ability to use fats as fuel; typically fuels aerobic activity

heterotroph
(Gr. *heteros,* different + *trophos,* feeder) an organism, such as an animal, fungus, and most prokaryotes and protists, that takes in preformed nutrients from external sources

autotroph
(Gr. *auto,* self + *trophos,* feeder) an organism, such as a plant, that can manufacture its own food

electromagnetic spectrum
the full range of electromagnetic radiation in the universe, from highly energetic gamma rays to very low-energy radio waves

photons
a vibrating particle of light radiation that contains a specific quantity of energy

absorption spectrum
the wavelengths of light absorbed by a pigment

chlorophyll
(Gr. *chloros,* green + *phyllon,* leaf) light-trapping pigment molecules that act as electron donors during photosynthesis

carotenoids
plant pigments that absorb green, blue, and violet wavelengths and reflect red, yellow, and orange light

chloroplast
an organelle present in algae and plant cells that contains chlorophyll and is involved in photosynthesis

stroma
in chloroplasts, the space between the inner membrane and the thylakoid membranes

thylakoid
(Gr. *thylakos,* sac + *oides,* like) a stack of flattened membranous disks containing chlorophyll and found in the chloroplasts of eukaryotic cells

light-dependent reactions
(also known as *energy-trapping reactions*) the first phase of photosynthesis, driven by light energy; electrons that trap the sun's energy pass the energy to high-energy carriers such as ATP, where it is stored in chemical bonds

carbon-fixing reactions
(also known as *light-independent reactions* or the *Calvin-Benson cycle*) the second stage of photosynthesis in which the energy trapped and converted during the light-dependent reactions is used to combine carbon molecules into sugars

For further review, exercises, practice quizzes, and more, log into the LIFE Web site at 4ltrpress.cengage.com/life

Chapter in Review

cell cycle
the events that take place within the cell between one cell division and the next

epidermis
the outer layer of cells of an organism

dermis
the skin layer just below the epidermis or outer layer; the dermis contains tiny blood vessels, sweat glands, hair roots, and nerve endings

subcutaneous
literally below the skin; often refers to fat (adipose) cells that bind the skin to underlying organs found below the dermis layer

basal layer
the deepest layer of the epidermis, the outer layer of the skin; the basal layer contains cells that divide and replace dead skin cells; also called *germ layer*

basal cells
cells that lie in a layer just below the epidermis

division phase
during the cell cycle, the partitioning of the cells' internal organelles, and the dividing of the cell in two

interphase
the period between cell divisions in a cell; during this period, the cell conducts its normal activities and DNA replication takes place in preparation for the next cell division; interphase is divided into three periods: G_1, S, and G_2

chromosome
a self-duplicating body in the cell nucleus made up of DNA and proteins and containing genetic information; a human cell contains 23 pairs of chromosomes; in a prokaryote, the DNA circle that contains the cell's genetic information

chromatid
a daughter strand of a duplicated chromosome; duplication of a chromosome gives rise to two chromatids joined together at the centromere

replication
the copying of one DNA molecule into two identical DNA molecules

alignment
the positioning of chromosomes on the mitotic or meiotic spindle

separation
the movement of chromatids or chromosomes away from each other toward opposite poles of the dividing cell during mitosis or meiosis

sister chromatids
the two rods of a replicated chromosome

centromere
the point on the chromosome where the spindle attaches and also where the two chromatids are joined

kinetochore
a group of proteins located at the centromere that attaches to long fibers called *spindle fibers*

spindle fibers
the cytoskeletal rods (microtubules) that move chromosomes toward the cell poles and that cause cell poles to separate during cell division

Introduction An understanding of cancer and effective new treatments will require a good understanding of the growth and division cycles or cell cycles that cells undergo, including mitosis and meiosis, how each is governed, and how aberrant controls can lead to tumor formation.

LO1 Cell Growth and Cell Division A growth of cells is called *proliferation*. The alteration of normal growth and division is called the *cell cycle*. During the division phase, cell parts are duplicated and/or partitioned in two. The growth period between two division phases is called *interphase*. Interphase has three portions: the G1 phase or active growth phase during which the cell manufactures new cell components in preparation for cell division; the S phase during which DNA is replicated and each chromosome now consists of two identical chromatids; the G2 phase, a time of protein manufacture before cell division; and the M phase or mitosis, during which the nuclear material is divided, followed by the division of cytoplasm in cytokinesis.

LO2 Mitosis and Cell Division After the nucleus divides in mitosis, the cytoplasm divides by means of cytokinesis. In animal cells, a contractile ring pinches the cell in two; in plant cells, a cell plate forms and partitions the cell in half. Some kinds of cancer chemotherapy attack the spindle of dividing cancer cells or prevent it from forming. Radiation can mutate or break the chromosomes of cancer cells.

LO3 Control of Cell Division Cells like the basal cells of skin's epidermal layer can continue to divide, thus they are stem cells. Studies of basal cell carcinomas have revealed that a mutated gene called *patched* allows the cells in basal cell tumors to go on dividing and dividing. The patched gene encodes a receptor for a signaling protein called *sonic hedgehog*. When the patched gene is mutant (defective), it can turn on cell division in basal cells, but it can't turn them off again, and the result is a basal cell carcinoma.

LO4 Meiosis: Cell Division Preceding Sexual Reproduction In meiosis I, a diploid parent cell divides, forming two haploid daughter cells. In meiosis II, those two daughters divide again, resulting in four haploid cells. In human females, only one of the four becomes

Figure 4.16
Mitosis and Meiosis Compared

(a) Mitosis

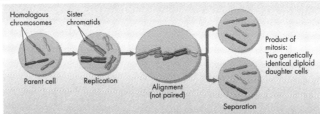

(b) Meiosis

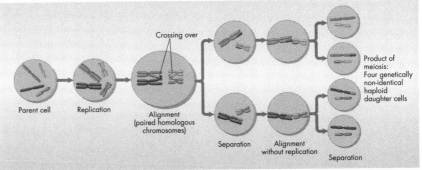

G_1 phase
the portion of the cell cycle that follows mitosis but precedes DNA synthesis

S phase
the portion of the cell cycle during which the cell synthesizes DNA

G_2 phase
the portion of the cell cycle that follows DNA synthesis but precedes mitosis

M phase
the portion of the cell cycle during which the nucleus divides by mitosis and the cytoplasm divides by cytokinesis

mitosis
the process of nuclear division in which replicated chromosomes separate and form two daughter nuclei genetically identical to each other and the parent nucleus; mitosis is usually accompanied by cytokinesis (division of the cytoplasm)

cytokinesis
the process of cytoplasmic division following nuclear division

prophase
the first phase of nuclear division in mitosis or meiosis, when the chromosomes condense, the nucleolus disperses, and the spindle forms

metaphase
the period during nuclear division (mitosis) when the spindle microtubules cause the chromosomes to line up at the center of the cell

anaphase
a period during nuclear division when the chromosomes move toward the poles of the cell

telophase
the final phase of nuclear division when the chromosomes are at opposite poles of the cell, the nuclear membrane and nucleolus reappear, and the spindle disappears

mitotic spindle
a weblike structure of microtubules that suspends and moves the chromosomes; formed during prophase in mitosis

centriole
pairs of short, rod-shaped organelles that organize the cytoskeletal fibers called *microtubules* into scaffolds; these intracellular frameworks help maintain cell shape and move chromosomes during cell division

contractile ring
the ring of cytoskeletal elements (actin filaments) that separates one cell into two during the division of the cytoplasm

cell plate
in plant cells, a partition that arises during late cell division from vesicles at the center of the cell and that eventually separates the two daughter cells

stem cells
a normal body (somatic) cell that can continue to divide, replacing cells that die during an animal's life

growth factors
proteins that can enhance the growth and proliferation of specific cell types

receptor
a protein of a specific shape that binds to a particular chemical

an egg; the other cells are polar bodies. There is a reshuffling of maternal and paternal chromosomes during meiosis called *genetic recombination* involving either crossing over or independent assortment. Genetic recombination explains the incredible genetic diversity resulting from sexual reproduction and leads to survival differences that fuel natural selection and evolution.

meiosis
the type of cell division that occurs during gamete formation; the diploid parent cell divides twice, giving rise to four cells, each of which is haploid

sexual reproduction
a type of reproduction in which new individuals arise from the mating of two parents

gamete
(Gr., wife) a specialized sex cell, such as an ovum (egg) or sperm, that is haploid; a male gamete (sperm) and a female gamete (ovum) fuse and give rise to a diploid zygote, which develops into a new individual

fertilization
the fusion of two haploid gamete nuclei (egg and sperm), which forms a diploid zygote

egg
the haploid female gamete

sperm
the haploid male gamete

gonad
an animal reproductive organ that generates gametes; testes and ovaries

ovary
egg-producing organ

testis (pl. testes)
the male reproductive organ that produces sperm and sex hormones

zygote
(Gr. *zygotos,* paired together) the diploid cell that results from the fusion of an egg and a sperm cell; a zygote may either form a line of diploid cells by a series of mitotic cell divisions or undergo meiosis and develop into haploid cells

germ cell
a sperm cell or ovum (egg cell) or their precursors; the haploid gametes produced by individuals that fuse to form a new individual

somatic cell
(Gr. *soma,* body) a cell in an animal that is not a germ cell

homologous chromosomes
chromosomes that pair up and separate during meiosis and generally have the same size, shape, and genetic information; one member of each pair of homologous chromosomes comes from the mother and the other comes from the father

diploid
a cell that contains two copies of each type of chromosome in its nucleus (except, perhaps, sex chromosomes)

haploid
having only one copy of a chromosome set; a human haploid cell has 23 chromosomes

meiosis I
the first division of meiosis, during which the number of chromosomes in a diploid cell is reduced from a diploid set of duplicated chromosomes to a haploid set of duplicated chromosomes

meiosis II
the second division of meiosis, during which a haploid cell with duplicated chromosomes divides to form two haploid cells with unduplicated chromosomes

polar bodies
haploid cells that form during meiosis in the female but do not become the egg

genetic recombination
the reshuffling of maternal and paternal chromosomes during meiosis, resulting in new genetic combinations

independent assortment
the random distribution of genes located on different chromosomes to the gametes; Mendel's second law, the principle of independent assortment

For further review, exercises, practice quizzes, and more, log into the LIFE Web site at 4ltrpress.cengage.com/life.

Chapter in Review

5

genetics
the study of genes and inheritance

hybrid
an offspring resulting from the mating between individuals of two different genetic constitutions

blending model of heredity
the idea that maternal and paternal characteristics *blend* to produce the characteristics found in the offspring; disproved by Mendelian genetics

particulate model of heredity
Mendel's idea that heredity could be governed by "particles" that retain their identity from generation to generation

self-fertilization
the ability of a plant or animal to fertilize its own eggs

cross-fertilize
to deliberately cross two organisms; in plants, to transfer pollen from one self-fertilizing flower to another

parental (P_I) generation
in Mendelian genetics, the individuals that give rise to the first filial (F_1) generation

first filial (F_I) generation
in Mendelian genetics, the first generation in the line of descent

dominant
in genetics, an allele or corresponding phenotypic trait that is expressed in the heterozygote (in other words, that shows in the hybrid)

recessive
an allele or corresponding phenotypic trait that is hidden by a dominant allele in a heterozygote

second filial (F_2) generation
in Mendelian genetics, the second generation in the line of descent

allele
one of the alternative forms of a gene

phenotype
the physical appearance of an organism controlled by its genes interacting with the environment

genotype
the genetic makeup of an individual

heterozygous
(Gr. *heteros*, different + *zygotos*, pair) having two different alleles for a specific trait

homozygous
having two identical alleles for a specific trait

heterozygote
an organism with two different alleles for a given trait

homozygote
an organism with two identical alleles for a given trait

law of segregation
Mendel's first law, or principle, states that sexually reproducing diploid organisms have two alleles for each gene, and that during the gamete formation these two alleles separate from each other so that the resulting gametes have only one allele of each gene

Introduction Cystic fibrosis is an inherited disease, based on a mutated gene that brings about sticky mucus and clogged ducts in vital organs such as the lungs and pancreas. This chapter explains inheritance patterns like those for cystic fibrosis as well as many other aspects of genetics.

LO1 Universal Principles of Heredity Gregor Mendel, working in a quiet abbey garden in the mid-1800s, worked out the basic laws of heredity. He created hybrids by crossing pea plants with various pure-breeding traits and devised a particulate model of heredity to replace the widespread belief at that time in the blending model of heredity. In these hybrid experiments, the pure-breeding plants (for example, long-stemmed pea plants versus short-stemmed pea plants) formed the parental (P_1) generation. By cross-fertilizing the two plant types, Mendel produced a first filial (F_1) generation. He called the trait that showed up in the F_1 generation *dominant* and the one that did not *recessive*. He allowed F_1 plants to self-fertilize to produce the second filial (F_2) generation, and then looked for the pattern of inheritance of the two traits.

LO2 Rules Governing Inheritance of Single Traits The phenotypic ratio of dominants to recessives in the F_2 generation was 3:1. Mendel reasoned that particulate factors influence the traits and are not blended from one generation to the next. Modern geneticists call the factors *genes*. Mendel also reasoned that the particulate factors must come in different forms, now called *alleles*. These are either dominant or recessive, and each trait is governed by two alleles. An organism's visible or measurable physical traits are its phenotype, while its genetic make-up, based on its combination of alleles, is its genotype. Heterozygous individuals, or heterozygotes, have two different alleles for a given trait (one dominant and one recessive), while homozygous individuals, or homozygotes, have identical alleles for a given trait (either two dominant or two recessive). Mendel concluded that an individual's two allele copies for each trait come from the mother and father and that these become segregated during the production of sex cells. This is Mendel's law of segregation. Punnett squares are a useful tool for diagramming crosses and following allele segregations and combinations. Genetic principles rely on the laws of chance and probability.

Table 5.1

Principles of Heredity

1. A hereditary trait is governed by a gene.

2. Genes reside on chromosomes and are specific sequences of DNA in all cells, but they are RNA in some viruses.

3. A gene for each trait can exist in two or more alternative forms called *alleles*. An individual's alleles, interacting with the environment, determine its external appearance, biochemical functioning, and behavior.

4. Most higher organisms have two copies of each gene in body cells (they are diploid). Gametes (eggs or sperm), however, have only one copy of each gene (they are haploid).

5. Homologous chromosomes are two chromosomes that are similar in size, shape, and genetic content.

6. A homozygote has two identical alleles of a gene; a heterozygote has two different alleles of a gene.

7. An individual's physical makeup (the way it looks and functions) is its phenotype; an organism's genetic makeup is its genotype.

8. In a heterozygote, generally only one of the two alleles shows in the phenotype, while the other allele is hidden. The allele that shows is the dominant allele, and the hidden allele is the recessive allele.

9. Pairs of alleles separate, or segregate, before egg and sperm formation, so each gamete has a single copy of each gene. At fertilization, sperm and egg combine randomly with respect to the *alleles* they contain, and the resulting zygote in general has two copies of all genes.

10. Genes on different chromosomes assort independently of each other into gametes.

11. Linked genes lie on the same chromosome and tend to be packaged into gametes together.

Punnett square
in genetics, a diagrammatic way of presenting the results of random fertilization from a mating

pedigree
an orderly diagram of a family's relevant genetic history

carrier
[1] in genetics, a heterozygous individual not expressing a recessive trait but capable of passing it on to her or his offspring; [2] in biochemistry, a substance, often a protein, that transports another substance

mutant
the allele that results from a mutation; also used to refer to the organism containing such a mutation

sickle-cell anemia
a genetic condition inherited as a recessive mutation in a hemoglobin gene and characterized by pains in joints and abdomen, chronic fatigue, and shortness of breath

incomplete dominance
the genetic situation in which the phenotype of the heterozygote is intermediate between the phenotypes of two homozygotes

codominance
the genetic situation in which both alleles in a heterozygous individual are fully expressed in the phenotype; this is a characteristic of human blood types

major histocompatibility complex (MHC)
a complex of proteins that are specific for each individual and are the factors that cause the body to reject transplanted tissues; their main function is to aid in communication among immune cells

parental type
an offspring having the characteristics of one of the parents

recombinant type
an offspring in which characteristics of the parents are combined in new ways

independent assortment
Mendel's second law, or principle; the random distribution of genes located on different chromosomes to the gametes

dihybrid cross
a mating between two individuals in which the investigation follows the inheritance of only two traits

9:3:3:1 ratio
the ratio of phenotypes found in the offspring of two individuals, both of whom are heterozygous for two traits whose alleles assort independently

autosome
a chromosome other than a sex chromosome

sex chromosomes
pairs of chromosomes where the members of the pair are dissimilar in different sexes and are involved in sex determination, such as the X and Y chromosomes

X chromosome
the sex chromosome found in two doses in female mammals, fruit flies, and many other species

LO3 Analyzing Human Inheritance Patterns Using pedigrees, geneticists discovered that cystic fibrosis is inherited as a recessive trait. Heterozygous individuals who pass on a disease allele but do not show its effects are called *carriers*. A trait like sickle-cell anemia shows incomplete dominance; carriers show a mild form of the disease. Human blood types are an example of codominance, in which the heterozygous individual shows both phenotypes—for example, AB blood types. Some genes have more than two alleles, including human blood types. This explains why blood types can be A, B, O, or AB. Sometimes a single mutated gene causes several different effects (several different phenotypes).

Figure 5.7

Blood Groups, Incomplete Dominance, and Multiple Alleles

(b) Family studies

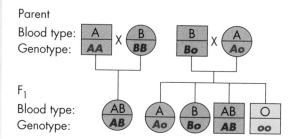

LO4 The Inheritance of Multiple Traits Offspring showing the same traits as parents are called *parental types,* while offspring with new combinations are called *recombinant types.* Diagramming crosses involving two traits or dihybrid crosses on an enlarged Punnett square produces a 9:3:3:1 ratio of phenotypes. This basic analysis works because hereditary factors segregate into gametes independently of each other; this is Mendel's principle of independent assortment.

LO5 Sex and Inheritance Males and females have several pairs of similar chromosomes or autosomes, and one pair that can have dissimilar members, the sex chromosomes, the X chromosome and Y chromosome. We inherit our mitochondrial chromosomes from our mothers. Environmental factors can influence gene expression.

LO6 Genetics and Societal Change Geneticists have learned to map individual genes to their specific locations, or loci, on chromosomes and discovered that chromosomes show genetic linkage—they carry many genes. The Human Genome Project is a modern effort to determine the nucleotide sequence of all 23 human chromosomes. Gene mapping can help researchers to isolate the genes for specific diseases.

For further review, exercises, practice quizzes, and more, log into the LIFE Web site at 4ltrpress.cengage.com/life.

Y chromosome
the sex chromosome found in a single dose in male mammals, fruit flies, and many other species

mutation
any heritable change in the base sequence of an organism's DNA

X-linked
characteristic of a heritable trait that occurs on the X chromosome

SRY
specific gene on the Y chromosome that has been isolated as the "sex-determining region" and necessary for causing male development in mammals

gene mapping
the assignment of genes to specific locations along a chromosome

locus (pl. loci)
the location of a gene on a chromosome

linkage
alleles of two genes located so close to each other on the same chromosome that they fail to assort independently

Human Genome Project
the research effort to sequence the entire set of human genes and to understand their functions

Chapter in Review

6

double helix
the term used to describe the physical structure of DNA, which resembles a ladder twisted along its long axis

transformation
the process of transferring an inherited trait by incorporating a piece of foreign DNA into a prokaryotic or eukaryotic cell

bacteriophage (or phage)
"bacteria eater"; a virus that infects bacterial cells

A, C, G, T (adenine, cytosine, guanine, thymine)
the four types of nucleotides contained in DNA; they are identical except for the bases they contain

x-ray diffraction
a process in which a beam of x-rays is passed through a crystalline material to help determine its three-dimensional structure

helix
a structure similar to a spiral staircase; DNA is a double helix

complementary base pairing
in nucleic acids, the hydrogen bonding of adenine with thymine or uracil, and guanine with cytosine; it holds two strands of DNA together and holds different parts of RNA molecules in specific shapes, and is fundamental to genetic replication, expression, and recombination

histone
protein in the nucleus around which DNA molecules of the chromosomes wind, allowing extremely long DNA molecules to be packed into a cell's nucleus

nucleosome
the basic packaging unit of eukaryotic chromosomes; a histone wrapped with two loops of DNA

chromatin
the substance of a chromosome

polymerization
the joining together of newly paired bases, creating a DNA strand identical to the original double helix strand of DNA

DNA polymerase
the enzyme that catalyzes the polymerization of DNA strands

semiconservative replication
the universal mode of DNA replication, in which only one of the two strands of DNA of the parent molecule is passed to each daughter molecule; this inherited strand serves as the template for the synthesis of the other strand of the double helix

genetic marker
any genetic difference between individuals that can be followed in a genetic cross; for example, areas of repeated base sequences along a DNA strand

Introduction Dr. Marilyn Menotti-Raymond and colleagues at the National Institutes of Health helped solve a murder case by carrying out lab procedures to positively identify the DNA in cat hair roots. The hairs were left in the lining of a jacket also bearing the murder victim's blood. The unique structure of DNA as well as repeated sequences of nucleotides that vary at different loci along the chromosomes from individual to individual allow researchers to create genetic "fingerprints."

LO1 Identifying the Hereditary Material Mendel discovered in the mid-1800s that hereditary "factors" determine an organism's physical, chemical, and functional characteristics. Biologists in the 1940s thought only protein was versatile enough to carry complex information, since there is an "alphabet" of 20 amino acids forming the millions of kinds of proteins. Researchers devised a way to test whether protein or DNA could carry information. They extracted carbohydrates, proteins, and DNA from disease-causing bacteria and added these separate extracts to nonlethal bacteria. Bacterial cells treated with carbohydrates and proteins remained nonlethal but those treated with DNA became lethal—able to cause pneumonia in mice and other mammals. Researchers called this transfer of an inherited trait (in this case, the ability to cause disease by the uptake of pure DNA) *transformation*.

LO2 DNA: The Twisted Ladder
The variability of DNA is the key to evolution by natural selection yet the stability of DNA determines an organism's resemblance to its parents. How does one molecule do both things? James Watson and Francis Crick knew several facts about DNA from other researchers' efforts. DNA is a very long, linear thread made up of a chain of nucleotides, A, T, G, and C (adenine, thymine, guanine, and cytosine). They knew A and T occur in equal proportions in DNA, and so do G and C. Finally, they had an x-ray diffraction photo from Rosalind Franklin that suggested two strands, probably in a helix. Watson and Crick built models that would fit all the available evidence and came up with the actual structure, a double helix.

Figure 6.2
Life Cycle of a Bacterial Virus

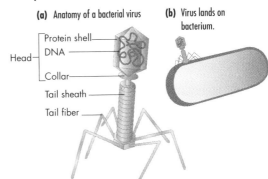

(a) Anatomy of a bacterial virus

Head — Protein shell, DNA, Collar, Tail sheath, Tail fiber

(b) Virus lands on bacterium.

(c) Virus injects its genes into the cell.

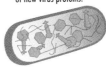

(d) Viral DNA replicates, and directs the synthesis of new virus proteins.

(e) Virus particles assemble.

(f) Cell bursts, releasing new virus particles.

(g) Protein with "hot" sulfur from virus stays outside the bacterial cell while DNA with "hot" phosphorus—and genes—enters the cell.

Protein shell labeled with radioactive sulfur

DNA labeled with radioactive phosphorus

LO3 DNA Structure Modern geneticists know that DNA has two nucleotide chains, oriented in opposite directions like the northbound and southbound lane of highway: they are antiparallel. Sugar-phosphate backbones form the uprights of the twisted ladder and A–T G–C pairs, joined by complementary base pairing, form the ladder rungs. Each chromosome is made up of one long, tightly wound DNA molecule coiled around spools of protein called *histones*. A nucleosome is one spool wrapped with two loops of DNA. Adjacent nucleosomes form coiled cords and the cords are packaged into chromatin, the substance of a chromosome. During the interphase of mitosis, the spools are unwound and diffuse. During prophase, the chromatin is compacted and the chromosomes are visible.

Figure 6.4

The Structure of Double-Stranded DNA

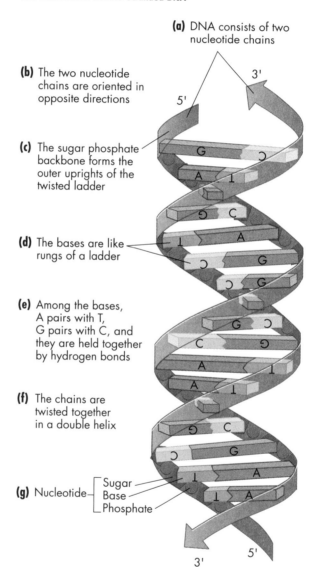

(a) DNA consists of two nucleotide chains

(b) The two nucleotide chains are oriented in opposite directions

(c) The sugar phosphate backbone forms the outer uprights of the twisted ladder

(d) The bases are like rungs of a ladder

(e) Among the bases, A pairs with T, G pairs with C, and they are held together by hydrogen bonds

(f) The chains are twisted together in a double helix

(g) Nucleotide— Sugar Base Phosphate

LO4 DNA Replication The steps of DNA replication are (1) separation, during which the double helix unwinds and enzymes break the hydrogen bonds between complementary base pairs; (2) complementary base pairing during which free-floating bases pair up and bond to the newly unattached bases; and (3) joining, during which two new double helices form. The joining or polymerization requires the enzyme DNA polymerase.

The three-step process is also known as semiconservative replication because only one of the two strands in the DNA molecule is completely new. This contributes to the amazing accuracy of DNA replication.

For further review, exercises, practice quizzes, and more, log into the LIFE Web site at 4ltrpress.cengage.com/life.

Chapter in Review

9

inheritance of acquired characteristics
the long-disproved belief that changes in an organism's appearance or function during its lifetime could be inherited

descent with modification
the notion that all organisms are descended with changes from common ancestors

natural selection
the increased survival and reproduction of individuals better adapted to the environment

fossil
traces or remains of a living thing from a previous geologic time

sedimentary rock
layer upon layer of sand and dirt accumulated over thousands or millions of years and eventually forming rock layers that sometimes entomb fossilized organisms from different eras

homologous elements
elements (such as a leg, flipper, or wing) in different species that derive from a single element in a common ancestor

vestigial organ
a rudimentary structure with no apparent utility but bearing a strong resemblance to structures in probable ancestors

biogeography
the study of the geographical location of living organisms

divergent evolution
the splitting of a population into two reproductively isolated populations with different alleles accumulating in each one; over geologic time, divergent evolution may lead to speciation

adaptive radiation
evolutionary divergence of a single ancestral group into a variety of forms adapted to different resources or habitats

convergent evolution
evolution of similar characteristics in two or more unrelated species; often found in organisms living in similar environments

phyletic gradualism
the concept that morphological changes occur gradually during evolution and are not always associated with speciation; distinct from punctuated equilibrium

punctuated equilibrium
the theory that morphological changes evolve rapidly in geologic time; in small populations, the resulting new species are distinct from the ancestral form; after speciation, species retain much the same form until extinction; distinct from phyletic gradualism

speciation
the emergence of a new species; speciation is thought to occur mainly as a result of populations becoming geographically isolated from each other and evolving in different directions

Introduction Wayne Chedwick has lost four toes to a bacterial infection that destroyed soft tissue and bone. That same infection, lodged in an ankle bone, has threatened the entire appendage. The infection is especially dangerous because the *Staphylococcus* bacteria are resistant to the common antibiotic methicillin. The emergence of antibiotic-resistant species like this one represents evolution in action.

LO¹ Emergence of Evolutionary Thought Most 19th-century scientists believed that species were created individually and remained unchanged throughout time. Jean Baptiste Lamarck suggested a variation upon this with "created" species able to change over time to better compete in their environments. Lamarck's hypothesis, the inheritance of acquired characteristics, was wrong. The notion of change over time, however, was correct. Charles Darwin and Alfred Wallace posed a third theory after observing and collecting plants and animals on extensive voyages. They both postulated descent with modification from common ancestors, by means of natural selection, during which selection pressure from the environment affects individuals and their inheritable variations. Through this, nature "selects" favorable traits or adaptations that are passed along to new generations. Evolution acts on populations. Traits that confer selective advantage increase an individual's chances of survival within a population in a given environment.

LO² Evidence for Evolution Fossils of intermediate form show points along evolutionary pathways. Homologous elements derive from a single element in a common ancestor. The forelimbs of whales, people, cheetahs, and bats are homologous and support the idea of descent with modification. Vestigial organs are evolutionary "leftovers" that are now useless but resemble an ancestor's useful structures. By comparing the base pair sequences of genes and the amino acid sequences of proteins from different species, geneticists can create molecular family trees that are remarkably similar to trees based on fossil data. Other evidence for evolution comes from biogeography, the geographic distribution of organisms.

Figure 9.3
Comparative Anatomy Supports Descent with Modification

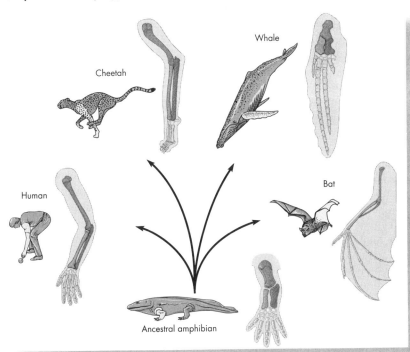

Cheetah

Whale

Human

Bat

Ancestral amphibian

synthetic theory of evolution
in the 1930s and 1940s, biologists began to combine evolutionary theory with genetics; the synthetic theory suggests that (1) gene mutations occur in reproductive cells at high enough frequencies to impact evolution; (2) gene mutations occur in random directions unrelated to the organism's survival needs in its environment; (3) natural selection acts on the genetic diversity brought about by such random mutations

neutral mutations
single-gene mutations that leave the gene's function basically intact and neither harm nor help the organism

gene duplication
one method that may lead to the evolution of new genes with new functions; this can occur when a chance error in DNA replication or recombination creates two identical copies of a gene

gene pool
the sum of all alleles carried by the members of a population; the total genetic variability present in any population

Hardy-Weinberg principle
in population genetics, the idea that in the absence of any outside forces, the frequency of each allele and the frequency of genotypes in a population will not change over generations

Hardy-Weinberg equilibrium
a proposed state wherein a population, in the absence of external pressure, has both stable allele and stable genotype frequencies over many generations

gene flow
the incorporation into a population's gene pool of genes from one or more other populations through migration of individuals

genetic drift
unpredictable changes in allele frequency occurring in a population due to the small size of that population

population bottleneck
a situation arising when only a small number of individuals of a population survive and reproduce; therefore only a small percentage of the original gene pool remains

bottleneck effect
the reduced genetic diversity that results from a drastic drop in a population's size

founder effect
in evolutionary biology, the principle that individuals founding a new colony carry only a fraction of the total gene pool present in the parent population

inbreeding
nonrandom mating that occurs when relatives mate with each other rather than with unrelated individuals

inbreeding depression
a situation of weakened genetic viability that occurs when a population has many more individuals that are less fit than in a normally breeding population

directional selection
a type of natural selection in which an extreme form of a character is favored over all other forms

LO3 Pathways of Descent Marine foraminifera are good examples of gradual evolutionary change. The squirrels living on opposite rims of the Grand Canyon were split into two populations historically and are a good example of divergent evolution. The 20 species of Hawaiian honeycreepers adapted to surviving on different foods are good examples of adaptive radiation. Flying squirrels and sugar gliders are unrelated but resemble each other closely; they are good examples of convergent evolution. The model of phyletic gradualism holds that all lines change at about the same rate over time, while the model of punctuated equilibrium holds that structural changes occur in fits and starts. The formation of a new species is called *speciation*.

LO4 Genetic Variation: Evolutionary Raw Material Traits vary between individuals of the same species because of genetic variation. Single-gene mutations or changes in the DNA sequence of a single gene can alter gene function. Some of these are neutral mutations that don't help or harm the organism, while others can be harmful or lethal mutations. Genetic recombination can shuffle existing alleles (but the frequency in the population stays the same), while mutation can change the frequency in a population's gene pool. Gene duplication can lead to new genes with new functions. Some species have very little genetic variation. Humans, for example, have only one-quarter as much genetic variation as chimpanzees.

LO5 How Is Genetic Variation Inherited? A population without perturbing influences is in Hardy-Weinberg equilibrium, with stable allele and genotype frequencies over many generations. External pressures include mutations, migrations, small populations, nonrandom mating, and natural selection.

LO6 Agents of Evolution Mutations can change allele frequencies in a population. So can gene flow, which is based on the arrival or departure of members. Genetic drift, or unpredictable changes in allele frequencies, often happens in small populations. A population bottleneck can occur when a large population is cut dramatically by disease, famine, or other factors and recovers its numbers from a few survivors—a bottleneck effect. Genetic drift can also occur when a few individuals split off from a large population and establish an isolated one, termed the founder effect. Mating is often nonrandom. Inbreeding brings about changes in allele frequency.

LO7 Natural Selection: Adaptations to Environments In artificial selection, people (for example dog breeders) choose specific traits to emphasize in new generations. This can influence an individual's evolutionary fitness.

LO8 How Do New Species Arise? In nature, every true species is reproductively isolated from every other species. Mechanisms that bring about this isolation can be behavioral, physical, chemical, or biological. In allopatric speciation, species arise when a barrier separates their ranges into distinct areas. In sympatric speciation, new species arise without geographic barriers.

stabilizing selection
a mode of natural selection that results in individuals with intermediate phenotypes; under these selection pressures, extreme forms are less successful at surviving and reproducing

disruptive selection
a type of natural selection in which two extreme and often very different phenotypes become *more* frequent in a population

reproductively isolated
every true species in nature fails to generate fertile progeny with other species; the result is reproductive isolation

reproductive isolating mechanisms
any structural, behavioral, or biochemical feature that prevents individuals of a species from successfully breeding with individuals of another species

allopatric speciation
the divergence of new species as a result of geographical separation of populations of the same original species

sympatric speciation
a situation in which a population diverges into two species after a genetic, behavioral, or ecological barrier to gene flow arises between subgroups of the population inhabiting the same region

For further review, exercises, practice quizzes, and more, log into the LIFE Web site at 4ltrpress.cengage.com/life.

Chapter in Review

14

ecology of populations and communities
the study of how groups of organisms are distributed in a particular area at a particular time and how they interact with other species coexisting in the same locale

zero population growth
in a population, the number of individuals gained is exactly equal to the number lost

survivorship curve
a plot of the data representing the proportion of a population that survives to a certain age

late-loss survivorship curve
a plot of survivorship data indicating that an organism's life expectancy decreases with each passing year

early-loss survivorship curve
a plot of survivorship data indicating that most individuals in a population die young

life expectancy
the maximum probable age an individual will reach

fertility curve
generally a graph that plots reproduction rate versus the age of female population members

biotic potential
an organism's capacity for reproduction under ideal conditions of growth and survival

J-shaped curve
a plot of population growth with an upsweeping curve that represents exponential growth

exponential growth
growth of a population without any constraints; hence, the population will grow at an ever-increasing rate

S-shaped curve
a plot of population growth with a flat section, a steeply rising section, and then a leveled off section that represents logistic growth

logistic growth
growth of a population under environmental constraints that set a maximum population size

carrying capacity
the density at which growth of a population ceases due to the limitation imposed by resources

life history strategy
the way an organism allocates energy to growth, survival, or reproduction

Agricultural Revolution
the transition of a group of people from an often nomadic hunter-gatherer way of life to a usually more settled life dependent on raising crops, such as wheat or corn, and on livestock; it was under way in the Middle East by 8000 years ago

Industrial Revolution
the replacement of hand tools with power-driven machines (like the steam engine) and the concentration of industry in factories beginning in England in the late 18th century

demographic transition
a changing pattern from a high birth rate and high death rate to a low birth rate and low death rate

Introduction In the past three decades, fishers have decimated fish populations in the formerly rich coastal waters of Massachusetts. The goal of researchers there is to use the study of ecology to determine safe limits for fish catches and thus to manage marine resources to sustain healthier populations and communities in the future.

LO1 Ecological Levels A population is a group of interacting individuals of the same species that inhabit a defined geographical area. A community consists of two or more populations of different species occupying the same geographical area. An ecosystem consists of communities of living things interacting with the physical factors of their environment. The biosphere consists of all the ecosystems of Earth, including all living species; the atmosphere, oceans, and soil; and the climate patterns, wind currents, and nutrient cycles that affect living things.

LO2 Limits to Where Species Can Live Several factors determine where a species can or can't exist: physical factors such as temperature, water, sunlight, and nutrients; interactions with other species that may block a population's survival or distribution; and geographical barriers that prevent access such as seas, deserts, and mountains.

LO3 Limits to Population Size Part of restoring decimated populations to healthy levels is understanding population density, or the number of individuals that live in a certain amount of space. Death and birth affect population size, and are reflected in a survivorship curve. Humans follow a late-loss survivorship curve. Flounders follow an early-loss survivorship curve.

Exponential growth, or explosive population increase in which birth rate exceeds death rate, results in a J-shaped curve when graphed. Limited resources impact population growth, changing J-shape growth to logistic growth, indicated by an S-shaped curve. When individuals are using all the resources available to them, they have reached the environment's carrying capacity.

Figure 14.4
The J-Shaped Curve of Population Growth

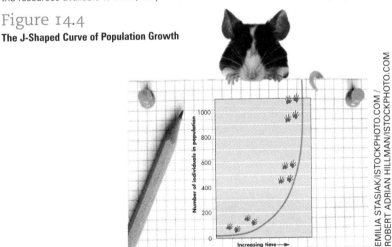

© EMILIA STASIAK/ISTOCKPHOTO.COM /
© ROBERT ADRIAN HILLMAN/ISTOCKPHOTO.COM

Figure 14.5
Sheep on Tasmania: The Growth of Real Populations Often Follows an S-Shaped Curve

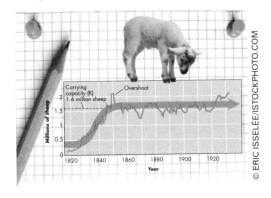

© ERIC ISSELÉE/ISTOCKPHOTO.COM

age structure
the number of individuals in each age group of a given population

habitat
the physical place within a species' range where an organism actually lives

niche
the role, function, or position of an organism in a biological community

fundamental niche
the potential range of all environmental conditions under which an organism can thrive

realized niche
the part of the fundamental niche that a species actually occupies in nature

interspecific competition
competition for resources—e.g., food or space—between individuals of different species

competitive exclusion
a situation in which one species eliminates another through competition

predator
an organism, usually an animal, that obtains its food by eating other living organisms

prey
living organisms that are food for other organisms

predation
the act of procurement and consumption of prey by predators

camouflage
body shapes, colors, or patterns that enable an organism to blend in with its environment and remain concealed from danger

chemical warfare
a defense strategy of prey species in which these organisms produce distasteful oils or other toxic substances that kill or harm predators

mimicry
the evolution of similar appearance in two or more species, which often gives one or all protection; for example, a nonpoisonous species may evolve protection from predators by its similarity to a poisonous model

parasite
a type of predator that obtains benefits at the expense of another organism, its host; a parasite is usually smaller than its host, lives in close physical association with it, and generally saps its host's strength rather than killing it outright

commensalism
a relationship between two species in which one species benefits and the other suffers no apparent harm

mutualism
a symbiotic relationship between two species in which both species benefit

succession
the process through which a regular progression of communities will regrow at a particular site

pioneer community
the species that are first to colonize a habitat after a disturbance such as fire, plowing, or logging

Figure 14.6

Overexploiting Limited Resources Can Lead to a Population Crash

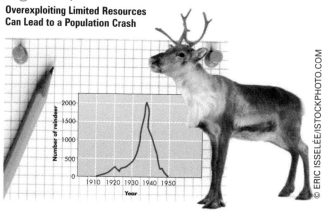

© ERIC ISSELÉE/ISTOCKPHOTO.COM

The physical environment limits population growth in several ways. Some growth-limiting factors originate outside the population—they are extrinsic; these include food supplies and weather. Some factors originate inside the population—they are intrinsic; for example, when crowded kangaroos resorb their embryos. The most important intrinsic population regulatory mechanism is competition.

LO4 The Human Population On all continents, the Agricultural Revolution and the Industrial Revolution accelerated human population growth. A population's age structure, the number of individuals in each age group, reflects its growth rate. Sweden currently has a bullet-shaped age distribution, with roughly equal numbers of people at most age levels up to old age, where there are smaller numbers. Uganda now has a pyramid-shaped age distribution, with many young people, fewer middle aged individuals, and even fewer old people.

LO5 Where Organisms Live and Thrive An organism resides in its habitat, its physical place in the environment. Its function role in the community is its niche. The potential range of all conditions under which an organism can thrive is its fundamental niche. The part of the fundamental niche that a species actually occupies in nature is its realized niche.

LO6 How Species Interact Ecologists have categorized interactions between species into four general types. In (1) competition and (2) predation, one or both of the species suffer. In (3) mutualism and (4) commensalism, neither species is harmed by the interaction.

LO7 Organization of Communities Communities change over time. The total number of species found in a community is its species richness, or species diversity. Many factors influence species richness, including latitude and isolation, resources, competition, and predation. Species richness and diversity help stabilize communities.

For further review, exercises, practice quizzes, and more, log into the LIFE Web site at 4ltrpress.cengage.com/life.

transition community
a community of organisms that establish themselves at a particular site based upon conditions produced by the activities of the pioneer community

climax community
the most stable community in a habitat and one that tends to persist in the absence of a disturbance

species richness
the total number of species in a community

Appendix A:
The Properties of Water

Water, Temperature, and Life

Anyone who has had frostbite knows that water behaves differently at different temperatures. When a person is caught in a blizzard without gloves, the liquid water in his or her fingers may may turn into ice crystals, which can tear apart cells and kill them, perhaps leading to loss of the fingers. It is fortunate for living things that water usually remains liquid in the normal temperature range found on Earth, instead of assuming one of its other physical forms—gas (water vapor) or solid (ice).

Living things are also lucky that water is slow to heat; that is, the amount of heat needed to raise the temperature of a certain volume of water is greater than for most other liquids. This property is a direct result of water's hydrogen bonds. Much of the heat energy applied to water goes into stretching or breaking hydrogen bonds instead of raising the water temperature. This helps ensure the relatively constant external and internal environments living organisms need.

A tennis player perspiring at the end of a vigorous match can appreciate another important temperature-related property of water: An unusually high amount of heat is required to turn liquid water into water vapor. Before a water molecule can evaporate, it must jostle about rapidly enough to fly off the surface of a water droplet. Before it can really jostle, the hydrogen bonds linking the molecule to its neighbors must be broken by the absorption of heat energy.

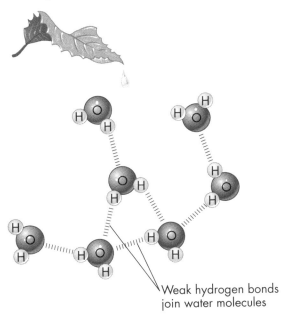

Weak hydrogen bonds join water molecules

In the process of absorbing heat, evaporating water cools its surroundings. For a wild horse escaping a predator, this property provides a natural cooling system and explains the evolution of sweat glands in horses, people, and some other mammals. Sweat pours from sweat glands in the skin and covers parts of the body surface. As the sweat evaporates, a large amount of body heat goes into breaking the hydrogen bonds in the water molecules. This cools the horse's body as sweat evaporates from the skin.

Physical Properties of Water

In addition to its properties related to temperature, water has several physical properties important to living things.

Water molecules exhibit *cohesion*, the tendency of like molecules to cling to each other, and *adhesion*, the tendency of unlike molecules to cling to each other—for example, water to paper, soil, or glass. Together, cohesion and adhesion account for *capillarity*, the tendency of a liquid substance to move upward through a narrow space against the pull of gravity, such as between the fibers of a paper towel being used to wipe up a spill, or up the inside of a narrow glass tube. Capillarity plays a part in the upward transport of water in many kinds of plants. Without the cohesion of water molecules to each other and adhesion to the walls of narrow tubes, there would be no tall trees such as redwoods or eucalypti.

One physical property of water must be overcome the moment a newborn baby draws its first breath. This property, called *surface tension*, is the tendency of molecules at the surface of liquid water to cohere to each other rather than adhere to the air molecules above them. The water molecules in a newborn's lungs tend to bind to each other and to the tissue more strongly than to air; for this reason, they tend to pull the walls of the lungs together, which could cause those delicate organs to collapse. The body, however, produces special molecules called

surfactants, which function like detergent molecules to lower the surface tension of the water in the lungs, thus preventing lung collapse. Premature babies born before their lungs are capable of generating surfactants sometimes die because their lungs collapse.

Water has yet another physical property with biological implications: the tendency of ice (solid water) to float in liquid water. The hydrogen bonds in ice are fairly rigid, creating an open latticework that holds water molecules farther apart than the more easily broken bonds of the liquid form. Thus, ice is less dense than liquid water, and floats in it. This is a unique property; other substances become more dense when they freeze. If ice did not become less dense, many lakes would freeze solid in winter, and only the top few centimeters would thaw in summer. Instead, with a frozen top layer insulating the lower depths, plants and animals can survive winter in the chilly liquid water beneath the ice.

Have you ever suffered from acid indigestion after eating too much spicy food too fast? This uncomfortable condition is caused when cells in your stomach secrete large quantities of hydrochloric acid (HCl). While the acid speeds up the digestion of food, it can also irritate your stomach lining. When hydrochloric acid dissolves in water (in your stomach or elsewhere), it releases H^+ into the solution:

$$HCl \rightarrow H^+ + Cl^-$$

As an antidote to acid indigestion, you may have taken some bicarbonate (HCO_3^-), the active ingredient in many over-the-counter heartburn remedies. Bicarbonate can act as a *buffer*, a substance that regulates pH by "soaking up" or "doling out" hydrogen ions as needed: When hydrogen ion concentrations are high, buffers bind to H^+, and when hydrogen ion concentrations are low, buffers release H^+.

When basic, or *alkaline*, substances dissociate in water, instead of giving off hydrogen ions, they combine with them, resulting in an excess of hydroxide ions, OH^-. For example, the base NaOH dissociates into sodium and hydroxide ions:

$$NaOH \rightarrow Na^+ + OH^-$$

The sodium ions dissolve in the water, and some of the freed OH^- ions combine with free H^+ to form H—OH (or, more familiarly, H_2O), leaving fewer hydrogen ions than before NaOH was added to the water.

pH

Why does the most acidic solution have the *lowest* number on the pH scale? And why does each pH unit represent a ten-fold difference in hydrogen ion concentration? Chemists measure the amount of substances in units called moles and the concentration of substances in moles per liter (mol/L). The pH scale indicates the concentration of hydrogen ions in this concentration unit. A pH of 1 is 0.1 moles of H^+ per liter, a pH of 2 is 0.01, and a pH of 10 is 0.000,000,000,1 moles of H^+ per liter. The pH is equivalent to the number of decimal places to the right of the decimal point. This accounts for the factor-of-ten difference between pH units. Because low pH values have few decimal places to the right of the decimal point, they have great concentrations of hydrogen ions. In a solution, the concentration of hydrogen ion (H^+) times the concentration of hydroxide ion (OH^-) is always the same. Whenever the concentration of hydrogen ions goes up, the concentration of hydroxide ions goes down, and vice versa.

pH scale

Extremely basic	14.0—Drain opener
	13.0—Bleach
	12.0—Ammonia
	11.0—Glass cleaner
	10.0—Great Salt Lake
	9.0—Baking soda
	8.0—Seawater, egg white
Neutral	7.0—Human blood and tears
	6.0—Cell interior
	Saliva, milk
	5.0—Black coffee
	4.0—Acid rain, tomato juice
	3.0—Vinegar, Coca-Cola
	2.0—Lemon juice
	1.0—Stomach acid
Extremely acidic	0.0—Concentrated nitric acid

pH meter

5.0

Appendix B:

Microscopes

How do we know that eukaryotic cells have a membrane-bound nucleus, chloroplasts, or any of the other organelles discussed in this book? Much of what we know about cells comes from biologists peering into microscopes and witnessing the beauty inside and on the surfaces of the cells. The three basic types of microscopes include the light microscope, the transmission electron microscope, and the scanning electron microscope.

Light microscopes are instruments containing optical lenses that refract, or bend, light rays so that an object appears larger than it really is (Figure a). Because it can illuminate and magnify, biologists use the light microscope extensively to locate cells in tissues, to observe the behavior of living cells (Figure b), and to detect cell organelles that can be stained bright colors, such as the nucleus, chloroplasts, and mitochondria (Figure c). If a specimen is thin enough for light to pass through, a light microscope can magnify its physical details to more than 2,000 times.

Colored stains can heighten the contrast between various structures in the specimen, making them easier to distinguish. Stains are usually used in combination with fixatives, agents that preserve the cells or tissues so that they remain unchanged. However, stains and fixatives kill cells, so to view living cells, biologists use differential interference contrast, or Nomarski light microscopes that augment the differences in light refraction between unstained structures so that the contrast between them is bright even without stains. (Figure d).

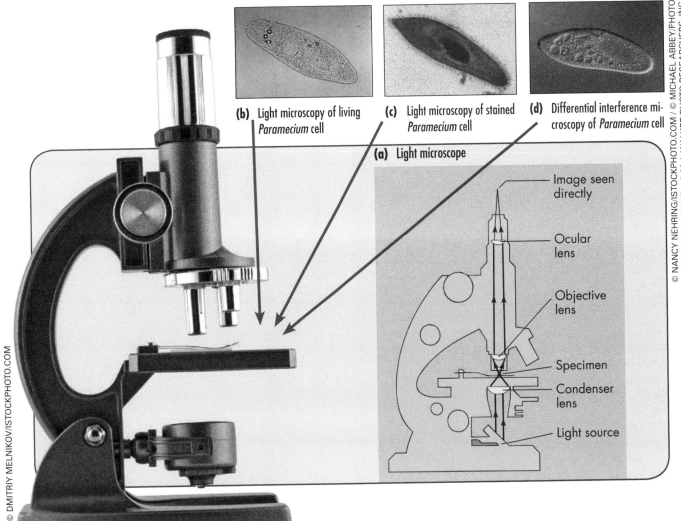

(b) Light microscopy of living *Paramecium* cell

(c) Light microscopy of stained *Paramecium* cell

(d) Differential interference microscopy of *Paramecium* cell

(a) Light microscope

- Image seen directly
- Ocular lens
- Objective lens
- Specimen
- Condenser lens
- Light source

Electron microscopes (EMs) use electrons with wavelengths 100,000 times shorter than visible light; these short wavelengths provide greater resolution, which allows greater magnification. Electron microscopes also use magnets rather than ground glass lenses to focus the electron beams. Electron microscopes opened a new and marvelous realm to biologists and have added much of our current knowledge of cell structure. *Transmission electron microscopes (TEMs)* generate images of thin slices of a cell, tissue, or object. These have revealed a level of complexity and detail in the cell never suspected until the middle of the twentieth century (Figures e, f). And *scanning electron microscopes (SEMs)* generate three-dimensional surface images. These have shown us a beautiful and sometimes bizarre vision of the intricate outer shapes of living cells and organisms (Figures g, h).

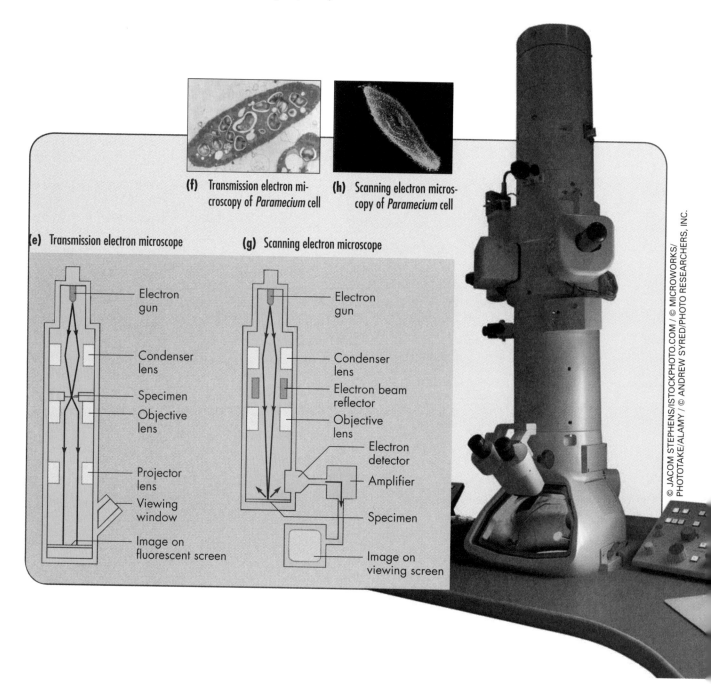

(f) Transmission electron microscopy of *Paramecium* cell

(h) Scanning electron microscopy of *Paramecium* cell

(e) Transmission electron microscope

- Electron gun
- Condenser lens
- Specimen
- Objective lens
- Projector lens
- Viewing window
- Image on fluorescent screen

(g) Scanning electron microscope

- Electron gun
- Condenser lens
- Electron beam reflector
- Objective lens
- Electron detector
- Amplifier
- Specimen
- Image on viewing screen

Appendix C:
The Hardy-Weinberg Principle

The *Hardy-Weinberg principle* provides an idealized standard against which a geneticist can compare what happens in a real population and thus detect evolutionary change.

The principle has two main points:

1. *The allele principle:* If left undisturbed, the frequency of different alleles in a population remains unchanged over time.
2. *The genotype principle:* With no disturbing factors, the frequency of different genotypes will not change after the first generation.

We can understand the principle by considering a population of snails (see figure) that can fertilize themselves or each other at random (Step 1). These snails possess a gene for shell color that shows partial dominance, with genotype AA causing a blue shell, *aa* resulting in a yellow shell, and Aa giving a green shell. By analyzing changes in frequency of this shell color gene with the Hardy-Weinberg equations, we can determine whether the snail population is evolving.

Each of the five snails shown in the figure is a diploid with two copies of the color gene. In this population's gene pool, there are ten alleles: six A alleles and four *a* alleles. If the symbol p represents the fraction of A alleles, then $p = 6/10$, or 0.6. If the symbol q represents the fraction of *a* alleles, then $q = 4/10$, or 0.4.

Because the number of A alleles plus the number of *a* alleles represent all of the alleles of this gene in this snail population, $0.6 + 0.4 = 1$, or in symbols, $p + q = 1$. This is the *allele pool equation*.

To see if allele frequencies change and evolution occurs, we must examine what happens when the snails reproduce, keeping in mind Mendel's rule that alleles separate in the formation of egg and sperm.

Notice that despite meiosis, the frequency of A and *a* alleles is the same in the gametes as it was in the original population, 6/10 A and 4/10 *a* (Step 2).

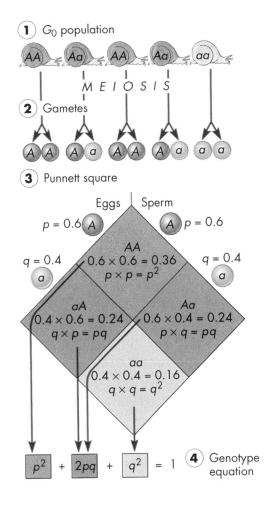

1 G_0 population

M E I O S I S

2 Gametes

3 Punnett square

Eggs | Sperm

$p = 0.6$ A ⬥ A $p = 0.6$

$q = 0.4$ *a* ⬥ *a* $q = 0.4$

AA
$0.6 \times 0.6 = 0.36$
$p \times p = p^2$

*a*A
$0.4 \times 0.6 = 0.24$
$q \times p = pq$

Aa
$0.6 \times 0.4 = 0.24$
$p \times q = pq$

aa
$0.4 \times 0.4 = 0.16$
$q \times q = q^2$

$p^2 + 2pq + q^2 = 1$ **4** Genotype equation

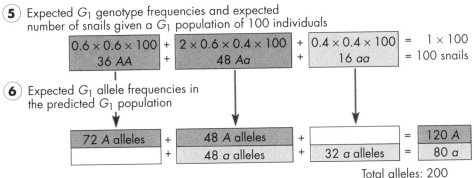

5 Expected G_1 genotype frequencies and expected number of snails given a G_1 population of 100 individuals

| $0.6 \times 0.6 \times 100$ | + | $2 \times 0.6 \times 0.4 \times 100$ | + | $0.4 \times 0.4 \times 100$ | $= 1 \times 100$ |
| 36 AA | + | 48 Aa | + | 16 aa | $= 100$ snails |

6 Expected G_1 allele frequencies in the predicted G_1 population

| 72 A alleles | + | 48 A alleles | + | | $= 120$ A |
| | + | 48 a alleles | + | 32 a alleles | $= 80$ a |

Total alleles: 200

Now what happens to allele frequencies at the time of fertilization? If we assume random mating, then we can write the frequencies into a Punnett square (Step 3). We can call $p^2 + 2pq + q^2 = 1$ the *genotype equation* (Step 4). This equation says that the sum of the individuals with *AA,* and *Aa,* and *aa* genotypes adds up to the entire population (the "1" in the equation).

To determine whether evolution has occurred in the snail population, we must look for a change in allele frequencies between generations. If five snails of the parental G_0 generation produce 100 snails in the G_1 generation, then we can expect the genotype frequencies and resulting genotype numbers shown in Step 5, barring outside influences. (Thus, the genotype equation predicts the number of each of the three different genotypes in the population.) What, then, are the frequencies of alleles in this new generation? Have they changed?

You can see from Step 6 that the frequency of *A* alleles is 120/200, or 0.6, and the frequency of *a* alleles

is 80/200, or 0.4—the same as in the original generation. From this generation on, the allele and genotype frequencies will remain the same, in the absence of outside influences, as you can prove for yourself by making another Punnett square and filling it in with the new data.

Applying the Hardy-Weinberg principle this way, we can predict that in populations without some outside influence, no evolution will occur over the generations. The Hardy-Weinberg equations provide a benchmark, a point of comparison for measuring any gene changes—or evolution—that might occur. If allele or genotype frequencies found in a population in nature are different from those predicted by the allele pool and the genotype equations, then there must be some outside influence, like mutation, natural selection, migration, nonrandom mating, or small populations. Biologists can then design experiments to see which outside influence may be important in any specific case.

> In populations without some outside influence, no evolution will occur over the generations.

Physiology

Body Function, Survival, and the Steady State

Learning Outcomes

LO¹ Examine how homeostasis contributes to survival

LO² Explore the body's hierarchy of organization

LO³ Explain the mechanisms for homeostasis

LO⁴ Describe processes of temperature regulation

LO⁵ Understand the mechanisms for salt and water balance

> ## 66 The central problem for a living thing is to maintain a steady state internally despite an often harsh and fluctuating external environment. 99

A Medical Pioneer in Orbit

The environment of deep space is about as hostile and lethal as environments come—a vacuum devoid of oxygen and blasted by subfreezing temperatures, lethal radiation levels, and a near or total absence of gravity, depending on the proximity of stars and planets. Today's space vehicles provide breathable air, liveable temperatures, and shielding from most radiation, but they can't reproduce Earth's

> **After working at a hard physical activity on a hot and dry day, a dehydrated student drinks several cans of beer. Will the student's thirst be quenched and the body rehydrated?**

gravity. Therefore, an astronaut's body must try to adjust to the sudden weightlessness of space in various ways through the delicate balancing act of homeostasis—how the body adapts to changes in the external environment and maintains constant internal conditions. However, the human body had not experienced the conditions of space before the 1950s, so it has no specifically evolved mechanisms to deal with weightlessness. The adjustments work well enough, however—at least in the short term.

Bearing no body weight in space, the bones start releasing some of their calcium and slowing the formation of new bone cells. In his 9 days and nearly 3 million miles in Earth's orbit, astronaut Bernard Harris lost almost 1 percent of his total bone. It is not yet clear whether astronauts on long flights will be able to recover from the substantial bone loss they accrue. His muscles, too, began to disassemble themselves in the absence of gravity and normal exercise. "I probably lost somewhere in the neighborhood of 10 to 15 percent of my muscle mass," he says, but this can be "rebuilt" back on Earth.

The courage of Harris and the other astronauts has helped biologists learn much more about the body's remarkable homeostasis and its constant adjustments to change. This change can be the radical shifts that occur in extreme environments such as deep space, deserts, high mountains, or polar caps. It can be the subtler variations in the temperate climates where most of us reside. Or it can involve alterations brought on by injury, disease, childbirth, or other processes. Regardless, homeostasis allows dozens of aspects of our blood and fluid chemistry and body functioning to stay within narrow *survivable* limits day after day.

As we explore body function, survival, and homeostasis in this chapter, we'll discuss how cells and tissues are organized in an animal's body. We'll also see how that structural order allows needed materials to reach—and wastes to exit—all parts of the body. As we go along, you'll find answers to these questions:

- ☑ How do tubes and transport mechanisms help supply the body with its daily needs?
- ☑ How is the complex animal's body organized into cells, tissues, and organs?
- ☑ How does an animal's body maintain the steady state of homeostasis?
- ☑ What mechanisms keep our salt and water content balanced?

homeostasis
the maintenance of a constant internal balance despite fluctuations in the external environment

microgravity
state of near-weightlessness

anatomy
the study of biological structures such as bones and kidneys

physiology
the study of how biological structures function

LO¹ Staying Alive: Problems and Solutions

The changes Bernard Harris experienced in space were specific to the state of near-weightlessness called microgravity. True weightlessness occurs in deep space; the shuttle and its passengers still receive a tiny tug of gravity while in orbit 240 miles above Earth.) The changes, nevertheless, are nearly identical to true weightlessness, and they represent a class of responses to environmental change that we will encounter again and again as we explore animal anatomy and physiology. Anatomy is the study of biological structures, such as bones, skin, and kidneys; physiology is the study of how such structures work—how bones grow, how skin cells make a tight body cover, how the kidneys cleanse the blood, and so on. Living organisms and their cells can be subjected to wide fluctuations in their immediate environments: changes in temperature, light, acidity, salinity, and availability of water, minerals, and nutrients. Changing environmental factors such as these, including microgravity while in Earth's orbit, create an external setting that is constantly shifting. Most living cells, however, can survive only within a narrow range of temperature, acidity, and other parameters. The central problem for a living thing, therefore, is to maintain a steady state internally despite an often harsh and fluctuating external environment. And the solution is homeostasis.

Maintaining Homeostasis

Living organisms are made up of cells, and essential life processes must go on within individual cells as well as within entire, many-celled animals. Essential life processes include

1. capturing energy and essential materials from the environment,

2. exchanging gases such as oxygen for energy harvest and the waste carbon dioxide, and

3. maintaining a body of a particular shape, fluid composition, and in some cases temperature that stays within a given range.

Single-celled organisms, such as amoebas, exchange materials with their environment by means of diffusion and active transport directly across the plasma membrane (see Chapter 4). Even some multicellular animals, such as flatworms, can rely on direct diffusion because their bodies are so thin and flat that each cell lies very close to the outside world.

Large bodies are generally too thick for each of their cells to exchange materials directly with the environment. A number of special systems evolved to overcome this problem for the cells and organs within multicellular organisms. For example, three systems service the cells of the pancreas. Their general function serves as a good overview of all the physiological systems in the body. Each system has a tube running from the outside environment to a location deep inside the body, capable of bringing supplies in to the cells or carrying away wastes. Each tube has special regions where substances inside the tube can be exchanged with body fluids bathing the tube. This exchange takes place over short distances via diffusion and by active transport. The body fluids surrounding each cell exchange oxygen, nutrients, wastes, and other substances with the circulatory system, which carries materials to every cell in the body in a moving stream, the blood. The substances can leave this stream by diffusion and can enter every body cell, again via diffusion and active transport, or wastes can be released by cells, enter the tube, and be carried away.

Let's see how this general strategy works in one particular physiological system, our astronaut's respiratory system (Fig. 16.1): Oxygen from the air in the space station enters his body through a tube (the windpipe; Step ①) and diffuses into the bloodstream in a special exchange region (the lungs; Step ②). The oxygen diffuses into the blood (Step ③), and the flowing stream of blood then carries the dissolved oxygen throughout his body (Step ④). Finally, the oxygen passes out of his blood and into individual body cells by diffusion (Step ⑤), where the cell uses the gas in aerobic respiration (Step ⑥).

Tubes and transport mechanisms give a many-celled organism some control over the immediate environment surrounding most of its cells. Still, each organism functions as a whole and directly contacts the physical environment with its skin, scales, fur, or other outermost surface and so remains subject to environmental fluctuations. We'll see in the next sections how a large array of structural, functional, and behavioral mechanisms come into play to keep both the organism and its cells on an even keel.

LO² Body Organization: A Hierarchy

If an animal's cells were crammed together haphazardly, gases, fluids, and other materials could not be transported around the body in a

Figure 16.1
Tubes and Diffusion: A Strategy for Exchanging Materials with the Environment

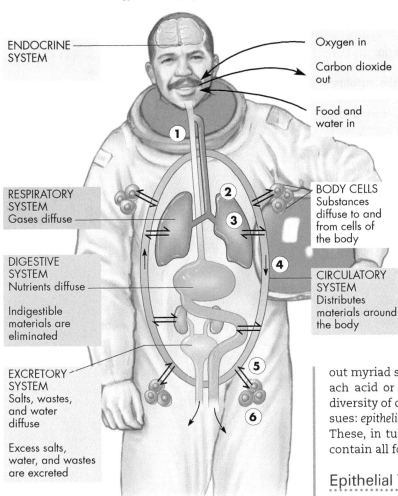

ENDOCRINE SYSTEM

Oxygen in

Carbon dioxide out

Food and water in

RESPIRATORY SYSTEM
Gases diffuse

BODY CELLS
Substances diffuse to and from cells of the body

DIGESTIVE SYSTEM
Nutrients diffuse

Indigestible materials are eliminated

CIRCULATORY SYSTEM
Distributes materials around the body

EXCRETORY SYSTEM
Salts, wastes, and water diffuse

Excess salts, water, and wastes are excreted

epithelial tissue
a major tissue type that covers the body surface and lines the body cavities, ducts, and vessels

exocrine gland
a gland with its own transporting duct that carries its secretions to a particular region of the body, and includes the digestive and sweat glands; contrasts with endocrine glands

endocrine gland
a gland that secretes hormones directly into the extracellular fluid or blood rather than into a duct; includes the pituitary, adrenal, and thyroid glands; contrasts with exocrine glands

The Four Types of Tissues

A person's body is a marvelously complex and integrated whole containing over 200 cell types that carry out myriad specialized roles such as secreting stomach acid or building hair proteins. Despite all this diversity of cell types, there are just four types of tissues: *epithelial, connective, muscle,* and *nervous* tissues. These, in turn, make up the organs, most of which contain all four tissue types.

Epithelial Tissue

Epithelial tissue lines or covers body surfaces with sheets of cells. We just saw that an epithelium lines the inner surface of the stomach, and it also covers us with the outer layers of our skin (Fig. 16.3a). Because epithelial sheets are often subject to abrasion, epithelial cells tend to divide continuously. Epithelial tissue has several crucial functions:

1. it receives environmental signals;
2. it protects the body from foreign substances;
3. it secretes sweat, milk, wax, and other materials;
4. it excretes wastes (in the kidney); and
5. it absorbs nutrients, drugs, and other substances (in the intestines) (Fig. 16.3b).

Since glands are organs that secrete, it's no surprise that epithelial tissue makes up the two major kinds of glands: the exocrine glands, which secrete substances such as sweat onto the skin and digestive juices into the gut, and some endocrine glands,

useful way. Instead, cells are organized into tissues, organs, and organ systems (Fig. 16.2).

A *tissue* is an integrated group of cells of similar structure performing a common function within the body. An *organ* is a unit composed of two or more tissues that together perform a certain function. Several organs can form an *organ system*, which is two or more interrelated organs that work together, serving a common function. Collectively, all the organ systems make up an organism—in the case of our central example, an astronaut.

An important part of understanding how homeostasis keeps a steady internal state is looking more closely at the kinds of tissues that make up organs, which we do in this chapter. Each of the next few chapters then introduces the functioning of organs within particular organ systems, such as the circulatory system or nervous system.

connective tissue animal tissue that connects or surrounds other tissues and whose cells are embedded in a collagen matrix; bones and tendons are mainly connective tissue

which secrete the internal chemical messengers within the body called *hormones*.

Epithelial sheets typically have one surface facing a space, such as the air, in the case of the skin, or the urine-storing cavity of the urinary bladder. Cell junctions (review Figure 2.14) bind adjacent epithelial cells tightly together and stop fluid (such as urine) from leaking across the lining and into the body. Junctions also link the inner surface of the epithelium to a thick underlying meshwork of protein and fibers, the basement lamina (also known as the *basement membrane*) (Fig. 16.3a). Without this firm bond, the skin would peel right off your body. Just beneath the basement lamina lies the second tissue type, connective tissue.

Connective Tissue

Connective tissue has relatively few cells, which are dispersed within a large amount of extracellular material. Connective tissue binds other tissues and supports flexible body parts, and connective tissue cells produce the extracellular material that forms a matrix, or framework, for other structures (Fig. 16.4a). This matrix usually includes fibers of the proteins collagen and elastin. Collagen is the most abundant protein in the body; weight for weight, it is as strong as steel. Connective tissue

1. fills spaces between muscles;

2. links epithelial layers to underlying organs;

3. stores fat;

4. makes up the tendons that attach muscles to bones and the ligaments that attach bones to other bones; and

5. forms cartilage.

Blood and bone are also types of connective tissue, even though blood is a liquid containing red and white cells, and bone is a hardened matrix housing bone-forming cells.

In space, Bernard Harris experienced bone loss. Why would homeostasis, a system evolved to keep the body functioning on an even keel, allow such a seemingly self-destructive process? Bone forms a rigid framework that withstands gravity, and it is a complex of proteins, phosphorus, and calcium. (The latter is an element needed for muscles to contract, for nerves to transmit information, and for blood to clot.) In space, Harris's bones sensed "mechanical unloading," or a sudden

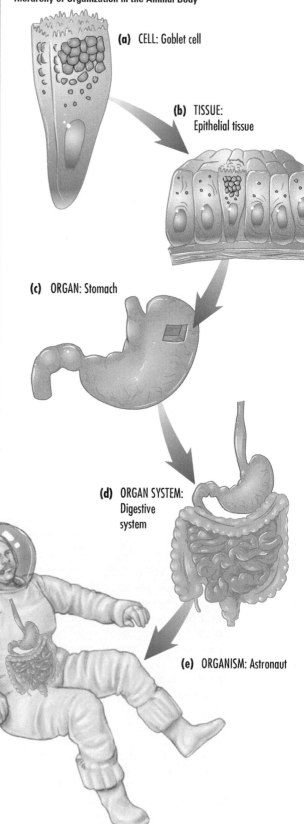

Figure 16.2
Hierarchy of Organization in the Animal Body

(a) CELL: Goblet cell

(b) TISSUE: Epithelial tissue

(c) ORGAN: Stomach

(d) ORGAN SYSTEM: Digestive system

(e) ORGANISM: Astronaut

Figure 16.3
Roles of Epithelial Tissue

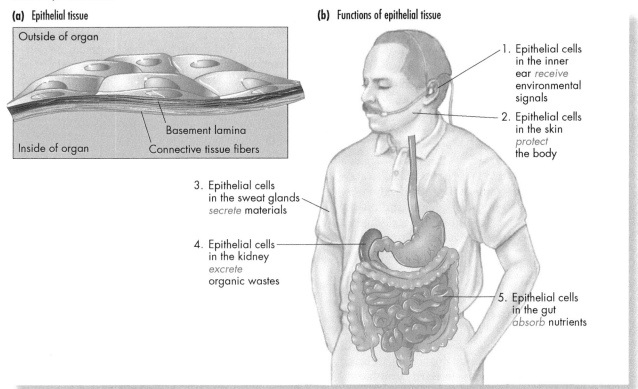

(a) Epithelial tissue

Outside of organ

Inside of organ

Basement lamina
Connective tissue fibers

(b) Functions of epithelial tissue

1. Epithelial cells in the inner ear *receive* environmental signals
2. Epithelial cells in the skin *protect* the body
3. Epithelial cells in the sweat glands *secrete* materials
4. Epithelial cells in the kidney *excrete* organic wastes
5. Epithelial cells in the gut *absorb* nutrients

Figure 16.4
Roles of Connective Tissue

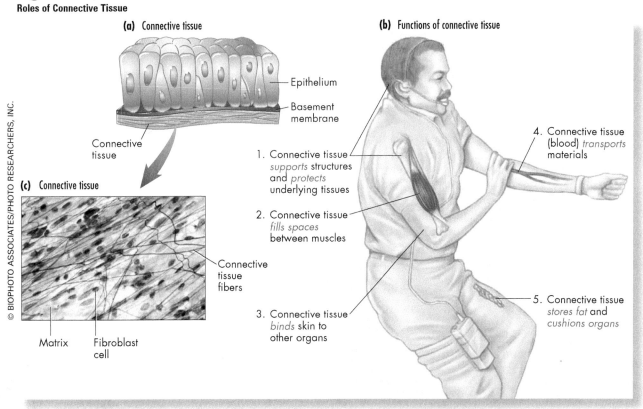

(a) Connective tissue

Epithelium

Basement membrane

Connective tissue

(c) Connective tissue

Connective tissue fibers

Matrix

Fibroblast cell

(b) Functions of connective tissue

1. Connective tissue *supports* structures and *protects* underlying tissues
2. Connective tissue *fills spaces* between muscles
3. Connective tissue *binds* skin to other organs
4. Connective tissue (blood) *transports* materials
5. Connective tissue *stores fat* and *cushions organs*

lack of body weight due to the absence of gravity. The homeostatic mechanisms of the body work to constantly remodel bone, depositing bone at points of heavy stress, such as the spots where very strong muscles attach, and removing bone where there is less stress. Because microgravity reduces stress virtually everywhere in the skeleton, hormonal signals told Dr. Harris's bones to start "remodeling" themselves by removing calcium and releasing it into the blood. Signals also slowed the formation of new bone. The same process goes on in a bedridden patient: The absence of muscular and mechanical stress leads to the removal of calcium and the slowdown of new bone production.

Bone remodeling is a good example of the general strategy of homeostasis: When external conditions change (in Bernard Harris's case, when gravity all but disappeared), natural mechanisms act to bring about a proper body response. In Harris's situation, the proper response would be dumping calcium, because keeping up a robust bone structure would "cost" more in energy expenditure than it would be "worth," since there is essentially no gravity pulling down on the body and strong structural support is less important. The bone remodeling and calcium dumping led to a thinning and weakening of Harris's bones and to an increase of calcium in the urine and in the blood. In postmenopausal female astronauts, the situation becomes even more pronounced. Shannon Lucid, for example, spent 188 days in space in 1996 at the age of 55. Even before her space flights, her bones were receiving a signal to release some stored calcium since, after menopause, the element would no longer need to be heavily "stockpiled" for building future fetal bones or producing milk. A woman who doesn't take estrogen supplements typically loses 1 or 2 percent of the calcium in her bones each year after menopause. This is why women may be concerned about osteoporosis, literally porous bones, due to calcium loss. An astronaut in space typically loses 1 or 2 percent of bone calcium per *month*. Unless postmenopausal women astronauts take estrogen, space flight could have a longer lasting effect on

them than on their male colleagues in terms of rebuilding weakened bones back on Earth.

Muscle Tissue

Thanks to a third tissue type, most animals are capable of movement: Muscle tissue contracts, or shortens, and thereby applies force against objects. (In Chapter 22, we'll see three types of muscle tissue: the striped or striated type that moves limbs and other body parts; the smooth type that propels internal organs; and the heart muscle that keeps this vital pump squeezing and moving blood through the body.) Grab your upper right arm with the left hand and raise your right hand up to your chin, bending your arm at the elbow. The hardening bulk you feel is muscle tissue as it changes from long, thin tubes to short, thick tubes to move the arm. Muscle cells are generally quite long and thin and are filled with protein fibers. The fibers slide past each other like two parts of a telescope, and cause the cell to shorten. During space flight, Harris's muscles atrophied—particularly those muscles that maintain the body upright against gravity, such as the calf muscle, the back portion of the thigh, the buttocks, and the muscles that keep the back straight and the head upright. Long periods of bed rest or disease can cause similar muscle wasting, as when you wear a cast on a broken limb. People are often shocked at the skinny arm or leg they see when a cast comes off after six or eight weeks. Atrophy of unused muscles is another good example of homeostasis: It prevents the body from spending valuable resources to build muscle tissue that is not being used as much as before.

Nervous Tissue

A fourth type of tissue, nervous tissue, helps control and coordinate the actions of organs, organ systems, and the whole body. Nervous tissue, in turn, makes up a system, the nervous system, encompassing the nerves, sense organs, and brain. Nervous tissue transmits electrochemical impulses;

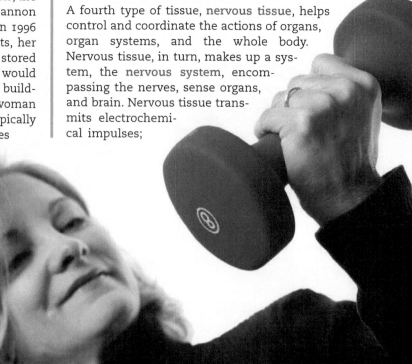

for example, you feel a pin prick on your fingertip because the pin deforms nervous tissue and this triggers a nerve impulse (see Chapter 21). The essential feature of nervous tissue is its ability to transmit signals and thereby communicate. Nerve cells, called neurons, sense changes in their environment. They then process that information and command muscles to contract or glands to secrete; these actions then help the animal adjust to the initial change. Nerve cells have very long, thin processes that act like telephone wires carrying messages from one place to another in the body. The longest cells of the body are nerve cells.

Nervous tissue accomplishes a key feature of homeostasis: the communication of various body parts with one another. Large animals need sophisticated avenues of coordination and communication, which integrate far-flung body parts so the left hand (or paw or tentacle) knows what the right hand is doing—at least most of the time—and the organism functions efficiently as a single entity. The electrical signals of nervous tissue and the nervous system rapidly integrate and regulate body functions. At the same time, blood-borne chemical signals (hormones) given off by the endocrine system cause slower, longer lasting body reactions and changes. We'll see more about the nerves and hormones in this and later chapters, and how they help organisms to maintain homeostasis—the internal constancy they need to survive.

LO³ How Do Our Bodies Maintain a Steady State?

When Dr. Harris performs routine checkups on patients, he can get a fairly accurate reading of how healthy they are by taking their temperature and blood pressure, listening to their heart and lungs, and analyzing the chemical content of their blood and urine. Since medical researchers have established a normal range of values for each measurement, chances are good that if the so-called vital signs fall within the correct ranges, the body is keeping the internal environment at a constant healthy level that, in turn, promotes the cells' efficient functioning.

On the space shuttle *Columbia*, Bernard Harris was both a physician and, in a sense, a medical guinea pig, providing information on astronauts' vital signs while subjected to microgravity. Dr. Harris outfitted himself and the other crew members with various types of electronic sensors. He collected data from those sensors, took blood and urine samples, and conducted tests before, during, and after the space flight. His goal was to determine baselines for body

functioning on Earth and then to compare them with changes astronauts experience during space flight, including increased urination, mild anemia, and bone and muscle wasting. The core of our story is not precisely what he and colleagues found but rather *how* an astronaut's body (and yours as well) establishes and maintains an internal even keel whether on a college campus on a warm, sunny day, or in the frigid darkness of space. The answers involve a set of marvelously integrated strategies based on feedback loops.

Feedback Loops: Mechanisms for Homeostasis

The thermostat in the space capsule and the one in your house employ the same general strategy for maintaining a steady condition with minor fluctuations. In your house, the thermostat *senses* the temperature, *evaluates* it (is it above or below the temperature range you set?), then *acts* by turning the furnace (or perhaps the air conditioner) on or off. The thermostat's activity requires: (1) a receptor to sense the environmental conditions (a thermostat contains a thermometer for that); (2) an integrator to evaluate the situation and make decisions (the internal workings of the thermostat signal the furnace or air conditioner to turn on or off), and (3) an effector to execute the commands (in your house, the furnace or air conditioner is the effector). Again and again in our discussion of animal homeostasis, you'll encounter these common elements: receptors, integrators, and effectors.

Now, these elements often interact in a feedback loop, a series of steps that *sense* a change in the external or internal environment, *evaluate* the new situation, and *react* in a way that modifies the original change (Fig. 16.5a,b). In a house, the feedback loop involves the thermostat's recognition of a temperature drop in the house; the triggering of the furnace to pour out more heat; and the thermostat's recognition of the new, higher temperature leading to a temporary shutdown of the furnace.

neuron
a nerve cell that transmits messages throughout the body; made up of dendrites, cell body, and axon

receptor
[1] a protein of a specific shape that binds to a particular chemical; [2] in physiology, a structure that carries out one of three primary elements of a homeostatic system to sense environmental conditions; also see effector and integrator

integrator
one of three primary elements characteristic of a homeostatic system; an integrator evaluates the situation and makes decisions; also see effector and receptor

effector
one of three primary elements characteristic of a homeostatic system; an effector executes the decisions; also see integrator and receptor

feedback loop
a control system involving a series of steps that sense a change and, in turn, influence the functioning of the process; can be positive or negative

negative feedback loop
a series of steps used to resist change in a homeostatic system; first by sensing a deviation from the baseline condition, then by turning on mechanisms that oppose that trend and thus bring things back toward the baseline

hypothalamus
a collection of nerve cells at the base of the vertebrate brain just below the cerebral hemispheres; part of the diencephalon and responsible for regulating body temperature, many autonomic activities, and many endocrine functions

positive feedback loop
a series of steps that brings about rapid change in a homeostatic system; amplifies an initial change of the external or internal environment in one direction further and further in the same direction

Feedback loops can be negative or positive. A negative feedback loop resists change by sensing a deviation from the baseline condition, then turning on mechanisms that oppose that trend and bring things back toward baseline. For example, your steady body temperature depends on a biological thermostat located in a small region of the brain called the hypothalamus lying above the roof of your mouth. The thermostat in the hypothalamus is set at about 37.8°C (100°F), which we measure as about 37°C (98.6°F) in the somewhat cooler mouth. Now suppose your body suddenly becomes too cold—think, for example, of the hundreds of people tossed into the icy North Atlantic as the *Titanic* sank in 1912. Specialized nerves in the hypothalamus detect the temperature change in blood flowing through the brain, while other nerves analyze information arriving from temperature receptors in the skin. The hypothalamus integrates the information and then causes muscles to begin to contract randomly (shiver), which generates heat; this heat counteracts the original change—the sudden cooling. The main point is that negative feedback loops tend to act to keep conditions constant—in this case, a constant body temperature.

Let's look at what happens when you have a fever. When virus particles or bacterial cells invade the body and begin multiplying, certain white blood cells release substances that can reset the brain's natural thermostat, the hypothalamus, to a value higher than normal (say, 38.8°C (102°F) rather than 37.8°C (100°F). The thermostat-resetting substances cause the local release in the hypothalamus of prostaglandins, molecules that turn up the body's thermostat. The body's "furnace," the muscles, start working overtime, contracting in uncontrollable shivers, even under heavy blankets, and the body temperature soars. This heat helps inhibit the bacterial or viral growth, perhaps by allowing more activity of the infection-fighting white blood cells. Aspirin brings down body temperature by interfering with the synthesis of prostaglandins. When the fever "breaks," the thermostat is reset once again to a lower temperature. Since the body is still hot, however, it initiates cooling behavior, largely by sweating.

Negative feedback loops can help an animal's body (including a person's body) resist internal change away from a baseline. But homeostasis employs another strategy: positive feedback loops that bring about rapid change. In a positive feedback loop, an initial change of external or internal environment in one direction is amplified further and further in the same direction. Probably the most familiar example of positive

Figure 16.5

**Feedback Loops
Prevent and Provoke Change**

(a) A negative feedback loop

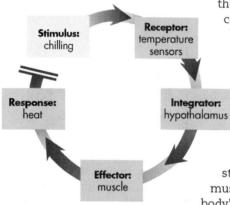

(b) A positive feedback loop

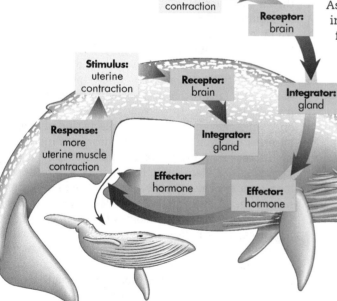

homeotherm
a "warm-blooded animal" in which the internal body temperature is fairly constant, based on physiological mechanisms that also control the distribution of its large reservoir of warm, moving fluid when the environment is too hot or cold

© GEORGE CAIRNS/ISTOCKPHOTO.COM

NEGATIVE FEEDBACK LOOPS CAN HELP THE BODY RESIST CHANGE; POSITIVE FEEDBACK LOOPS BRING ABOUT RAPID CHANGE.

feedback is the terrible screech you sometimes hear from a public-address system. A microphone picking up sound from the speakers sends the sound back, where it is further amplified. The microphone picks up that louder rebroadcast sound, the speakers reamplify it once more, and soon the sound mounts to an ear-piercing squeal.

In animals, positive feedback loops that disrupt the steady state are rarer than negative ones that maintain the steady state, and the positive loops usually act for a specific purpose. An example is the positive feedback loop that drives labor and delivery during birth (Fig. 16.5b). The hormone oxytocin is a chemical signal that causes the uterus to contract; these strong muscular actions cause more oxytocin to be released, more contractions to occur, and so on. The feedback produces stronger and longer contractions spaced closer and closer together until, at the climax of the cycle, a baby is born (review Fig. 8.10). This explosive action stops the loop and restores homeostasis—in this case, a noncontracting uterus. A colloquial way of describing a positive feedback loop is as a "vicious cycle."

LO⁴ Homeostasis, Circulation, and Behavior

Despite the bitter cold outside the orbiting space shuttle and *Mir* space station, Bernard Harris's body remained at about 98.6°F. The vehicles were heated, of course, but his own homeostatic mechanisms were responsible for the precise control over his body temperature. With our steady body temperature, we humans are considered homeotherms (*homeo* = same + *therm* = heat). This is also true of other mammals and birds: All are homeotherms or, colloquially, "warm-blooded" animals. Homeothermic animals have a large reservoir of warm, moving fluid whose distribution in the body can be controlled to a certain degree when the environment is too hot or cold.

Homeotherms maintain body temperature via feedback loops such as those we just described, as well as changes in blood circulation and in behavior. To see how these mechanisms work, think again about the victims of a boating accident—whether it be a rowboat in a lake to the *Titanic* in the North

vasoconstriction
contraction of blood vessel walls; regulates blood flow

vasodilation
relaxation of blood vessel walls; regulates blood flow

countercurrent flow (or countercurrent exchange)
a mechanism in which fluids with two different characteristics (such as temperature or solute concentrations) flow in opposite directions and can exchange energies or substances at points of contact along a concentration gradient

Atlantic. A person plunged into cold water may start shivering quickly, but the body does some other things automatically, as well: It shunts blood from one region to another, and it behaves in certain ways triggered by a survival instinct.

Shunting of Body Fluids

A warm-blooded animal's skin is crisscrossed by blood vessels that contain part of this blood "reservoir." When a mammal, say, a passenger on the *Titanic*, falls into cold water, tiny mus-cles divert blood from these surface vessels so that the warm blood and hence the person's body heat, stays in the body core instead of circulating in the periphery, where it would dissipate more easily into the cold water. The shunting of blood from the surface toward the core requires vasoconstriction, literally, blood vessel constriction, a rapid closing down of millions of tiny vessels near the body's surface and in extremities such as the nose, ears, limbs, fingers, and toes that sends a greater volume of blood toward the body core (Fig. 16.6a). If, on the other hand, an animal—a galloping horse, let's say, or an active tennis player—becomes over-heated on a hot day, blood can be shunted into these same surface vessels. This involves vasodilation, or blood vessel opening, during which millions of peripheral vessels quickly open wider and so blood from the body's core rushes to skin, head, and limbs (Fig. 16.6b). This conveys heat toward the body surface, where the surrounding lower temperature air or water can absorb it. Vasodilation also explains why your own skin may feel flushed and look glowing or even red in hot weather or during heavy exercise. Another mechanism called countercurrent flow, or countercurrent exchange, allows an animal's body to conserve the heat from exposed extremities—flippers, hands, feet, and so on.

Behavioral Adaptations

Let's go back once again to a person who has fallen overboard into cold water. A typical survival response would be to thrash around because, for the reasons we just saw, exercise does tend to warm you up. A victim might also try to grab another person or a piece of floating debris and desperately try to climb up and away from the freezing water. Ironically, a victim who moves around in cold water will lose body heat 35 percent faster than one who stays motionless. A person could survive up to three hours in water that's 50°F (10°C), but only by remaining still and keeping the

Figure 16.6
Temperature Regulation

© OLGA KORONEVSKA/ISTOCKPHOTO.COM

© SUZANNE TUCKER/ISTOCKPHOTO.COM

(a) Vasoconstriction—shunting of blood away from body surface if chilled

(b) Vasodilation—shunting of blood to body surface if overheated

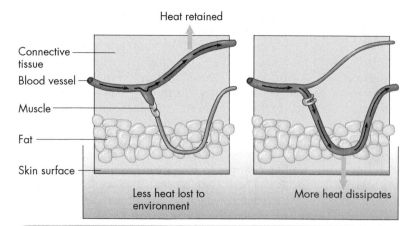

Heat retained

Connective tissue
Blood vessel
Muscle
Fat
Skin surface

Less heat lost to environment

More heat dissipates

head—which radiates fully 50 percent of your body heat—out of the water. The best behavioral strategy is to climb out onto floating debris, to cover the head, and never to flail or allow the head to remain in the water. A motionless person would warm up a thin film of water around the body. This layer would decrease heat loss compared to someone thrashing around, constantly recirculating cold water to the body surface.

In a sense, because *Homo sapiens* evolved in warm equatorial regions, we humans are still tropical organisms. We need special gear—warm and/or waterproof clothing, hats, boots, gloves, wetsuits, spacesuits—just to survive for extended periods in a cold environment. Even with all its mechanisms for maintaining a steady internal temperature, the body may fall behind in its efforts to keep up with heat loss during a long period in the cold, especially if not covered in the right protective gear. A state called hypothermia sets in if the body's core temperature drops below 35°C (90°F). (The inverse of this, hyperthermia, can set in when environmental temperatures are too high and exposure is too prolonged. Children or pets left in overheated cars sometimes suffer from hyperthermia, as can marathon runners on a hot day.)

During a lengthy exposure to cold air or water, rapid vasoconstriction shunts blood to the body core, leaving the extremities vulnerable to frostbite. Because vasoconstriction restricts blood flood to the brain, victims of hypothermia can also display confusion, poor judgment, drowsiness, and strange behavior. Activity slows in the nerves of the arms, legs, and other peripheral areas, and this helps explain the stumbling, clumsiness, and lethargy that are additional symptoms of hypothermia.

The thousands of warm-blooded bird and mammal species display a huge range of survival behaviors when confronted by overly cold or hot conditions. Hibernating in a tree trunk or cave is one familiar example. Another is seasonal migration to a more temperate area to ride out the winter months. Others include huddling together to preserve body heat, as do Emperor Penguins in the dead of the Antarctic winter; building or seeking shelters, like Arctic foxes; and restricting activity to warmer or cooler parts of the day, as do desert mice.

Variable-Heat Animals

With the elaborate mechanisms we've just seen—negative feedback, circulatory shunting, and behavioral adaptations—homeotherms have a marked advantage: their activity can remain high (including escaping from predators and capturing prey) regardless of environmental temperatures. The majority of animal species, however, are "cold-blooded," including some animals with backbones (amphibians, reptiles, and fish) and all animals without backbones (insects, jellyfish, worms, clams, crabs, and so on). How do they manage? "Cold-blooded" animals obtain most of their heat from the environment and their body temperatures can fluctuate widely. Biologists call animals with variable internal temperatures poikilotherms (POY-kill-oh-therms; *poikilo* = various + *therm* = heat) and have learned that many of their mechanisms for maintaining a livable temperature range are behavioral. A lizard or alligator, for example, instinctively moves in or out of the sun, does heat-generating "push-ups" or basks with its jaws gaping open—all strategies that keep its body temperature between 35°C and 40°C (95°F and 104°F). A sick lizard will actually induce its own artificial fever by baking itself in the sun until its body temperature soars and the bacterial or viral infection dissipates.

Some kinds of poikilotherms, however, have physiological adaptations in addition to behavioral

hypothermia
the state that sets in when the body's core temperature drops below 35°C (90°F)

hyperthermia
the state of elevated body temperature that sets in when environmental temperatures are too high and bodily exposure to heat is too prolonged

poikilotherm
an animal with variable internal temperature; colloquial synonym for poikilotherm is "cold-blooded animal"

American Alligator

water balance
a condition in which the amount of water entering the body equals the amount of water leaving

urine
a fluid that washes urea from the body

excretory system
system that [1] cleanses the blood of organic waste molecules and [2] carries them out of the body as urine or its equivalent through a special set of excretory tubes

intracellular fluid
the fluid inside cells

extracellular fluid
the fluid within the body but outside of cells

ones that help regulate body heat. In some oceangoing fishes, such as tunas and sharks, hardworking red-colored muscles enable the animals to swim rapidly and at the same time generate enough excess heat to warm the body core. Other poikilotherms have mechanisms that help them cope with variable body temperatures. Some freshwater fishes, for example, have two sets of cellular enzymes: one that functions best at cool temperatures and another that functions best at warm temperatures.

Body temperature is important but it's just one feature kept in check by homeostasis. To maintain an animal's total internal steady state, despite the often unpredictable external world, dozens of systems work simultaneously and under elaborate coordination and control. Let's return to Bernard Harris on the space shuttle and examine another homeostatic system that maintains constant internal conditions, in this case, the composition of the body fluids: the excretory system and the kidney.

LO⁵ Maintaining Salt and Water Balance

Facing the strange stress of microgravity, astronauts become keenly aware of their bodies' natural water balance and the role it plays in their lives. Picture a 2-liter bottle of soda pop or juice; that's how much body fluid shifted from Bernard Harris's legs and lower torso into his upper chest, neck, and face in the first few hours after entering the shuttle *Columbia*. The fluid shift made his face look round and smooth, and it caused an uncomfortable pressure in his head and sinuses. Over the next few days, however, his body eliminated some of the fluid by means of a homeostatic process that attempted to reestablish a steady state for fluid balance. Specialized receptors in the blood vessels leading to Harris's brain and heart started registering "Overfilled!" This triggered the release of chemical signals (particular hormones) that caused his body to excrete extra sodium and water in a higher-than-normal volume of urine. This removed some of the upper body fluid and relieved some of the con-

gestion in his head and chest. Unfortunately, it also eliminated some water from his blood (but no blood cells). The remaining blood cells therefore became more concentrated. This, in turn, triggered a negative feedback loop that slowed down the production of new red blood cells by his bone marrow and caused him to become slightly anemic. The key player in all of these homeostatic events is the *kidney*, an amazing living filtration device that maintains the chemical constitution of the blood and the level of water and salts in the body fluids despite enormous external changes, such as the sudden weightlessness of space. Obviously, the kidney and its functions evolved under terrestrial conditions as adaptations to challenges like thirst, extra salt in the diet, and waste products in the blood. But when the strange demands of space travel confront the body, the kidney's activity changes slightly to deal with the new stress.

Over a period of hours or days, the amount of water entering an animal's body must precisely equal the amount leaving—a condition called water balance. Animals take in water by eating and drinking, and as a product of metabolism (Chapter 3). Animals lose water by evaporation across the skin and respiratory surfaces, such as the lungs; in sweat and feces; and in other wastes, such as urine. Urine is a fluid that carries urea from the body; *urea* is the nitrogen-containing waste product formed by the breakdown of protein and nucleic acid molecules. The body must equalize water gained and lost each day so that it doesn't dry out or become waterlogged. The body must also rid itself of wastes. An animal's digestive system rids the body of undigested solid wastes, but the excretory system does two things: it (1) cleanses the blood of organic waste molecules and (2) carries wastes out of the body as urine or its equivalent through a special set of excretory tubes. As we will see, the kidneys are central to both excreting dissolved organic wastes and balancing water content by removing the right amount of water in the urine.

In complex animals, blood vessels carry blood adjacent to or very near every cell. The blood's fluid and salt content is normally maintained within narrow limits. What's more, inside each body cell, the pH, salt content, and waste concentration cannot vary too much, or individual cells will cease to function and the animal will die. The fluid inside cells, the intracellular fluid, makes up about two-thirds of the total body water. This intracellular fluid undergoes a continual exchange of materials with the extracellular fluid—fluid in the spaces between cells. Figure 16.7 illustrates this exchange. Extracellular fluid, in turn, is in equilibrium with the watery

Figure 16.7
Water Compartments in the Body

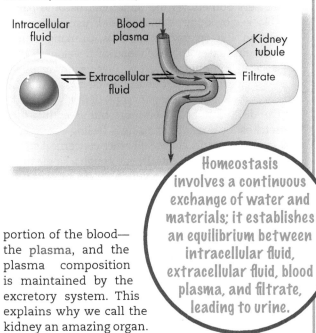

Intracellular fluid · Blood plasma · Kidney tubule · Extracellular fluid · Filtrate

Homeostasis involves a continuous exchange of water and materials; it establishes an equilibrium between intracellular fluid, extracellular fluid, blood plasma, and filtrate, leading to urine.

portion of the blood—the plasma, and the plasma composition is maintained by the excretory system. This explains why we call the kidney an amazing organ. By maintaining the contents of the blood, the kidneys indirectly maintain the intracellular fluid within each of the body's billions of cells. The kidney's crucial cleansing and fluid balancing activities, however, bear a high cost: The kidneys are metabolically more active than the heart! Without a continuous energy flow to these vital organs, the kidneys would fail and body fluids would become too salty or too watery for an animal to survive.

Nitrogen-Containing Wastes

If you've ever built a bookcase, then you know that short pieces of boards remain after you saw and hammer wood to build the furniture. In a similar way, residues of molecules remain unused after cells process nutrients and build from them new molecules and cell parts; these residues are wastes that must be removed. Excretion is the process that removes the byproducts of metabolism and rids the organism of excess water and salts. Excretion differs from elimination, the expulsion of solid wastes as feces (see Chapter 19). Undigested solid materials never leave the interior of the digestive tube; they never, in other words, actually enter the body or its cells. By contrast, metabolism within cells is the source of most waste products excreted in urine, and these wastes must be collected from every cell and floated away. Let's look more closely now at the excretion process and what it removes.

Three Types of Waste

When it comes to using energy, living cells are very flexible: they can burn fats, carbohydrates, and proteins for energy, depending on what's available. Cells burn fats and carbohydrates "cleanly," changing them to pyruvate. This molecule, you may recall, feeds directly into the Krebs cycle portion of aerobic respiration (see Fig. 3.6), and leads only to the waste products water and carbon dioxide. These small H_2O and CO_2 molecules diffuse out of cells and eventually may be expelled from the body. In contrast, before cells can use proteins for the production of ATP in aerobic respiration, they must first break the proteins down into amino acid subunits, and then chop each amino acid into a nitrogen-containing portion (the—NH_2, or amine group) and the carbon-containing remainder of the molecule (review Fig. 2.7). Cells transform the carbon-containing portion of the amino acid into pyruvate, which enters the Krebs cycle, but the amine becomes ammonia (NH_3), a strong-smelling alkaline ingredient we recognize from cleaning solutions, or the ion ammonium (NH_4^+). Even at low concentrations, ammonia is highly toxic to cells, so organisms must get rid of it quickly. Many animals that live in water excrete ammonia directly into the surrounding pond, stream, or seawater, where it is diluted so much that it becomes nontoxic. Land animals and certain other aquatic animals, however, turn the ammonia into less caustic, less damaging compounds before excreting it.

Birds, reptiles, insects, and land snails convert ammonia into the less toxic uric acid through special enzyme activities in the liver. The relatively insoluble substance continues to circulate suspended in the blood, like silt carried along in a river, and the kidneys gradually remove it. Producing uric acid as an excretory product helps land animals conserve water, because this relatively insoluble nitrogenous waste can pass out of the body as a paste containing little moisture. The white portion of the ubiquitous bird droppings that decorate window ledges, park statues, and the occasional human head is mainly uric acid. Uric acid can also be stored in almost solid form in a special part of a chick or turtle egg, away from the embryo. Without such an effective form of waste disposal, hard-shelled eggs (and the animals that hatch from them) might never have evolved.

plasma
the liquid portion of blood

excretion
the elimination of metabolic waste products from the body; in vertebrates, the main excretory organs are the kidneys

uric acid
a water-insoluble nitrogenous waste product excreted by birds, land reptiles, and insects

urea
a water-soluble nitrogenous waste product formed during the breakdown of proteins, nucleic acids, and other substances, excreted by mammals and some fishes

kidney
the main excretory organ of the vertebrate body; filters nitrogenous wastes from blood and regulates the balance of water and solutes in blood plasma

ureter
the tube that carries urine from the kidney to the urinary bladder

kidney stones
crystals usually formed of calcium and organic compounds that painfully block the ureter

urinary bladder
a single storage sac into which the two ureters dump fluids for excretion; when full, it stretches local nerves, causing a feeling of urgency

renal cortex
one of the kidney's three distinct visible zones, where initial blood filtering takes place

renal medulla
the kidney's central zone, divided into a number of pyramid-shaped regions; helps conserve water and valuable dissolved materials (solutes)

nephron
the functional unit of the vertebrate kidney; each of the million nephrons in a kidney consists of a glomerulus enclosed by a Bowman's capsule and a long attached tubule; the nephron removes waste from the blood

Mammals and a few kinds of fishes turn ammonia into urea, a combination of ammonia and carbon dioxide. This conversion also takes place in the liver. Just as dirty dishwater goes through sewer pipes to a central water treatment facility for final disposition, mammal and fish livers secrete urea, which dissolves in water, into the blood. The bloodstream then carries the urea to the kidneys, where they remove it from the blood and excrete it in urine, the fluid wastes excreted by the kidney.

The Human Excretory System

If you've ever been hungry, tired, and cold and had a very full urinary bladder simultaneously, then you'll probably understand why urination is sometimes called our most compelling bodily function. And imagine having to do it in the space shuttle or a space station with nearly zero gravity where drains don't work! (In case you've ever wondered, Dr. Harris reveals that astronauts visit small lavatory compartments and use devices that vacuum the droplets so they don't wind up floating around the cabin interior for the rest of the flight!) This urgency associated with excretion—whether assisted by gravity or not—has to do with the necessary waste-removal role of the excretory system and with its particular anatomy.

In humans, as in other vertebrates, the main organ of the excretory system is the kidney. A person's two plump, crescent-shaped kidneys, each about the size of your fist, are located just below and behind the liver, and they receive a large, steady flow of blood (Fig. 16.8). From the blood, the kidneys filter and remove excess water and waste substances, and these materials collect as concentrated urine in a central

cavity in each kidney. Wastes leave the central cavity and then flow down a long tube called the ureter (yer-EET-er). Sometimes the ureter can become painfully blocked by kidney stones, crystals usually formed of calcium and organic compounds. Drinking plenty of water decreases the likelihood of developing this excruciating condition. The two ureters dump urine into a single storage sac, the urinary bladder, which in an adult can hold about 500 ml (1 pt) of fluid. The bladder can distend to hold a bit more, but when it is full, it stretches local nerves, causing a feeling of urgency that can temporarily eclipse all other concerns. During urination, bladder contents drain through a single tube, the urethra (yoo-REE-thruh), which carries urine out of the body.

A cross-section of a kidney reveals three distinct visible zones (Fig. 16.9a):

1. an outer renal cortex (a bit like a thick orange peel); this is where initial blood filtering takes place.

2. a central zone, or renal medulla, divided into a number of pyramid-shaped regions (Fig. 16.9b). The medulla helps conserve water and valuable dissolved materials (solutes). The functional units of the kidney, twisted tubules called nephrons, reach from the cortex down into the medulla (Fig. 16.9c).

Figure 16.8
The Human Excretory System

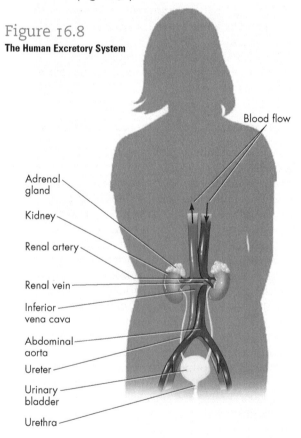

Blood flow

Adrenal gland

Kidney

Renal artery

Renal vein

Inferior vena cava

Abdominal aorta

Ureter

Urinary bladder

Urethra

3. a funnel-shaped, hollow inner compartment, or *renal pelvis*, inside these two zones, where urine is stored before it passes into the ureter and then collects in the bladder.

An Overview of the Nephron's Activity

The kidney has three basic processes—filtration, reabsorption, and secretion (see Fig. 16.10 on page 20). Filtration occurs at the bulbous tip of the nephron. During this first stage, blood pressure forces small molecules, such as glucose, amino acids, ions, water, and urea, out of the blood plasma through a filter, and into the cavity of the nephron. Large protein molecules and blood cells are left behind in the blood because they are too large to fit through the pores in the filter.

During tubular reabsorption, the nephron sorts the small molecules, shunting useful ones back to the blood and retaining the wastes in the nephron.

Finally, during tubular secretion, the nephron checks the blood supply one last time and removes from circulation excess ions, drugs, or other wastes that still remain and secretes them into the forming urine.

The way the kidney performs the three basic functions of filtration, reabsorption, and secretion is truly a wonder of natural engineering. This "engineering" is based largely on the delicate loops within the nephrons and the flow of blood around them.

Structure of the Nephron

Each nephron is a long, twisted, looping tubule that carries out filtration, absorption, and secretion in the healthy kidney with efficiency and ease (Fig. 16.9c). Each human kidney contains roughly 1 million nephrons, each extending from the outer cortex through the medulla and draining into the renal pelvis. If all the nephrons in an adult's kidney were straightened out and placed end to end, they would form a microscopically slender tube about 80 km (50 mi) long.

Near the outer surface of the kidney, one end of the nephron, called the Bowman's capsule, is cup-shaped like a punched-in balloon (Fig. 16.9c,d). The other end of the nephron drains away urine toward the bladder. Between these two ends, the tubule meanders and tangles like a long strand of spaghetti. The capsule leads into the convoluted proximal ("near") tubule, which then dips sharply down into the medulla. There, it makes a hairpin curve and

filtration
the process in the vertebrate kidney in which blood fluid and small dissolved substances pass into the kidney tubule, but large proteins and blood cells are filtered out and remain in the blood

tubular reabsorption
in the vertebrate kidney, the process whereby nutrients are returned from the kidney tubule to the blood

tubular secretion
in the vertebrate kidney, the process whereby ions and drugs are secreted from the blood into the kidney tubule

Bowman's capsule
in the vertebrate kidney, the bulbous unit of the nephron that surrounds the blood capillaries of the glomerulus; the region that filters water and solutes from the blood

proximal tubule
in the vertebrate kidney, the convoluted tube between the Bowman's capsule and the loop of Henle

Figure 16.9

Anatomy of the Human Kidney: A Blood-Cleansing Organ

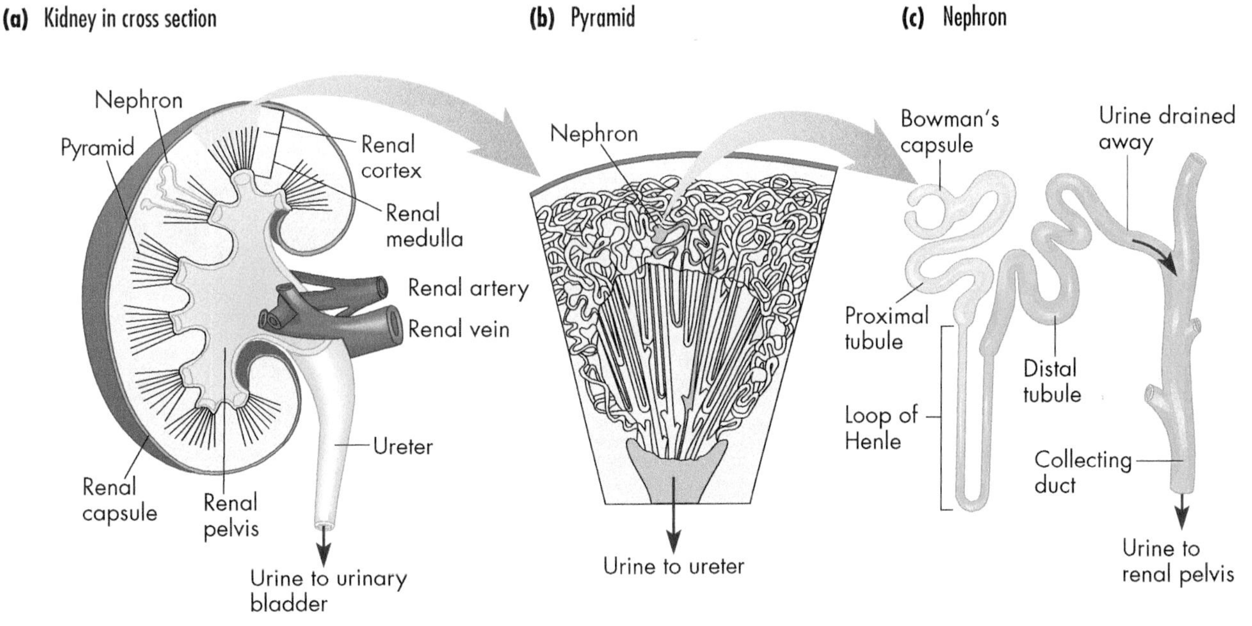

(a) Kidney in cross section

(b) Pyramid

(c) Nephron

loop of Henle
U-shaped region of vertebrate kidney tubule chiefly responsible for reabsorption of water and salts from the filtrate by diffusion

distal tubule
the convoluted tubule in the vertebrate kidney that receives the forming urine after it has passed through the loop of Henle

glomerulus
(L., a little hall) in the vertebrate kidney, a collection of tightly coiled capillaries enclosed by the Bowman's capsule

heads back up into the cortex. The U-shaped section of the nephron, known as the loop of Henle, is chiefly responsible for reabsorption of water from the tubule contents back into the blood. The loop of Henle connects to the part of the nephron farthest from Bowman's capsule, the distal ("far") tubule. Distal tubules from various nephrons join and form large *collecting ducts*, which receive liquid wastes from several distal tubules, drain into the renal pelvis, and carry away the urine. About every 15 seconds, a small amount of urine collects in this pelvis or hollow inner compartment, and waves of muscle contraction in the ureter sweep the urine through the ureter to the urinary bladder for storage and eventually for excretion through the urethra. (Consider for a minute what would happen to an astronaut if gravity, rather than these peristaltic waves of

contraction, caused urine to move from the kidney into the bladder.)

Blood Flow Around Nephrons

At any given time, about one-fifth of the total blood in our bodies is passing through the blood vessels to and from the kidneys. The pathway of blood flow around each nephron is critical to kidney function and is similar to the action of an incredibly delicate coffee filter. Blood makes its closest contact with the nephron in the Bowman's capsule, as a small artery branches (Fig. 16.9d, Step ①) and brings blood to the glomerulus, a wad of capillaries, which are fine, thin-walled blood vessels (Fig. 16.9e). Minute holes pierce the cells that make up the capillary walls (Fig. 16.9e), and fluid from the blood percolates through the delicate filter and into the Bowman's capsule. The fineness of these capillary pores is ultimately responsible for the nephron's blood filtration activities.

When capillaries leave the capsule, they do not merge directly into veins, but instead rejoin to form another small artery or arteriole, which exits the capsule (Fig. 16.9d, Step ②). This arteriole carries blood into a second network of capillaries that surrounds

Figure 16.9 Continued
Anatomy of the Human Kidney: A Blood-Cleansing Organ

(d) Blood vessels and nephron

(e) Bowman's capsule

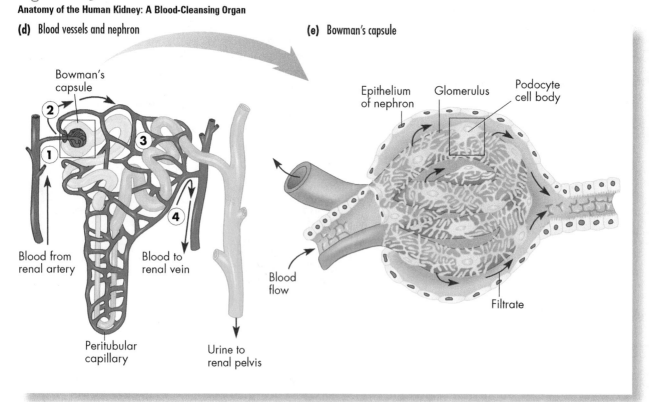

the looped portion of the nephron (Step ③). These capillaries finally merge into a small vein that connects to the large vein that leaves the kidney (Step ④). These veins carry blood away from the kidney and toward the heart.

Nephrons at Work

During his first few hours in microgravity, Dr. Harris's kidneys were working overtime as his rate of urine production increased to counteract the rush of blood and tissue fluid to his head and chest. In times of water overload, it's almost embarrassing how well the kidneys work to remove fluid and chemical wastes while at the same time conserving mineral ions, glucose, and other needed materials. Each day in an adult human, about 180 L (48.5 gal) of fluid—enough to fill a bathtub—passes from the blood into the cavities of the kidneys' Bowman's capsules. We do not, of course, urinate 180 L a day, but rather the much more reasonable amount of about 1.5 L (3 pt) per day. Clearly, the nephrons accomplish a great deal of water conservation before they produce that smaller quantity of urine.

Filtration

This first stage of urine formation occurs in the Bowman's capsule (Fig. 16.9e). In the cup of the capsule, the walls of the capillaries are built of thin cells perforated by pores, with the blood on one side of the cells and a thick basement membrane or lamina on the other. Across the basement membrane lie the epithelial cells that form Bowman's capsule. On the other side of those cells is the cavity (lumen) of Bowman's capsule. The epithelial cells of each

Bowman's capsule are called podocytes (literally, "foot cells"). Each podocyte has thousands of fingerlike projections that enclasp each capillary completely, like fingers wrapping around a hose. Blood pressure forces some of the plasma, the yellowish fluid portion of blood, through tiny pores in the walls of the capillaries (on page 21, see Fig. 16.11, Step ①), just as water pressure forces water out of a perforated garden hose or lawn sprinkler. The filtered liquid, containing various dissolved substances but lacking blood proteins, then passes through the fingers of the podocytes into the cavity of the Bowman's capsule. The transport of water; sodium, potassium, and chloride ions; and sugars, amino acids, and urea out of the capillaries and into the cavity of the Bowman's capsule is passive and does not require any special output of energy other than blood pressure. The fluid, or filtrate, in the capsule is still very much like blood plasma, except that it contains no large proteins.

Tubular Reabsorption

As soon as the filtrate enters the nephron's twisted proximal tubule, reabsorption begins and returns to the blood most of the water, sodium, potassium, and chloride ions, sugars, and amino acids that were just filtered out of the blood into the Bowman's capsule (Fig. 16.11, Step ②). Cells move these materials out through the walls of the proximal tubule and into the extracellular space, and finally the materials pass back into the blood plasma of the capillaries entwining the proximal tubule. Instead of being driven passively by blood pressure as in the process of filtration, tubular reabsorption depends on active transport of solutes (at a continuous cost of ATP energy) across the plasma membranes of nephron cells. As the tubule reabsorbs ions in this way, 80 to 85 percent of the water

podocytes
the epithelial cells of each Bowman's capsule (literally, "foot cells")

filtrate
in the vertebrate kidney, the fluid in the kidney tubule (nephron) that has been filtered through the Bowman's capsule

© ISTOCKPHOTO.COM

Figure 16.10

Filtration, Reabsorption, and Secretion: The Roles of the Nephron

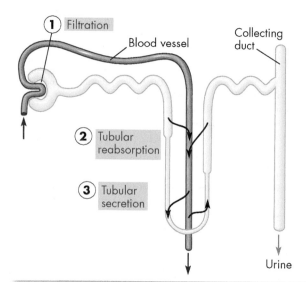

In filtration (Step ①), water and other small molecules are filtered from the blood and enter the nephron.

In tubular reabsorption (Step ②), water, salt, and nutrients are returned to the blood.

In tubular secretion (Step ③), some ions and drugs are secreted from the blood back into the nephron; from there they move with the urine into the collecting duct, renal pelvis, and ureter and pass into the bladder for elimination.

in the original filtrate passively follows the ions back into the capillaries via the process of osmosis, the movement of water from a solution with a few dissolved materials across a membrane into a concentrated solution (Step ③).

Next, the filtrate—minus most of its water but still containing urea and salts—passes through the loop of Henle. Here, the cells of the nephron use energy to pump chloride ions (Cl⁻) into the extracellular fluid surrounding the tissue cells of the kidney's medulla, and sodium ions (Na⁺) follow passively (Fig. 16.11, Step ④). As a result of this ion pumping, the innermost part of the medulla becomes very salty compared to the upper part, as suggested by the gradient of grey in Figure 16.11. This means that the concentration of Na⁺ and Cl⁻ is lowest toward the outside of the kidney and grows increasingly higher toward the inner part of the medulla, the part containing the hairpin curve of the loop of Henle (see Fig. 16.9c). Because the tissue surrounding the loop is salty, water diffuses out of the loop by osmosis and reenters the blood of the nearby capillaries (Fig. 16.11, Step ⑤). This exodus of water ends, however, as the filtrate rounds the bend and moves up the loop, because that part of the tube is not permeable to water (Step ⑥).

From the water-tight region of the tubule, the filtrate, still containing urea, some salt, and some water, passes toward the collecting duct (Fig. 16.11, Step ⑦). In that duct, once again, the walls are permeable to water, and even though the filtrate passing through is already quite concentrated, the surrounding tissues are still saltier. Thus, still more water diffuses out of the collecting ducts by osmosis and

enters the blood of the capillaries (Step ⑦). In addition, the walls of the collecting duct allow a certain amount of urea to pass back out, rather than being excreted in the urine. This urea increases the brinelike concentration in the inner medulla and causes still more water to be removed and conserved.

By the time the filtrate (at this point called urine) has reached the part of the collecting tubule in the innermost (and saltiest) region of the medulla, much of the water has been reabsorbed (Fig. 16.11, Step ⑧). In fact, about 99 percent of the water originally filtered from the blood in the Bowman's capsule has by now been returned to the body's circulation. That's why we excrete 1.5 liters of urine each day, as opposed to 180 liters, and why the urine has a high concentration of wastes relative to water content.

Tubular Secretion

The kidneys' activities—specifically filtration and reabsorption—are mainly responsible for the volume of the urine produced. (In an astronaut, that volume is initially higher than normal because of the blood and fluid shift toward the head and the body's homeostatic response to the problem.) The kidneys' third major activity, *tubular secretion*, is responsible for removing unneeded materials from the blood. The proximal and distal tubules remove many kinds of undesirable substances from the extracellular fluid surrounding the nephron and secrete them into the forming urine. These materials include hydrogen and potassium ions, ammonia, and certain drugs, such as the antibiotic penicillin and the sedative phenobarbital (Fig. 16.11, Step ⑨). Tubular secretion, therefore, is an important blood-cleansing process. It can also help maintain an appropriate pH level in the blood, because nephron cells secrete more hydrogen ions into the urine if the blood is too acidic and fewer hydrogen ions if the blood is too alkaline.

Tubular secretion is the physiological process that makes drug testing possible—checking a person's urine to see if he or she has taken drugs. Various laboratory techniques can detect even minute traces

Figure 16.11
How the Nephron Makes Urine

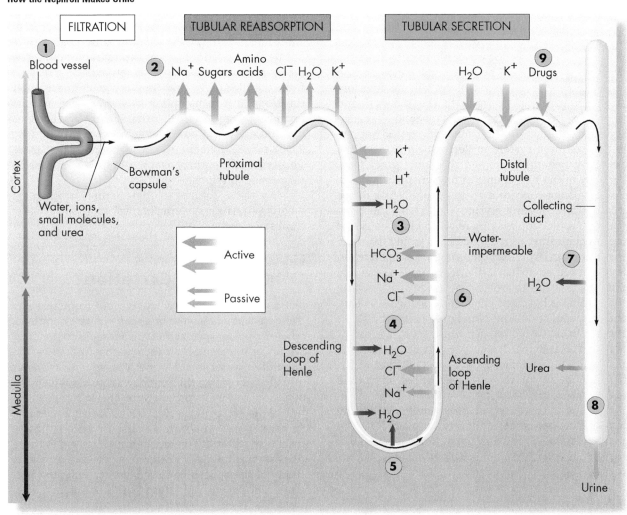

of the metabolic breakdown products of marijuana, cocaine, heroin, sleeping pills, tranquilizers, morphine, codeine, and many kinds of prescription drugs. If a person takes a drug overdose and loses consciousness and no one is sure which drug was consumed, physicians quickly test the urine to identify the drug and determine the best treatment for saving the patient's life. Two additional uses—testing athletes and employees for drug use on the playing field or on the job—are currently common but have created considerable controversy.

The Kidney and Homeostasis

During his weeks in space, Dr. Harris's kidneys helped his body adjust to the dramatic loss of gravity. These organs not only cleansed his blood of urea but also helped reestablish and maintain constant body con-

ditions in several ways. As we already saw, the kidneys helped Harris's body get rid of the excess fluid in the blood and tissue spaces that migrated up into his head and chest after gravity stopped tugging it toward his feet.

The extra urine production decreased Harris's blood volume and lessened the puffiness in his upper body and face. However, it created a secondary problem: As water was removed from his blood in the first couple of days in space, Harris's blood cells grew more concentrated just the way draining a reservoir in the autumn concentrates the fish. The body has a feedback loop involving a hormone called *erythropoietin* (ee-RITH-ro-POY-i-tin) that deals with changes in the concentration of blood cells. Normally, if the concentration of red blood cells drops below about 45 percent or so of the total blood volume, the kidney senses the blood's decreased oxygen-carrying

antidiuretic hormone (ADH)
a posterior pituitary gland hormone that regulates the amount of water passing from the kidney as urine

diuresis
abundant urine production

capacity and responds by secreting erythropoietin (Fig. 16.12). The hormone travels through the blood to the bone marrow, where it stimulates new red blood cells to form. The increased concentration of red blood cells carries more oxygen to the kidneys, and the organs respond by releasing less erythropoietin. Consider what would happen to this feedback system in Bernard Harris after his excretory system eliminated the extra water from his body in the first couple of days in space and his blood cells got concentrated as a result. His kidneys would stop secreting erythropoietin and the bone marrow would stop making new red blood cells and the concentration of red blood cells would decrease as the older cells die. Now, what would happen when Harris returned to Earth's mighty pull? He would drink extra water to replace the fluids now draining away from his head and chest and sinking to his legs, and this would dilute his blood cells, creating a slight anemia. What would happen to the level of erythropoietin at this point? It would rise, causing the bone marrow to increase blood cell manufacturing activities and once again raise the level of red blood cells to normal.

Harris's kidneys helped him maintain a steady internal environment a third way, related to the proximal tubule's tendency to reabsorb calcium ions. Recall that when a person is weightless or nearly so,

negative feedback mechanisms in the bones sense too much calcium, then begin to dismantle the bones and dump the extra calcium ions into the blood. When the blood passes through the Bowman's capsules in the kidneys, the calcium ions pass into the filtrate. As the filtrate passes through the tubule, the process of tubular reabsorption removes calcium ions from the filtrate, so that they can once more enter the blood. But reabsorption can bring calcium ions up only to a certain level. If that level is exceeded, as it is with massive bone degradation accompanying space travel, then the excess appears in the urine. This leads to the worry over irreversible bone loss on long space missions.

Now let's return to the actual mechanism whereby Harris's system "knows" to remove water from the blood.

How Do Hormones Control Water Excretion?

Just as you can adjust a faucet's tap to increase or decrease water flow, your body can regulate nephrons, resulting in an increase or decrease in urine flow. We've looked at several factors that influence the amount of water in the urine: The amount of water initially filtered into the Bowman's capsule, which can be influenced by blood pressure; the salt concentration of the extracellular fluid in the kidney's medulla; and the degree to which the distal tubule is impermeable to water. Two hormones are involved in these processes: antidiuretic hormone regulates the permeability of the collecting duct to water, while the hormone aldosterone regulates salt reabsorption.

Antidiuretic Hormone

Have you ever heard someone say that coffee and beer are diuretics? That means that substances in these beverages cause the body to produce higher than normal amounts of urine. Antidiuretic hormone (ADH, also called vasopressin) is aptly named because it slows down diuresis, or abundant urine production. ADH controls how much water the nephron reabsorbs from the filtrate and returns to the blood. Special nerve cells in the hypothalamus of the brain produce ADH, and long extensions of those cells extend to a nearby region, the pituitary gland, and store the hormone (Fig. 16.13). When the concentration of salt and other solutes rises in the body—say, after you eat a bag of salty potato chips (Fig. 16.13, Step ①)—the hypothalamus detects the changes and causes the pituitary gland to release some of its stored ADH into the blood (Step ②). Upon reaching the kidney, ADH makes the walls of the distal tubule and col-

Figure 16.12

How the Kidney Maintains Red Blood Cell Concentrations

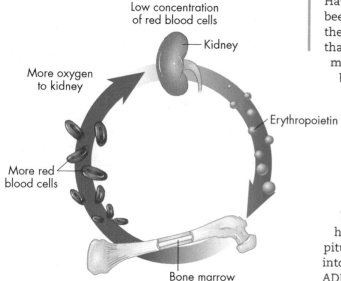

Low concentration of red blood cells

Kidney

More oxygen to kidney

Erythropoietin

More red blood cells

Bone marrow

lecting ducts temporarily more permeable to water (Step ③) so more water is reabsorbed into the bloodstream, diluting the too-high concentration of blood solutes (Step ④). Since water is drawn from the filtrate into the blood, the blood becomes less salty, but at the same time, the urine becomes more concentrated (Step ⑤). Finally, less salty blood causes the brain's secretion of ADH to decrease (Step ⑥), thus completing a negative feedback loop.

As beer drinkers occasionally discover to their dismay, alcohol inhibits ADH secretion, leading to the excretion of sometimes embarrassing quantities of urine. This causes dehydration—a major contributor to the hangover a person can feel after drinking too much alcohol.

Aldosterone

While ADH "adjusts the tap" to control the body's reabsorption of water, another hormone, aldosterone, secreted by the adrenal glands (which sit on top of the kidneys) controls the absorption of salt. In brief, if either the concentration of sodium ions or the blood pressure drops, the kidney secretes the enzyme renin. Renin initiates a signal cascade in the blood that eventually produces angiotensin II, which triggers the release of aldosterone from the adrenal gland. Aldosterone causes the distal tubule and collecting duct to reabsorb sodium ions from the tubule contents into the blood. Chloride ions follow passively, and the increasingly salty blood slows the release of renin. This completes the negative feedback loop and, in turn, maintains the concentration of sodium in the blood within the narrow range that is best for the activity of nerve cells and other crucial internal activities.

Studies of astronauts in space have shown that their blood is low in sodium ion concentrations and, in fact, low in the concentrations of all particles. No one knows yet why this condition exists. Future experiments will have to be conducted on astronauts in space to explain why weightlessness seems to result in mysterious shifts in blood chemistry.

Kidneys: Adapted to the Environment

Organisms have evolved to survive in environments that are hot, cold, dry, wet, acidic, salty, and every imaginable combination and variation. We've seen the close association between a kidney's filtering, balancing, and secreting functions and its multilayered, nephron-packed structure. It's no surprise that biologists have found striking variations in the kidneys—specifically in the nephrons—of animals with markedly different life histories. For example, take the kangaroo rat, a small rodent inhabiting the deserts of the western United States. This animal conserves water to an extreme degree, and each of its nephrons has a very long loop of Henle. With this modification, its kidneys can

aldosterone
a steroid hormone released by the cortex of the adrenal gland that regulates salt reabsorption in the kidney

renin
an enzyme released by the kidney that converts a blood protein into the hormone angiotensin II

angiotensin II
a hormone that causes blood vessels to constrict, counteracting falling blood pressure; it can also trigger the adrenal glands to secrete aldosterone, which results in sodium and water reabsorption and thus even higher blood volume and pressure

Figure 16.13
How Hormones Regulate Salt and Water Balance

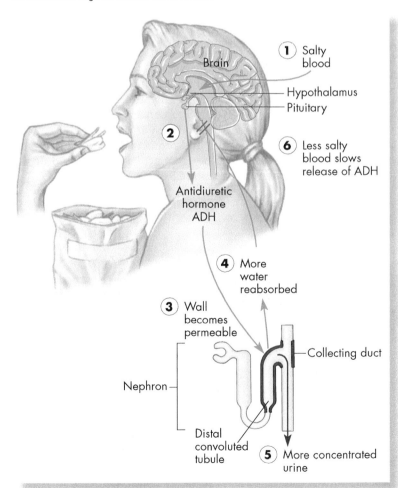

reabsorb practically all the available water back into the animal's body as the filtrate moves through the long loop. As a result, the kangaroo rat can produce urine 25 times more concentrated than its own blood—the highest concentration of any mammal.

In contrast, look at an aquatic mammal such as a beaver. It takes in a great deal of water in its food and through its skin and must get rid of the fluid, not conserve it. In a beaver's kidney, the loops of Henle are short and reabsorb less water; as a result, the animal produces great quantities of urine with only twice the concentration of its own blood. Humans have a combination of long and short loops of Henle and so produce a urine of variable concentration, depending on how much water is available in the environment at a given time.

Salt and Water Balance

Ever wonder why a thirsty sailor can't simply drink seawater? The answer lies with the salt and water balance we have been discussing: Human kidneys cannot make urine as salty as seawater. For every 1 L (1.06 qt) of seawater we humans would consume, we would produce 1.3 L (1.37 qt) of urine. This would cause rapid dehydration. In contrast, a camel *can* drink seawater because its kidneys can make urine

that is more concentrated than seawater. Likewise, marine animals such as sharks, flounder, or sea gulls drink seawater readily. Obviously, animals face different osmotic challenges depending on the saltiness, dryness, and wetness of their natural environments. Let's look at another important aspect of homeostasis on land, at sea, and in fresh water: osmoregulation, the regulation of osmotic balance.

Salt and Water Balance in Land Animals

We land animals are bathed in a sea of air, and so we tend to lose water through evaporation across the body and breathing surfaces as well as through urination. This brings about needs so familiar we rarely think about them: (1) the need to drink water, (2) the need to dump excess salt by sweating and urinating (or in some animals, excreting salt through special salt glands), and (3) the need to conserve water through physical and behavioral mechanisms. Our human skin surface, for example, is dry and helps seal in water— though not as well as an insect's waxy cuticle, a reptile's scaly skin, a bird's feathers, or a mammal's fur. In one experiment, researchers sheared a camel, and the animal's water expenditure increased by 50 percent!

The moist skin of an earthworm, snail, or amphibian allows those animals to lose much more water through evaporation, so they tend to behave in ways that help them conserve water: Amphibians, for example, tend to remain in cool, wet places, and snails tend to come out only in the cool, damp night air. People exhibit water conserving behaviors, too: Desert dwellers tend to wear clothing that minimizes evaporation and protects them from the sun, and they tend to be most active at dawn and dusk, when temperatures are lower.

Salt and Water Balance in Aquatic Animals

You might think that fishes, seals, crabs, and other aquatic animals have it made when it comes to conserving water and balancing salts, since they don't have to face the problem of constant evaporation like we land animals do. In fact, though, they simply have a *different* continual problem due to their body fluids having a salt concentration either higher or lower than the surrounding water. If an animal lives in an aquatic environment saltier than its internal fluids—in the ocean, say, or a salt lake—water tends to diffuse outward and leave the animal dehydrated. If an animal lives in an aquatic environment less salty than their blood—as in a freshwater lake or river—then water tends to diffuse into their bodies and waterlog the organisms. To overcome these challenges, various adaptations have evolved in different groups for excreting water and balancing salt.

The easiest solution to osmoregulation is to have body fluids with the same concentration as the surrounding water, and that is the situation in invertebrates such as oysters and sea stars. The salt levels of their body fluids conform to their surroundings, whether they are salty or dilute. Other marine invertebrates, such as crabs and brine shrimp, have internal mechanisms to maintain steady levels of water and salts regardless of environment.

In fishes, marine mammals such as seals, and other aquatic vertebrates, body fluids can be more or less concentrated than their surroundings, but the concentrations remain more or less steady through homeostatic mechanisms and anatomical structures. Sharks, for example, have very little net change in their internal water concentration because their body fluids have roughly the same concentration of dissolved substances as seawater. The retention of urea by the shark's kidney contributes to this high concentration of dissolved substances in the blood. Any salts that build up are excreted by a special rectal gland.

In freshwater fishes and amphibians, the blood has a higher salt concentration than the environment. Water tends to flow in across the skin by osmosis, so these animals have no need to drink; instead, their kidneys produce large amounts of dilute urine, which rids the body of excess water. Unfortunately, salt also tends to leave the body and

Who knew?

While initially any cold drink satisfies thirst receptors in the mouth and throat, making the student feel less thirsty, the alcohol in the beer inhibits the action of antidiuretic hormone (ADH), causing less water to be reabsorbed by the kidneys and rehydration to be delayed. After a while, the student's thirst will return (and his or her bladder will be full).

diffuse into the water. The gills of freshwater fishes are able to actively accumulate and absorb salt from the lake or river water.

Finally, for most ocean-dwelling fish and mammals, the seawater is saltier than their body fluids and thus the animals tend to lose needed water through their skin and gain excess salt. As an evolutionary consequence, saltwater fish *do* drink seawater, and they retain most of the water. They produce very little urine, and their gills actively pump out excess salt. Sea lions, whales, and other marine mammals have a different solution: They never need to drink and instead take in salt water only with food. Their very efficient kidneys conserve water strongly and excrete excess salt.

It is clear from these descriptions that whatever an animal's environment, its excretory system works continuously to keep water and dump salt, or the reverse, depending on what's needed to maintain a steady state in the body tissues. Homeostasis—whether of body fluid content, oxygen levels in the tissues, calcium in the blood and bones, or body temperature—is costly but necessary to survival. Understanding the many body parts and mechanisms that contribute to this steady state helps us appreciate the beauty of our own physiology and that of other animals. It also encourages us to take care of our health in intelligent ways. And it gives us a deeper understanding of the extreme environments explorers like Bernard Harris have faced and overcome in the high mountains, desert, polar regions, ocean abyss, and the radiation-blasted darkness and weightlessness of space.

Freshwater fishes do not drink, but saltwater fishes do.

CHAPTER 17

Circulation *and* Respiration

Learning Outcomes

LO[1] Understand the role of blood in the circulatory system

LO[2] Compare open and closed circulatory systems

LO[3] Explain the anatomy and the activity of the blood vessels and heart

LO[4] Explain the structure and activity of the respiratory system

> ❝*Fully one-third of the approximately 75 trillion cells in your body are red blood cells.*❞

A Life-Saving Substitute

Blood is a life-giving, oxygen-bearing commodity that we tend to take for granted. We often assume that in a modern, industrialized country, it will be quickly available should we have the misfortune to need it. But blood shortages are growing more common as fewer and fewer people—less than 5 percent of the population—are willing donors. Exhaustive testing for the viruses that cause AIDS and hepatitis and for other contaminants has made our blood supply safe, but at a price: A hospital patient can now pay hundreds of dollars for a single unit (pint) of blood.

What do you know?

Snorkelers often hyperventilate before a deep dive. Why might this be dangerous?

To researchers, there's a straightforward answer to this dilemma: Artificial blood. Doctors have spent nearly two decades in pursuit of a blood substitute that works well and won't harm patients. Artificial blood has, in fact, been a top research goal for many drug companies and for the U.S. Army. But as simple and worthy as this search may sound, it's an unbelievably complicated thing to do.

The creation of artificial blood is our case study in this chapter and serves as a lead-in to the two main subjects. The first is circulation—how blood moves through the body carrying oxygen and nutrients to tissue cells and carrying wastes away. The second is respiration—how sufficient oxygen is drawn into the body and transferred to blood, and in return, how carbon dioxide is expelled. The two systems and their vital organs, the heart, lungs, and blood vessels, are delicately intertwined. While exploring these critical systems, you'll find the answers to these questions:

- ☑ What is blood and how does it reach tissues throughout the body?
- ☑ How does the heart circulate the blood and what is the lymphatic system?
- ☑ How are heartbeat and blood pressure controlled?
- ☑ How does oxygen leave the blood and enter cells, and why do those cells need oxygen?
- ☑ How do the lungs draw in air and expel carbon dioxide, and how does the body control breathing rate?
- ☑ What are comparable strategies for gas exchange in other animals?

LO¹ Blood: A Liquid Tissue for Transport

A safe human blood substitute is clearly needed. But why is making one so difficult? To understand that, let's look at what the blood does in the healthy body or when transferred into a

circulation
the path of blood or a blood equivalent such as hemolymph as it moves through an animal's body, carrying oxygen and nutrients to tissue cells and carrying wastes away

respiration
the process by which oxygen is drawn into the body and transferred to blood, and carbon dioxide is expelled

erythrocyte
a red blood cell; its main function is transporting oxygen to the tissues

leukocyte
a white blood cell; functions in the body's defense against invading microorganisms or other foreign matters

platelet
a disk-shaped cell fragment in the blood important in blood clotting; also called a *thrombocyte*

plasma
the liquid portion of blood

antibody
a protein produced by the immune system in response to the entry of specific antigens (foreign substances) into the body

albumin
a group of large blood proteins that helps maintain osmotic pressure and binds to toxic substances in the blood

fibrinogen
a protein in blood plasma that is converted to fibrin during clotting

surgery patient and how it carries out those many roles.

Components of Blood

If you prick your finger with a sterile pin then press out a small drop of blood onto a glass slide, you'll immediately see the bright red color. If you examined the drop with a microscope, you'd see the reason for the hue: Your view would be nearly filled with red blood cells, or erythrocytes (*erythro* = red + *cyte* = cell) (Fig. 17.1a). You'd also see a much smaller number of white blood cells, or leukocytes (*leuko* = white) in the same microscope field, along with some platelets, which are small globular cell fragments, and a watery yellow fluid surrounding all the solid elements.

Since blood is red, one might assume that the most common element is the red blood cell. But is it? To find out, you'd need not just a droplet of blood but a few

milliliters of blood in a test tube. Then you'd need to put the tube in a centrifuge, an apparatus that spins a sample rapidly and separates components according to their density. What you'd see is that within the centrifuged blood, the top half or so is the pale yellow liquid, called plasma, which is more than 91 percent water (Fig. 17.1b). Plasma's main function is transporting blood cells and dissolved substances, including salts, sugars, and fats, from the foods we eat. Plasma also contains water and a storehouse of important dissolved salts and proteins, which additional laboratory procedures can separate out. One group of plasma proteins, the globulins, includes antibodies, defensive molecules that attack invaders (described in Chapter 18). The albumins, another group of large blood proteins, help maintain osmotic pressure and bind to toxic substances in the blood. A third plasma protein, fibrinogen, is essential for blood clotting. To make substitute blood plasma in the laboratory, one would need to add the proper amount of salts to sterile water. The liver and other organs would then provide proteins like albumin and fibrinogen.

In a test tube of centrifuged blood, the dense portion below the yellowish plasma is the part that proves hardest to reconstruct in artificial blood. This 45 to 50 percent has two bands (Fig. 17.1b): on top is a thin gray band representing less than 1 percent of blood volume and consisting of white blood cells plus cell fragments, the platelets, which help blood to clot. The lower, much wider red band contains red blood cells. A physician can use the width of

Figure 17.1

Blood and its Components

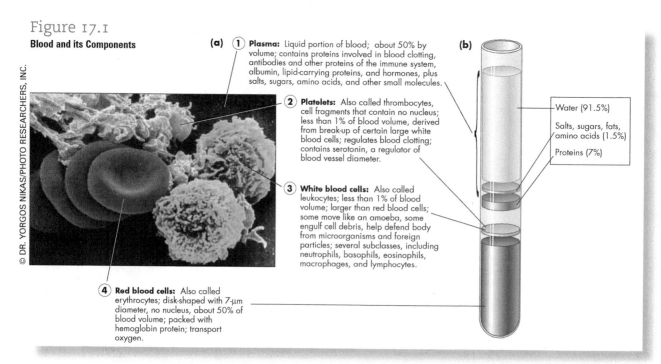

(a)

① **Plasma:** Liquid portion of blood; about 50% by volume; contains proteins involved in blood clotting, antibodies and other proteins of the immune system, albumin, lipid-carrying proteins, and hormones, plus salts, sugars, amino acids, and other small molecules.

② **Platelets:** Also called thrombocytes, cell fragments that contain no nucleus; less than 1% of blood volume, derived from break-up of certain large white blood cells; regulates blood clotting; contains serotonin, a regulator of blood vessel diameter.

③ **White blood cells:** Also called leukocytes; less than 1% of blood volume; larger than red blood cells; some move like an amoeba, some engulf cell debris, help defend body from microorganisms and foreign particles; several subclasses, including neutrophils, basophils, eosinophils, macrophages, and lymphocytes.

④ **Red blood cells:** Also called erythrocytes; disk-shaped with 7-μm diameter, no nucleus, about 50% of blood volume; packed with hemoglobin protein; transport oxygen.

(b)

Water (91.5%)

Salts, sugars, fats, amino acids (1.5%)

Proteins (7%)

© DR. YORGOS NIKAS/PHOTO RESEARCHERS, INC.

this band of red blood cells to help diagnose medical problems. If the band is too narrow, the person has too few red blood cells and is probably *anemic*, perhaps suffering from fatigue and shortness of breath. Anemia can result from heavy blood loss, iron deficiency, poor vitamin B_{12} absorption, sickle cell disease (see Chapter 5), certain infections, and other causes. The red blood cells are simple, but crucial to blood's role in carrying oxygen, and constructing them—or something that performs their functions—is the major challenge to biologists trying to make artificial blood.

Red Blood Cell Shape and Function

Fully one-third of the approximately 75 trillion cells in your body are red blood cells. Let's look at those 25 trillion cells, see how they work, and discuss what it would take to replace them. Clues to red blood cell function come from the shape of the cells and their contents. Each red blood cell resembles a doughnut without a hole (Fig. 17.1a)—biologists call it a *biconcave disk* shape. In contrast, white blood cells are shaped more like golf balls, and many other body cells are shaped like ice cubes. So why does the red blood cell have that particular disklike shape? Being rounded, they move through vessels fairly easily. Their flattened shape allows more of the cell contents to be close to the cell's surface compared to a spherical cell; this suggests that cell surface exchanges are especially crucial for red blood cell function. Proteins of the cytoskeleton just inside the cell membrane help maintain the red blood cell's disk shape (see Fig. 2.10). Embedded in that membrane are the proteins and carbohydrates that give the cell its A, B, O, or AB blood type. Infusing a patient with the wrong blood type can lead to a dangerous clumping reaction in the blood vessels. Artificial blood lacking blood cell membranes, surface markers, and hence blood types would avoid this potential problem.

Although humans are eukaryotes, their mature red blood cells lack a nucleus, mitochondria, and other cell organelles. That's because these organelles are squeezed out as the red cells grow and develop, and are not replaced. The loss of organelles leaves more space for important proteins in the cell. Red blood cells help to transport carbon dioxide to the lungs, partly because they contain the enzyme **carbonic anhydrase**. This enzyme speeds the conversion of carbon dioxide (CO_2) and water (H_2O) to bicarbonate (HCO_3^-) and hydrogen ion (H^+). When there is lots of carbon dioxide in the environment, the extra hydrogen ions turn the blood more acidic. Most of all, though, the red blood cells are chock full of the protein hemoglobin, which transports oxygen. The flattened shape of red blood cells makes sense in that they allow more of each cell's millions of hemoglobin molecules to lie near the outer membrane than if red blood cells were spheres. Any artificial blood substitute would therefore need some type of oxygen-transporting molecule that somehow mimics this flattened "wrapper" or at least the cell membrane's ability to allow fast, efficient gas exchange between the blood and its surroundings.

carbonic anhydrase
an enzyme contained by red blood cells that speeds the conversion of carbon dioxide (CO_2) and water (H_2O) to bicarbonate (HCO_3^-) and hydrogen ion (H^+)

hemoglobin
a blood protein with iron-containing heme groups that bind and transport oxygen

Hemoglobin: An Oxygen-Carrier Molecule

Hemoglobin molecules are far smaller than red blood cells. In fact, each red blood cell contains about 350 *million* hemoglobin molecules. Hemoglobin's specialized structure allows it to act like an oxygen sponge and enables a pint of blood, let's say, to soak up 70 times more oxygen than could a pint of water. Hemoglobin has a unique structure with four polypeptide chains (called globin chains). Two of these, the alpha-globin chains, are identical, as are the other two, the beta-globin chains. Each of the four globins in a hemoglobin molecule is wrapped around a heme group, a series of chemical rings surrounding an iron atom. Heme is red in color and hence makes your blood red. Oxygen binds to the single iron atom at the center of each heme (see Fig. 17.2 on the next page).

Researchers have tried the most direct approach to making a blood substitute: eliminating the red blood cell "wrapper" and putting naked heme groups directly into a test animal's blood vessels. The problem, though, is that the heme binds so tightly to oxygen that it won't release the gas to cells that need it—hardworking muscle cells in the legs, let's say. This fact helps us understand the role of the hemoglobin's protein portion, the globin chains: They cause the heme to take up and release oxygen under appropriate physiological conditions. The plain heme idea didn't work. But it does help us see the complexity of blood's functioning in the body.

With its four globin chains and central heme group, the hemoglobin molecule is a wonder of adaptation. It not only picks up oxygen in the lungs and carries it to the tissues but also picks up carbon dioxide from the tissues and releases it in the lungs. Carbon dioxide binds directly to the protein chains, not to the central heme group. Furthermore, the versatile hemoglobin molecule binds more or less easily to oxygen, depending on the conditions. The blood in the body's brain and muscle tissues, for example, is more acidic than the blood in the lungs. That's because the active brain and muscle cells are giving off carbon dioxide from the burning of food molecules for energy. Carbonic anhydrase enzymes in the red blood cells (mentioned earlier) quickly convert CO_2 and water to bicarbonate and hydrogen ion, and this conversion makes the blood more acidic. Under these more acidic conditions, hemoglobin binds oxygen less readily, thus O_2 tends to break away from hemoglobin and diffuse from the bloodstream into tissue cells, which need it. This helps insure that cells will get the oxygen they need. But it also adds another level of complexity for those trying to make a successful blood substitute.

Production of New Red Blood Cells

We said that red blood cells are relatively short lived and can't divide and reproduce themselves. So how fast does the body make new blood cells, how long do they stay in circulation, and where do they arise in the body? The answers are additional considerations when designing artificial blood: If a person's body could produce a new crop of red blood cells in just a couple of hours, then when he or she became injured, artificial blood could be added for a very short time, mainly to keep the blood volume at a normal level, and soon the missing cells would be replaced naturally. However, if red blood cells form slowly over days or weeks, then a replacement would have to last much longer. It turns out that individual red blood cells die after about 120 days of circulating in the body and are replaced from stem cells in the bone marrow. The bone marrow stem cell populations are self-regenerating: When a stem cell divides in two, one daughter cell begins to differentiate into a mature blood cell, while the other differentiates into another stem cell and in effect replaces the original one. Some stem cells give rise to red blood cells; others generate white blood cells and the precursors to platelets.

In Chapter 16, we saw that the body has an important feedback mechanism that can sense

Figure 17.2

Hemoglobin

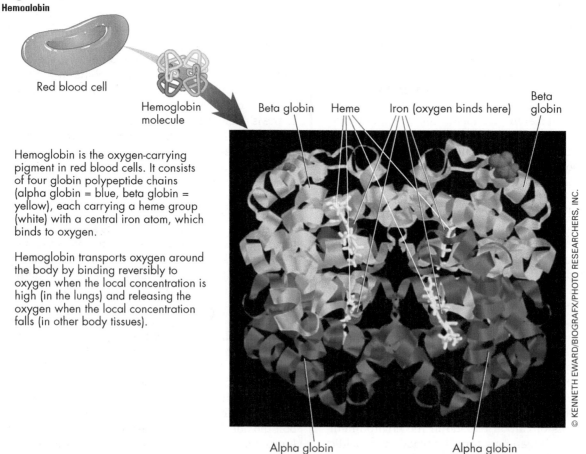

Red blood cell

Hemoglobin molecule

Beta globin   Heme   Iron (oxygen binds here)   Beta globin

Hemoglobin is the oxygen-carrying pigment in red blood cells. It consists of four globin polypeptide chains (alpha globin = blue, beta globin = yellow), each carrying a heme group (white) with a central iron atom, which binds to oxygen.

Hemoglobin transports oxygen around the body by binding reversibly to oxygen when the local concentration is high (in the lungs) and releasing the oxygen when the local concentration falls (in other body tissues).

Alpha globin   Alpha globin

a drop in red blood cell concentration after a sudden blood loss, as from a wound, and tells the bone marrow to begin making new cells (Fig. 17.3). A sudden blood loss can signal the bone marrow, too. The feedback mechanism starts when a decrease in the number of red cells in the blood lowers oxygen levels to the liver and kidneys. These organs then begin to produce the protein hormone erythropoietin (eh-RITH-ro-po-EE-tin; Greek, red + to make). This hormone travels through the bloodstream to the bone marrow, where it stimulates stem cells to divide and differentiate more quickly; as more red blood cells are produced, they carry more oxygen to tissues and organs throughout the body, including the liver and kidney. As a result, these organs slow their production of erythropoietin, and division of bone marrow stem cells slows. It takes about five days for a cell to pass down the "assembly line" of red blood cell differentiation, so the first brand new red blood cells won't appear in the blood in substantial numbers until about five days after the initial blood cell loss. Ideally, then, a blood substitute would last at least five days while the body generates new cells of its own to restore the original concentration.

Figure 17.3
Replacing Lost Blood Cells: A Negative Feedback Loop

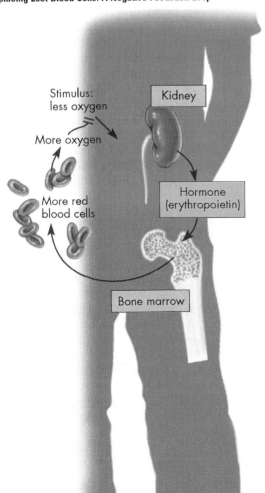

As you might imagine, erythropoietin could be an important supplement to artificial blood to help stimulate new blood cell production after blood loss from an accident, surgery, or a battle. Indeed, there are effective erythropoietin drugs on the market that do stimulate red blood cell formation. Unfortunately, some unscrupulous athletes have tried using these drugs to gain an advantage without putting in the necessary training work. They've resorted to taking erythropoietin ("epo") to stimulate an increase in red blood cells in the hopes of increasing oxygen delivery to their muscles. For someone without blood loss, however, this may be counterproductive, because the increased concentration of red blood cells also increases blood viscosity; this in turn makes the heart work harder than normal, trying to pump the thicker, more molasses-like fluid through the vessels.

> **erythropoietin**
> a hormone that stimulates the production of new red blood cells

White Blood Cells: Defense of the Body

For every 500 red blood cells, there is only one white blood cell, or *leukocyte* (*leuko* = white + *cyte* = cell; see Fig. 17.1). White blood cells are larger than red blood cells, and they retain their nucleus when they mature. Some leukocytes can move like an amoeba, an ability that allows them to squeeze through blood vessel walls and patrol the fluid-filled spaces between cells. Some can also engulf and take in debris (see Chapter 2). These characteristics help leukocytes to defend the body against invasions by microorganisms and other foreign materials, and to consume cell debris. There is so much to say about leukocytes and their role in the body's immune defense that Chapter 18 is devoted entirely to the subject.

Platelets: Plugging Leaks in the System

We saw that blood has a third cellular component, the platelets (also called *thrombocytes*; see Fig. 17.1). Platelets are not entire cells, but are irregular fragments that have broken off from large specialized cells in the bone marrow. Platelets are crucial blood components because they help to plug small leaks in the circulatory system. Were it not for the blood-clotting action of platelets, an animal's entire blood supply might literally drain away through even a minor wound. Even if a person or other animal were to lose a significant amount of blood through an unexpected trauma, however, the remaining blood would contain enough platelets to keep up the blood's normal clotting functions.

All of the blood's components are essential to its collective functions in the body: oxygen delivery; carbon dioxide removal; blood clotting; immune defense; and helping maintain the body's proper fluid volume. Artificial blood for emergency use can be simpler: just a sterile saline solution for the right blood volume and osmotic conditions, and some red-blood-cell equivalent to carry oxygen and carbon dioxide. The latter characteristic is the real challenge, as we'll see. But first, let's explore the intricate system of vessels through which the blood flows, as well as alternative systems for both blood and circulation in other animals.

LO² Circulatory Systems

In a town without roads, delivery trucks would be useless. Likewise, blood—whether authentic or artificial—would be of little value to an animal unless it could circulate its cargo of gases, nutrients, and other substances throughout the body. The human circulatory system has a highly branched network of vessels totalling thousands of miles in length—its "road system," if you will. A constant flow of blood passes through the vessels to within 0.1 mm (0.004 in.) of each body cell. A distance this tiny allows materials in the blood to diffuse quickly into cells and replenish nutrients and other necessary materials. Animals living in various kinds of environments have a range of different needs for gases, nutrients, and waste removal, as well as numerous kinds of restrictions upon what would be an appropriate delivery system. The range of solutions tells us something fundamental about the range of needs. So let's look at the circulatory systems of other animals.

Open Circulatory Systems

Tarantulas have an open circulatory system (Fig. 17.4a) in which a clear blood equivalent called *hemolymph* circulates rather freely in the body unconfined by tubes or vessels. Most other arthropods also have open circulatory systems, as do mollusks. The tarantula's heart is little more than an elongated, pulsating tube that runs from the rear of the body to the front (Fig. 17.4b). The heart's pumping action sends hemolymph in the direction of the animal's brain, where it leaves the heart tube and percolates toward the back of the animal through the open body cavity, bathing the tissues in the animal's gut and other internal organs. Finally, the hemolymph returns to the heart tube through special pores. An open circulation is not a very efficient transport system, but it suffices for spiders, insects, and many other invertebrates.

Closed Circulatory Systems

Segmented worms such as earthworms and vertebrates such as humans have a closed circulatory system, with its blood completely contained inside a system of vessels (Fig. 17.5a).

A closed circulatory system has several advantages over an open one. First, fluid contained within a network of closed tubes can be more easily shunted to

Figure 17.4
An Open Circulatory System

(a) An open circulation system

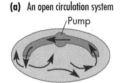

Pump

(b) Circulatory system of a tarantula

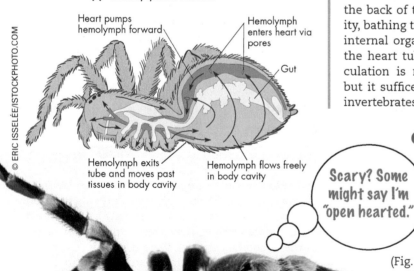

Heart pumps hemolymph forward

Hemolymph enters heart via pores

Gut

Hemolymph exits tube and moves past tissues in body cavity

Hemolymph flows freely in body cavity

Scary? Some might say I'm "open hearted."

specific areas where it is needed, much as a farmer can send the water in irrigation pipes to different fields. Second, because the fluid is completely contained within pipelines, the circulatory system can exert more pressure on the blood, forcefully distributing blood to areas distant from the pump, as in a giraffe's head or a whale's tail. You've no doubt discovered the results of pressurized fluid yourself: You can squirt water on an unsuspecting friend much farther away when you partially close off the opening of a garden hose with your thumb than you can by dribbling the water out of the unobstructed hose end.

The features of the closed circulatory system allow it to deliver blood more efficiently throughout larger, more complex, and more active organisms than an open system could. The human circulatory system is just one variation on this basic theme (Fig. 17.5b).

LO³ The Human Circulatory System

It takes an immense network of circulatory "tubing" to carry the 25 trillion red blood cells that deliver gases and materials to your body's other 50 trillion cells (Fig. 17.5b,c). If all of the blood vessels in your body were stitched end to end, the single long pipeline would circle the Earth twice! To keep the blood flowing through all these vessels, your heart must beat with a regular rhythm and maintain the flow at a pressure that is high enough to force blood into your brain, nose, toes, and all the tissues in between. These enormous tasks are possible because of both the anatomy and the activity of the blood vessels and heart. This vital system is also subject to many diseases and conditions, as we'll see later.

An Overview of Circulation

Let's start by exploring the pathways that blood takes through the human circulatory system. Blood leaving the right side of the heart passes to the lungs, organs that bring blood into contact with oxygen from the environment. Oxygen

Figure 17.5
A Closed Circulatory System

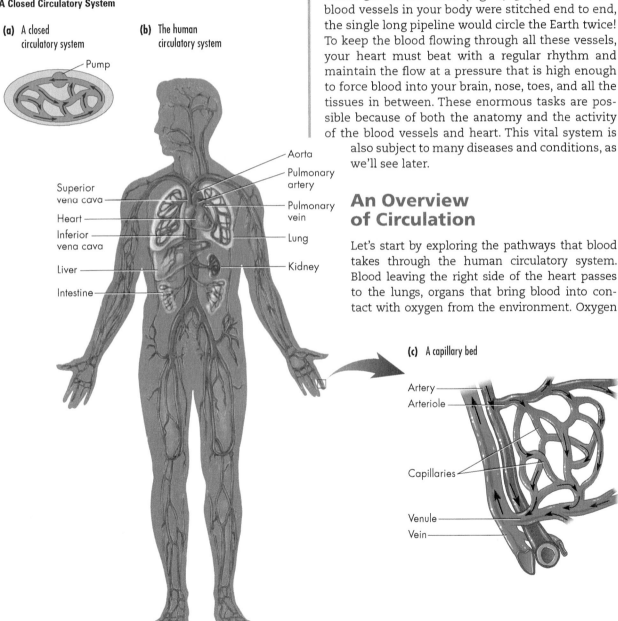

(a) A closed circulatory system

Pump

(b) The human circulatory system

Aorta
Pulmonary artery
Pulmonary vein
Lung
Kidney

Superior vena cava
Heart
Inferior vena cava
Liver
Intestine

(c) A capillary bed

Artery
Arteriole
Capillaries
Venule
Vein

pulmonary circulation
the blood vessel system that carries oxygen-poor blood from the heart to the lungs, where gas exchange occurs, and carries oxygen-rich blood back to the heart

systemic circulation
the blood vessel system that carries oxygen-rich blood from the heart to the body and returns oxygen-poor blood to the heart

artery
a large blood vessel with thick, multilayered muscular walls, which carries blood from the heart to the body

blood pressure
a force of liquid blood within the circulatory system; created by blood moving within a closed system and propelled by contractions of the heart and muscular artery walls

arteriole
a thinner-walled, smaller branch of an artery, which carries blood from arteries to the capillaries in the tissues

capillary
tiny blood vessels with walls one cell thick that permeate the tissues and organs of the body

capillary bed
a network of capillaries that links arterial and venous blood vessels

venule
a small thin-walled blood vessel that arises from capillaries and carries blood from the tissues to the veins

vein
a large thin-walled blood vessel that brings blood from the body to the heart

diffuses from the air in the lung sacs into the blood. Once the blood has picked up oxygen, it returns to the left side of the heart for further pumping. The left side of the heart then pushes the blood with enough force to deliver oxygen to every cell, tissue, and organ in the body. On this circuit, for example, the blood moves through the gut, where it picks up nutrients (details in Chapter 19); through the kidneys, where it dumps waste materials for excretion from the body (see Chapter 16 for details); to the muscles and brain, where it unloads oxygen and picks up carbon dioxide; to endocrine organs, where it picks up hormones (see Chapter 20), and so on. Eventually, the blood returns to the right side of the heart and begins another circuit.

This arrangement can be thought of as two separate circulatory loops. In the lung loop, or pulmonary circulation, the right side of the heart pumps blood directly to the lungs and back to the left side of the heart. In the second loop, a body loop called the systemic circulation, the left side of the heart pumps blood to all organs except the lungs, and the blood returns to the right side of the heart. Because of this double loop arrangement, oxygen-rich and oxygen-poor blood never normally mix. Furthermore, the body can control the two circulatory systems somewhat independently, with the right side of the heart using less pressure to pump blood to the nearby lungs, and the left side of the heart using high pressure to reach all body tissues quickly. Not all vertebrates have this two-loop arrangement, as biologists have learned by studying the evolutionary origin of the circulatory systems in fish, reptiles, amphibians, birds, and mammals.

Blood Vessels

"Vessels" is a catch-all phrase for thick-walled tubes wider than your thumb, delicate pipelines much finer than a hair, and everything in between. All the vessels must contain fast-moving blood cells. So what are our blood vessels like?

Blood moves away from the heart in arteries, vessels with thick, multilayered, muscular walls ranging in size from the diameter of a garden hose to the thickness of a pencil or less (see Fig. 17.5c). The contraction of these wall muscles, along with the beating of the heart, helps keep blood under pressure—the force we call blood pressure. The pulse you can feel in your neck and wrists is actually sequential spurts of blood passing through arteries. Arteries branch and form smaller vessels called arterioles. These vessels are too small to be seen without a microscope, and the muscle layer surrounding them is thinner than in the arteries. Arterioles branch again into the dense, weblike network of delicate capillaries, minute vessels that permeate the fingertips, earlobes, lungs, liver, and all the tissues of the body. Capillaries are microscopic vessels only about 8 micrometers (0.0003 in.) in diameter, and rarely more than about 0.1 mm (0.004 in.) from any body cell. A capillary's diameter is so small that red blood cells can pass through only in single file. Capillary walls are just one cell layer thick, so they are very delicate. Capillaries are so numerous, however, that they make up almost all of a person's blood vessels; if all capillaries were filled with blood at the same time, they could contain the entire 5 L (10.5 pints) of human blood. The capillaries' ultrathin structure is one key to the efficiency of the circulatory system, because materials can readily diffuse into and out of the narrow capillaries and the single cell layer that encompasses them. Any successful design for artificial blood must easily pass through these capillaries and leave them unharmed.

One of the most marvelous features of the vertebrate circulatory system is the capillary beds, networks that link the arterial and venous sides of the circulation (see Fig. 17.5c). The arterial side of each capillary bed conveys fresh blood (pictured in red) *away from the heart* and to the capillaries. Oxygen, nutrients, carbon dioxide, and metabolic wastes can move quickly across the capillary walls and into and out of the extracellular fluid and nearby tissue cells. The oxygen-depleted blood (shown in blue) then continues to move through the bed to the venous side; there the capillaries leading away from the tissues feed into larger vessels known as venules, which in turn merge and become veins. Veins carry blood *toward the heart,* where the circulation cycle begins again. Perhaps you can see the bluish veins close to the skin surface of your wrists. These blue vessels

Figure 17.6

Valves Maintain a One-Way Blood Flow in Veins

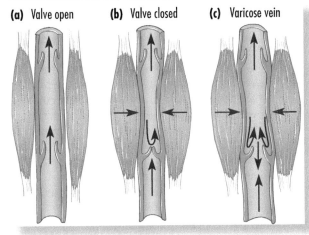

(a) Valve open   **(b)** Valve closed   **(c)** Varicose vein

contain hemoglobin with less oxygen bound to it and this is not as bright red as oxygen-rich blood.

Blood in the veins is under lower pressure than blood in arteries. This is because blood in the veins has already traveled some distance from the heart and has been slowed by passage through the narrow capillaries, and because veins have a larger diameter and less muscular walls that squeeze their contents less forcefully than do artery walls. This low-pressure fluid flows toward the heart's right side and does not flow backward or pool in the extremities owing to a system of valves—tonguelike flaps that extend into the internal space (or *lumen*) of the vein (Fig. 17.6). The heart has valves, too, as we'll see; these are similar to but distinct from the venous valves. Like a one-way door, when blood pushes a valve from one direction, it opens and allows blood to pass, but when blood pushes from the other direction, the valve slams shut. If venous valves become damaged, blood can flow backward, causing the vein to distend and become visible as a large blue bulb, a *varicose vein*. Whatever form artificial blood takes, it must not be unduly damaged by the slamming shut of the valves or the small eddies they create.

The Heart

At the physiological center of the circulatory system lies the heart (see Fig. 17.5b). Roughly the size of a large, lopsided apple, your heart pumps a teacupful of blood with every three beats, 5 L (5.3 qt) of blood every minute, and upwards of 7,200 L of blood every day of your life. Over a lifetime, this amounts to 2.5 billion heartbeats and enough blood to fill a building six stories high and a city block long. Although medical engineers have tried valiantly, replacing the living circulatory pump has proved exceedingly difficult.

This tireless organ, and the hearts of all mammals, has four chambers divided into two pairs: the right atrium and right ventricle, and the left atrium and left ventricle. Each atrium (pl., *atria*) receives blood from veins. (In ancient Rome, an atrium was a roofless room with a pool to collect rainwater.) The more muscular chamber, the ventricle, receives blood from the atrium and pumps it through an artery to either the pulmonary or systemic circulation. Let's follow the pathway of blood through the heart, starting with the pulmonary circulation (see Fig. 17.7 on the next page):

Step ①. The right ventricle of the heart pumps oxygen-poor blood past a one-way valve, the pulmonary semilunar valve, with three half-moon-shaped flaps, into the Y-shaped pulmonary arteries.

Step ②. The pulmonary arteries carry oxygen-poor blood to capillaries in the lungs, where the blood picks up oxygen from inhaled air and unloads carbon dioxide into exhaled air.

Step ③. The freshly oxygenated blood flows to the pulmonary veins (the only veins in an adult person that carry oxygen-rich blood) and then passes to the heart's left atrium.

Step ④. The left atrium pumps the oxygenated blood through another one-way valve, the mitral or left atrioventricular valve, into the heart's left ventricle. This chamber sucks in much of the blood as it relaxes. (For a comparison, clench your fist tightly and then relax your fingers, and see how air is sucked into the space inside your fist.)

Step ⑤. The thick walls of the muscular left ventricle contract around this blood in a wringing motion until enough pressure develops to push open yet another one-way valve,

valve
a tonguelike flap extending into the internal space of a vein that helps regulate the flow of blood

heart
a muscular organ that pumps blood through vessels

atrium (pl., atria)
(L., hallway) a chamber of the heart that receives blood from the veins

ventricle
a muscular chamber of the heart that pumps blood to the lungs or to the rest of the body

pulmonary semilunar valve
one-way valve with three half-moon-shaped flaps through which the right ventricle of the heart pumps oxygen-poor blood toward the lungs

pulmonary artery
the artery that carries blood from the heart's right ventricle to the lungs

pulmonary veins
vessels that carry oxygenated blood from the lungs to the heart's left atrium

aorta
in a vertebrate animal, the main artery leading directly from the left ventricle of the heart; supplies blood to most of the animal's body

superior vena cava
one of the two largest veins in the human body; carries blood from the head, neck, and arms to the right atrium of the heart

inferior vena cava
one of the two largest veins in the human body; carries blood from the legs and most of the lower body to the right atrium of the heart

cardiac muscle
the specialized muscle tissue of the heart

intercalated disks
an intercellular connection that links heart muscle cells electrically

the aortic semi-lunar valve, and squirt the blood into the aorta—the main artery leading to the systemic circulation. This body loop conveys blood to capillary beds in brain, muscle, kidney, and other distant tissues, then returns it via venules and veins that lead back to the right atrium again.

Step ⑥. The right atrium receives oxygen-poor blood from the body tissues via two large veins, the superior vena cava and the inferior vena cava. These vessels collect blood from the upper and lower body, respectively. Finally, the right atrium pumps its load of oxygen-poor blood into the right ventricle through a fourth valve, the petal-shaped tricuspid or right atrioventricular valve, which prevents blood from flowing back when a ventricle contracts. Again, the ventricle provides negative pressure that sucks blood into the cavity. The circuit is now complete, and as the right ventricle contracts, it pushes blood once more into the pulmonary circulation.

How Does the Body Control the Heartbeat?

Like the muscles in your arm, each of the heart's four chambers is made up of specialized cells organized into contractile fibers. In your arm, however, your biceps muscle can contract either weakly (e.g., when you pick up a pencil) or more strongly (when you pick up your backpack), and the strength of contraction depends on what percentage of the muscle fibers contract at any given time. In your heart, however, all the fibers in the cardiac (heart) muscle contract with each heartbeat. Blood flow through the heart increases mainly by faster beating.

What accounts for this specialized "all or none system" so characteristic of heart muscle? First, heart muscle cells are linked electrically by special regions, the intercalated (in-TER-cal-ated) disks. Junctions (see Chapter 2) between cells in these disk regions pass electrical impulses instantaneously from muscle cell to muscle cell, and these electrical signals stimulate muscle contraction. As a result, neighboring sections of the heart wall contract and relax together in a superbly coordinated pumping action that keeps blood flowing smoothly through the system.

Figure 17.7

Pathways of Blood Flow

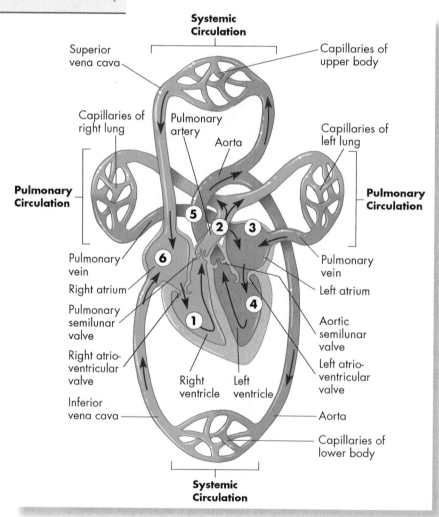

Systemic Circulation

Superior vena cava

Capillaries of upper body

Capillaries of right lung

Pulmonary artery

Aorta

Capillaries of left lung

Pulmonary Circulation

Pulmonary Circulation

5

2

3

6

Pulmonary vein

Pulmonary vein

Right atrium

Left atrium

Pulmonary semilunar valve

1

4

Aortic semilunar valve

Right atrioventricular valve

Left atrioventricular valve

Inferior vena cava

Right ventricle

Left ventricle

Aorta

Capillaries of lower body

Systemic Circulation

Second, cardiac muscle contracts automatically—that is, without stimulation from the nervous system. (Nerves do help speed or slow the heart rate, however, as Chapter 21 describes.) Different subsets of heart muscle cells have different intrinsic rates of contraction. Some, called pacemaker cells, contract slightly faster than all the others, and because each contraction spreads quickly throughout a region of the muscle, pacemaker cells ignite contractions in the entire heart and set the rate of the heartbeat.

Pacemaker cells are located near the upper right atrium in a region called the sinoatrial (SA) node (Fig. 17.8a). Immediately before a beat, an electrical impulse spreads from the SA node across the walls of both right and left atria, causing the two chambers to contract in unison. A second node, the atrioventricular (AV) node (Fig. 17.8b), is another area of modified cardiac muscle cells located at the junction of the right atrium and right ventricles. When the electrical signal generated by the SA node reaches the AV node, there is a brief delay before the signal

passes to the ventricles. Upon reaching the ventricles, the signal triggers a contraction of these chambers. The brief delay in the transmission of the pacemaker impulse at the AV node is necessary for an efficiently beating heart: If the atria and ventricles were to contract simultaneously, blood in the atria might flow back into the veins instead of forward into the ventricles.

Each time a heart's atria or ventricles contract, they are said to be in systole (SISS-toe-lee). The opposite, or relaxed, phase is known as diastole (die-AST-oh-lee). Together, these two phases make up the cardiac cycle—the contraction/relaxation sequence of atria and ventricles that makes up a single heartbeat. As the ventricles relax in diastole, they suck blood from the atria into their chambers, a bit like a turkey baster drawing up juice.

pacemaker cells
cells that set the rate of the heartbeat

sinoatrial (SA) node
a lump of modified heart muscle cells near the upper right atrium that is spontaneously electrically excitable; the pacemaker that governs the basic rate of heart contractions in vertebrates

atrioventricular (AV) node
a bundle of modified cardiac muscle cells between the heart's atria and ventricles that relays electrical activity to the ventricles

systole
the contraction phase of the heart muscle

diastole
the relaxation phase of the heart muscle

cardiac cycle
the contraction/relaxation (systolic/diastolic) sequence of atria and ventricles that makes up a single heartbeat

Figure 17.8
Electrical Impulses Drive the Heartbeat

(a) Signal from SA node: atria contract

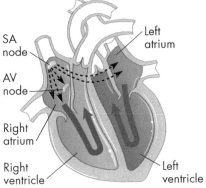

(b) Signal from AV node: ventricles contract

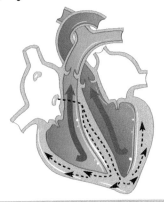

Blood Pressure

When a person loses blood from a major wound, there is a disastrous decrease in blood pressure because the pressurized system has been breached. The main reason for giving blood transfusions in the battlefield or at an accident scene is to maintain blood pressure. Often, paramedics will simply infuse saline because fresh whole blood of the right blood type is not available in an ambulance. In a sense, saline was the first successful blood substitute because it helps restore blood volume and pressure. It doesn't carry much oxygen, however. Normal blood pressure, generated by muscles in the walls of the heart and arteries, is substantial: blood spurts out more than 2 m (6.5 ft) high from a severed aortic artery! To deliver blood quickly and continuously to cells far from the heart, blood pressure must remain adequate; an extreme blood pressure drop can send a person into shock and actually be fatal in itself.

Blood Pressure and Disease

A healthy young adult male at rest has a typical blood pressure of about 120 mm Hg during systole and about 80 mm Hg during diastole. This is written as 120/80 and stated as "120 over 80." A nurse

atherosclerosis
the formal name for cardiovascular disease, a condition in which waxy deposits or plaques build up inside the arteries and gradually obstruct blood flow

coronary arteries
the arteries of the heart

myocardial infarction (heart attack)
medical condition resulting from the blockage (from a blood clot) of the heart's arteries, causing complete cutoff of blood flow to a section of the heart muscle and subsequent damage or destruction of that muscle tissue

stroke
paralysis or numbness caused by destruction of brain tissue due to a blood clot or blood vessel break

or doctor measures your blood pressure in millimeters of mercury (mm Hg); a pressure of 120 mm Hg could literally lift a column of mercury 120 mm high (4.5 in.). Young women and people who exercise regularly tend to have blood pressure readings lower than 120/80. Patients are considered to have high blood pressure or hypertension if their readings are persistently higher than 140/90. Hypertension is often called "the silent killer" because it can cause considerable damage to blood vessels long before it causes pain or disability.

High blood pressure causes local thickening in the smooth muscle cells surrounding blood vessels. You've probably heard of *arteriosclerosis*, a disease characterized by thickened artery walls (*sclero* = hard). In one form of this disease, called atherosclerosis, cholesterol accumulations lead to waxy deposits or *plaques* that build up inside the arteries and gradually obstruct blood flow. Obstructing blood flow increases blood pressure the way tightening a nozzle boosts water pressure inside a running hose. To overcome the mechanical obstruction and resistance of plaque buildups, the heart's ventricles must work harder. If plaques accumulate in the heart's own arteries (the coronary arteries), the muscle can become oxygen-deprived and this can lead to *angina pectoris*, a condition of squeezing chest pressure and pain. Plaques in coronary arteries can attract platelets and these, in turn, sometimes cause blood clots to form. If a clot breaks off, it can lodge further down the artery's interior and completely cut off blood flow to a section of heart muscle. This clotting and sudden blockage is called a *heart attack* or myocardial infarction, and it can cause disability or even death. If the blood clot forms in a brain artery and cuts off

blood flow to brain tissue, the event is called a stroke, and this can result in deficits of speech and/or movement.

People can prevent or at least manage hypertension by maintaining ideal weight, exercising several times per week, avoiding tobacco, reducing salt and alcohol consumption, and controlling stress. Certain drugs can also help, including diuretics to reduce blood volume (and hence pressure) and beta blockers to reduce heart contraction and blood pressure.

Blood pressure is obviously a key to cardiovascular health. So what do the numbers 120/80 actually mean? When a medical worker wraps an inflatable cuff around your upper arm and vigorously pumps in air, it increases the pressure in the cuff to, say, 200 mm Hg, and this constriction temporarily prevents blood from flowing into the main artery in your arm. The worker will listen through a stethoscope placed on the artery inside your elbow, but won't hear anything yet because the artery is closed by the pressure. The medical worker then releases air from the cuff until the pressure drops below that of the beating heart ventricle (say, 120 mm Hg). He or she can hear the artery open when the ventricle contracts, but then slaps shut from the force of the cuff when the ventricle relaxes. Next the worker releases more air from the cuff, dropping its pressure to below that of the ventricles, even at rest (say 80 mm Hg). Once again, he or she will hear no sound because the artery is permanently open. In this example, the patient's blood pressure is 120 over 80.

Blood traveling away from the heart has its high pressure (for example, 120) because of the heart's muscular pumping. As blood moves through the arteries, however, and into the voluminous capillary beds, the pressure dissipates (e.g. to about 40). This lowered pressure allows veins to serve as the body's blood reservoir, capable of holding as much as 80 percent of total blood volume at any given time. The movement of muscles in the arms, legs, and rib cage gently "milks" blood through individual veins, while the one-way valves in vessels in your extremities prevent backflow and keep the blood moving toward the heart. If no muscular milking takes place over a long period of time—for example, while you're sitting throughout a long plane ride—blood and other fluids accumulate in the extremities.

Regulation of Blood Flow

From moment to moment, the distribution of blood varies in an animal's arteries, veins, and capillaries, depending on oxygen consumption. During vigorous exercise, for example, a higher volume of blood moves to your oxygen-starved muscles. Later, if you eat an energy bar, your intestines absorb nutrient molecules that, in turn, move into a suddenly increased blood supply in the digestive tract (see Chapter 19). When one region of the body, say, the leg muscles, uses oxygen more rapidly, then the walls of arterioles in other body regions contract and cut down blood flow. As we saw in Chapter 16, contraction of the vessel walls is called *vasoconstriction* ("vessel constriction"); it causes a decrease in the diameter of blood vessels and restricts blood flow while more blood moves to other regions. In the body regions requiring a greater blood flow, a reverse process, *vasodilation*, takes place. The diameter of the vessels increases, and more blood can move through.

Local blood flow is also regulated by precapillary sphincters, or rings of smooth muscle around the capillary's upstream origin (Fig. 17.9a,b). When we get extremely cold, vasoconstriction and the closing of precapillary sphincters can decrease blood flow in capillary beds near the skin surface in the fingers or toes. The decrease in bright red oxygenated blood in these tissues can make the skin take on a yellowish or bluish cast. Likewise, eyedrops that "get the red out" contain chemicals that constrict the eyeball's arterioles so they appear less prominent. When we are very warm, as during active exercise, vasodilation allows the capillary beds to become engorged, and the skin can feel hot and look red.

Several factors regulate the tension of arteriole muscles and so modulate vessel diameters. Among these are neurotransmitters and the gas nitric oxide (see Chapter 21); hormones (see Chapter 20); and finally, oxygen itself. In artificial blood experiments, it became clear that hemoglobin circulating freely in the bloodstream must disrupt one or more of these controls. But which? Current evidence points to both nitric oxide and the oxygen supply.

Nitric oxide (NO) is a gaseous molecule containing one nitrogen atom and one oxygen atom. NO is produced locally by the cells that line the blood vessels (endothelial cells), and causes the smooth muscle fibers surrounding arterioles to relax and thus increases local blood flow. During sexual arousal, for example, cells lining blood vessels in the penis release NO, extra blood flows into the penis as a result, and this causes an erection. Experiments

Figure 17.9
Evidence of Blood Flow

(a) Vasoconstriction

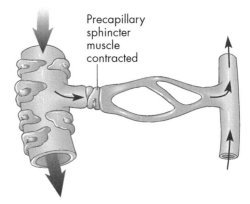

Precapillary sphincter muscle contracted

(b) Vasodilation

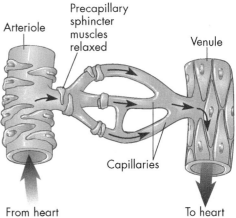

Arteriole

Precapillary sphincter muscles relaxed

Venule

Capillaries

From heart

To heart

precapillary sphincters
rings of smooth muscle around a capillary on the arterial (as opposed to venous) side of a capillary bed

nitric oxide
the simple chemical compound NO; it occurs as a gas under normal atmospheric conditions and has been found to act as a neurotransmitter during penile erection and certain other physiological processes

have shown that free hemoglobin mops up NO, and thus decreases its local concentration. Without it, the arteriole muscles can't relax and in fact tighten up further, decreasing blood flow to the tissue cells.

On top of this NO mechanism, free hemoglobin molecules carry more oxygen than the same molecules would inside red blood cells. Experiments show that an increased oxygen supply can trigger vasoconstriction. This prevents a local tissue area from getting too much oxygen delivered and not having enough carbon dioxide carried away.

Blood Clotting

A patient suffering drastic blood loss needs something else in addition to normalized blood pressure: a way to stop the bleeding. Fortunately, as you have probably experienced throughout your life, we have a natural system that plugs up wounds—a system biologists call the blood-clotting cascade. In a cut vessel, several separate events take place that halt the flow of blood (Fig. 17.10a): (1) Smooth muscles in the walls of the damaged vessel contract and partly close off the vessel. (2) Platelets, the circulating cell fragments we saw earlier, react by releasing the hormone *serotonin* that keeps the muscles contracting. (3) Platelets at the injured site begin sticking to each other and to rough surfaces at torn edges of the wound, forming a plug. (4) The next stage is coagulation, the actual formation of a blood clot.

The formation of a blood clot (coagulation) involves a series of steplike changes in blood proteins (Fig. 17.10b). First, injured cells release activators (Step ①), which, in a cascade of reactions, stimulate the conversion of an inactive protein (prothrombin) into an enzyme (thrombin) (Step ②). This enzyme transforms *fibrinogen* (a protein that normally circulates dissolved in the plasma) into tough, insoluble threads of a related protein, fibrin (Step ③). Fibrin threads in turn become woven into a strong, wiry mesh that traps red blood cells, creating a blood clot (Step ④).

People with hemophilia lack a functional copy of a gene encoding a protein in the clotting cascade. As

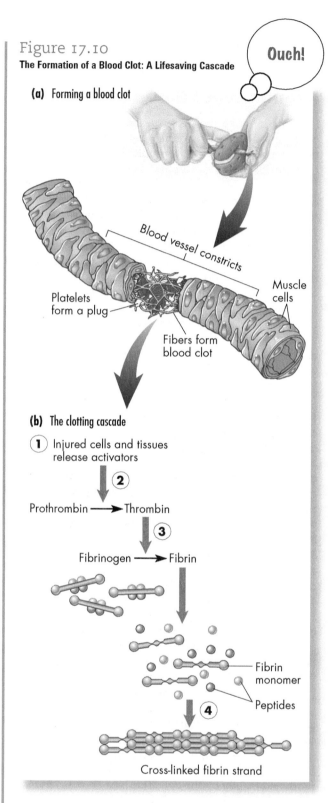

Figure 17.10
The Formation of a Blood Clot: A Lifesaving Cascade

Ouch!

(a) Forming a blood clot

Blood vessel constricts

Muscle cells

Platelets form a plug

Fibers form blood clot

(b) The clotting cascade

① Injured cells and tissues release activators

②

Prothrombin ⟶ Thrombin

③

Fibrinogen ⟶ Fibrin

Fibrin monomer

Peptides

④

Cross-linked fibrin strand

a result, they do not form normal blood clots. Unless a person with hemophilia receives periodic intravenous injections of solutions containing the normal protein, even a minor wound can lead to major blood loss and possibly death. A successful blood substitute must allow normal clotting but not stimulate unwanted clots. These clots could clog blood vessels in vital organs such as the heart, causing a heart attack, or in the brain, causing a stroke. In fact, quickly administering clot-dissolving enzymes to heart attack or stroke victims can dramatically reduce damage to the heart or brain.

The Lymphatic System

Our human circulatory system and that of many other vertebrates is so highly pressurized that it forces fluid from the blood plasma through the thin walls of capillaries. This fluid—water plus dissolved plasma components—then accumulates in the spaces between cells. A second system of fluid-containing vessels, the lymphatic system, drains this squeezed-out fluid from extracellular spaces and returns it to the bloodstream (Fig. 17.11a). Lymphatic vessels also play a major role in the immune system (see Chapter 18).

Unlike the blood vessels, the lymphatic vessel system consists of capillaries and larger vessels that do *not* form a totally enclosed circulatory loop. Instead, lymphatic capillaries are minute tubes that are closed at one end and siphon off excess fluid from the body tissues. After seeping through the thin walls

> **lymphatic system**
> in vertebrates, a collective term for a system of vessels carrying lymph (fluid that has been forced out of the capillaries) back to the bloodstream

Figure 17.11
The Human Lymphatic System

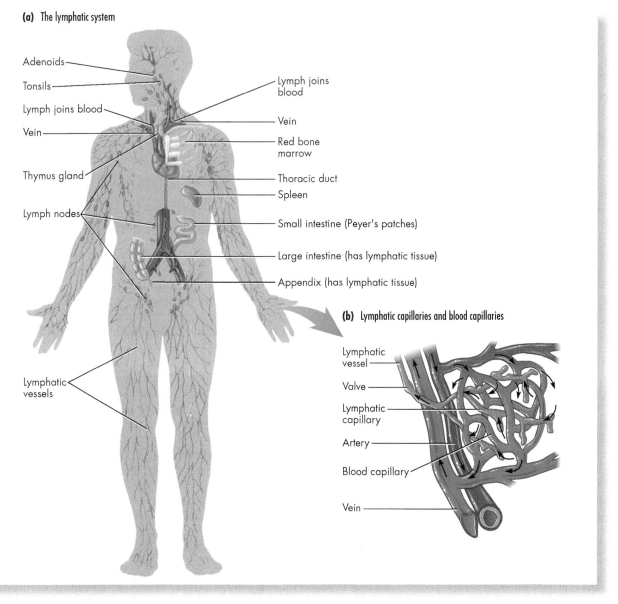

(a) The lymphatic system

Adenoids
Tonsils
Lymph joins blood
Vein
Thymus gland
Lymph nodes
Lymphatic vessels

Lymph joins blood
Vein
Red bone marrow
Thoracic duct
Spleen
Small intestine (Peyer's patches)
Large intestine (has lymphatic tissue)
Appendix (has lymphatic tissue)

(b) Lymphatic capillaries and blood capillaries

Lymphatic vessel
Valve
Lymphatic capillary
Artery
Blood capillary
Vein

lymph
fluid forced out of capillaries, occupying spaces between cells, and draining into the lymphatic system

lymph node
a bean-shaped filtering organ and part of the immune system that stores lymphocytes and prevents debris in the lymph from mixing into the blood

lymphocyte
a white blood cell formed in lymph tissue; active in the immune responses that protect the body against infectious diseases

thymus
a gland in the neck or thorax of many vertebrates; makes and stores lymphocytes in addition to secreting hormones

spleen
organ about the size and shape of a banana in an adult person that lies just behind the stomach; the spleen filters blood, produces phagocytic (debris-gobbling) white blood cells, and stores platelets and some blood cells

organismal respiration
the manner in which a whole animal exchanges carbon dioxide and oxygen with the atmosphere

into the lymphatic capillaries, the fluid is called the lymph. Lymph contains mostly water, but also white blood cells, salts, proteins, dead cells, and sometimes invasive microorganisms, such as bacteria and viruses. Lymphatic capillaries merge, like creeks joining to form a stream, and streams combining to form a river (see Fig. 17.11b), and finally, two major lymphatic vessels emit a surge of lymph into veins near the heart. The lymph fluid is then merged once again with the plasma portion of circulating blood.

Bean-shaped filtering organs called lymph nodes prevent debris in the lymph from mixing into the blood (see Fig. 17.11a). As lymph moves along a lymph vessel, it percolates through the nodes, like oil passing through an oil filter, and the node filters out dead cells and other debris. The nodes also harbor large numbers of infection-fighting lymphocytes (a type of white blood cell), which help protect the body from bacteria and other foreign materials. You've probably experienced painful, swollen lymph glands in the neck, underarms, or groin area during a bout of infection; the swelling indicates that these organs have increased their filtering activities. Unfortunately, just as lymph vessels can carry dead cells away from an infection site, they can also transport migrating cancer cells to new sites. This is why doctors often remove lymph nodes and vessels along with cancerous tissue in cancer patients.

Like veins, lymphatic vessels transport fluids under low pressure. Valves keep the lymph flowing in one direction, and the squeezing force of contractions in muscle tissue surrounding the lymph vessels propels the fluid. A person with inactive muscles, say, an injured skier in a hospital bed, can suffer lymph accumulation, which results in swelling or *edema* (eh-DEE-muh).

The lymphatic system also has two organs that are somewhat separate from the network of vessels.

The soft, V-shaped thymus located at the base of the neck in front of the aorta plays a role in the body's immunity (Chapter 18). The spleen, about the size and shape of a banana in an adult, lies just behind the stomach. The spleen filters blood, produces phagocytic (debris-gobbling) white blood cells, and stores platelets and some blood cells. Despite these functions, surgeons can remove a person's injured spleen without causing any severe consequences to overall health because the bone marrow and liver can perform essential spleen functions. However, the spleen will collect red blood cells infected by the malaria parasite. The spleen also collects and destroys the hemoglobin in most blood substitutes developed so far.

LO⁴ The Respiratory System

Blood transports many important substances around the body, with oxygen being the most "time sensitive." Any successful blood substitute would have to do the same. Nature has provided us with an elegant system for picking up needed oxygen and eliminating carbon dioxide wastes. Let's explore the structure and activity of the respiratory system to examine the challenges of gas exchange and the evolutionary solutions that have arisen in different animal groups.

Why Do Animals Have a Respiratory System?

Think back to Chapter 3 for a moment and to the cell's harvest of energy from food molecules. In the process of cellular respiration, enzymes in an organism's mitochondria remove energized electrons from food molecules, passing them to electron carriers and releasing carbon dioxide as a waste product (review Fig. 3.7). The carbon dioxide produced this way diffuses from the cell and the electron carriers pass electrons to mitochondrial proteins. These proteins eventually pass the electrons to oxygen gas (along with hydrogen ions), and water molecules form. Cells use the energy released by electron transport to make ATP, the cell's energy currency (Fig. 17.12). Cells in a large complex animal such as a human take up oxygen from the watery fluid that surrounds the cell and also dump carbon dioxide there. Where does the extracellular fluid get its oxygen? From a group of organs specialized to extract oxygen from the environment: the respiratory system.

Biologists use the term "respiration" in two ways. We just reviewed cellular respiration. In contrast, organismal respiration is the way a whole animal

Figure 17.12
Gas Exchange at the Organismal, Cellular, and Molecular Levels

(a) A silkmoth caterpillar's spiracles

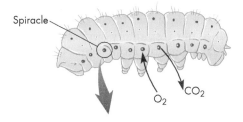

Spiracle

O_2

CO_2

(b) The silkmoth caterpillar's respiratory system

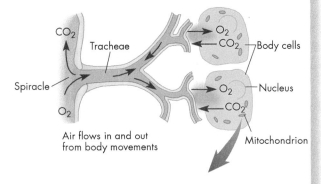

CO_2

Tracheae

O_2
CO_2 — Body cells

Spiracle

O_2

O_2 — Nucleus

CO_2

Air flows in and out
from body movements

Mitochondrion

(c) Mitochondrion: the source of carbon
dioxide and the sink of oxygen

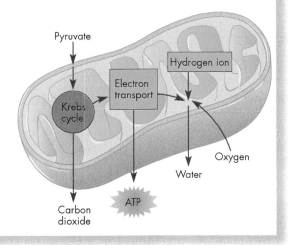

Pyruvate

Hydrogen ion

Electron
transport

Krebs
cycle

Oxygen

Water

ATP

Carbon
dioxide

exchanges carbon dioxide and oxygen with the atmosphere. We mammals respire when we breathe, but other animals have other solutions.

Respiration and Diffusion

We saw in Chapter 16 that large animals rely on systems of tubes to bring oxygen into the complex multicelled body and dump carbon dioxide out. They rely on different tubes—the circulatory system—to transport the gases to and from each body cell. And the two systems interact (review Fig. 16.1). Less complicated animals have the same needs but simpler solutions. Take a caterpillar (a moth larva), for example (Fig. 17.12a). Atmospheric gases enter and leave the body through spiracles, portholes that open onto branching tubes called tracheae (TRAY-key-ee). At the farthest tips of those tubes deep inside the insect's body, oxygen directly enters the surrounding fluid, and from there diffuses to surrounding tissue cells (Fig. 17.12b). The oxygen passes across the plasma membranes, enters the cells' cytoplasm, and moves to the mitochondria, where oxygen takes part in cellular respiration (Fig. 17.12c). In each step, the oxygen passes by diffusion, the spontaneous migration of a substance from a region of higher concentration to a region of lower concentration.

Diffusion underlies gas exchange at the subcellular, cellular, and sometimes organismal levels. The need for gas exchange via diffusion has powerfully influenced how the shapes and functions of respiratory structures evolved:

spiracle
a hole in the body wall of insects that forms the opening of the air tubes (tracheae)

tracheae
branching networks of hollow air passages used for gas exchange in insects

1. Because water generally surrounds cells, gases must reach cells by passing through a layer of liquid.

2. Diffusion is much slower in water than in air—an amazing 300,000 times slower. As a consequence, each animal cell must be close to a source of oxygen and a sink for carbon dioxide so that gases can diffuse to and from each cell quickly. Flatworms don't have a respiratory system because their bodies are so thin and flat that the "deepest" interior cells are never more than about 0.5 mm from the surface. Oxygen and carbon dioxide therefore can diffuse quickly and directly between cells and the animal's moist surroundings.

3. The greater the exposed surface for exchange, the more gas can diffuse between a liquid and the atmosphere, or between two liquids. If you hang wet laundry on a line, for example, and expose a large surface area to the atmosphere, the water will evaporate faster than if you leave the laundry in a heap with a small surface area-to-volume ratio.

4. Diffusion rates speed up or slow down depending on the gas concentrations and gas pressures in the liquid and in the surrounding

gill
a specialized structure that exchanges gases in water-living animals

gill filaments
tiny subdivisions of the gill bar that support many thin, platelike structures, which help extract dissolved oxygen from water

lamellae
tiny platelike structures supported by gill filaments; help aquatic animals respire efficiently in water

swim bladder
a bag of gas that can be inflated or deflated slightly and helps a fish maintain its depth in the water without sinking or floating

atmosphere. Returning to the laundry analogy, water leaves the liquid phase in the clothes and enters the atmosphere much faster if the air is dry than if the humidity is high.

These four principles of diffusion have influenced the shape and activities of animal bodies. Let's look at solutions for gas exchange in fish, frogs, birds, and humans.

Strategies for Gas Exchange

Fish, tadpoles, and many other animals that live in the water have gills: organs specialized for gas exchange that develop as outgrowths of the body surface. A developing fish has several tunnels connecting the inside of the mouth with the external environment. A fish's gills form from bars of tissue in between these tunnels (Fig. 17.13a). Each gill bar is subdivided into hundreds of flexible gill filaments, which, in turn, support many thin, platelike structures. These delicate plates, or lamellae, hold the key to how a large, active, aquatic animal can respire efficiently in water, even though most lake, river, or ocean water holds only one twentieth as much oxygen as air. Embedded within each lamella is a lacy meshwork of capillaries lying just one cell layer away from the water that passes through the gill filament. This proximity of blood to oxygen-bearing water means that oxygen readily diffuses across the cells into capillaries, while carbon dioxide easily diffuses outward. The pumping heart then circulates the oxygen-rich blood throughout the animal's body.

The steady opening and closing of a fish's mouth pumps a constant stream of water through the mouth to the gills, over the gills, then out through a flap (the operculum) that protects the gills (Fig. 17.13a). This water flow moves in the opposite direction to blood flow within the capillaries inside the gill's lamellae (Fig. 17.13b). The result is a *countercurrent exchange*, in which two fluids with different characteristics (here, different oxygen contents) flow in opposite directions (Fig. 17.13c). As they flow, materials are exchanged along all their points of contact owing to diffusion

> **Diffusion is much slower in water than in air—an amazing 300,000 times slower.**

from high to low concentrations. As a result, the animal can collect enough oxygen for aerobic cellular respiration and an active lifestyle even though water holds so much less oxygen than air.

We land animals have access to the higher oxygen content of air, but we face a different threat: the drying out of our respiratory surfaces, which would bring gas exchange to a lethal halt.

Respiratory Adaptations in Land Animals

The only animals that live surrounded entirely by dry air are terrestrial arthropods and mollusks, such as spiders and snails, and land vertebrates, including reptiles, birds, and mammals. Not coincidentally, the arthropods and vertebrates have evolved specialized internal respiratory channels. We saw how a spider's tracheae bring oxygen deep into its body. The standard solution in air-breathing vertebrates is, of course, lungs.

A few species of fish that live in the warm, stagnant, oxygen-poor water of swamps have evolved lungs, blind-ended internal pouches that connect to the outside by a hollow tube (see Fig. 17.14a on page 46). These swamp fishes get a meager amount of oxygen through their gills, and the lungs supplement it. In many fishes, the lung pouch loses its connection to the exterior and serves not as a true lung, but as a swim bladder, a bag of gas that helps the fish maintain its depth in the water without sinking or floating.

In an amphibian, such as a frog (Fig. 17.14b), the lungs are simple sacs with walls that are richly endowed with a dense lacework of blood capillaries. The uncomplicated baglike lungs of amphibians have far less surface area for gas diffusion than the convoluted lungs of reptiles, birds, and mammals; however, gases can also diffuse through an amphibian's moist skin, which supplements the lungs so that the animals can obtain enough oxygen to support their way of life.

In contrast to amphibians, air flows through a bird's more complicated set of air sacs and tubes in a one-way path (Fig. 17.14c). Because this one-way flow through the lungs prevents the mixing of fresh and "stale" air, birds can sustain extremely high levels of activity for much longer periods than we mammals can manage. Birds can even flap actively over the top of Mt. Everest while most humans standing still at the peak need oxygen tanks to avoid passing out.

Figure 17.13

Fish Gills, Water Flow, and Countercurrent Exchange Allow Oxygen Harvest from the Water

(a) Water flow

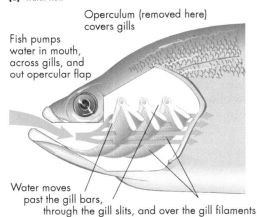

Operculum (removed here) covers gills

Fish pumps water in mouth, across gills, and out opercular flap

Water moves past the gill bars, through the gill slits, and over the gill filaments

(b) Gill function

Deoxygenated blood flows into the gill filament

Oxygen diffuses from the water into the blood

Oxygenated blood leaves the gill filament headed for the rest of the body

(c) Countercurrent exchange

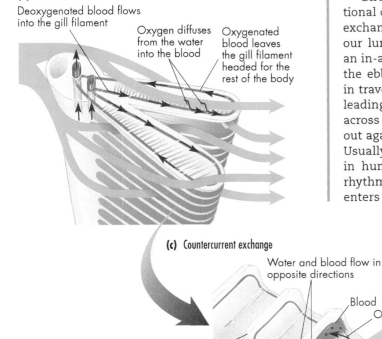

Water and blood flow in opposite directions

Blood

Oxygen

Lamellae

Water

Thus, along the entire route, the concentration of oxygen (red dots) in the water is always a bit higher than in the blood

The Human Respiratory System

Most mountain climbers attempting to scale Mt. Everest carry supplemental oxygen (and never reach the summit, anyway). A handful of people, however, have climbed to the top breathing on their own. Swedish climber Göran Kropp, for example, rode a bicycle from his home to Kathmandu, Nepal, more than 7,000 miles away. He proceeded to Everest base camp with 150 pounds of gear in his backpack and with no assistance from hired Sherpas. He then trudged to the summit without an oxygen tank, descended once again to Kathmandu, and then pedaled his bike back home to Sweden. The human respiratory and circulatory systems can obviously adapt to low-oxygen environments—even extreme ones.

Birds and fish have the benefit of a unidirectional current of air or water moving past their gas exchange surfaces, but we mammals don't. Instead, our lungs operate more like an amphibian's with an in-and-out air flow or tidal ventilation, a bit like the ebb and flow of the tides. The air we breathe in travels through an inverted tree of hollow tubes leading into the lungs. There, gases are exchanged across a thin, moist membrane before the air moves out again through the same branching set of tubes. Usually, a quantity of air (about 500 ml, or a pint, in humans) is inhaled and exhaled in a regular rhythm. This tidal pattern means that fresh air enters the lungs only during half of the respiratory cycle and that a quantity of unexpelled, stale dead air (the so-called residual volume) filled with carbon dioxide remains in the lungs and airways at all times, mixing with the fresh air that enters from outside. Nevertheless, we have special adaptations that increase the rate of gas exchange and compensate for an in-and-out ventilation system.

Respiratory Passageways for Air Flow

When a mammal breathes in, air enters the respiratory system through the nose and sometimes through the mouth. The moist cavities of the mouth or nose warm and humidify the air, and open toward the back (posteriorly) into the pharynx (FAIR-inks) or throat (see Fig. 17.15a on page 47). The pharynx

tidal ventilation
the in-and-out flow of air that characterizes mammalian respiration

pharynx
[1] in vertebrates, a tube leading from the nose and mouth to the larynx and esophagus; conducts air during breathing and food during swallowing; the *throat;* [2] in flatworms, a short tube connecting the mouth and intestine

esophagus
the muscular tube leading from the pharynx to the stomach

trachea
the "windpipe," the major airway leading into the lungs of vertebrates

larynx
a cartilaginous structure containing the vocal cords; it is also known as the voice box

epiglottis
a flap of tissue just above the larynx that closes during swallowing and prevents food from entering the lungs

bronchi (sing., bronchus)
two hollow passageways that branch off the trachea and enter the lungs

bronchiole
one of the thousands of small branches from the bronchi that lead to the alveoli in the lungs

alveoli (sing., alveolus)
in the lungs, tiny bubble-shaped sacs where gas exchange takes place

branches into a pair of tubes; one, the esophagus (ih-SOFF-uh-gus; Greek, gullet), leads to the stomach. The other, the windpipe, or trachea (TRAY-key-uh), is the airway leading into the lungs. At the forward (anterior) end of the trachea lies the larynx (LAIR-inks), or voice box, housing the vocal cords. Just above the opening to the larynx is a flap of tissue called the epiglottis (*epi* = above, *glot* = language), which normally shields the larynx during swallowing and prevents food from accidentally entering the lungs.

A few centimeters below the human larynx, the trachea branches into two hollow passageways called bronchi (sing., *bronchus*), each of which enters a lung. Finer and finer branchings of these tubes create an inverted tree with thousands of narrowed airways, or bronchioles. These eventually lead to millions of tiny, bubble-shaped sacs called alveoli (al-VEE-oh-lie; sing., *alveolus*) where gas exchange actually takes place (Fig. 17.15b). A moist layer of epithelial cells lines each alveolus, and blood capillaries surround this layer. Human lungs contain roughly 300 million alveoli, and if the linings of all these delicate bubbles were stretched out simultaneously, they would occupy about 70 square meters—enough surface area to cover a badminton court, or 20 times the body's entire skin surface! Oxygen diffuses readily out of the alveolus and into red blood cells that squeeze down through the center of the nearby capillaries (Fig. 17.15c). Meanwhile, carbon dioxide leaves the blood, diffusing out of the capillary and entering the

alveolus. From the alveolus, carbon dioxide is expelled to the outside with the next exhalation.

Cells lining the larger airways produce a sticky mucus ideally suited to capturing any dirt particles or microorganisms we accidentally inhale. Brushlike cilia on cells lining the airways continuously clear this mucus from the bronchi and sweep any trapped debris up toward the pharynx, where they can be swallowed or expelled. Inhaled tobacco smoke damages the cells lining the alveoli and paralyzes the cilia in the airways. The smoke from a single cigarette can immobilize

Figure 17.14
Pouches and Air Exchange

(a) Fish

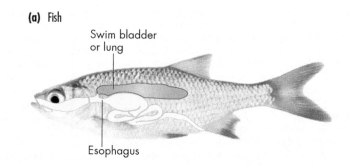

Swim bladder or lung

Esophagus

(b) Amphibian

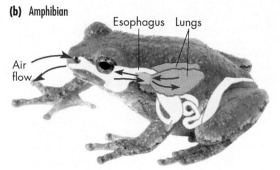

Esophagus   Lungs

Air flow

(c) Bird

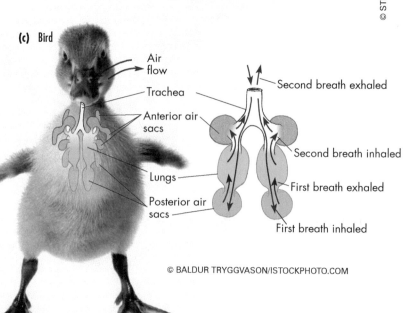

Air flow

Trachea

Anterior air sacs

Lungs

Posterior air sacs

Second breath exhaled

Second breath inhaled

First breath exhaled

First breath inhaled

Figure 17.15

The Human Respiratory System

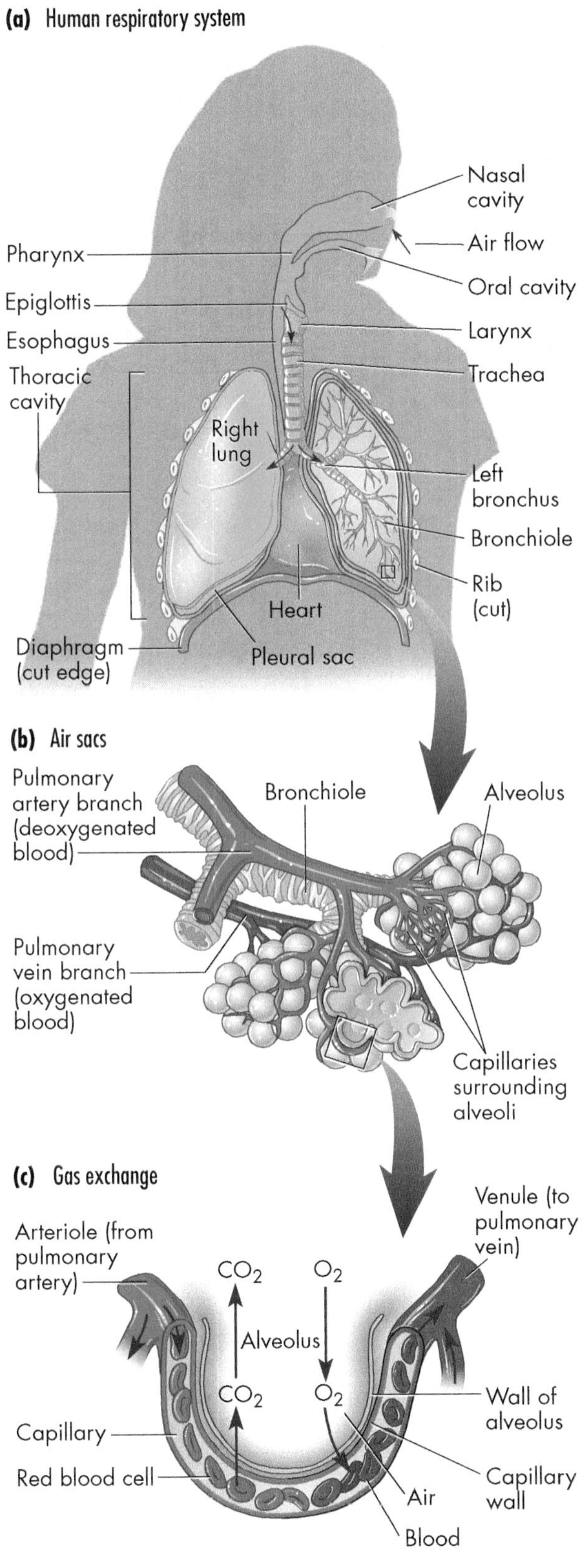

(a) Human respiratory system

© ISTOCKPHOTO.COM

Nasal cavity
Air flow
Oral cavity
Larynx
Trachea
Left bronchus
Bronchiole
Rib (cut)

Pharynx
Epiglottis
Esophagus
Thoracic cavity
Right lung
Heart
Diaphragm (cut edge)
Pleural sac

(b) Air sacs

Pulmonary artery branch (deoxygenated blood)
Bronchiole
Alveolus
Pulmonary vein branch (oxygenated blood)
Capillaries surrounding alveoli

(c) Gas exchange

Arteriole (from pulmonary artery)
Venule (to pulmonary vein)
CO_2 O_2
Alveolus
CO_2 O_2
Capillary
Red blood cell
Air
Blood
Wall of alveolus
Capillary wall

the cilia for hours and lead fairly quickly to a hacking smoker's cough—the respiratory system's attempt to rid itself of airborne garbage that accumulates because the cilia no longer sweep it out.

Ventilation: Moving Air Into and Out of Lungs

Healthy lungs look like pink, spongy, deflated balloons. A fluid-filled pleural sac surrounds each lung, which hangs in the thoracic cavity, the region within the rib cage, over a domed sheet of muscle called the diaphragm (Fig. 17.15a and see Fig.17.16a). The fluid surrounding the lungs is under lower pressure than the air inside, and this pressure difference enables the lungs to remain slightly expanded even when no air is being taken in. A collapsed lung results when a pleural sac is punctured and the fluid drains away or air enters.

Several special adaptations we mammals have give us a powerful bellowslike air intake. Part of the intake depends on anatomy. The ventilation of the lungs is possible because the dome-shaped diaphragm muscle pulls down toward the stomach during inhalation or the drawing in of fresh air (Fig. 17.16b). You can feel this if you place both hands on your chest with a couple of fingers on ribs and the other on your abdomen, then breathe in. Exhalation, the passive release of air from the lungs, occurs when these steps are reversed (Fig. 17.16c).

Control of Ventilation by the Brain

In each of us, respiratory control centers in the brain help determine when and how we breathe. For example, the diaphragm and the muscles between ribs (the intercostal muscles) respond to nerve impulses generated by the medulla oblongata. This region in the brain connects with the spinal cord (see Fig. 17.16a). When one set of nerve cells in the medulla oblongata fires, the breathing muscles contract and we inhale. During

pleural sac
one of two fluid-filled sacs that enclose the lungs

thoracic cavity
the region within the rib cage directly over the heart, in which the lungs and heart are suspended

diaphragm
the muscle sheet that separates the thoracic cavity from the abdominal cavity and helps draw air into the lungs during breathing

ventilation
the process of inhalation and exhalation of the lungs of many vertebrates

inhalation
the drawing in of fresh air

exhalation
the passive release of air from the lungs

intercostal muscles
the muscles between ribs

medulla oblongata
the lowest region of the brainstem, the most posterior part of the brain; involved in keeping body conditions constant

Figure 17.16
Control of Breathing

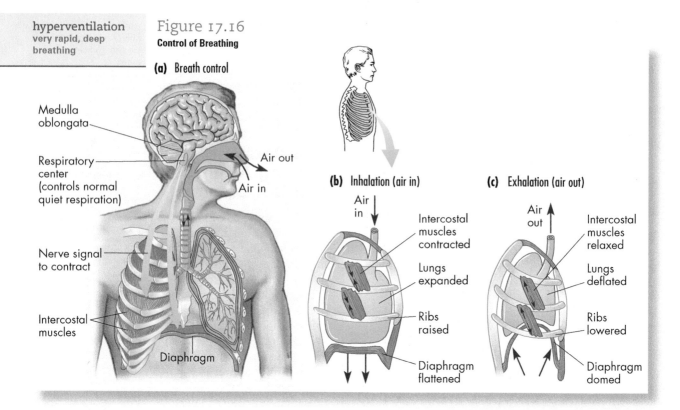

(a) Breath control

Medulla
oblongata

Respiratory
center
(controls normal
quiet respiration)

Air out

Air in

Nerve signal
to contract

Intercostal
muscles

Diaphragm

(b) Inhalation (air in)

Air
in

Intercostal
muscles
contracted

Lungs
expanded

Ribs
raised

Diaphragm
flattened

(c) Exhalation (air out)

Air
out

Intercostal
muscles
relaxed

Lungs
deflated

Ribs
lowered

Diaphragm
domed

normal, relaxed breathing, these inspiratory nerve cells stop firing after about two seconds, allowing the diaphragm and intercostal muscles to relax and us to exhale. During panting, however, the inspiratory nerve cells signal expiratory nerve cells, they trigger stronger muscle contraction, and exhalation is more forceful. We can, of course, regulate our breathing consciously to some extent, and that's because nerve cells located in other parts of the brain can exert control over the medulla oblongata's respiratory centers.

Try holding your breath for the count of ten seconds. Cessation of breathing has two effects on the body: it decreases the blood level of oxygen, and at the same time increases the blood level of carbon dioxide. Which gas does the body monitor to control breathing? Biologists have known the answer since 1875, when three French physiologists found it through a dramatic and disastrous experiment on themselves. The three ascended to a high altitude in a hot-air balloon equipped with bags of pure oxygen to be used as needed. Their balloons passed the 7,500 m (24,600 ft) level (about 1,000 m lower than the summit of Mt. Everest), but they felt no need to use the oxygen. One of the scientists recorded—in an oddly scrawled handwriting—that they were feeling no ill effects at all. When the balloon finally descended, two of the three were dead. The survivor's sad conclusion: The human body is very poor at sensing its own need for oxygen when deprived of it at high altitude.

In contrast, the brain readily senses an increase in carbon dioxide. If a person again and again rebreathes a small volume of air in a stuffy room, the concentration of carbon dioxide gradually rises, and this is detected by sensors in the brain's medulla oblongata and in chemical receptors in the aorta and the carotid arteries. (These receptors also respond to low oxygen levels.) The sensors notify the brain's respiratory center that carbon dioxide levels have increased, and the brain deepens and speeds the person's ventilation, reestablishing the blood's optimal oxygen-carbon dioxide balance. Sensors in the muscles and joints can also detect body movements, and they trigger the brain to increase breathing rates even before carbon dioxide levels in the blood begin to change. The Göran Kropps of the world obviously have very sensitive carbon dioxide sensors and an exaggerated response to the "low oxygen" signal.

Most of the rest of us tend to show periodic breathing when traveling above 9,000 ft: our breathing grows rapid and increasingly deep, then is followed by shallower breathing that eventually stops completely for up to 10 seconds. This pattern, repeated over and over, is apparently based on the body's attempt to balance two conflicting situations. Rapid breathing at high altitude brings more oxygen into the blood, but expels huge quantities of carbon dioxide. The same is true when you blow on the coals of a campfire or inflate an air mattress with very rapid, deep breathing

"The human body is very poor at sensing its own need for oxygen when deprived of it at high altitude. In contrast, the brain readily senses an increase in carbon dioxide."

or hyperventilation. The decrease in carbon dioxide causes the blood to become more alkaline. Recall that carbon dioxide and water combine and form carbonic acid, which breaks down to bicarbonate and hydrogen ions that acidify the blood. When carbon dioxide concentrations are low, on the other hand, including after hyperventilation, the blood becomes more alkaline. Apparently, when you temporarily stop inhaling at high altitude, carbon dioxide builds up and this helps restore the blood's normal pH.

Engineering a Blood Substitute

The high altitude studies are a great training ground for the artificial blood studies, because they prove that it is not enough to just have some kind of hemoglobin. It has to pick up oxygen and deliver it in the correct ways, and if you understand those mechanisms, it is possible to design workable substitutes.

There are many critical uses for artificial blood:

- Emergencies such as earthquakes and tornadoes, after which local blood supplies can run out quickly.

- Battlefields, accident scenes, and medical surgeries in remote rural areas.

- A replacement for whole blood in places such as Africa and Mexico where HIV, hepatitis, and other contaminants have tainted some banked blood supplies.

- Routine scheduled surgeries during which patients need a unit or two of blood but can't donate and stockpile their own weeks before surgery. Instead, the patient could donate blood

in the operating room immediately before the start of the surgery, then he or she could receive a pint or two of blood substitute as a blood volume stabilizer. During the surgery, the patient's own blood could then be transfused back with less chance of contamination, mislabeling, or wrong blood typing that costs lives every year in American hospitals.

- Blood banks for explorers in deep-sea submersibles, polar research stations, and even space stations or other planets.

Many companies around the world are testing artificial blood products. It seems likely that our biological knowledge of blood, blood circulation, and respiration will soon lead to a safe, effective substitute that many of us will someday need.

Who knew?

Think about the unfortunate balloonists, who experimented on themselves to find out if high elevation affected humans. Since they couldn't sense the lack of oxygen, they didn't realize they needed to come down, and instead passed out and died. Now, imagine that you performed a similar experiment on yourself, only underwater! What will happen when you pass out? Hyperventilation doesn't increase oxygen in the blood, but it does lower carbon dioxide to such low levels that the snorkeler doesn't feel the urge to breathe (remember that we're much more sensitive to carbon dioxide concentration) before the oxygen has run out.

Defense
Against
Disease

Learning Outcomes

LO[1] Identify the body's nonspecific resistance to disease

LO[2] Understand the body's specific resistance to disease

LO[3] Explain how the body regulates the immune system

LO[4] Compare and contrast passive and active immunity

> **❝** *Once aroused, natural immune protection can form a lifelong defense against particular threats.* **❞**

The Uncommonly Unpleasant Cold

A cold is the manifestation of a viral infection of the respiratory tract. It involves nasal symptoms such as a stuffed-up or runny nose and throat symptoms such as cough or soreness. Most of the time, it also affects the sinuses and inner ear. The culprit, a virus, is typically one of 100 different strains of *rhinovirus* (literally, "nose virus"). But very similar symptoms can result from

> **Although antibodies are proteins and proteins are coded by genes, we can manufacture more kinds of antibodies than we have genes. Explain how this paradox can occur.**

five or six other types of viruses, including influenza virus and respiratory virus. A cold virus usually enters through the nose and then defeats the body's first line of defense—the skin lining the nose and sinus passages, the mucus given off by those skin cells, and the beating cilia that also line the sinuses. As the cilia sweep the viral invaders toward the back of the throat, they encounter perfect protein entry ports on the nasal cell membranes. Through these ports, the virus gains entrance to the nasal cells. Once inside, the virus inserts its nucleic acid into the nasal membrane cell and commandeers the cell's growth mechanism to make new virus particles. These, in turn, burst out, kill the cell, and reinfect new cells nearby.

Surprisingly, this cellular takeover and destruction do not cause the cold symptoms we're all familiar with. Rather the runny nose, sore throat, and so on result from our body's second line of defense against intruders—*inflammation*, with its redness, heat, and swelling. The nasal passages' copious production of mucus is part of this response and is an early attempt to "wash" viral particles away from the cells and tissues.

The body also has a third line of defense that is slower but more specific and involves the entire immune system, with its network of protective organs, tissues, and cells. White blood cells, for instance, produce targeted proteins called *antibodies* that attack only very specific invaders—in this case, a particular strain of rhinovirus. Unfortunately, it takes two weeks for the white blood cells to gear up and mass produce these molecular weapons if needed, and in the meantime, most cold sufferers will have turned to over-the-counter drugs for relief.

In this chapter, we'll see how our disease-resistance mechanisms enable us to recognize and eliminate invaders. We'll also see how, once aroused, natural immune protection can form a lifelong defense against particular threats. Along the way, you'll find answers to these questions:

- ☑ What are the body's nonspecific responses to invasion by microbes or viruses?
- ☑ How does the immune system provide specific resistance against invaders?
- ☑ How does the body regulate immunity and what goes awry in diseases such as arthritis?
- ☑ How do medical workers use vaccines to deliberately transfer immunity?

immune system
the network of cells, tissues, and organs that defends the body against invaders

pathogen
a disease-causing agent

nonspecific resistance
cellular functions that fight disease in the same way regardless of the invader's characteristics

specific resistance
the body's ability to combat particular species or strains of pathogens and other invaders; works more slowly than nonspecific resistance

immunity
specific resistance, or immunity, is a slow series of reactions based on lymphocytes and antibodies (in vertebrates) that is more targeted to particular invaders or damaged cells within the organism than are nonspecific responses

interferons
a class of antimicrobial proteins that are released by certain virus-infected cells that diffuse to other cells and, in turn, cause them to produce proteins that inhibit viral replication

complement system
a group of about 20 plasma proteins (a type of antimicrobial protein) that attack and destroy microbes and stimulate inflammation

LO¹ Disease Defense and Nonspecific Resistance

Our body's ability to fight off disease-causing agents (or pathogens) such as a rhinovirus is called *resistance*. As we saw in the introduction, we have two types of resistance. Nonspecific resistance to diseases includes a first line of defense in the form of physical barriers to entry and a second line of defense based on nonspecific cell activities—cellular functions that fight disease in the same way regardless of the invader's characteristics. These two lines of defense protect us from a wide variety of pathogens, and they work quickly. Because of their general nature, however, they can fail to combat many important disease-causing organisms. The second type of resistance (and our third line of defense) is specific resistance to disease, or immunity. Immunity has the advantage of combating particular species or strains of pathogens and other invaders. Its disadvantage is that it works more slowly than nonspecific resistance.

Disease resistance is based on three main functions: recognizing the invader, communicating between defensive cells, and eliminating the invader. In this section, let's investigate how the physical barriers and cellular activities of nonspecific resistance protect the body. Then in the next section, we'll explore the more complicated mechanisms of specific resistance to disease.

Nonspecific Resistance to Disease

Cold symptoms actually result from your body's nonspecific defenses. Regardless of the type of invader—virus versus bacteria, for example—nonspecific defenses can involve:

1. *physical barriers* such as the skin and mucous membranes.

2. *nonspecific substances* (listed below) that fight many different sorts of viruses and bacteria. (In contrast, specific substances, including antibodies, are highly targeted to recognize and stop only particular species and strains of bacteria or viruses.)

3. the *cellular activities* of natural killer cells, an attacking type of white blood cell; of phagocytes, patrolling cells that engulf particles; and of many cell types that produce inflammation, with its redness and swelling.

The First Line of Defense: Physical Barriers

If you are holding a tack and your finger slips, you might puncture your skin. The skin and the mucous membranes that line the respiratory and digestive systems are the body's first line of defense against unwanted intruders (Fig. 18.1, Step ①). They form a physical barrier that keeps out most microorganisms capable of multiplying within the body and causing infection. Any break in this smooth, elastic barrier can allow dirt and microorganisms to enter the bloodstream. Fluids secreted by the skin or mucous membranes can help the body resist disease by washing away pathogens in a nonspecific way. Furthermore, some of these secretions, such as sweat, saliva, and tears, contain lysozyme (Chapter 3), an enzyme that can dissolve certain kinds of bacterial cell walls and hence kill bacterial cells.

The Second Line of Defense: Nonspecific Substances and Cellular Activities

Returning to the tack in your finger, the metal point would probably introduce microbes into your system and these would quickly come into contact with growth-inhibiting antimicrobial proteins in body fluids. The interferons are an important class of antimicrobial proteins released by certain virus-infected cells. Interferons diffuse to other cells and, in turn, cause them to produce proteins that inhibit viral replication (Fig. 18.1, Step ②). Another type of antimicrobial proteins is the so-called complement system, a group of about 20 plasma proteins that attack and destroy microbes and stimulate inflammation. These proteins can become activated by either antibody binding to its target or by components in a bacterium's cell wall. This activation then intensifies (or complements) other disease-fighting mechanisms, both nonspecific and specific.

Bacteria entering with the tack may encounter natural killer cells, which are a type of white blood cell that can kill many kinds of infectious microbes and some types of tumor cells in a nonspecific fashion. Natural killer cells can recognize some cell surface molecules and release proteins called *perforins* that perforate or poke a hole in bacterial plasma membranes (Fig. 18.1, Step ③).

An invading bacterium might also encounter *phagocytes*, or specialized scavenger cells that devour debris (Fig. 18.1, Step ④; review Chapter 2). Once consumed by a phagocyte, the microbe is killed by enzymes stored in the little bags called *lysosomes* that we discussed in Chapter 2.

Finally, a tack puncture—a mechanical breech—can induce a series of nonspecific internal resistance reactions called the inflammatory response, or *inflammation*, which includes redness, pain, heat, and swelling. Inflammation captures invaders at the site of the injury and prepares the tissue for repair. An even better example of inflammation is a cold. A rhinovirus attack upon and entry into the nasal membrane cells is a biological breech (see Fig. 18.2 on the next page, Step ①). The virus particles infect the nasal cells, take over their information-processing machinery, and cause them to start churning out new virus particles. This eventually causes some cells in the nasal membrane to burst and die (Step ②). Damaged tissues such as virus-infected membrane cells release inflammation mediators, or chemical signals that provoke inflammation reactions (Step ③). Inflammation mediators include the large proteins called *complement proteins*; small hormones called prostaglandins; and short proteins called cytokines. These mediators cause scavenging white blood cells (phagocytes) to leave the bloodstream and converge on the injured area in search of invaders.

natural killer cell
a type of white blood cell that can kill many kinds of infectious microbes and some types of tumor cells; part of the nonspecific defense of the body

inflammatory response
the body's response to intruders, composed of a series of nonspecific internal resistance reactions including redness, pain, heat, and swelling

inflammation mediators
chemical signals released by damaged tissues that provoke inflammation reactions

prostaglandins
a fatty acid–derived hormone secreted by many tissues; for example, prostaglandin from the uterus produces strong contractions in the uterine muscle, causing menstrual cramps or inducing labor

cytokine
a short protein that acts as an inflammation mediator

Figure 18.1
Nonspecific Defenses

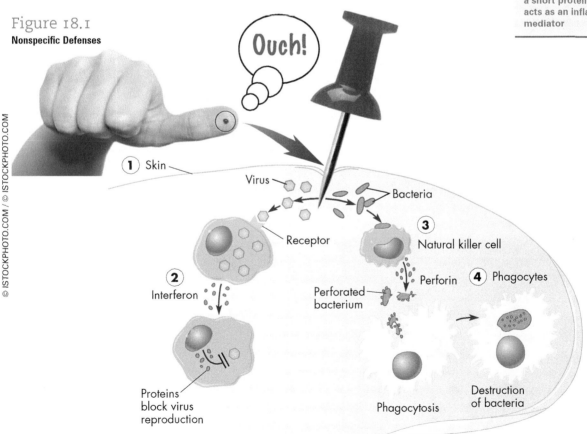

© ISTOCKPHOTO.COM / © ISTOCKPHOTO.COM

mast cell
a round cell that occupies connective tissue in the skin and mucous membranes, contains little packets of chemicals, and releases histamine and heparin when triggered by certain antigens

histamine
a chemical released by mast cells that causes capillaries to dilate; part of the inflammatory response

heparin
a chemical released by mast cells that binds to clot-inhibiting proteins; part of the inflammatory response

The phagocytes devour the intruders and clean up debris by phagocytosis (Step ④).

Inflammation mediators also act on mast cells, round cells that occupy connective tissue in the skin and mucous membranes and are filled with little packets of chemicals called histamine and heparin (Fig. 18.2, Step ⑤). Mast cells stimulated by inflammation mediators such as prostaglandins or cytokines release the chemicals from these packets into the space surrounding the cell. Released heparin prevents blood from clotting so that more leukocytes can get to the infected site. Released histamine binds to surface receptors on the cells of nearby capillaries and on smooth muscle cells. This binding, in turn, causes capillaries to dilate and become leaky (Step ⑥). Dilation brings more blood to the infected area, and allows fluid to leak into tissue spaces, causing redness, nasal congestion, and swelling around the

nose and eyes. (We take the drugs called *antihistamines* to combat these symptoms.) Finally, inflammation mediators also stimulate mucous glands to secrete more of the slippery coating; sneezing, nose blowing, and coughing up this mucus flushes away debris from the nasal passages (Step ⑦).

The small hormones called *prostaglandins* also stimulate mucus secretion, and a mucus buildup in the throat often stimulates a hacking cough. Prostaglandins produced by mast cells cause smooth muscle cells in the bronchioles to constrict as well, and this probably makes breathing more difficult. Finally, prostaglandins also participate in resetting the body's thermostat, and this contributes to a fever (see Chapter 16). Some over-the-counter and prescribed medications diminish a cold's miserable symptoms, although they don't fight the cold viruses themselves. A few drugs actually block viral replication and researchers are working on various kinds. So far, however, they tend to be only partially effective and to have bothersome side effects. Perhaps future drugs will be able to quickly and specifically target the particular viral culprits behind each person's cold. In the meantime, our body's own specific resistance does eventually gear up—albeit slowly—to fight colds and flu and return us to health.

Figure 18.2
Nonspecific Defenses and a Cold Sufferer's Symptoms

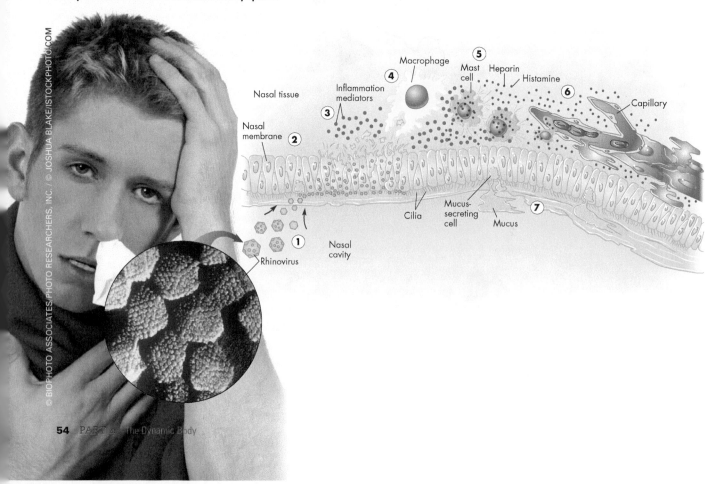

LO² Specific Resistance to Disease

Our first and second lines of defense are a fast-acting "one size fits all" approach to combating disease that, as we've seen, can also cause the "overreactions" of inflammation. On the other hand, specific resistance—our third line of defense—acts more slowly, but tailors a defensive response to the invading agent. Specific resistance involves your body's complete immune system, a large network of organs, cells, and molecules (Table 18.1). The organs include your bone marrow, spleen, lymph nodes and thymus. The cells include several classes of white blood cells that constantly circulate in the bloodstream and lymph. Finally, the molecules include special cell surface molecules called *major histocompatibility complex (MHC) proteins*; signaling chemicals secreted by white blood cells; and the uniquely targeted attack proteins we mentioned earlier, the antibodies. A remarkable and unique feature of the immune system is that it features immunologic memory: it can remember an invader to which it has already been exposed, such as last year's strain of cold virus. This memory feature is one of the reasons people get on average only two or three colds each year. To understand how this wonderful and specific defense system works, we need to investigate the cells and molecules of the immune system in more depth.

Molecules of the Immune System

The immune system's silent battles are fought at the level of molecules. These can be molecules on the surfaces of invading viruses or microbes, for instance, acting as antigens (defined below). And they can be antibodies, regulatory proteins, and other examples of the body's defensive molecules.

Antigens

Antigens are chemicals that generate an immune response. You can start to understand antigens by

immunologic memory
the capability of memory B cells in vertebrates to produce a more rapid and vigorous immune response based on former encounters with antigens

antigen
(Gr. *anti* = against + *genos* = origin) any substance, including toxins, foreign proteins, and bacteria, that when introduced into a vertebrate animal causes antibodies to form

Table 18.1

Players in the Immune Response

Molecules	Cells	Organs
Antigens: Foreign substances that stimulate an immune response	**B cells:** Lymphocytes that after stimulation by antigens divide and differentiate into cells that produce antibodies	**Bone marrow:** Origin of B cells
Antibodies: Immune proteins that bind to antigens and help eliminate them	**T cells:** Lymphocytes that mature in the thymus, regulate the immune response, and can directly kill some invaders	**Thymus:** Origin of T cells
Interleukins: Growth factors that enhance the immune response	**Macrophages:** Large cells that devour foreign substances, process them, and present them to other immune system cells	**Lymph nodes** **Spleen**
Major histocompatibility complex (MHC) proteins: Cell surface proteins that mark the cells of the individual and aid in communication among immune system cells		Storage sites of lymphocytes

Ag, Stimulation, B, Secretion, Binding, Ab, IL, Macrophage, MHC, T, Secretion

interleukin
a protein that speeds or slows the dividing and maturing of other immune cells

B cell or B lymphocyte
a type of white blood cell that makes and secretes antibodies in response to foreign substances (antigens)

T cell or T lymphocyte
a type of white blood cell that kills foreign cells directly and also regulates the activities of other lymphocytes

macrophage
an animal cell that ingests other organisms and substances; in the immune system, a cell that engulfs invaders and consumes debris

antibody-mediated immune response
a type of immunity in which antibody proteins circulate freely in the body, bind to invaders, and help eliminate them

examining the structure of the rhinovirus in Figure 18.2. Notice that the viral surface is bumpy, with individual proteins projecting by a few amino acids here and a few there. Each stretch of three to six amino acids has a specific shape characteristic for that particular amino acid sequence. The immune system can recognize each specific molecular shape of about this size when attached to a larger molecule and initiate a response to it. Any substance that can stimulate an immune response is called an *antigen*, and the class includes the surface proteins of a rhinovirus. Many antigens are proteins, but carbohydrates and lipids can also act as antigens. Even small molecules, when attached to a larger protein, can act as antigens. Invaders can have many recognizable surface proteins; the outer coats of most viruses, bacteria, fungal cells, and larger parasites (such as the malaria agent we encountered in Chapter 11) contain many different proteins and carbohydrates functioning as antigens.

Antibodies

The immune system responds to antigens by producing *antibodies*, protective proteins made by special types of white blood cells and secreted into the blood and lymph (Table 18.1 and see Fig. 18.3 on page 58). An antibody acts by binding to an antigen projecting from the surface of an infecting rhinovirus, bacterium, or other foreign agent. The antibody is therefore recognizing the invader and at the same time marking it for elimination.

Regulatory Proteins

Besides antigens and antibodies, specialized white blood cells make an additional group of proteins that work together in regulating the immune response. We saw that some of these, the cytokines, are actors in the nonspecific response to invaders such as

One way to keep these molecules straight is to remember that an *antigen* *generates* an immune response, and an *antibody* is made by your *body*.

rhinoviruses. Some immune cells secrete proteins called interleukins (Table 18.1) that speed or slow the dividing and maturing of other immune cells. In this way, interleukins are involved in the immune system's communication activities. Other immune system molecules stud the surfaces of white blood cells, especially the proteins in the MHC. These MHC proteins are specific for each individual and are the factors that cause the body to reject transplanted tissues such as skin grafts or organs such as donated kidneys. Their main function is to aid communication among immune system cells; the tissue "labeling" leading to transplant rejection is just a side effect.

Cells of the Immune System

Several types of white blood cells cooperate in generating immunity (Table 18.1), but among them, lymphocytes are the driving force. *Lymphocyte* means "cell of the lymph system" and indeed, these small, round, colorless white blood cells spend much of their time inside lymphatic tissues (review Fig. 17.11). One major type of lymphocyte called a B cell (short for B lymphocyte) is formed in the *bone* marrow. B cells are vitally important to our health because these cells make and secrete the antibody proteins that coat free-floating invaders such as rhinovirus, other viruses, and bacteria, and mark them for destruction.

The other major type of lymphocyte, called a T cell (short for T lymphocyte), originates in the bone marrow but matures in the thymus. T cells kill foreign cells, often eukaryotic invaders such as malarial parasites or body cells no longer recognized as "self" because they have become cancerous or infected with virus. Certain T cells also help regulate the activities of other lymphocytes. A third kind of white blood cell is the macrophage (literally, "big eater"). Macrophages are large, specialized phagocytes that, along with some other cell types, help lymphocytes recognize antigens; this stimulates the lymphocytes to attack invaders. Then the macrophages help clean up by consuming debris from the dismantled intruders.

The Specific Immune Response in Action

The body's specific resistance involves two main types of immunity. One is the antibody-mediated immune response, in which antibody proteins circulate freely throughout the body, bind to the invaders, and help to eliminate them. The other is the *cell-mediated immune response*, in which specific T lymphocytes circulate through the body and the immune cells themselves directly attack the invader. Because the body's attack on rhinovirus involves mainly the antibody-mediated immune response, we'll discuss it first. You can follow these steps in Figure 18.3 on the next page.

1. The virus attacks nasal lining cells and reproduces itself inside them, and cells begin dying as the virus particles break out and spread. Cellular debris, including rhinovirus proteins, begins to accumulate and may leak into the bloodstream and lymphatic system.

2. As the circulating debris floats past B cells, Y-shaped antibodies anchored in the plasma membranes of some of these stationary B cells bind to antigens—the bumps on the rhinovirus (see Fig. 18.2). In addition, phagocytes that have engulfed virus particles can pass (or "present") viral antigens to the membrane-bound antibody on B cells, where they bind. This binding represents recognition of the invader and leads to a specific immune response tailored for this strain of rhinovirus.

3. Certain T cells that are members of a class called *helper T cells* also become activated by the viral antigen and then interact with B cells that have bound themselves to the rhinovirus antigen.

4. The helper T cells secrete interleukins.

5. These protein growth factors communicate with B cells and stimulate them to divide into 2, 4, 8, 16, and eventually hundreds of B cells identical to the initial cells.

6. Many members of the clone differentiate into antibody-secreting "factories" known as plasma cells. Other members of each clone of cells may become *memory cells* (which we'll discuss shortly).

7. Once mature, each of the plasma cells (nestled in the tonsils, spleen, and lymph nodes) secretes into the lymph fluid over 1,000 copies of a free-floating antibody molecule. This molecule can bind specifically to the antigen on the surface of the rhinovirus and to it alone.

8. The secreted antibodies, carried in the lymphatic vessels, now leave the tonsils, spleen, and lymph nodes. The lymph drains back into the bloodstream near the heart, carrying the defense molecules with it into the blood, which then distributes them throughout the body.

9. The antibodies pass from blood capillaries into spaces between cells all over the body, and wherever they encounter their target—a rhinovirus—they zero in and bind to it like a dart in a bull's eye.

10. This binding of antibodies to rhinovirus proteins neutralizes the virus by causing virus particles to clump together. The body eliminates these clumps because the antibody coating attracts macrophages like chocolate frosting attracts ants, encouraging the scavenging macrophages to devour, digest, and destroy the antibody–virus complexes.

plasma cell
a type of B cell clone that generates antibodies

immunoglobulin
globular proteins of the immune system that comprise antibodies; classes of immunoglobulins include IgG, IgA, IgM, and IgE

heavy chains
the two longest of the four polypeptides, or chains of amino acids, which compose an immunoglobulin molecule

light chains
the two shortest of the four polypeptides, or chains of amino acids, which compose an immunoglobulin molecule

It's a marvel of biological research that we can understand in such detail how the body fights an infection through the rapid nonspecific resistance response followed by the slower-acting but specific immune response. In fact, biologists and physicians know much, much more about the activities of antibodies, B cells, and T cells. So let's explore a little deeper.

How Antibodies Work

The antibodies you make to a particular infecting rhinovirus strain will protect you from another cold caused by the same strain, but you're likely to catch another cold within several months anyway. Why? The answer requires a better understanding of what antibodies are, how they perform their functions, and the limits to their powers.

Antibody Structure

Antibodies are immunoglobulins (im-you-no-GLOB-you-lins), or globular proteins of the immune system. Each antibody consists of four polypeptides, or chains of amino acids (see Fig. 18.4 on page 59). Two of these chains are longer and are called heavy chains, and two are shorter and are called light chains. In any given antibody molecule, the two heavy chains are identical to each other, and the two light chains are identical to each other. Linked together, the four chains make a molecule shaped like the letter Y, with a stem made only of two heavy chains and two arms, each made of a light chain and part of a heavy chain (Fig. 18.4).

Antibodies' two main functions are related to this Y-shaped structure. (1) They recognize antigens by binding to them. The tips of the two upper arms each bind to an antigen of complementary shape like a lock fits a key. (2) They mark antigens for elimination from the body. Once the antibody's Y arms bind to an antigen, the lower stem of the Y stimulates components of the immune system such as macrophages to attack and destroy whole antibody–antigen complexes (see Fig. 18.3, Step ⑩).

To understand how antibodies do their jobs, researchers have compared the exact amino acid sequences of different antibody proteins directed against different antigens. By doing this, they've discovered that in the main class of antibody circulating in the blood, the stem section always has the same amino acid sequence, and hence the same shape. This is true whether the antibody is directed against a rhinovirus, a strain of *E. coli* bacteria, a tetanus toxin, or some other antigen. In contrast, the tips of the two arms have a

Figure 18.3
The Body's Specific Defenses: An Immune Response to a Rhinovirus

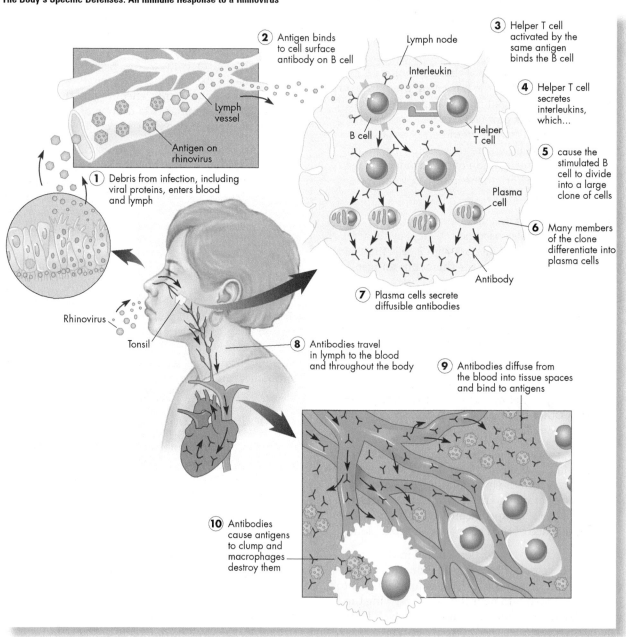

② Antigen binds to cell surface antibody on B cell

③ Helper T cell activated by the same antigen binds the B cell

④ Helper T cell secretes interleukins, which...

⑤ cause the stimulated B cell to divide into a large clone of cells

⑥ Many members of the clone differentiate into plasma cells

⑦ Plasma cells secrete diffusible antibodies

① Debris from infection, including viral proteins, enters blood and lymph

⑧ Antibodies travel in lymph to the blood and throughout the body

⑨ Antibodies diffuse from the blood into tissue spaces and bind to antigens

⑩ Antibodies cause antigens to clump and macrophages destroy them

Lymph node
Interleukin
B cell
Helper T cell
Plasma cell
Antibody
Lymph vessel
Antigen on rhinovirus
Rhinovirus
Tonsil

Figure 18.4

Y-Shaped Antibodies: Variable "Arms" Bind Different Antigens

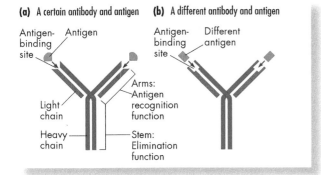

(a) A certain antibody and antigen   **(b)** A different antibody and antigen

huge variety of different amino acid sequences and thus a huge range of different shapes. These many shapes can bind in complementary key-in-lock fashion to an enormous array of antigens—each antibody to an antigen of a particular shape (Fig. 18.4). But because antibodies are so specific, an antibody against one rhinovirus strain may not protect against any of the hundred or so other strains.

Antigen-Binding Sites: Specificity and Diversity

The antibody molecules made by a single clone of B cells will bind only to an antigen of a single shape. Luckily, though, a person can make more than 100 million distinct types of antibody molecules, each with a unique binding site. By adding antibodies from all the clones of B cells together, an individual's antibodies can recognize and combine with 100 million different antigens, including pollen from a wide spectrum of different flowers, the outer coats of thousands of different viruses and bacteria, and the cell walls of many different molds.

Doctors have harnessed the huge spectrum of antibody shapes and activities as a powerful tool for diagnosing illnesses. One example of this is an accurate test for specific antibodies to the AIDS virus, HIV. When HIV first enters a person's body, he or she begins to make antibodies to it according to the scheme outlined in Figure 18.4. Blood tests can identify these antibodies against HIV. Anyone who has these antibodies in their blood is then called *HIV-positive*, a term that indicates exposure to the virus. Unfortunately, these antibodies do not protect against the virus because the virus wreaks its havoc *inside* cells, where it is hidden from the antibodies. Nevertheless, identification of HIV-positive individuals can be used to help slow the spread of the virus. By identifying HIV-contaminated blood from exposed people, medical workers can avoid accidental transfusions to other patients and help prevent new cases of AIDS.

How Antibodies Trigger Elimination of an Invader

We've seen that the arms of a Y-shaped antibody bind to an antigen, while the stem of the Y triggers the elimination of an invader. We've also seen that in the main class of antibody circulating in the blood, all molecules have the same amino acid sequence of their stem section, while the sequences differ in their arms, allowing them to bind differently shaped antigens. In addition to this main class, biologists have identified other classes of antibodies with different elimination activities. Each class varies slightly from other classes in the amino acid sequence of the stem (and hence the stem shape) (Fig. 18.4).

One stem class circulates in the blood and efficiently eliminates rhinovirus and other viruses and bacteria. These antibodies can also cross the placenta from a pregnant woman into her baby, providing the baby with some protection for a few weeks after birth. The blood protein fraction called gamma globulin is rich in this class of antibody. Doctors sometimes inject gamma globulin into a patient who has just had surgery, or a patient headed for a country with hepatitis, typhoid, or other endemic diseases, to provide that traveler with immediate protection.

Another class of antibodies has a stem shape that allows these molecules to enter bodily secretions such as saliva, tears, milk, and the mucus from a runny nose or the intestinal lining. These molecules can pass to a nursing infant through the mother's milk and can temporarily help protect the child from diseases to which the mother is immune—for instance, the strain of her last cold bug. Passing along antibodies is a strong rationale for breast-feeding.

A third antibody class binds to mast cells in the skin and intestinal lining. Recall that mast cells contain bags of chemicals that cause the swelling associated with inflammation (see Fig. 18.2, Step ⑤). Cells bound to this antibody class help fight parasites but also produce the irritating condition we call allergy, which acts much like the body's nonspecific responses to a cold. Sometimes allergies can be dangerous: If the mast cells throughout the body react all at once to an antigen—let's say toxin from a bee sting—then vessels dilate throughout the entire body. This can lead to a life-threatening drop in blood pressure known as anaphylaxis.

gamma globulin
a blood protein fraction that is rich in the class of antibody (IgG) effective at eliminating viruses and bacteria

allergy
an extreme reaction to foreign substances or allergens that mimics a body's nonspecific resistance reaction

anaphylaxis
a life-threatening drop in blood pressure brought on by an extreme allergic reaction

cell proliferation
the body's process of duplicating B cells for the purpose of fighting off invaders such as the rhinoviruses that cause the common cold

clonal selection mechanism
the combined process of the binding of a B cell to an antigen and proliferation into a clone of B cells

memory cell
a type of B cell clone that can proliferate when stimulated by the type of antigen that triggered the original B cell, forming its own clone of both plasma and memory cells; also called *memory B cell*; responsible for the secondary immune response

primary response
the initial immune response to an invader

secondary response
a stronger, swifter reaction to an invader or other antigen when encountered a subsequent time

B Cells in Action

Antibodies are obviously talented with their single basic Y-form and their millions of uniquely shaped recognition sites. But why does it take them so long to help a cold sufferer? This time lag between infection and elimination stems from the way the immune system produces antibodies. Every B cell is a small, colorless, rough-surfaced sphere that carries in its membrane many copies of the kind of antibody it will secrete when an antigen of the appropriate shape comes along and stimulates it. Immunologists have discovered that each individual B cell carries and secretes antibodies with binding sites of *only one shape.* "One cell, one antibody" is the shorthand way to remember this important phenomenon.

We're protected from most pathogens because our bodies contain millions of different B cells and each one is able to make an antibody of a different shape. These cells are lodged in lymph nodes and tonsils or are present in blood and lymph. Each B cell responds to a different antigen, and the response involves the initiation of cell proliferation, as you can see in Figure 18.5.

1. Each B cell has on its surface copies of an antibody with a unique shape based on the amino acid sequences of the Y-shaped antibody molecule.

2. When rhinovirus antigens enter the body, some bind to antibodies on the B cells that fit them best.

3. This binding of antigen to antibody stimulated the B cell to divide rapidly and thus *selected* it to proliferate into a *clone*, a group of cells all descended from a single parent cell.

4. In about 10 days, each single B cell generated a clone of 1,000 daughter cells. The combined process of selection by antigen and proliferation into a clone is called the clonal selection mechanism of antibody formation.

5. Some of the daughter cells in each clone in the tonsils stop dividing and differentiated into

Figure 18.5

B Cells: Clonal Selection and Antibody Production

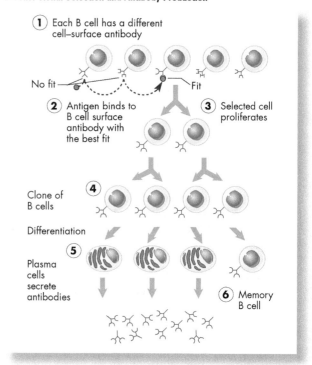

plasma cells, living antibody factories. Plasma cells focus their energy on antibody production and survive only a few days.

6. Other cells of the clone did not differentiate immediately into antibody-secreting factories. Instead, they became memory B cells, or memory cells. Like the original B cell, memory B cells advertise their antibody on their surface and can proliferate when stimulated by the same type of antigen that triggered the original B cell. With this second round of division, the memory B cells form their own clones of both plasma and memory cells, all with the ability to make antibodies of the same specificity as those carried by the original B cell.

The first time a specific antigen stimulates an animal, only a few cells may respond. This first response is known as a primary response. But the next time the animal encounters the same antigen, say, the same strain of rhinovirus, it is better prepared because it has a large pool of memory cells partway along the road to becoming differentiated plasma cells. The net result is a stronger, swifter reaction to the invader—a secondary response. Memory B cells can thus make the difference between resisting disease and succumbing to it.

By the time healthy newborns grow to adolescence, they will have developed many sets of protective memory cells, providing immunity to many kinds of infections. Memory cells can survive for several decades, and this explains why most of us rarely contract measles or chicken pox a second time. If a grandparent had measles as a second-grader and is then exposed to measles while babysitting a sick grandchild, a large pool of memory cells in the older person is stimulated to produce antibodies that help eliminate the viruses before they have a chance to cause disease.

The message about cells bears repeating: Each type of antigen stimulates specific individual B cells to form a clone of daughter cells. Some of these identical daughter cells will secrete antibodies that target and destroy invaders immediately like guided missiles. Others will remain in reserve as memory cells in case of later exposure to the same antigen.

The Antibody Diversity Puzzle

Your body contains B cells that can form an antibody to virtually any antigen you could ever encounter: a rare virus from Borneo, a pollen grain from a Mongolian steppe grass, and even molecules of an organic chemical just invented by a chemist in the laboratory! *But how?* How can your cells contain the huge number of genes necessary to code for millions of different antibodies, including antibodies against molecules you will probably never encounter and some that haven't even been invented yet? Recall from Chapter 7 the "central dogma" of biology: that each polypeptide is encoded by a single gene. Does that mean there is a different gene for each different antibody? If that were true, we'd need more genes for making individually shaped antibodies than for all our other body functions combined. In a sense, the immune system contradicts this dogma. To see how, consider two familiar kinds of restaurants. In one, a particular main dish comes with certain set side dishes—no substitutions. That's how most genes work. In another, you can build a unique dinner by selecting one appetizer from six choices, one salad from four selections, one entree from twenty alternatives, and one dessert from five. In a similar way, a mature antibody gene is built from gene parts put together from three or four subparts, each with many different possible base pair sequences. By this special mechanism of gene recombination, a relatively small number of genes can create an almost infinite number of antibody protein shapes.

T Cells in Action

T cells help regulate immune responses and are involved in the cell-mediated immune response. During this, T cells directly attack and eliminate foreign intruders, usually large invaders such as parasites, cancer cells, some virus-infected cells, or tissue transplants, rather than small invaders such as rhinovirus or bacteria.

Types of T Cells

While all B cells have the same function—to produce antibodies—T cells play at least three different roles in the immune response:

1. Half of all T cells are cytotoxic T cells, which destroy foreign cells, including cells transplanted to a person from another individual, or body cells transformed by virus infection or cancer.

2. Helper T cells communicate via chemical signals with B cells and with the other types of T cells; this "dialogue" can initiate an immune response or augment an existing one.

3. Suppressor T cells slow or stop ongoing immune responses.

How T Cells Work

Viewed through a microscope, T cells are practically indistinguishable from B cells: both are small, spherical, and colorless. But the two types of lymphocytes differ in their pathways of development. B cells arise in the bone marrow and mature there before eventually migrating to either the spleen, tonsils, or lymph nodes. T cells arise in the bone marrow, too, but pre-T cells then migrate to the thymus, where they acquire their definitive capabilities as one of the several types of mature T cells (see Fig. 18.6 on the next page, Step ①). Mature T cells eventually leave the thymus and lodge in the lymph nodes, spleen, and skin. The thymus shrinks as a person matures, and the immune system functions less effectively. This helps explain why many senior citizens need flu shots at the start of each winter's flu season.

T Cell Receptors: Key to T Cell Function

While in the thymus, pre-T cells develop the ability to bind specific antigens. Antigen-binding ability comes from antigen-binding proteins embedded in their cell surface membrane, just as in B cells. In

cell-mediated immune response
a type of immunity in which T cells directly attack invaders

cytotoxic T cell
a type of T cell that destroys foreign cells, including cells transplanted to a person from another individual or body cells transformed by virus infection or cancer

helper T cell
a type of T cell that communicates via chemical signals with B cells and the other types of T cells to trigger or to augment an immune response

suppressor T cell
a type of T cell that can stop or slow ongoing immune responses

T cell receptor
the receptor protein of a T cell

coreceptor
in a T cell, a molecule associated with the T cell receptor that enhances the T cell's ability to bind specific antigens

major histocompatibility (MHC) proteins
(Gr. *histos*, web of a loom, or tissue) cell surface proteins that mark an individual's cells for self-recognition and aid in communication among immune system cells

B cells, however, the receptor protein is an antibody, while in T cells it's a special T cell receptor (Fig. 18.6, Step ②). Another protein, called the coreceptor, is associated with the T cell receptor, and researchers picture it as a cane-shaped molecule like the ones in Figure 18.6.

Different types of T cells display different coreceptors on their surfaces. Helper T cells have a coreceptor called CD4, and young cytotoxic T cells have CD8 coreceptors (Fig. 18.6, Step ③). After T cells mature in the thymus, they migrate to lymph nodes (Step ④), where they sometimes encounter invaders.

Self and Nonself: Major Histocompatibility Proteins

The T cell receptor binds antigen only when a macrophage or other immune cell presents antigen to it along with the self-marking membrane molecules called major histocompatibility proteins (MHC) (*histos* = web of a loom, or tissue). MHC molecules are a key to the T cell's two main functions: the ability to directly kill cells bearing antigens and the ability to regulate the immune response.

Each person's cells have a unique array of MHC proteins serving as cellular fingerprints that distinguish self from nonself. Biologists first recognized MHC proteins for their role in determining whether an animal will accept or reject a tissue graft, such as skin transplanted from a donor onto a burn victim. That transplant can be rejected if the MHC "fingerprints" of the graft's cells differ from the recipient's. You've probably heard of desperate searches by

Figure 18.6
T Cells at Work

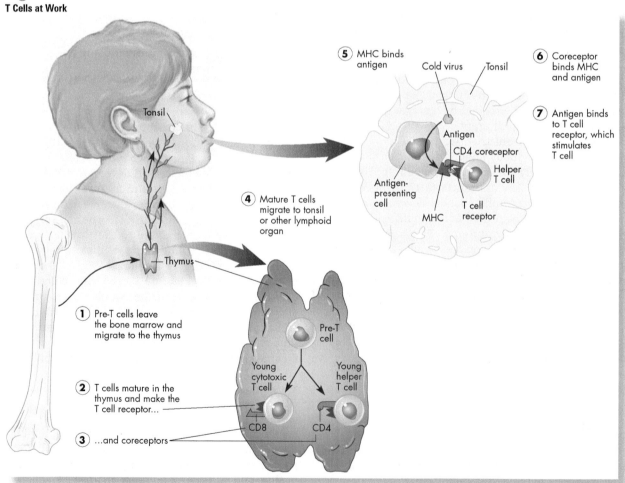

⑤ MHC binds antigen

⑥ Coreceptor binds MHC and antigen

⑦ Antigen binds to T cell receptor, which stimulates T cell

Cold virus

Tonsil

Antigen

CD4 coreceptor

Helper T cell

Antigen-presenting cell

MHC

T cell receptor

④ Mature T cells migrate to tonsil or other lymphoid organ

Tonsil

Thymus

① Pre-T cells leave the bone marrow and migrate to the thymus

Pre-T cell

Young cytotoxic T cell

Young helper T cell

② T cells mature in the thymus and make the T cell receptor...

CD8

CD4

③ ...and coreceptors

doctors and families to find compatible donors of bone marrow, livers, kidneys, or other organs to save a gravely ill loved one. What physicians are searching for in cases like these are organs with MHC proteins very similar or identical to the patient's. If the MHC proteins are different, the patient's cytotoxic T cells will recognize the grafted tissue as nonself and attack it, usually causing rejection.

During an immune response to a foreign invader, MHC proteins and coreceptors work in concert with the T cells. As Figure 18.6 shows, phagocytes attach foreign antigens to their MHC proteins (Step 5). The coreceptor on a T cell then binds to this MHC–antigen complex (Step 6), bringing the two cells very close together. The antigen then binds to the T cell receptor (Step 7), which activates the T cell and causes it to divide into a clone. The clone of activated T cells can then do its job: helping B cells produce antibodies (see Fig. 18.3, Step 3), killing virus-infected or cancerous host cells, or attacking and destroying invaders.

Even in cases of mild illness such as a cold, T cells are doubly important. First, helper T cells stimulate B cells to divide rapidly in the cold sufferer or other patient (see Fig. 18.3). Second, cytotoxic T cells can directly target and kill virus-infected cells, such as nasal membrane cells infected with rhinovirus. Cytotoxic T cells can kill other cells in a manner similar to natural killer cells: releasing perforin proteins, which poke holes in the target cell (see Fig. 18.1, Step 3). Both of these T cell actions help a cold sufferer or other patient regain her health.

LO³ Regulating the Immune System

Whether a person has a devastating illness such as AIDS or a mild infection such as a cold, the human immune system, with its ability to recognize and eliminate specific molecules, is crucial to our daily lives. Its precision is so impressive, in fact, you have to wonder why it can produce antibodies and cytotoxic T cells against foreign cells but doesn't usually attack and destroy its own proteins. The answer is self-tolerance, the lack of an immune response to one's own molecules. Biologists think that self-tolerance develops because the B cells capable of responding to our own antigens are selectively killed off when we are fetuses and newborns. The few self-reactive cells that manage to survive are apparently held in check by interactions with special suppressor T cells in a way that biologists don't yet fully understand.

Unfortunately, sometimes tolerance goes awry, leading to autoimmune diseases, attacks on certain cells or tissues by the person's own immune system.

This may be the result of misdirected helper T cell activity. Rheumatoid arthritis is an autoimmune disease that afflicts millions of people in the United States alone. In people with this condition, the joints swell painfully, the fingers can become gnarled and twisted, and everyday movements, such as buttoning a shirt, can be painful or even impossible. Multiple sclerosis is another autoimmune disease, in which a person's immune system reacts to substances (myelin) that surround and protect nerve cells. In some types of diabetes, a patient's immune system destroys some of the pancreatic cells that normally produce insulin. This hormone helps regulate the levels of sugar in the blood, and without it, metabolism is disrupted.

Pregnancy is an interesting exception to the immune system's recognition and elimination of foreign antigens. The human fetus, containing some of the father's histocompatibility proteins, burrows into the uterus. So why doesn't the mother's body reject the half-foreign fetus? Studies have shown that the uterus is a special immunological zone during pregnancy. During these nine months, a woman's body rejects a graft from the fetus if it is placed anywhere but the uterus. Researchers are still studying how embryos are protected in the womb, but it must be quite complicated, precise, and efficient in order to defend the tiny cluster of tissues from the mother's powerful network of immune cells and organs.

Despite this protection, the fetus sometimes does come under attack. About one couple in 15 have Rh incompatibility, a situation in which their newborn infant can contract a serious anemia called *erythroblastosis fetalis*. Many people have Rh antigen on the membranes of their red blood cells and are thus said to be Rh-positive. Others, however, lack the Rh antigens and are Rh-negative. When an Rh-positive man and an Rh-negative woman produce a baby, the infant may be Rh-positive (see Fig. 18.7 on the next page, Steps 1 and 2). If the baby's blood cells mingle with the mother's during delivery (Step 3)

self-tolerance
the lack of an immune system response to components of one's own body

autoimmune disease
a disease in which a person's immune system attacks the body's own cells or tissues

rheumatoid arthritis
an autoimmune disease in which joints swell painfully; in hands affected by this condition, the fingers can become gnarled and twisted, and everyday movements such as buttoning a shirt can be painful or even impossible

multiple sclerosis (MS)
an autoimmune disease in which a person's immune system reacts to and damages or destroys the myelin sheaths that surround and protect nerve cells

Rh incompatibility
a situation in which a pregnant woman is Rh-negative but her fetus is Rh-positive, leading the mother's immune system to attack the fetus's red blood cells

and its Rh antigens enter her bloodstream, they may stimulate her immune system to produce antibodies against the Rh antigen (Step ④). Because it takes several days for antibodies to form, the newborn is safe from harm. The antibodies against the Rh antigen don't affect the mother, either, because her cells don't produce Rh antigen (if they did, she'd be Rh-positive, not Rh-negative) (Step ⑤). During a subsequent pregnancy, however, the antibodies against the Rh antigen already present in the mother's blood from the first delivery can cross the placenta and attack the new fetus's red blood cells if they carry Rh antigen (Steps ⑥ and ⑦). Debris from the attacked cells can lead to fetal anemia, brain damage, or even death.

Physicians prevent this dangerous situation by injecting an Rh-negative mother with antibodies against the Rh antigen at the birth of her first Rh-positive child. These antibodies (called *Rhogam*) bind to the Rh antigens on fetal blood cells that may have entered the mother's circulation during delivery. Covered by these injected antibodies, the Rh-positive antigen fails to stimulate the mother's immune system, and the next fetus will be safe from attack.

LO⁴ Immunization

In the last 200 years, medical practitioners have learned to manipulate the immune system to help patients in two ways, termed *passive* and *active immunity*.

Passive Immunity with Borrowed Antibodies

Let's say you were out hiking and suddenly saw a rattlesnake, which reared up and bit you on the leg. Not only would you be shocked and frightened, but there would be no time to spare. The venom contains toxic proteins that stop nerves from functioning and that damage blood vessels. You would need a quick-acting remedy to keep these poisons from harming or even killing you. The best treatment would be

Figure 18.7
Pregnancy and Rh Disease

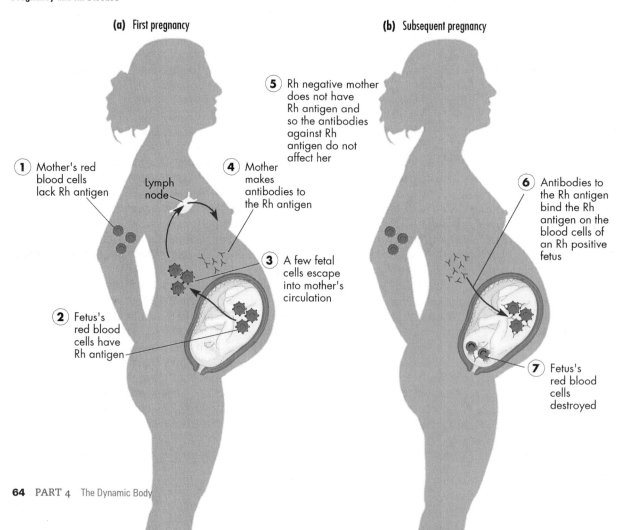

(a) First pregnancy   **(b)** Subsequent pregnancy

⑤ Rh negative mother does not have Rh antigen and so the antibodies against Rh antigen do not affect her

① Mother's red blood cells lack Rh antigen

Lymph node

④ Mother makes antibodies to the Rh antigen

③ A few fetal cells escape into mother's circulation

② Fetus's red blood cells have Rh antigen

⑥ Antibodies to the Rh antigen bind the Rh antigen on the blood cells of an Rh positive fetus

⑦ Fetus's red blood cells destroyed

© ISTOCKPHOTO.COM

passive immunization: injecting antibodies made by one individual into another individual (Fig. 18.8). Technicians prepare the anti-snake-venom antibodies by injecting a horse or rabbit with inactivated snake venom, which induces the mammal to form antibodies against the venom proteins. Workers then collect these antibodies, now called antivenin. When you rush into a clinic after a snakebite, a doctor injects this antivenin into you immediately and it quickly circulates through your bloodstream. There it can combine with (neutralize) the snake toxin in a typical antigen–antibody fashion before, one hopes, the venom can destroy any of your nerve cell function.

Figure 18.8

Passive Immunization: Transferred Antibodies

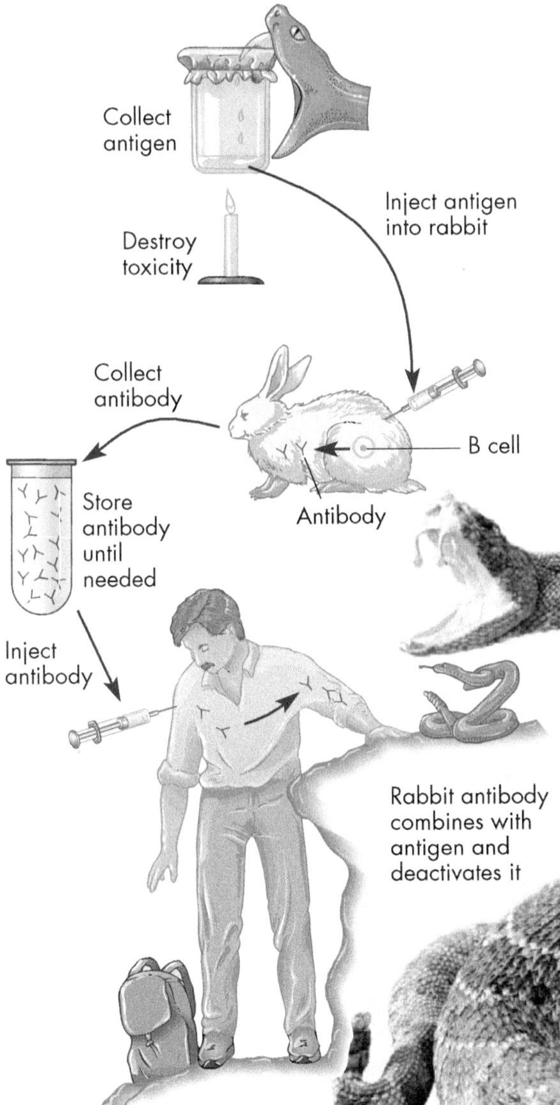

Collect antigen

Inject antigen into rabbit

Destroy toxicity

Collect antibody

Store antibody until needed

B cell

Antibody

Inject antibody

Rabbit antibody combines with antigen and deactivates it

© MARIA DRYFHOUT/ISTOCKPHOTO.COM

Passive immunization has one great advantage: It works very fast. But it also has the disadvantage of acting for only a short time. Your immune system would soon recognize the borrowed antibody molecules as foreign and eliminate them. With the antibody molecules would go your passive protection, leaving you vulnerable to snake venom if bitten again.

Active Immunity with Altered Antigen

You've probably received many vaccines in your lifetime for diseases such as polio, diphtheria, and measles. Unlike antivenin, which provides short-term passive immunity, vaccines such as these provide long-term protection by stimulating active immunity, the production of antibodies or antigen-specific T cells by the individual's own immune system. Safer and more effective than most drugs, vaccines provoke a specific response aimed at one microbe or toxin, and nothing else in the body.

Edward Jenner, an 18th-century English country physician, developed the first vaccine almost 200 years ago. To help protect people from smallpox, a severely disfiguring disease that killed one out of every four people in Jenner's time, he injected people with a small amount of cowpox virus (the word vaccination, in fact, comes from the Latin, *vacca* = cow). Jenner based his technique on the observation that milkmaids who contracted cowpox from the cows they milked always recovered and almost never got smallpox. Indeed, the cowpox virus he injected caused mild sickness and discomfort, but it still protected people against smallpox. By 1978, modern vaccines based on Jenner's original ones had successfully eradicated smallpox worldwide.

passive immunization
the injection of antibodies generated in one individual into another individual

antivenin
an antibody that counteracts snake venom; antivenins are prepared by technicians who inject horses or rabbits with inactivated venom and then collect the antibodies produced by the mammal to fight the antigen

active immunity
the production of antibodies or antigen-specific T cells by an individual's own immune system

vaccination
a form of long-term protection produced by stimulating active immunity aimed at one microbe or toxin

booster shot
a second dose of a vaccine; can induce memory cells to differentiate and form still more antibody-producing and memory cells

Modern vaccines are made of microbes and toxins that have been killed or otherwise modified in the laboratory so they can't cause disease. The first shot with altered germs stimulates the production of antibody-producing cells and memory cells (review Fig. 18.5). A booster shot, which is simply a second dose of the same vaccine, can then induce the memory cells to differentiate and form still more antibody-producing and memory cells. If a vaccinated person later comes in contact with live bacteria, virus, or toxin carrying those antigens, his or her body will already contain many antibodies and memory cells that can quickly eliminate the dangerous agents and prevent disease. Vaccination is a slow-acting process, requiring a booster shot and several weeks for the development of adequate protection. Nevertheless, the active immunity it stimulates lasts a long time, sometimes a lifetime.

Many medical researchers see new vaccines as the best hope for combating infectious diseases that can't be treated or cured by other approaches. Unfortunately, many viruses, including rhinovirus, come in many different strains. And other invaders, such as the malarial parasites we encountered in Chapter 11, can change their surface properties so often that they evade active immunity. Although it's been two centuries since Jenner's first vaccine, medical workers still have developed only about 20 safe, effective vaccines. Contemporary researchers are

Who knew?

Antibodies go one step beyond the typical gene–protein relationship. By combining different elements from a number of gene sequences, they can form an amazing array of different proteins from a limited number of genes.

using recombinant DNA and other forms of biotechnology to create synthetic vaccines against influenza, HIV, and other viruses that can "outwit" the immune system.

Research has shown that, for unknown reasons, a person makes circulating antibodies to the rhinovirus only about half the time they catch a cold. And because there are over 100 different strains of rhinovirus, it's going to be hard—maybe impossible—to make safe, effective vaccines against each one. In the meantime, researchers are aiming for new antiviral drugs that will directly eliminate cold viruses or keep them from spreading. And they continue to recommend over-the-counter measures (antihistamines, pain killers, and cough suppressants) to block the side effects from our nonspecific responses, while they continue to search for new and better drugs that will actually fight the rhinovirus and other viral invaders.

Vaccination is a slow-acting process, requiring a booster shot and several weeks for the development of adequate protection.

"It's easy to read, it outlines important topics, and it's relevant. Thanks for the good stuff on the website, I think it will **really help with tests**.

– Thomas Scholtes, Student at University of Maryland, College Park

REVIEW

HE DID

LIFE puts a multitude of study aids at your fingertips. After reading the chapters, check out these resources for further help:

• **Chapter in Review cards**, found in the back of your book, include all learning outcomes, definitions, and visual summaries for each chapter.

• **Online printable flash cards** give you three additional ways to check your comprehension of key biology concepts.

Other great ways to help you study include **interactive biology games, podcasts, audio downloads, and online tutorial quizzes with feedback**.

You can find it all at **4ltrpress.cengage.com/life**.

Learning Outcomes

LO^1 Identify essential dietary nutrients

LO^2 Explain how animals digest food

LO^3 Understand how the digestive tract functions

LO^4 Describe the human digestive system

LO^5 Review the current understanding of healthy nutrition

Animal Nutrition and Digestion

"How can P.B. live so long and contentedly on the koala diet when you couldn't do it for a day?"

Up a Tree

She's so fuzzy and adorable that people come from hundreds of miles away just to watch her sit in a tree and sleep. Her favorite food is her only food. She rests or sleeps 80 percent of the time, eats during half of her waking hours, and moves about for just 4 minutes a day. Meet Point Blank ("P.B." for short), the oldest koala in captivity.

What do you know?

Explain the model for how leptin and insulin regulate body fat.

Koalas eat nothing but eucalyptus leaves. No vitamins, no special treats for good behavior, nothing.

Here is a mammal that lives without shelter in the branches of eucalyptus trees in its native Australia, rarely comes down to the ground, virtually never drinks water, and exists for decades on nothing but the moisture and nutrients in leathery, gray-green eucalyptus leaves. If you tried this regimen you'd lose weight fast! That's because the leaves contain few nutrients and have a bitter, nauseating, turpentine flavor due to their toxic essential terpene oils and tannins. The fact that your body could never absorb enough nutrients from these nasty-tasting leaves is only the beginning. You'd also dry out from water loss, have a continuously full digestive tract from the bulky, fibrous leaves, and be hungering for your old foods within a matter of hours.

How can P.B. live so long and contentedly on the koala diet when you couldn't do it for a day? For that matter, how can a robin eat mostly worms, or a hyena eat raw meat, hide, and bones, or a cow eat mostly grass and hay? You'll discover the answers in this chapter as we explore the subjects of digestion and nutrition: How do animals, which are heterotrophs, obtain energy and materials—including amino acids, sugars, fatty acids, vitamins, and minerals—from the foods they ingest? And how do the energy and materials, in turn, fuel activity, growth, and maintenance in these multicellular organisms? You'll see, too, how for every animal, digestive anatomy and physiology are closely tied to what the animal eats and what its body needs. Along the way, you'll find out why eucalyptus leaves poison virtually all mammals except the koala. And you'll find answers to the following questions:

- ☑ What are nutrients?
- ☑ How do animals digest food?
- ☑ What are the parts of the digestive tract?
- ☑ What is the form and function of the human digestive system?
- ☑ How can we make sense of the voluminous but conflicting and frequently changing information on healthy diets and proper nutrition?

© ISTOCKPHOTO.COM

nutrition
the science concerned with the amounts and kinds of nutrients needed by the body

dietary fiber
cellulose plant fibers and cell walls that cannot be digested; fiber is important for helping to propel wastes through the digestive system; also called *roughage*

LO¹ Nutrients: Sources of Energy and Elements

To plan out the right diet for P.B.—even a diet as simple as straight eucalyptus leaves—doctors rely on nutrition, the study of precisely how much protein, carbohydrates, lipids, vitamins, and minerals, and how many calories of food energy an animal must consume to stay alive and healthy. Without this knowledge, zoo workers could never be sure their koalas, camels, cobras, and hippopotami were getting enough of the right foods to fend off disease. Without scientific investigation of human nutrition, parents might wonder if their children were getting the elements essential for full mental and physical development. And adults would wonder if they were eating the right foods to prevent cancer, heart disease, and obesity, yet have enough energy for their daily activities and exercise.

Even with their highly specialized diet, koalas—as heterotrophs—still need a supply of organic and inorganic nutrients, including carbohydrates, lipids, proteins, vitamins, minerals, and total calories, just as do other zoo animals and zoo visitors. We encountered these molecules in Chapters 2 and 3. Here we explore their roles in the animal body.

Carbohydrates: Sources of Carbon and Energy

The sugars in fruit; the starches in potatoes, rice, bread, and pasta; and the cellulose in the cell walls of eucalyptus leaves are rich sources of energy and of carbon atoms. Together, these and certain other foods provide the nutrients we call carbohydrates. As Chapter 2 explained, carbohydrates include monosaccharides, such as the glucose found in honey; disaccharides, such as sucrose, or table sugar; and polysaccharides, such as potato starch and cellulose (recall Fig. 2.6).

Our human digestive system can derive glucose from the sugars in grapes or peaches or from the starch in rice, wheat, corn, or potatoes. After a meal, the simple sugars pass into the bloodstream, and the circulatory system carries them to cells throughout the body, where they supply most of the energy for glycolysis and aerobic respiration (Fig. 19.1a). Nerve cells in the brain and throughout the body are particularly sensitive to fluctuations in blood glucose levels. If starving, the body will break down its fat stores first, then move on to its own muscle tissues, converting the subunits to glucose and providing the sensitive nervous system cells with what they need to stay fully active.

The cellulose fibers in plant cell walls, including the cells of leaf blades, and the "strings" in celery stalks, are also complex carbohydrates. We can't digest these cellulose fibers and neither can other animals. So how can strict vegetarians such as koalas, cows, termites, and zebras get what they need from their all-plant diets? The answer is they have cellulose-digesting microbes in their digestive tracts, and these microbes break down the cellulose into glucose subunits, providing the animals with energy. Even with its cellulose-digesting microbes, the koala still has a challenging diet because eucalyptus leaves contain a large amount of lignin, an indigestible material that strengthens plant cell walls (see Chapter 23). The koala can digest a small part of the lignin, although experts aren't sure how. But eucalyptus leaves are 36 to 56 percent cell walls—more fibrous than All-Bran high-fiber cereal, at 32 percent. Analysis shows that because of the high percentage of cellulose and lignin in the leaves, koalas get most of their nutrients (87 percent) from the fluid inside the eucalyptus leaf cells. We get some cellulose in our own diets—in vegetables, fruits, and whole-grain cereals—but because we can't digest it at all, it provides the dietary fiber or *roughage* we need to help propel wastes through the large intestine.

Soluble fiber comes from pectin, a polysaccharide that helps glue adjacent cell walls together in plants. Pectin is particularly abundant in apples, citrus fruits, and strawberries. Soluble fiber forms a gel when mixed with water, and nutrition researchers think that dietary soluble fiber helps lower a person's cholesterol (and thus decreases the risk of arterial disease) by binding to and eliminating from the body a substance made from cholesterol, called *bile*. Insoluble fiber won't dissolve in water, and it's plentiful in bran. This fiber type helps move material through the intestines faster, and researchers think that because of this characteristic, insoluble fiber may help decrease the risk of colon cancer.

The koala, of course, gets a huge amount of fiber—so much that it poses a problem: How can a small animal have a big enough digestive tract to hold all this bulky material while bacteria ferment some of it and release energy compounds? We'll see the answer later.

When it comes to carbohydrates, we often hear, "Avoid table sugar, desserts, and other sugary foods." The fact is, sugar provides calories of food energy, our largest nutritional need. Table sugar doesn't provide many vitamins or minerals, but neither do honey, brown sugar, or raw sugar. The issue is whether a person substitutes sugar-laden foods for more nutritious ones—a candy bar, say, instead of an apple. Bacteria in a person's mouth also prefer sucrose as a fuel, and the sugar allows the microbes to grow rapidly and produce acid that can cause cavities in your teeth. Some people crave sugars and other carbohydrates to the point of overeating, and this has led to the promotion of the low-carbohydrate, high-protein diets many now follow. We'll revisit that later, too.

Lipids: Energy-Storage Nutrients

Most people have only to visualize the solid white fat of a bacon slice or the slippery golden oil in salad dressing to know what a lipid is. Eucalyptus leaves are also filled with toxic oils that are lipid based. Like carbohydrates, lipids supply food energy, but animals generally store much more energy in the form of lipids than of carbohydrates, as our waistlines often reveal. Even a lean person, though, with no visible "spare tire," stores about seven times as much lipid as glycogen (a storage form of glucose). Why is lipid a better form for storing energy? First, lipids provide about twice as much energy per gram as carbohydrates (9 Calories per gram versus 4.5). After a meal of oily sunflower seeds or fatty meat, an animal breaks down lipids to products that move directly into the Krebs cycle (Fig. 19.1b). The Krebs cycle harvests energy from these products, and their carbon atoms become intermediates for building amino acids and other substances the body needs.

A second reason animals often store fat rather than carbohydrate is that fats and water don't mix, while carbohydrates tie up twice their weight in water. In fact, if you stored carbohydrates instead of fats, your body would weigh twice as much. Without fat stores, walruses couldn't live through an Arctic winter, hummingbirds couldn't migrate across the Gulf of Mexico, and wolves would have more trouble surviving between the rabbits and other prey they catch as irregular meals.

Finally, certain essential nutrients, including vitamins A, D, E, and K, are fat soluble, and lipids help the digestive tract absorb these vitamins and deliver them to cells. The human body can't generate one key fatty acid—linoleic

Figure 19.1
How the Body Gets Energy and Materials from Foods

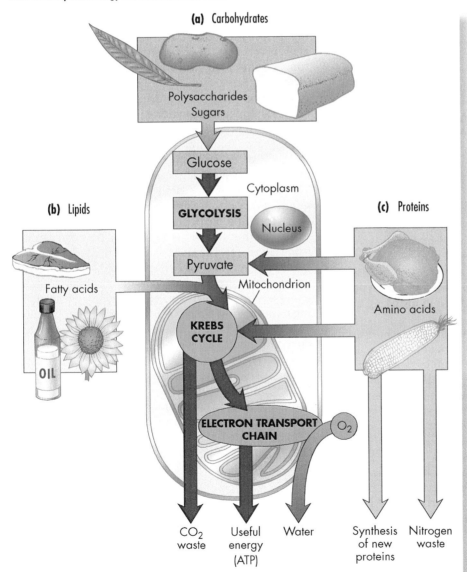

(a) Carbohydrates

Polysaccharides
Sugars

Glucose

Cytoplasm

(b) Lipids

GLYCOLYSIS

Nucleus

(c) Proteins

Fatty acids

Pyruvate

Mitochondrion

Amino acids

KREBS CYCLE

OIL

ELECTRON TRANSPORT CHAIN   O₂

CO₂ waste

Useful energy (ATP)

Water

Synthesis of new proteins

Nitrogen waste

acid—from component parts, so it becomes an essential fatty acid that we must eat in our diets in order to build parts of the cell membrane involved in importing materials. Lipids, then, are necessary nutrients and important storage molecules. But many of us eat a diet too rich in fats and oils, and this increases one's risk of obesity, colon cancer, and heart disease.

Protein: Source of Amino Acids

Both a koala's thick, silvery fur and its sharp claws curved for tree-climbing are made almost totally of a single type of protein, keratin. In marsupials and in all other mammals, skin, cartilage, tendons, bone, muscle tissue, and even the cornea that covers the eye are largely protein. So are enzymes, antibodies, hemoglobin, and some hormones, all necessary for life to continue and for cells to divide or recycle their constituents. The ubiquity of protein and its constant turnover means that animals need a continuous supply of the nutrient; from it, their digestive systems can extract amino acids and build new proteins (see Fig. 19.1c).

For a koala, getting enough protein is a real challenge and it helps explain why the animal eats so much. The protein concentration in eucalyptus leaves (8 percent by weight, excluding water) is very low compared with other plant foods such as oats (13 percent) or almonds (21 percent). Furthermore, the poisonous tannins and terpenes in eucalyptus leaves inhibit the animal's body from digesting and absorbing protein.

A 150-pound (68-kg) human is much larger and much more active than a 20-pound (9-kg) koala, and requires about 1 g (0.04 oz) of protein per kilogram (2.2 lb) of body weight per day. A college student of average height and weight needs at least one-sixth of a pound (about 75 g) of pure protein each day to replace daily losses. This is about what you would obtain from a single cooked chicken breast. Some experiments with lab animals have suggested that eating too much protein can lead to kidney damage, because those organs must work overtime to excrete the nitrogen wastes derived from the amino acids in a high-protein diet. This, however, is in dispute; the advocates of low-carbohydrate, high-protein diets see these kidney-damage studies as flawed.

The amounts of protein needed are one current nutritional issue; the types of protein needed are another, and this has important implications for vegetarians. The body can synthesize many of the 20 amino acids it needs as long as the amino (nitrogen-containing) portion of the molecule is available (review Fig. 2.7). Just as your body can't make linoleic acid for lipids, however, it can't make eight amino acids: lysine, leucine, phenylalanine, isoleucine, tryptophan, valine, threonine, and methionine. For us, these are essential amino acids (Fig. 19.2) that we must eat in our foods every day, since our bodies don't store free amino acids. Children also need extra supplies of the amino acids histidine and arginine, because their bodies make enough for maintenance but not enough for growth.

Without one or more of the essential amino acids, the body can't build the full spectrum of proteins it needs to replace worn-out parts or to generate new cells. We saw in Chapter 7 that cells manufacture proteins by adding one amino acid at a time to a growing polypeptide chain. If even one of these amino acids is missing, the chain stops elongating, a bit like running out of red yarn while knitting a blue and red striped sweater; the project stops until you can get more. That's why lacking even one essential amino acid can stop protein synthesis in the body.

Most animal proteins in foods such as meat, cheese, eggs, and milk contain the eight essential amino acids as well as the other twelve. Many plant proteins, however, don't have the eight essentials. This is why vegans, strict vegetarians who avoid all animal products, including eggs and dairy products, must combine particular vegetable foods each day to ensure that they'll get enough of the right amino acids. Rice, for example, contains little lysine but plenty of methionine, so they'll eat rice together with beans, which are deficient in methionine but contain enough lysine (see Fig. 19.2). Some people in developing nations show symptoms of protein deprivation—swollen belly, skin and hair loss, and low levels of energy—because they eat a diet consisting mostly of starchy cereals and/or root crops that can lack essential amino acids. As a result, their bodies draw proteins from their own tissues, dismantling them and using their essential amino acids for new protein synthesis. Excess amino acids from their foods are simply excreted and wasted. When a human being starves, it's usually the lack of protein, rather than the lack of food energy, that leads to death.

Vitamins and Minerals: Important Nutrients

An animal's body, whether human or koala, needs relatively large amounts of protein and carbohydrate each day for building, repair, and energy. It needs

Figure 19.2
Essential Amino Acids

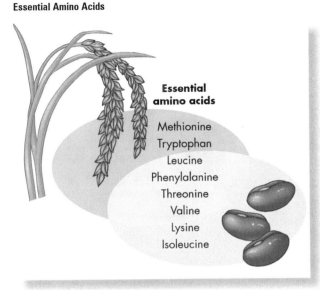

Essential
amino acids

Methionine
Tryptophan
Leucine
Phenylalanine
Threonine
Valine
Lysine
Isoleucine

another set of nutritive substances too, the vitamins and minerals, but only in minute amounts.

Vitamins

Vitamins are organic compounds needed in small amounts for normal growth and metabolism. Animals can't synthesize or, in some cases, store vitamins in large quantities, so they must take in a set of specific vitamins every day in their food.

Nutritionists doing research on human diets have found that people require 14 vitamins. Vitamins A, D, E, and K are soluble in fat, while the B vitamins and vitamin C are water soluble. Fat-soluble vitamins tend to be stored in the body's fat tissues; because accumulations can produce serious side effects, nutritionists warn against taking high doses of vitamins A, D, E, or K.

Rather than being stored in fat tissues, water-soluble vitamins move from the digestive system directly into the bloodstream and are then picked up as needed by the tissue cells. Our kidneys filter out and eliminate any amounts beyond the cells' immediate needs. That's why nutritionists say it's pointless to take huge amounts of vitamin C, for example. Koalas need vitamins, too; a few of these are supplied by the leaves, and the rest by bacteria that ferment leaves in the animal's digestive tract. Bacteria in our digestive tracts also provide us with some vitamins.

Minerals

An animal's body also needs small amounts of another type of nutrient: minerals, specific inorganic chemical elements. *Major minerals* are those elements we need in amounts greater than 0.1 g each day; *minor minerals* are those we need in amounts less than 0.01 g daily. An adult person has about 2 kg (4.5 lb) of minerals in his or her body—mostly the calcium and phosphorus in bones and teeth. Our tears, blood, and sweat taste salty because of the sodium, potassium, and chlorine in the fluids. Sulfur is found in many proteins, and magnesium in many enzymes; the bones also hold a reservoir of magnesium along with calcium. The human body contains less than 1 teaspoon of minor minerals, but these elements are still critical to survival. Perhaps most important is iron, lying at the center of the hemoglobin molecule in our blood and essential to the transport of oxygen (see Chapter 17). Thyroid hormones contain the element iodine; zinc is an important component of some enzymes and gene-regulating proteins; and we need fluorine for healthy bones and teeth. Studies of koalas in the wild reveal that while they tend to get most of the minerals they need from eucalyptus leaves and dirt, they occasionally have mineral deficiencies such as too little copper in the bloodstream and liver.

A person's need for specific minerals can change over time. For example, prior to menopause, a woman needs more iron every month because of periodic blood loss, and she requires extra iron throughout pregnancy to supply nutrients for the fetus's blood. She also needs extra calcium while pregnant for building fetal bones, and even more calcium while nursing. After menopause, natural declines in estrogen cause a loss of calcium that can lead to osteoporosis, so postmenopausal women, too, need to consume enough calcium.

Because vitamins and minerals are required in such small quantities, most people in affluent countries get more than enough of both simply by eating a well-balanced diet. A poor diet due to poverty or poor eating habits can indeed lead to vitamin or mineral deficiencies, however, with potentially serious consequences. A long-term absence of vitamin A, for instance, can lead to blindness, while a prolonged lack of B vitamins may lead to convulsions and other neurological disorders.

Food as Fuel: Calories Count

Most Americans have a far greater problem with overeating and obesity than with malnutrition.

vitamin
(L. *vita* = life + *amine* = of chemical origin) an organic compound needed in small amounts for growth and metabolism and must be obtained in food

mineral
an inorganic element such as sodium or potassium that is essential for survival and is obtained in food

overweight
having body weight that is more than 10 percent above ideal

obese
having body weight that is more than 20 percent above ideal

basal metabolic rate
the rate at which the body uses energy while resting

Figure 19.3
Ideal-Weight Chart

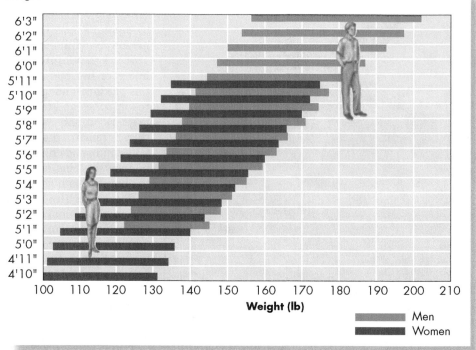

Height

Weight (lb)

Men
Women

While most children and half of adults are in a healthy weight range (Fig. 19.3), fully 25 percent of teenagers and 50 percent of adults are either overweight or obese (a body weight more than 10 or 20 percent over ideal, respectively). Research shows that obesity contributes to cardiovascular diseases, some forms of diabetes, joint problems, generally poor health, and an overall decrease in the quality of life, including reduced earning power due to illness and prejudice against their appearance.

Food energy is usually measured in kilocalories (kcal), also called *Calories* (Cal). A calorie (lower case "c") is the amount of energy needed to raise the temperature of 1 mL of water 1°C; 1,000 cal (1 kilocalorie or 1 Cal) is therefore a thousand times that energy amount. A large apple contains about 100 Cal worth of energy-producing compounds; and jogging 1.6 km (1 mi) burns about 100 Cal of stored energy.

How much energy do we need? That varies with age, sex, body size, and activity level. A normally active female college student needs around 1,800 to 2,000 Cal a day to fuel her total metabolic needs; a male college student needs about 2,200 to 2,500 Cal. Carbohydrates and protein each provide about 4.5 Cal/g, while fat provides 9 Cal/g. A female college student, then, would typically need the equivalent of about 400 g (14 oz) of pure sugar to provide the necessary calories. One of the strategies koalas have evolved to help overcome the small amount of calories in their spartan diet is to minimize their basal metabolic rate, the rate at which their bodies use energy while resting. Their rate is about half of our rate and is probably among the lowest of all

mammals. Koalas require only about 500 Cal each day, about the amount of energy in 200 g (a large bowl) of breakfast cereal or 500 g (a large pile) of eucalyptus leaves.

Figure 19.4 provides a revealing look at calories and energy, and a simple way to understand weight gain and loss. It shows the calories in three common snack foods and the amount of energy you'd have to expend in various physical activities to work off that food. For example, it takes 30 minutes to run off the calories in a cheeseburger, or an hour to burn them off playing tennis, but 6 1/2 hours to use them up sitting in a chair watching television! When an animal's food intake exceeds its energy needs, the inevitable result is storage of the leftover energy as body fat. The secret of weight control is basically this: take in only as many kilocalories as the body needs for fuel. Sound weight-loss programs combine calorie reductions, primarily through the decreased intake of sugar and fat, with increased physical activity. The result is less energy *in* and more energy *out,* with the differences made up gradually from the body's fat reserves. The koala eats such a low-calorie, high-fiber food source that it has to take a reverse strategy with regard to exercise: To conserve calories and hide from predators, it spends only four minutes a day moving about!

{ Mirror, mirror . . . }

While obesity is common in North America, some people become so obsessed with body weight and thinness that it seriously threatens their health. In the disorder called **anorexia nervosa**, a person (typically a middle-class teenaged girl) restricts her food intake severely, becomes cadaverously thin, and yet still sees herself as overweight. In a separate disorder called **bulimia**, a person secretly binges on huge helpings of cake, ice cream, cookies, bread, or other high-calorie foods, then purges with self-induced vomiting, laxatives, diuretics, fasting, or vigorous exercise. Both disorders have social, psychological, and probably neurochemical roots and can lead to organ damage and even death if untreated.

anorexia nervosa
an eating disorder in which a person restricts food intake severely, becomes cadaverously thin, and yet still sees himself or herself as overweight

bulimia
an eating disorder in which a person secretly binges on high-calorie foods, then purges with self-induced vomiting, laxatives, diuretics, fasting, or vigorous exercise

Apple
70 calories

58 min
12 min
9 min
7 min
6 min
5 min

© OLIVER WOLFSON/
ISTOCKPHOTO.COM

Cheeseburger
470 calories

Resting — 6 hr 30 min
Walking — 82 min
Tennis — 61 min
Swimming — 43 min
Cycling — 39 min
Jogging — 32 min

Figure 19.4
Food and Exercise Equivalents

Slice of Pizza
185 calories

2 hr 32 min
32 min
24 min
17 min
15 min
12 min

© ISTOCKPHOTO.COM

© TODD SMITH/ISTOCKPHOTO.COM

Figure 19.5
Strategies for Digestion

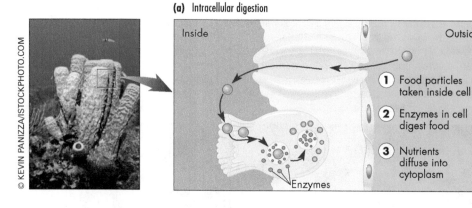

(a) Intracellular digestion

Inside   Outside

1. Food particles taken inside cell
2. Enzymes in cell digest food
3. Nutrients diffuse into cytoplasm

Enzymes

(b) Extracellular digestion

Inside   Outside

1. Cell secretes enzymes into cavity
3. Cell absorbs digested nutrients
2. Enzymes break down food outside of cell

LO² How Animals Digest Food

A koala chewing tough, leathery leaves; a polar bear devouring a seal; and a college student eating a chef's salad in the school cafeteria are all consuming food in forms that their cells can't use directly. Animal digestive systems must break down foods into usable small molecules and absorb them into the bloodstream, where they can then be distributed to body cells.

Intracellular and Extracellular Digestion

In the simplest animals—the sponges—some body cells take in tiny whole food particles directly from the water and break them down enzymatically to release usable nutrients. This strategy is called intracellular digestion (Fig. 19.5a), and it circumvents the need for the mechanical breakdown of food in a mouth or for the chemical digestion of food in a gut or other cavity. Intracellular digestion is clearly a simpler strategy, but it puts an upper limit on the size of food particles an animal can take in, and, in turn, limits its dietary choices.

Evolutionary changes brought about a way animals could exploit larger food particles. Extracellular digestion is the enzymatic breakdown of larger pieces of food into constituent molecules outside of cells, but usually within a special body organ or cavity (Fig. 19.5b). Nutrients from the broken-down foods pass into body cells lining the organ or cavity, and take part in body metabolism. Because the vast majority of animals rely on it, let's explore extracellular digestion in more detail.

Patterns of Extracellular Digestion

In rather simple animals, such as a cnidarian or flatworm (see Chapter 13), extracellular digestion takes place in the gastrovascular cavity, an internal sac with a single opening through which whole particles of food enter and undigested wastes leave. This system works well for small, thin organisms, but has important limitations: The animal doesn't break food pieces apart mechanically. As a result, digestive enzymes in the saclike gut can only break down the outer portions of ingested food chunks.

More complex animals have digestive tracts with two openings (Fig. 19.6). Food enters the mouth at one

© KEVIN PANIZZA/ISTOCKPHOTO.COM

© TOM BRANCH/PHOTO RESEARCHERS, INC.

end of the digestive tract, moves in a single direction through the gut, or gastrointestinal tract, and wastes exit at the other end of the tube, the anus. Between the two ends, a variety of specialized regions perform particular digestive roles. The overall result is the absorption of nutrients into the circulatory system. The circulatory system then distributes nutrients to each cell in the body.

LO³ The Digestive Tract

Let's return to the koala and its diet of nothing but eucalyptus leaves. This diet poses three main problems: (1) it has few nutrients; (2) it has a high concentration of bulky, indigestible dietary fiber; and (3) it has a large number of compounds that are toxic to most other mammals. Somehow, the koala's digestive tract must solve these problems despite the animal's small size. Let's look at digestive tracts, and compare the koala's to our own to see how that fuzzy marsupial solves its problems.

In people, koalas, and other vertebrates, the digestive tract is divided into five main regions:

mouth, esophagus, stomach, small intestine, and large intestine (see Fig. 19.7 on the next page). Together, these form the alimentary canal, or *gut*. In addition, nearby accessory organs, such as the salivary glands, liver, gallbladder, and pancreas, produce enzymes, bile, and other materials and deliver them into the tract at appropriate times, which aids digestion. Together, the alimentary canal and accessory organs accomplish the step-by-step conversion of foods into nutrients that circulate in the bloodstream and supply all the body's cells.

Now let's contrast the human digestive system to a koala's, displayed diagrammatically in Figure 19.7. The most remarkable feature of the koala gut is its huge cecum (SEE-cum), a dead-end sac with a 2 L capacity that is six times as long as the animal itself! As you can see from its position, the koala's cecum corresponds anatomically to the human appendix, which is vestigial and no bigger than your little finger. The koala's cecum is the largest of any mammal's, and about 40 percent of a koala's weight is the material inside this sac. Imagine if you had a 50- or 60-pound appendix! The koala's proximal colon is huge relative to our colon, but its distal colon is very narrow, containing lumps of compacted waste leaf material. What are the functions of the koala's cecum and colon? Other mammals that eat mostly leaves, such as cattle, have large stomach-like sacs that act as fermentation chambers. Bacteria growing in the cow's sac (or rumen) break down the cellulose and provide energy to the cow. But as we've seen, a koala gets only 13 percent of its energy from cellulose in cell walls and the rest from the contents of eucalyptus leaf cells. So what is the cecum doing if it is not fermenting cell walls? To understand the specialized gut of the koala, we first need to understand the function of a generalized gut.

gut (gastrointestinal tract)
the food processing or alimentary canal made up of the mouth, esophagus, stomach, small intestine, and large intestine

anus
the end of the digestive tract where waste products exit the body

alimentary canal
the gastrointestinal tract; includes the mouth, esophagus, stomach, and small and large intestines

accessory organ
one of several organs that aid digestion, including the salivary glands, liver, gallbladder, and pancreas

cecum
a feature of the large intestine; a dead-end sac that is vestigial in the human but can be large in other animals, including the koala

Figure 19.6
Basic Strategy of the Digestive System

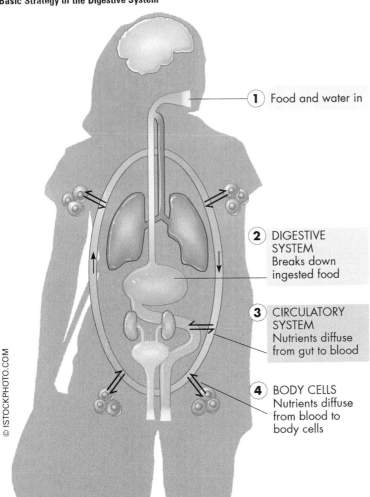

1. Food and water in

2. DIGESTIVE SYSTEM
Breaks down ingested food

3. CIRCULATORY SYSTEM
Nutrients diffuse from gut to blood

4. BODY CELLS
Nutrients diffuse from blood to body cells

© ISTOCKPHOTO.COM

Functions of the Gastrointestinal Tract

Within the alimentary canal, a four-step digestive process that extracts nutrients from food takes place. The steps include ingestion and mastication, digestion, absorption, and elimination (Fig. 19.7 center). First, the animal brings food into its mouth (ingestion, Step ①). It then breaks the food into small pieces (mastication). In many mammals and other vertebrates, this mastication involves slicing or grinding by teeth. In the case of many birds, mastication occurs in a muscular sac called the gizzard, which usually contains stones that grind against each other and pulverize food. (Researchers have also found huge gizzard stones in some dinosaur fossils.) Enzymes secreted into the gut tube break down the large macromolecules of food into smaller molecules, or monomers (digestion, Step ②).

Figure 19.7

The Gastrointestinal Tract and Steps of Digestion

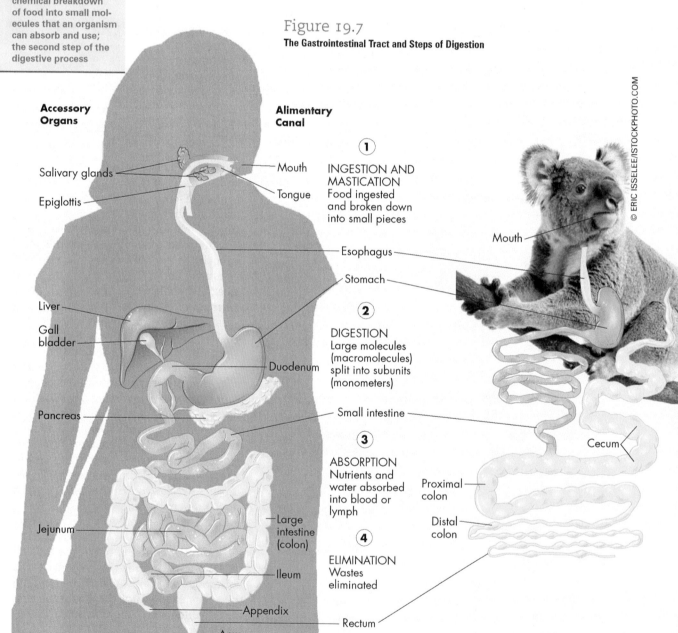

Accessory Organs

- Salivary glands
- Epiglottis
- Liver
- Gall bladder
- Pancreas
- Jejunum
- Ileum
- Appendix
- Anus

Alimentary Canal

- Mouth
- Tongue
- Esophagus
- Stomach
- Duodenum
- Small intestine
- Large intestine (colon)
- Ileum
- Rectum

① INGESTION AND MASTICATION
Food ingested and broken down into small pieces

② DIGESTION
Large molecules (macromolecules) split into subunits (monometers)

③ ABSORPTION
Nutrients and water absorbed into blood or lymph

④ ELIMINATION
Wastes eliminated

Mouth
Cecum
Proximal colon
Distal colon

© ERIC ISSELEE/ISTOCKPHOTO.COM

Next, in the process of absorption (Step ③), monomers pass across the gut wall into the animal's lymphatic system or bloodstream, which transports the small nutrient molecules to each cell in the body. Finally, most of the water in the food is absorbed and undigested residues are eventually eliminated (elimination, Step ④).

Tissues of the Gastrointestinal Tract

As we saw in Chapter 13, the gut is a long tube, and these alimentary functions are facilitated by the tube's four tissue layers. The innermost layer, which faces the cavity of the digestive tract, is a mucous membrane, or mucosa (Fig. 19.8). Some mucosa cells produce digestive enzymes, while others secrete mucus, a slimy coating that lubricates food passing through and keeps the gut from digesting itself.

Surrounding the mucosa is the submucosa, a connective tissue that is richly supplied with blood and lymph vessels and with nerve cells. Next is the muscularis, a double layer made of muscle fibers, in longitudinal, circular, and oblique orientations.

The contraction and relaxation of these fibers, or peristalsis, knead the food, mix it with digestive juices, and propel it along with rhythmic sequential contractions like toothpaste squeezed through a tube. Finally, a thin outermost layer, the serosa, forms a band around the other tissues and joins to the sheet (the mesentery) that attaches the gastrointestinal tract to the inner wall of the body cavity.

LO⁴ The Human Digestive System

Most vertebrates share these strategies of digestion, and we're no exception. Because we have such a varied diet, however, the human digestive system (Fig. 19.7) makes a better general model than the koala's highly specialized digestive system or that of many other animals. You might be surprised to learn that our gut, from mouth to anus, is approximately 8 m long, or about the height of a two-story house. All the sandwiches, brownies, apples, milk, and other foods

Figure 19.8
Anatomy of the Alimentary Canal

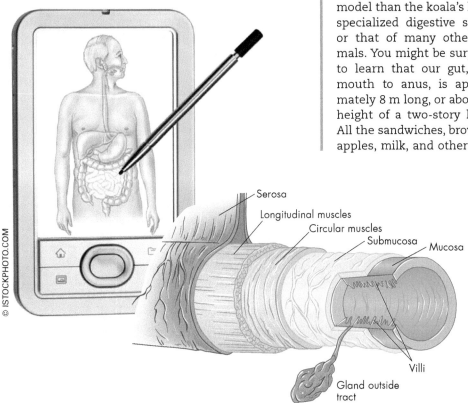

Serosa
Longitudinal muscles
Circular muscles
Submucosa
Mucosa
Villi
Gland outside tract

© ISTOCKPHOTO.COM

absorption
in this, the third step of the digestive process, small molecules pass across the gut wall into the animal's lymphatic system or bloodstream, which transports the small molecules to each cell in the body

elimination
in this last step of the digestive process, most of the water in intestinal wastes is absorbed and undigested residues are eventually eliminated

mucosa
the innermost layer of the lining of many vertebrate canals and organs, such as the uterus, reproductive tracts, and alimentary canal; often consists of mucus-secreting cells; in the alimentary canal, the mucosa contains enzyme-secreting cells

mucus
a slimy coating secreted by mucosa cells that lubricates food passing through the gastrointestinal tract and that coats the respiratory and reproductive tract linings

submucosa
a connective tissue outside the mucosa of the digestive tract that is richly supplied with blood and lymph vessels and nerves

muscularis
a double layer outside the submucosa of the digestive tract that is made of muscle fibers, in longitudinal, circular, and oblique orientations

peristalsis
(Gr. *peristaltikos*, compressing around) in animals, successive waves of contraction and relaxation of muscles along the length of a tube, such as those in the digestive tract that help move food

serosa
the outermost layer of the alimentary canal

mesentery
the sheet of tissue that is joined to the serosa and attaches the gastrointestinal tract to the inner wall of the body cavity

lumen
the central cavity; in a blood vessel, the central space where the blood flows

enamel
the substance covering teeth that is composed of calcium salts and protein; the hardest substance in the body

tongue
a muscular organ on the floor of the mouth of most higher vertebrates that carries taste buds and manipulates food

bolus
a soft, round mass of chewed food, shaped by the tongue and suitable for swallowing

salivary gland
a gland that secretes saliva

saliva
a watery liquid secreted by the salivary glands that moistens food particles for swallowing; contains the starch-digesting enzyme amylase

amylase
a digestive enzyme that begins the breakdown of carbohydrates

hard palate
the part of the oral cavity that forms the floor of the nasal cavity and most of the roof of the mouth

soft palate
the posterior part of the roof of the mouth

epiglottis
a flap of tissue just above the larynx that closes during swallowing and prevents food from entering the lungs

a person eats pass through the central cavity, or lumen, of this tube and undergo one digestive process after another. Let's follow a turkey sandwich through its digestive journey to see how the nutrients are liberated.

The Mouth, Pharynx, and Esophagus

Your teeth are superbly adapted to the job of cutting, tearing, and grinding the plant and animal tissues that omnivorous mammals (such as ourselves) eat (Fig. 19.9a). Teeth can stand up to regular wear and tear because the enamel covering them, made up of calcium salts and protein, is the hardest substance in the body. The enamel on a person's permanent teeth will actually generate sparks if struck against steel! Working along with the teeth is a muscular tongue, the principal organ of taste, but also, in our species, an organ that along with the *larynx*, or voice box, forms the sounds of spoken language (Fig. 19.10a). When you take a bite of a sandwich, your tongue moves some of the food toward the molars for grinding and some to the incisors for cutting, and shapes each small bite into a soft, moist lump, or bolus, that you can easily swallow.

Koalas have the same basic types of teeth as you do, but each of its molars have four V-shaped ridges that leave characteristic marks on a eucalyptus leaf as they break up the leaf blade into cells and crush the cells to release their nutritive contents (Fig. 19.9b). When these ridges wear down after years of cutting up tough leaves, a koala (especially one in the wild) can't access the leaf's contents, and the animal often dies of diseases and/or malnutrition.

As a mammal chews (Fig. 19.10a), three large pairs of salivary glands that lie in the tissues surrounding the oral cavity secrete clear, watery saliva, which mixes with the food. Saliva contains primarily mucus and water, and these moisten food particles and help them cling together in a bolus. Saliva also contains small amounts of amylase, a digestive enzyme that begins the breakdown of carbohydrates (such as the starch in the bread or in the lettuce and tomato of the sandwich). Just before swallowing begins (Fig. 19.10b), the tongue pushes the bolus of food up and back against the hard palate, which forms the floor of the nasal cavity and most of the roof of the mouth. Next, the food encounters the soft palate at the back of the mouth above the throat. This flexible muscular sheet rises as swallowing starts, preventing food from entering the nasal cavity. The flaplike epiglottis

Figure 19.9
Teeth: Unspecialized and Specialized

(a) Human teeth

(b) Koala teeth

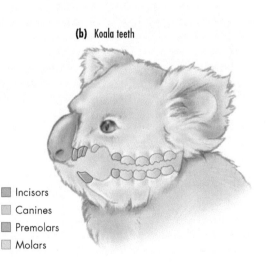

- Incisors
- Canines
- Premolars
- Molars

Figure 19.10

Anatomy and the Swallowing Reflex

(a) Chewing

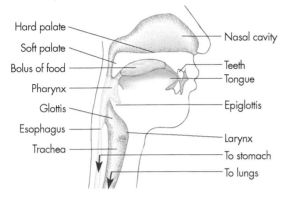

Hard palate
Soft palate
Bolus of food
Pharynx
Glottis
Esophagus
Trachea

Nasal cavity
Teeth
Tongue
Epiglottis
Larynx
To stomach
To lungs

(b) Swallowing

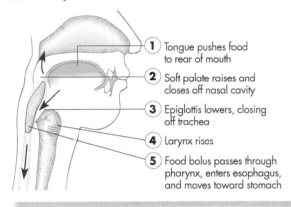

1 Tongue pushes food to rear of mouth

2 Soft palate raises and closes off nasal cavity

3 Epiglottis lowers, closing off trachea

4 Larynx rises

5 Food bolus passes through pharynx, enters esophagus, and moves toward stomach

moves backward and downward, closing off the opening to the trachea, or windpipe. This opening is called the glottis. Next the food bolus moves through the pharynx, the passageway for food between the mouth and esophagus and for air between the nose and throat. Food entering stimulates a reflexive swallowing action in the pharynx.

Swallowing then delivers the food bolus to the esophagus (eh-SOF-eh-gus), the pipeline to the stomach. To enter the stomach, the bolus passes through the cardiac sphincter (SFINGK-ter), a ring of muscle located at the junction of the stomach and esophagus (see Fig. 19.11a,b on the next page). This muscular ring usually stays tightly contracted, like the drawstring on a purse, preventing the stomach's contents from backing up into the esophagus. People often experience "heartburn" when the stomach is very full; this burning sensation is due to small amounts of stomach acid seeping out past the cardiac sphincter into the esophagus, which lacks the stomach's heavy mucous lining. Despite their names, neither heartburn nor the cardiac sphincter is related to the heart.

The Stomach

Next, the food bolus (here, of chewed turkey sandwich) passes into the elastic, J-shaped bag called the stomach (Fig. 19.11b). The stomach stores food for later processing—an adaptation that enables large animals to eat larger meals and hence feed less often. The average human stomach can comfortably hold about 1 L (about a quart; recall that the little koala's cecum holds twice as much!). When the stomach is full, waves of peristalsis in the muscular stomach wall churn and mix the contents with an acid bath of gastric juice secreted by glands in the stomach wall.

Gastric juice is a mixture of water, hydrochloric acid (HCl), mucus, and pepsinogen, a precursor to the protein-cleaving enzyme, pepsin. The hydrochloric acid makes gastric juice acidic enough to kill off most bacteria or fungi contaminating foods. This acid contributes to the breakdown of food pieces into constituent protein fibers, fat globules, and so on, and it also converts pepsinogen into pepsin. Pepsin breaks the peptide bonds that link amino acids in proteins. Therefore, during the time that protein-containing foods (such as the turkey in a sandwich) are in the stomach, they are partially digested to short polypeptide segments. Although digestion of the starch in the bread of the sandwich begins in the mouth, once food enters the stomach, very little additional digestion of starches and other carbohydrates (or of fats, like those in mayonnaise) takes place. This takes place later, in the small intestine.

The result of the chemical activity and mixing waves in the stomach is a pasty, milky, and highly acidic soup called chyme (KIME) (Fig. 19.11c). Chyme passes through another sphincter, the pyloric sphincter, into the small intestine at a rate of about a teaspoonful every three seconds after a meal (Fig. 19.11d). It usually takes one to four hours for the

glottis
the opening to the trachea, which is also known as the windpipe

pharynx
in vertebrates, a tube leading from the nose and mouth to the larynx and esophagus; conducts air during breathing and food during swallowing; the *throat*

esophagus
the muscular tube leading from the pharynx to the stomach

cardiac sphincter
a ring of muscle located at the junction of the stomach and esophagus

stomach
an expandable, elastic-walled sac of the gut that receives food from the esophagus

pepsinogen
a precursor to the protein-digesting enzyme pepsin

pepsin
an enzyme secreted by the stomach that digests proteins

chyme
the semifluid contents of the stomach consisting of partially digested food and gastric secretions

pyloric sphincter
a muscular ring located at the junction of the stomach and small intestine where chyme passes from the stomach to the small intestine

stomach to process a meal and for the chyme to pass, spoonful by spoonful, into the small intestine—less time for a high-carbohydrate meal, more time for a fatty meal.

Pancreas, Liver, and Gallbladder

The small intestine carries out most chemical digestion of food, as well as most absorption of nutrients. This portion of the gut tube, however, does not accomplish these tasks alone. Three accessory organs assist this portion of the gut tube—the pancreas, the liver, and the gallbladder—by dumping in substances that aid digestion and absorption.

The Pancreas and Its Digestive Enzymes

The pancreas is a narrow, lumpy organ situated close to where the stomach joins the small intestine (see Fig. 19.7). The pancreas produces a host of digestive enzymes and secretes them into the small intestine. These pancreatic enzymes include proteases, which break down proteins; lipases, which digest fats; and enzymes such as amylase, which complete the digestion of carbohydrates. The pancreas also secretes bicarbonate ions (the main ingredient in many antacids), which buffer or neutralize stomach acid entering the small intestine. This buffering is vital because, unlike stomach enzymes, pancreatic enzymes can't function in an acidic environment, and the acid could damage the small intestine.

Some pancreatic cells secrete the hormones insulin and glucagon directly into the bloodstream. These hormones help keep the levels of blood glucose within a certain range (see Chapter 18); when that homeostasis fails, a person can develop diabetes or other blood sugar disorders.

Figure 19.11
Function of the Stomach

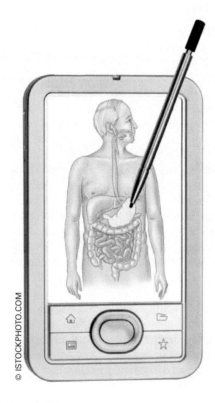

© ISTOCKPHOTO.COM

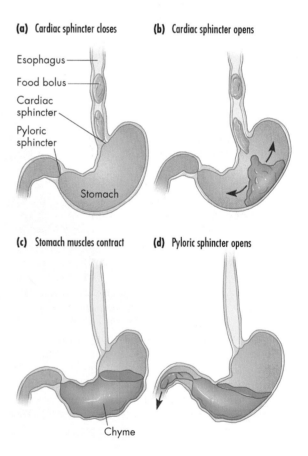

(a) Cardiac sphincter closes   **(b)** Cardiac sphincter opens

Esophagus
Food bolus
Cardiac sphincter
Pyloric sphincter

Stomach

(c) Stomach muscles contract   **(d)** Pyloric sphincter opens

Chyme

The Multipurpose Liver and the Gallbladder

The smooth, lobed, rather hemispherical liver is the largest gland in the human body (see Fig. 19.7). It weighs about 2 kg (4.5 lb) in an adult and performs biological tasks as diverse as destroying aging red blood cells, storing glycogen, and dispersing glucose to the bloodstream as circulating levels of the sugar drop. One of the liver's most important functions is to produce bile salts, molecules of modified cholesterol. Bile salts are stored as the yellow-green liquid bile in the gallbladder, a pear-shaped sac on the underside of the liver. Bile salts act like detergents and break up fat droplets in the small intestine (Fig. 19.12). Cholesterol-lowering drugs bind to bile salts and cause them to pass down the intestinal tract without being absorbed. This prevents the recycling of cholesterol from bile salts and thus decreases the amount of cholesterol in the blood.

Besides synthesizing bile, the liver picks up, stores, and sometimes synthesizes amino acids, glucose, and glycogen, and stores some vitamins and other compounds that cells need to function normally. Certain liver cells also contain special enzymes that can detoxify poisons. For example, the liver transforms molecules of ammonia—a toxic, nitrogen-containing waste created by the breakdown of amino acids—into urea, which is less toxic and is excreted in urine. The liver also detoxifies alcohol; but if the liver is overloaded with the drug year after year, it can become

liver
a large, lobed gland that destroys blood cells, stores glycogen, disperses glucose to the bloodstream, and produces bile

bile salts
molecules of modified cholesterol that break up fats in the small intestine

bile
a bitter, alkaline, yellow fluid produced by the liver that is stored in the gallbladder and released into the small intestine that aids in the digestion and absorption of fats

gallbladder
the sac beneath the right lobe of the liver that stores bile

Figure 19.12
Fat Digestion

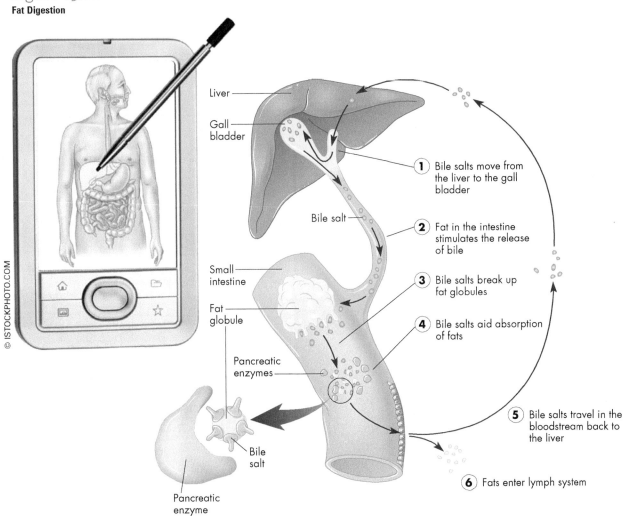

Liver
Gall bladder
Bile salt
Small intestine
Fat globule
Pancreatic enzymes
Bile salt
Pancreatic enzyme

1. Bile salts move from the liver to the gall bladder
2. Fat in the intestine stimulates the release of bile
3. Bile salts break up fat globules
4. Bile salts aid absorption of fats
5. Bile salts travel in the bloodstream back to the liver
6. Fats enter lymph system

© ISTOCKPHOTO.COM

small intestine
a coiled tube, about 6 meters (20 feet) long, that is the main site of carbohydrate and fat digestion and is also where protein digestion is completed, allowing nutrients to be absorbed into the blood

duodenum
the upper section of the small intestine

jejunum
the central section of the small intestine

ileum
the lower section of the small intestine

villus (pl., villi)
(L., a tuft of hair) a fingerlike projection of the intestinal wall that increases the surface area for absorption of nutrients

microvillus (pl., microvilli)
one of hundreds of tiny fingerlike projections extending from the surface of cells lining the walls of the intestine that increases the surface area available for absorption

Figure 19.13
Highly Absorptive Lining of the Small Intestine

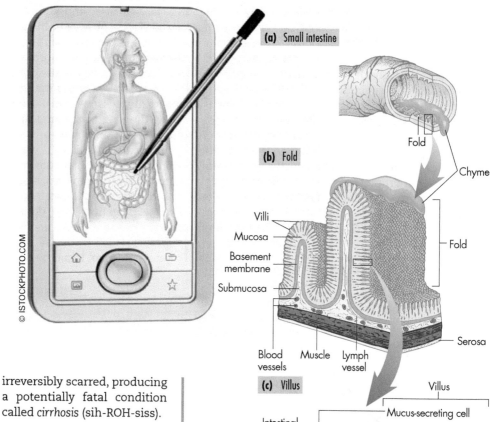

© ISTOCKPHOTO.COM

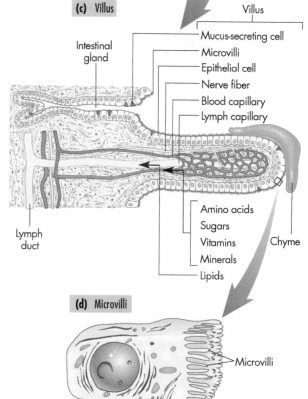

(a) Small intestine

(b) Fold

Villi
Mucosa
Basement membrane
Submucosa

Fold
Chyme
Fold
Serosa

Blood vessels   Muscle   Lymph vessel

(c) Villus

Villus

Intestinal gland

Mucus-secreting cell
Microvilli
Epithelial cell
Nerve fiber
Blood capillary
Lymph capillary

Lymph duct

Amino acids
Sugars
Vitamins
Minerals
Lipids

Chyme

(d) Microvilli

Microvilli

irreversibly scarred, producing a potentially fatal condition called *cirrhosis* (sih-ROH-siss).

The Small Intestine: Digestion and Absorption

The small intestine is a remarkable coiled tube about 6 m (20 ft) long. It's the main site of carbohydrate and fat digestion, and is also the place where protein digestion is completed so that nutrients can be absorbed into the blood. The small intestine begins just below the stomach and has three main regions along its length: the upper section, or duodenum (doo-oh-DEE-nuhm), the central jejunum, and the remainder, the ileum (see Fig. 19.7).

The small intestine is a marvel of compact biological engineering. If the surface of its inner lining were a smooth tube like a garden hose, there would be a relatively small surface area for digestion and absorption. Instead, that inner lining is so convoluted that it houses a huge absorptive surface. The intestinal lining is pleated into large numbers of folds (Fig. 19.13a,b), and each fold is covered with fingerlike extensions known as villi (sing., villus), which project into the lumen and come into contact with chyme (Fig. 19.13c). Further, cells on the outer layer of each villus are carpeted with microvilli (sing., microvillus), microscopic brushlike projections of the plasma membrane (Fig. 19.13d). The combination of folds, villi, and microvilli creates a total surface area in the human small intestine the size of a tennis court.

By the time the turkey sandwich you ate for lunch is reduced to chyme and reaches the small intestine, it contains partially digested carbohydrates and proteins, as well as undigested fat. Here, enzymes secreted by the intestine and the pancreas interact with bicarbonate ions and bile salts. Together, they gradually complete the digestion of the carbohydrates (from bread, lettuce, and tomato) into simple sugars; the proteins (from turkey meat) into amino acids; and the fats (from mayonnaise) into fatty acids and glycerol. These nutrient molecules are small enough to move across the plasma membranes of the microvilli and enter the intestinal cells. The amino acids and sugars then pass into blood capillaries, along with most of the available vitamins and minerals from the tomato slice and lettuce, while lipids enter tiny lymph capillaries (see Fig. 19.13c). The remaining contents of the small intestine, including the small amount of indigestible roughage in the bread, lettuce, and tomato, pass into the large intestine.

The Large Intestine: Site of Water Absorption

The last 1.2 m (4 ft) of the human alimentary canal is the large intestine, or colon. This section of the gut tube ascends on the right side of the body cavity, cuts across just below the stomach, then descends on the left side and ends in a short tube called the rectum (see Fig. 19.7). Extending from the colon near its junction with the small intestine is the small cecum with its extension, the appendix. This, as we saw, is a miniature version of the koala's giant cecum. A person's finger-shaped appendix plays no known role in digestion, but it may help fight infections in the gut (as may the koala's cecum). An inflamed appendix, most often based on blockage by hardened waste matter, can lead to the medical emergency called *appendicitis*.

The colon absorbs water, ions, and vitamins from the chyme. The rectum stores the semisolid undigested wastes, or feces, and helps excrete them. The colon is twice as wide as the small intestine, but its walls lack the many folds and villi of the small intestine. The smoother surface has a lower surface area for absorption, but it also presents less resistance to the movement of chyme through the tube.

Each day, about 0.5 L (about 1 pt) of chyme (now minus the nutrients absorbed in the small intestine) reaches the colon, along with 2 to 3 L (approx. 2 to 3 qt) of water, some from food and the rest secreted by the stomach and intestines themselves. The body can't afford to lose this much water, however, and much of the water is reabsorbed as the chyme moves slowly through the colon over a period of 12 to 36 hours. This absorption gradually transforms the chyme from fluid to semisolid, and the wastes (including undigestible cellulose fiber from the bread, lettuce, and tomato of the turkey sandwich we started with) are stored until their pressure against the colon wall triggers a *bowel movement* (defecation), the muscular expulsion of wastes through the rectum and out the anus.

Digestion is never 100 percent efficient, and some nutrients invariably pass into the colon from the small intestine. A variety of bacteria, including *Escherichia coli* and *Lactobacillus* and *Streptococcus* species, reside in the human intestine and live on these remaining nutrients; in the process, they produce a number of vitamins, including thiamine (vitamin B_1), riboflavin (vitamin B_2), vitamin B_{12}, and vitamin K. The colon absorbs these vitamins along with fluids.

Coordination of Digestion

As your turkey sandwich moves through your digestive system, the food is mechanically and then chemically broken down and most of its nutrients are absorbed. This complex process can't take place willy-nilly, and in fact, it is closely controlled by your nervous system and your endocrine (hormonal) system. Nerves throughout the digestive tract communicate between "upstream" and "downstream" regions, speeding or slowing the propulsion of food appropriately. Nervous activity in the brain and spinal cord can also speed up or slow down digestion. For example, the sight, taste, smell, or even thought of food (see Fig. 19.14 on the next page, Step ①) can cause signals from higher brain centers to travel via nerves to the salivary glands (Step ②), causing them to secrete saliva, and to secretory glands in the stomach lining, causing them to secrete gastric juices—hydrochloric acid and pepsinogen—into the stomach. Food arriving in the stomach and pushing against the stomach wall can trigger the same response.

colon (large intestine)
the last 1.2 meters (4 feet) of the human alimentary canal, which leads to the rectum

rectum
the terminal portion of the colon that stores and helps remove solid waste by defecation

appendix
finger-shaped vestigial organ that plays no known role in digestion, but may help fight infections in the gut

feces
semisolid undigested waste products that are stored in the rectum until excreted

gastrin
a digestive hormone secreted in the stomach that causes the secretion of other digestive juices

ulcers
craterlike sores in the mucosa of the stomach or small intestine

secretin
a digestive hormone secreted by the small intestine that causes the pancreas to secrete bicarbonate, which neutralizes stomach acid

cholecystokinin
a digestive hormone secreted by the small intestine that triggers the pancreas to release protein-digesting enzymes

Food in the stomach also lowers the acidity of the contents (Fig. 19.14, Step ③), and this triggers stomach-lining cells to secrete a hormone called gastrin (Step ④). Gastrin acts on other nearby stomach cells, causing them to secrete more hydrochloric acid (Step ⑤). This raises the acidity (lowers the pH) of gastric juice, and helps speed the breakdown of the food (Step ⑥). When the pH drops to about two again, the stomach stops secreting gastrin and, in turn, the extra acid. Food literally helps to stimulate its own digestion through a negative feedback loop for regulating stomach acid. Long periods of emotional stress can stimulate acid production in some people (and in lab animals) and lead to ulcers, craterlike sores in the mucosa of the stomach or small intestine. Research has shown that a bacterial species called *Helicobacter pylori* can be the causative agents in certain ulcers and can be treated with antibiotics.

Several other hormones help coordinate the timing and amount of enzyme secretion after you eat. For example, the peptide secretin from your small intestine causes your pancreas to secrete bicarbonate ion, which then enters your small intestine and neutralizes the stomach acid. Partially digested proteins cause the small intestine to release a second hormone, cholecystokinin (CCK; KOH-luh-SISS-toe-KEY-nin). This hormone triggers your pancreas to release protein- and fat-digesting enzymes. CCK also works on regulatory centers in the brain and produces the sensation of being full. This is why nutritionists often advise dieters to eat the protein foods in a meal first, so they'll feel satisfied sooner.

Working together, nerves and hormones—the body's rapid- and slow-acting control agents—fine-tune the secretion of digestive juices, making enzymes and ions instantly available to break down food but only when food is present and the powerful agents are needed.

The Koala's Survival Strategy

So far, we've seen that koalas stay alive by eating only one food, a food that few other animals can stomach. We've also seen that koalas have the animal kingdom's biggest cecum, and that while it's filled with fermenting bacteria that can break down cel-

Figure 19.14
Nerves and Hormones Coordinate Digestion

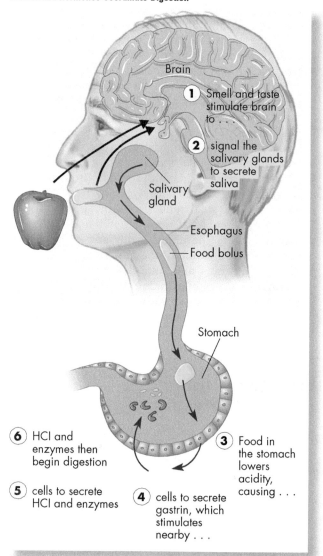

① Smell and taste stimulate brain to . . .

② signal the salivary glands to secrete saliva

③ Food in the stomach lowers acidity, causing . . .

④ cells to secrete gastrin, which stimulates nearby . . .

⑤ cells to secrete HCl and enzymes

⑥ HCl and enzymes then begin digestion

Brain · Salivary gland · Esophagus · Food bolus · Stomach

lulose, koalas still get 87 percent of their food energy from the contents of eucalyptus leaf cells and only 13 percent by fermenting the cell walls themselves. Looking at these facts, you've got to wonder what the huge cecum and swollen proximal colon are doing if they're not serving as fermentation chambers for bacteria that digest cellulose. And you've also got to wonder, if a koala relies primarily on cell contents for energy, how it can ever obtain enough food calories given the enormous mass of indigestible cell walls filling up the gut (in P.B.'s case, 80 pounds of it a week)?

Koala researchers solved these puzzles by studying how solid fibers and soluble components move through the koala's gut. It turns out that it takes about nine days for small particles and dissolved nutrient compounds to pass through the digestive system, but only about a day for large particles such as leaf fragments to move through. The retention time for small particles is one of the longest among all mammals. Apparently, the colon's back-and-forth squeezing movements wash dissolved substances and small particles into the cecum. There, bacteria can ferment them and help detoxify some of the tannins and other poisonous compounds from the leaves. (Enzymes in the liver detoxify the terpenes and other essential oils, and the "disarmed" compounds are excreted in the urine.) Meanwhile, larger leaf fragments from the animal's diet settle in the distal colon, where water can be recovered and most of the bulk quickly eliminated. Through these digestive sorting processes, the furry animals can quickly move through and excrete large quantities of tough, fibrous leaves while retaining the most easily digested parts—the cell contents—for longer periods to extract more nutrients from them. This sorting strategy, coupled with the animal's low basal metabolic rate, sleepy demeanor, and minimal energy expenditure, insures that the koala can survive on a meager, otherwise toxic diet that other animals shun. Until the late 1800s, when hunters took huge numbers of koalas for their thick, soft pelts, Australia's eucalyptus forests were filled with millions of the marsupials. Today, the living teddy bears are rare.

LO⁵ Healthy Diets and Proper Nutrition

You might be surprised to learn that the koala's feeding strategy has lessons for our own nutrition. If a person wants to lose weight, he or she needs to eat food with low energy content and high roughage content, while still maintaining an adequate intake of amino acids, vitamins, and minerals, and couple that with increased exercise and stepped up basal metabolic rate. That's hard for most overweight people to do but it's an equation that works and recent animal research shows why.

Enormously obese mice led researchers to discover how hormones regulate body weight. Obese mice have a mutation that blocks a feeling of fullness and so they keep on eating even when their energy intake levels exceed their energy expenditures. The mutation, in other words, seems to block the normal "stop eating" signal, and it was this that allowed biologists to understand how weight-regulating hormones function in both mice and humans. The hormone called leptin is produced by fat cells. A second hormone involved in fat regulation is the insulin secreted by the pancreas. Figure 19.15 on the next page shows how these two hormones influence human fat formation. Fat cells secrete leptin (Step ①)

leptin
a weight-regulating hormone produced by fat cells

and also cause the pancreas to liberate insulin (Step ②). These hormones travel in the blood to the brain (Step ③), where they can activate neural circuits that speed energy use (Step ④) and repress neural circuits that control the desire to eat (Step ⑤). During a meal, when the "I'm full" factors we discussed earlier, such as cholecystokinin, act on the brain, they interact with leptin/insulin-sensitive nerve cells, and cause the individual to stop eating (Step ⑥). These interactions result in energy balance (Step ⑦), by modulating the size of the fat cells and their production of leptin (Step ⑧). Obviously, if the "stop eating" signal is broken as in the mutant mouse, the animal will keep eating and become obese.

Investigation of a few rare human families whose members are extremely obese demonstrated that, with slight differences, the basic regulatory pathway works the same way in people. And just as in mutant mice, giving leptin to obese humans that have a mutation in the leptin gene reduces weight markedly. While most obese people do not have a mutation in leptin, they may have genetic variation in other elements of the pathway, such as the activity of brain hormones (Fig. 19.15, Steps ③–⑥). This gives real hope that treatments for obesity could become available in the future.

Look again at Figure 19.15 and think of the way you feel when you go on a diet. You slow down your intake of food, and your fat cells start to shrink. You are going to start to feel slim and trim and full of energy, right? Wrong! You feel hungry all the time, constantly fatigued, and can't think of anything but food. As you can see from Figure 19.15, while dieting, your fat cells start to shrink, produce less leptin, and signal the pancreas to make less insulin. The drop in leptin revs up your brain circuits that stimulate eating and conserving energy and now you feel like eating larger meals and sitting around and exercising less. What a cruel trick! This is what makes dieting and maintaining weight loss so difficult. This plus the fact that American consumers find fat- and sugar-laden foods in every restaurant, cafeteria, supermarket, convenience store, and vending machine they pass.

Given this discouraging picture, how can one turn on fat-burning enzymes, reduce the size of fat cells, and cut body weight to an ideal level? Nutritionists recommend cutting sugars, because in an already overweight person, when the blood sugar levels are high, glucose is often rapidly converted to fat and stored in fat cells rather than entering muscle cells, where the sugar can be burned. Some people have found that high-protein, low-carbohydrate diets reduce food cravings, helping them to eat the right number of calories each day to lose weight or maintain weight loss.

Most importantly, dieting must be accompanied by increased daily physical activity. Exercising most or all days of the week seems to turn up the metabolic rate so that the body burns more fat—not just during exercise sessions, but for many hours at rest, as well. Exercise decreases fat tissue and increases muscle mass, making the body look and feel trimmer. Finally, moderate daily exercise reduces the appetite, whereas both fasting (such as adhering to very-low-calorie diets) and inactivity increase appetite. In other words, eat low-calorie, high-fiber foods like a koala, but don't exercise like one!

Who knew?

After a meal, fat cells secrete leptin and cause the pancreas to secrete insulin. Leptin and insulin circulate to the brain, stimulating neural circuits that increase energy use. Appetite-suppressing factors such as cholecystokinin act on the leptin/insulin-sensitive nerve cells to reduce the desire to eat. If you go on a diet and your fat cells start to shrink, you feel hungry all the time; your fat cells produce less leptin, and the pancreas makes less insulin. This stimulates eating and slows metabolism.

Figure 19.15
Hormones Regulate Body Weight

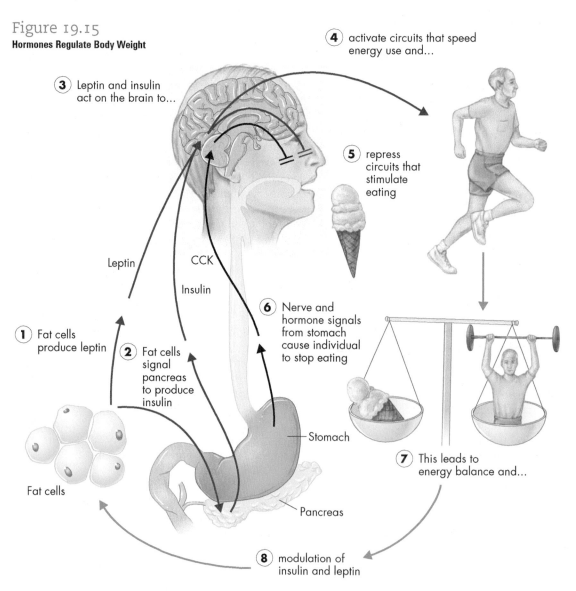

3 Leptin and insulin act on the brain to...

4 activate circuits that speed energy use and...

5 repress circuits that stimulate eating

Leptin

CCK

Insulin

6 Nerve and hormone signals from stomach cause individual to stop eating

1 Fat cells produce leptin

2 Fat cells signal pancreas to produce insulin

Fat cells

Stomach

Pancreas

7 This leads to energy balance and...

8 modulation of insulin and leptin

Learning Outcomes

LO^1 Identify the parts and functions of the nerve cells

LO^2 Describe how nerve cells communicate

LO^3 Identify the parts and functions of the animal nervous system

LO^4 Identify the parts and functions of the sense organs

The Nervous System

> ## **"** *More than any other organ, the brain is plastic: Its functioning is both flexible and resilient.* **"**

Silence on the Mind

Sherry Greer has lived in silence for a quarter century. She inherited a genetic condition from her two deaf parents and was herself born deaf. Each snail-shaped structure or *cochlea* in Sherry's inner ears formed abnormally when she was a fetus, and as a result, they could never receive sounds and transmit aural patterns to her brain. But Sherry's years have been rich in language communication, because on the day she was born, her parents began speaking to their infant daughter through the gestures of American Sign Language (ASL).

What do you know?

Despite our large brains and capacity for learning, we also exhibit many reflexive behaviors. Name three different human reflex activities and state their common features.

When Sherry is communicating in ASL, her brain is more fully active than is a hearing person's brain while reading, talking, or listening to spoken language. How does Sherry know what's going on in her own brain? She doesn't officially, but Dr. Helen Neville does, because she has tested Sherry in her lab at the University of Oregon. For two decades, Neville has studied a somewhat surprising subject: How experience inscribes the brain, shapes its nerve circuits, and molds its activity. Her work is part of neuroscience, the study of the brain and nervous system, and more specifically, the part relating to brain "plasticity." More than any other organ, the brain is plastic: Its functioning is both flexible and resilient. Neville and colleagues in her field around the world have discovered that a range of factors can shape how the brain adapts to changes and rebounds from injuries, how it senses the world, how it reacts to various stimuli, and how it regulates the body's activities. The factors that shape the brain can include mental stimulation (sights, sounds, smells, movements, and so on), deprivation (the absence of sound or some other type of sensation), and disease or trauma that physically alters the brain. For many kinds of brain activity, this plasticity is greatest in the developing child. But at some point, a window of time closes—a so-called *critical period*—after which experience no longer has as powerful a stimulating and shaping effect.

This chapter explores the basic biology of the nerves and their electrical impulses. It covers the sense organs and how they take in stimuli from the environment. And finally, this chapter discusses the brain, with its global processing and control of reactions, movements, sensations, body systems, thoughts, language, and imagination.

You'll encounter many examples of neural activity in this chapter, and we'll discover the answers to these questions:

- ☑ How do individual nerve cells receive and transmit information?
- ☑ How do nerve cells communicate with each other in networks?
- ☑ How does the brain function and how is its activity coordinated with the nervous system?
- ☑ How do sense organs work?

neuroscience
the study of the brain and nervous system

© ISTOCKPHOTO.COM

nervous system
an animal's network of nerves; includes the brain and spinal cord as well as the peripheral nerves; integrates and coordinates the activities of all the body systems

neuron
a nerve cell that transmits messages throughout the body; made up of dendrites, cell body, and axon

glial cell
a non-neural cell of the nervous system that surrounds the neurons and provides them with protection and nutrients

dendrite
(Gr., *dendron* = little tree) the branching projections of a neuron or nerve cell that transmit nerve impulses to the cell body

cell body
the major portion of the neuron; houses the nucleus and other organelles

axon
the portion of a nerve cell that carries the impulse away from the cell body

nerve
a group of axons and/or dendrites from many different neurons operating together in a bundle and held together by connective tissue

LO¹ The Structure and Function of Nerve Cells

When Sherry communicates through ASL, her brain directs the movement in her hands and arms. When she "listens" in ASL, she perceives language signs with her eyes, and her brain decodes these visual signals as words and phrases. All these events are possible because of her nervous system, a network of specialized cells in humans and virtually all other animals. These specialized cells send messages—usually directly—to other specific cells in the body. The nervous system has the crucial task of controlling and coordinating the activities of an animal's many body systems. It *receives* information from the environment; it *integrates* this information (in other words, it makes sense of it for the animal), and it *affects*, or causes a change in, the way the body functions. All these roles require *communication*. This communication can take place at the microscopic level between different parts of an individual nerve cell or between neighboring nerve cells. And it can take place at the macroscopic level between different individuals in a community, allowing animals to eat, flee from, or mate with other animals at appropriate times. We'll follow these micro and macro levels of communication in this chapter, first examining the way single nerve cells "talk" to each other, then how networks of nerve cells communicate, and finally, how an animal's sense organs detect what's happening in its environment and allow it to react and behave appropriately.

Nerve Cell Structure

Sherry Greer's nervous system—and in fact, every person's—contains over 1,000 different kinds of cells.

Some, like the nerve cells that control hand and finger movements, are about two feet long. Others, like the nerve cells that link one brain region to another, may be only a few millimeters long or less. All 1,000 cell types in the nervous system, however, can be classified as either neurons, the nerve cells that accomplish the actual communication tasks, or glial cells (GLEE-al; Greek, *glia* = glue), support cells that surround, protect, and provide nutrients to neurons and may influence them in as yet unknown ways. The human brain contains 100 billion neurons supported by 10 times as many glial cells (1 trillion).

Anatomy of a Nerve Cell

All neurons—including the billions of brain neurons that help Sherry Greer understand and speak American Sign Language—function by *collecting* information and *relaying* it to other cells in the body. Specific portions of each neuron perform these collecting and relaying functions (Fig. 21.1).

Neurons gather information by means of fine, branching cell processes called dendrites (from the Greek for *little tree*). Dendrites pick up signals from other nerve cells and pass these impulses in one direction, toward the cell body, the major portion of the neuron. The cell body houses the usual complement of intracellular organelles, including nucleus, mitochondria, endoplasmic reticulum, Golgi apparatus, and ribosomes. With this cellular machinery, the cell body produces the proteins that make up the rest of the nerve cell and the enzymes that assist the cell's activity.

After passing down the dendrites and across the cell body, the nerve impulse—still traveling in a single direction—enters the neuron's long, thin cell extension, its axon (Greek for *axle*). In some of your spinal nerves, the axon extends all the way from your spinal cord to your toe muscles, while the cell body and dendrites of those same neurons are located back in the spinal cord itself. A neuron may have dozens of dendrites with up to thousands of branches, but it usually has just one axon. A nerve is actually a group of axons and/or dendrites from many different neurons gathered in a bundle like a telephone cable.

Also like a telephone wire, the terminals or tips of an axon (it can have a few branches, too) stop at the receiver: They are the site of communication between cells. When a nerve impulse moves from dendrites to the axon and reaches the tips, it enters bulblike processes or axon terminals located very close to the cell membranes of other cells (Fig. 21.1). The two nearly contacting membranes plus the minute gap or cleft between them is a unit

Figure 21.1

Neurons Transmit Information from One Cell to Another

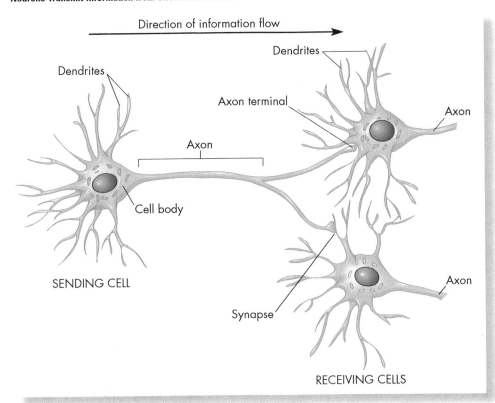

Direction of information flow

Dendrites

Dendrites

Axon terminal

Axon

Axon

Cell body

SENDING CELL

Synapse

Axon

RECEIVING CELLS

---

synapse
the region of communication between two neurons or between a neuron and a muscle cell

presynaptic cell
the neuron that sends a message down its axon and across a synapse to another cell, the postsynaptic cell

postsynaptic cell
the nerve cell that receives the message that has crossed a synapse from a presynaptic cell

nerve impulse
a change in ion permeabilities in a neuron's membrane that sweeps down the cell's axon to its terminal, where it can excite other cells

---

known as a synapse (SIN-apps), and a neural impulse can cross this synapse quickly. A neuron's axonal terminals may form synapses with a dendrite, a cell body of another neuron, another axon, a muscle cell, or a secreting cell (see Chapter 22).

Sending and Receiving Cells

The two cells on either side of a synapse have different functions. The *sending cell* (or presynaptic cell) transmits a message down its axon and across a synapse to the other cell, the *receiving cell* (or postsynaptic cell) (Fig. 21.1). This cell, in turn, may propagate the same message down its axon. Just as information flows in one direction within a neuron, it flows in one direction between neurons, from sending cell to receiving cell.

The axon of a sending cell may branch and rebranch, forming synaptic junctions with up to 1,000 other cells. Conversely, 1,000 other neurons might form synapses with the dendrites and the cell body of a single neuron, like hundreds of hands reaching out to touch a central object simultaneously. With these multiple links, an animal's communication network is literally a net. The 100 billion neurons of the human brain, for example, make 1,000

trillion synaptic contact points—more than all the known stars and planets in the universe. This most intricate lacework of interconnected neurons allows for all the simple and complex behavior we observe among animals. At one end of the continuum, it lets a sea slug withdraw its siphon when touched. At the other end, it lets a human being speak and understand the complicated symbols of ASL, such as those for "I'm going to class now."

Recall that an animal's nervous system receives and integrates data, and this affects a change in body function. Within a given neuron, the dendrites act as the receptors, the cell body acts as the integrator, and the axon and synapse act as the effectors of a nerve signal. Let's see what a nerve signal is, how it moves along a cell, and then later, how it can contribute to complex behavior such as language.

A Nerve Cell at Rest

Neuroscientists sometimes monitor a subject's brain waves to detect the electrical activity of nerve cells, specifically the nerve impulse, an electrochemical reaction that allows specific electrically charged atoms to rush into and out of the nerve cell.

The Resting Potential

The best way to see how neurons generate a nerve impulse is to focus on a single patch of a resting

Figure 21.2
A Neuron's Resting Potential

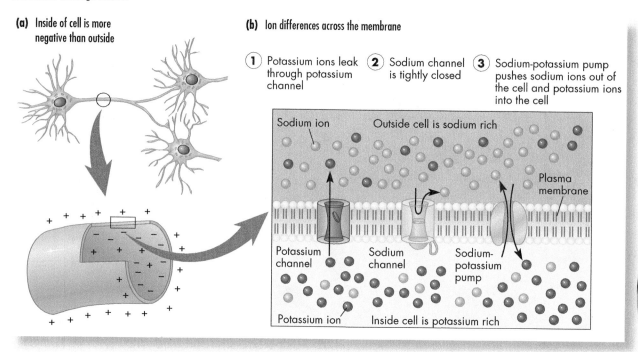

(a) Inside of cell is more negative than outside

(b) Ion differences across the membrane

1 Potassium ions leak through potassium channel

2 Sodium channel is tightly closed

3 Sodium-potassium pump pushes sodium ions out of the cell and potassium ions into the cell

Sodium ion

Outside cell is sodium rich

Plasma membrane

Potassium channel

Sodium channel

Sodium-potassium pump

Potassium ion

Inside cell is potassium rich

---

resting potential
potential energy that is the difference in electric charge between the cell's exterior and interior; measured in volts like a battery

potassium channel
a protein-lined pore in a cell's plasma membrane that permits potassium ions to flow in and out of the cell

neuron's plasma membrane. Like all cells, nerve cells have an electrical difference across their plasma membranes, even when unstimulated. That is, the inside of the cell is negatively charged with respect to the outside (Fig. 21.2a). This difference in electric charge, which can be measured in volts like a battery, represents an amount of potential energy called the resting potential.

A cell's resting potential is due to differences in the ions (electrically charged atoms) inside and outside the cell. The most important ions for nerve signaling are sodium (Na+), potassium (K+), and chloride (Cl−).

Cells are bathed in a fluid that has a high concentration of sodium ions and a relatively low concentration of potassium ions (Fig. 21.2b). In contrast, the fluid inside the neuron is relatively rich in potassium ions and low in sodium ions. The high concentration of sodium ions outside the plasma membrane is like

the thousands of music fans pushing and straining to get into an amphitheater for a rock concert. In contrast, the musicians and their crew inside the stadium warming up before the concert are like the potassium ions inside the cell. The musicians and crew can occasionally leave the stadium through the stage doors, but to keep the fans out requires strong gates and security officers to throw out the occasional fan who sneaks inside. Neurons have proteins in their membranes that act like these doors, gates, and security guards.

Protein Channels and a Pump

Three proteins are primarily responsible for maintaining a neuron's resting potential. The potassium channel is a protein pore through the membrane. The potassium channel pore contains a single gate that can open or close; thus the channel acts a bit like the stage door that permits the music crew to pass out of the stadium in that it allows potassium ions to pass slowly through the membrane and leak down their concentration gradient from the inside of the cell to the outside (Fig. 21.2b). Recall that a

> Neurons have proteins in their membranes that act like stadium doors, gates, and security guards.

cell's cytoplasm is a gel-like substance containing many proteins. These proteins are mostly negatively charged and are too bulky to pass through the membrane. The slow leak of positively charged potassium ions out of the cell thus leaves the inside of the cell with a slight negative charge.

In contrast to the potassium channel, a second protein pore, the sodium channel, acts more like the secured gates before the concert. It closes tightly and allows almost none of the sodium ions outside the cell to leak inward. The sodium channel has two gates, an activation gate and an inactivation gate. These act in a coordinated way, finely controlling the length of time the channel is open. At rest, one gate is open and the other closed.

The third protein that helps maintain the neuron's resting potential is the sodium-potassium pump. Like the security guards, the pump opposes the inappropriate leakage of ions through the channels by using energy to force sodium ions out of the cell. The pump also escorts potassium back into the cell. Note that the pump keeps the potassium and sodium ions from falling down their concentration gradients. *This takes work.* Similar pumps act continuously in every animal cell and collectively use more ATP than any other body activity (see Chapter 3).

The actions of these three proteins in a neuron's plasma membrane maintain a steady voltage differential between the cell's outside and its inside. In its resting state, the neuron is said to be *polarized*—it has an imbalance of electrical charges, negative on the inside and positive on the outside.

The Action Potential: A Nerve Impulse

A nerve impulse, or action potential, is the *reversal* of the charge on a resting cell; it's a bit like what happens when the gates finally open and all the fans suddenly rush into the stadium.

How, then, does this reversal come about? It all starts with a stimulus, such as a light flash, the sizzling taste of a chili pepper, the sight of an ASL word being signed, or an impulse from another nerve cell. The stimulus tweaks a resting neuron (see Fig. 21.3a on the next page), causing the second of the two gates in some of the sodium channels to open

(Fig. 21.3b). With both gates open, sodium ions begin to leak into the cell. As more sodium ions enter the cell, the difference in charge between the inside and outside begins to decrease. The cell begins to *depolarize*, or lose its state of electrical polarization.

When the original difference in charge between the outside and inside decreases enough, a threshold is passed and something quite dramatic occurs: In the patch of plasma membrane where the stimulus first arrives, most of the sodium ion channels open wide (Fig. 21.3b). Sodium ions can now rush into the cell, and the inside of the neuron becomes positively charged with respect to the outside. This reversed polarity is the action potential.

Sodium channels in the area of the action potential remain open for only about 1/1,000 of a second, and then inactivate as the inactivation gates close (Fig. 21.3c). For a few thousandths of a second after closing, the sodium channels cannot open again. This temporary state of nonresponsiveness limits the number of action potentials a neuron can fire each second.

About the time the sodium channels close, the potassium channels open fully, allowing potassium ions to rush out of the cell (Fig. 21.3c). With this outpouring, the electrical potential falls to a level below the original resting potential.

Eventually, the potassium channels close. The "bailing" action of the sodium-potassium pump restores the neuron to its original resting potential (Fig. 21.3d). The neuron is now ready for another stimulus to trigger a new action potential. The entire process of stimulus, action potential, and recovery has taken only a few milliseconds.

What would happen to an action potential if the gates in the ion channels were stuck shut? You have probably experienced the answer to this in your dentist's office. He or she will often inject novocaine as a pain-killing anesthetic before a procedure. Novocaine works by preventing the opening of the ion channels in nerve endings in the gums, tongue, and lips. Because the gates are closed, ions cannot pass through and there can be no action potentials in the neurons that relay pain signals to your brain. Without action potentials, you feel little pain, even if the dentist's drill touches an exposed nerve.

sodium channel
a protein-lined pore in the plasma membrane through which sodium ions can pass

sodium-potassium pump
a protein that maintains the cell's osmotic balance by using ATP energy to transport sodium ions out of the cell and potassium ions into the cell

action potential
a temporary all-or-nothing reversal of the electrical charge across a cell membrane; occurs when a stimulus of sufficient intensity strikes a neuron

Action potentials have a peculiar property: They are all-or-none responses; that is, either they don't occur at all, or they do occur and are always the same strength for a given neuron, regardless of how powerful the stimulus may be. A jab to the ribs is more intense than a tender caress, but it's not because the jab causes larger or faster action potentials. Instead, the jab simply causes more cells to fire more impulses more frequently than the caress.

How Does a Nerve Impulse Travel Down a Cell?

How does an action potential travel down an axon? The process is rather like the wave of rising and cheering fans that travels around a sports stadium. Each individual in the stadium represents a sodium channel, and standing up, throwing arms in the air, and sitting down again represents the opening and closing of sodium channels. Just as each individual stands because the person sitting nearest has just started to rise, so too does each sodium channel open because the channel next to it has just opened. The open gates allow sodium ions to rush into the cell and generate an action potential that itself propagates along the axon.

Direction of Impulse Travel

Interestingly, within the body, the impulses in a given neuron travel in one direction only (from spine to finger, for example, but not from finger to spine), because of the short nonresponsive period. For a few thousandths of a second after an action potential, a membrane patch cannot experience another action potential because the sodium channel is temporarily inactivated. Again, it's a bit like the wave that passes around a sport stadium; once you've stood, raised your arms, then sat back down, you don't want to do it all again too soon. The result of the temporary inactivation in the neuron is that the signal moves forward to the next patch but never moves backward toward the previous one.

The Speed of Impulse Travel

In many invertebrates, a nerve impulse traveling down a neuron moves only about 2 m (6.5 ft) per second. Think how sluggish a tennis match would be if players had to wait a full second for an impulse to travel from their brains to their toes! One way

Figure 21.3

How a Neuron Generates an Action Potential

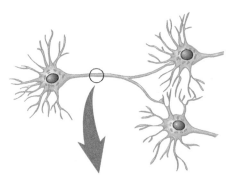

(a) Resting potential

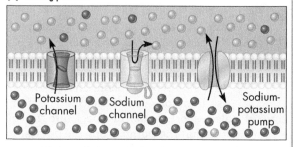

Potassium channel   Sodium channel   Sodium-potassium pump

(b) Sodium channels open; potassium channels close

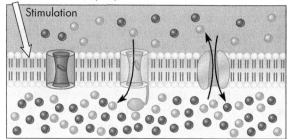

Stimulation

(c) Sodium channels close; potassium channels open

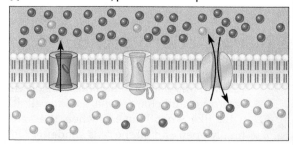

(d) Potassium channels close; pump restores resting potential

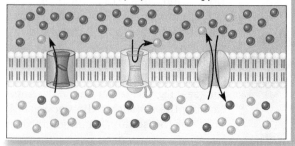

to speed the travel of nerve signals along an axon is for the diameter of the axon to increase. Just as a wider pipe has less resistance to water flow than a narrower one, a larger axon has less resistance to the flow of ions. A few invertebrates, such as the fast-moving squid, have in fact evolved huge axons over 1 mm in diameter that carry impulses rapidly. A person, however, could never make do with giant axons: To contain the 100 billion neurons and 1,000 trillion interconnections we need to produce our own complex actions, thoughts, and language, our heads would have to be 10 times bigger! Instead, vertebrates have evolved a means of rapid impulse propagation without giant neurons.

Insulating Sheaths Speed Impulse Travel

We vertebrates have greatly speeded nerve impulses because many of our neurons are insulated with fatty sheaths. We said earlier that the nervous system has ten times more glial, or supportive, cells than actual neurons. Some specialized glial cells situate themselves along an axon like fatty sausages on a string and wrap their plasma membranes around the axon surface like an electrician wraps a wire with black tape (Fig. 21.4a). Together, these special glial cells called *Schwann cells* form a lipid-rich layer, the **myelin sheath**, that insulates

the axon from the fluid outside the cell (Fig. 21.4a,b). In the tiny gaps between these insulating "sausages" lie bare regions, and ions can flow across the axon membrane only in these uninsulated nodes. Between the nodes, electrical current flows in the cytoplasm and extracellular fluid, and when this current reaches the next node, it causes sodium channels to open there. The result of this glial cell arrangement is that the nerve impulse moves rapidly from one node to the next, bouncing along the axon 20 times faster than if the axon lacked the myelin sheath. Even at their fastest, however—in neurons carrying impulses associated with touch, for example, or that conduct impulses to skeletal muscles—nerve impulses are transmitted only about 130 m (400 ft) per second, 2,000 times slower than the speed of electricity in a wire. Although most of our neurons have myelin sheaths, many neurons that communicate from one neuron to the next don't.

myelin sheath
a lipid membrane made up of Schwann cells that forms an insulating layer around neurons and speeds impulse travel

Mutant mice that have been bred with axons lacking insulating sheaths shiver uncontrollably. In the absence of the sheaths, nerve impulses can move erroneously between the axons from side to side as well as from end to end. Likewise, the human disease multiple sclerosis (MS), whose symptoms usually first appear in early adulthood, causes some nerve cells to lose their insulating sheath. Without this insulating layer, nerve impulses can't move rapidly from node to node along the cell, and transmission slows, leading to double vision, weakness, and wobbly limbs.

LO² Communication Between Nerve Cells

Just as ASL helps one person communicate with another, action at the special cell junctions called synapses helps some neurons communicate with other cells. The nerve impulse can pass information across a synapse from one neuron to another neuron, or from a neuron to a muscle cell. In either case, the signal moves in just one direction from the axon part of the neuron to the neighboring cell. Some neurons send impulses to other cells through direct electrical contact, like plugging in an electrical cord. Most neurons in the human body, however, talk to other cells chemically.

Figure 21.4
An Insulated Axon Propagates Impulses More Efficiently

(a) An insulated axon

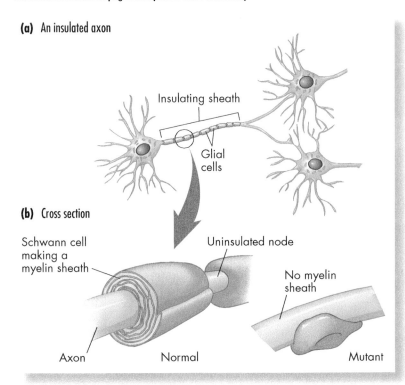

Insulating sheath

Glial cells

(b) Cross section

Schwann cell making a myelin sheath

Uninsulated node

No myelin sheath

Axon

Normal

Mutant

Chemical Synapses: Messages Spanning Gaps

We saw earlier that in a synapse, the bulblike axon terminal end is separated from a bulging structure on a receiving cell by the narrow synaptic cleft (Fig. 21.5a,b). A neural impulse can pass from the sending cell when a tiny amount of a chemical moves across the cleft and touches off a new impulse in the receiving cell. But what is this chemical and how does it work?

Within the axon's tip, enzymes synthesize a chemical signal called a neurotransmitter. The neurotransmitter enters small round vesicles, and in an axon at rest, these accumulate at the axon terminal. When an action potential moves along a neuron and reaches the end of the axon, special channels open and allow calcium ions to rush into the bulbous terminal (Fig. 21.5a, Step ①). The increase in calcium ion concentration causes the little bags of neurotransmitter in that sending cell to fuse with the cell's outer membrane. This releases thousands of neurotransmitter molecules into the synaptic cleft that separates the sending and receiving cells. The neurotransmitter molecules diffuse across the cleft (Step ②) in less than a millionth of a second and bind to receptor proteins embedded in a trough-shaped plasma membrane of the receiving cell's (usually) knoblike process (Step ③). This binding can cause the receiving cell to generate an action potential (Step ④). If the receiving cell is a muscle cell, it will contract; if it is another neuron, an action potential might be generated in it.

Cocaine Addiction: Action at the Synapse

Just after a neurotransmitter enters the synaptic cleft and triggers an action potential in the receiving cell, enzymes break down the chemical signal or the sending cell reabsorbs it (Fig. 21.5a, Step ⑤). Without this rapid cleanup, the messenger molecules would remain in the cleft and would continuously stimulate the receiving cell.

Figure 21.5

At a Chemical Synapse, Neurons Transmit Information Across a Cleft

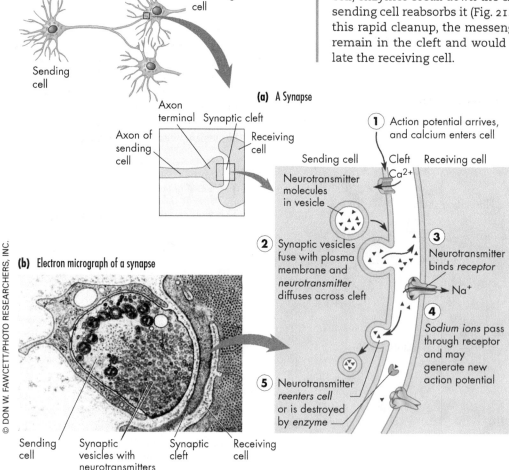

© DON W. FAWCETT/PHOTO RESEARCHERS, INC.

Receiving cell

Sending cell

(a) A Synapse

Axon terminal   Synaptic cleft

Axon of sending cell

Receiving cell

(b) Electron micrograph of a synapse

Sending cell   Synaptic vesicles with neurotransmitters   Synaptic cleft   Receiving cell

① Action potential arrives, and calcium enters cell

Sending cell   Cleft   Receiving cell
Ca²⁺

Neurotransmitter molecules in vesicle

② Synaptic vesicles fuse with plasma membrane and neurotransmitter diffuses across cleft

③ Neurotransmitter binds receptor

→ Na⁺

④ Sodium ions pass through receptor and may generate new action potential

⑤ Neurotransmitter reenters cell or is destroyed by enzyme

A faulty cleanup operation is central to the high people feel when taking cocaine. Cocaine blocks the cleanup in brain cells of a specific neurotransmitter called *dopamine*. The blocked cleanup occurs in the cells of the so-called central reward system. Because the neurotransmitter remains for a longer time at these pleasure synapses, the person feels euphoria and excitement.

The body begins to compensate by stepping up its ability to destroy the dopamine. This jazzed-up destruction mechanism, however, works faster and more efficiently whether cocaine is present or not and brings about drug tolerance: When the narcotic is gone, the reward center is starved of stimulation, and the user can no longer enjoy normally pleasurable activities such as good food and good sex. Instead, the addict's body craves more cocaine, and this causes the destructive cycle of drug-seeking behavior called *addiction*. Dopamine is so powerful in the brain's pleasure center that addiction to cocaine (especially the form called "crack") takes hold faster than addiction to other drugs, including heroin and tobacco.

Types of Neurotransmitters

The dopamine involved in cocaine addiction is just one of more than 50 different known chemicals that can serve as neurotransmitters in the nervous systems of various animals.

Of the many other neurotransmitters biologists have studied, the two they understand best are *acetylcholine* and *norepinephrine*. Like most neurotransmitters, acetylcholine transmits nerve impulses within the brain. But it also relays nerve signals to the skeletal muscles that help maintain posture, breathing, and limb movements, including the gestures of ASL; in addition, it is released by the vagal nerve, slowing the heart rate. Norepinephrine is found in synapses throughout the brain (and elsewhere in the nervous system), and biologists agree that it helps keep our moods and behavior on an even keel. People suffering clinical depression, with its pessimistic moods, disturbed sleep, altered appetite, and diminished energy levels, may actually have norepinephrine deficiencies within the brain. Conversely, the condition called *mania*, characterized by overactivity, irritable moods, and recklessness, may stem from too much norepinephrine in the brain.

LO³ Animal Nervous Systems

The learning of human language depends on nervous system activity. It depends on *sensing* signals—sounds or sights—from other people, *integrating* the signals to understand them, and *reacting* with a coordinated response to the communicated information. This is true whether the communication is spoken, written, signed, postural, or chemical (as in many other animal species). Regardless, sensing, integrating, and reacting require highly organized networks of neurons. Let's look, now, at how nervous systems are constructed and function, focusing mainly on the nervous systems of vertebrates such as ourselves.

The Vertebrate Nervous System

The grouse's elaborate mating dance, the cobra's hypnotic weaving, the vigorous kicks and turns of an aerobic dancer—all of these depend on a highly organized nervous system, and in vertebrates, that system is organized into two main units. The central nervous system (CNS) is the director, thinker, and information processor (see Fig. 21.6 on the next page). The CNS consists of the brain, which performs complex neural integration, and the spinal cord, which carries nerve impulses to and from the brain. The CNS also allows reflexes, or involuntary but predictable responses to stimuli. The peripheral nervous system (PNS) is the "go-between" or "middleman"; it includes sensory neurons that directly sense the

central nervous system (CNS)
the part of the nervous system consisting of the brain and spinal cord that performs the most complex nervous system functions

brain
the body organ that performs complex neural integration and, along with the spinal cord, forms the central nervous system

spinal cord
a tube of nerve tissue that runs the full length of a vertebrate's spine

reflex
involuntary but predictable responses to stimuli

peripheral nervous system (PNS)
the part of the nervous system that consists of the sensory and motor neurons and connects the central nervous system with the sense organs, muscles, and glands of the body

sensory neuron
a nerve cell that receives information from the external or internal environment and transmits this information to the brain or spinal cord

© CARLOS SANTA MARIA/ISTOCKPHOTO.COM

motor neuron
a neuron that sends messages from the brain or spinal cord to muscles or secretory glands

reflex arc
an automatic reaction, involving only a few neurons and requiring no input from the brain, in which a motor response quickly follows a sensory stimulus

environment and the motor neurons that directly contact muscles and glands and make them work. The peripheral nervous system connects the central nervous system with the sense organs, muscles, and glands of the body. The interplay between the central and peripheral nervous systems allows an animal to sense environmental stimuli, integrate the information, and respond appropriately, providing all the fascinating behaviors we can see in ourselves and other animals.

A Reflex Arc

Have you ever stepped on a tack or sharp piece of gravel with your bare toe? If so, the muscles in your leg lifted your toe immediately, even before you realized what had happened (Fig. 21.7). That muscle response was driven by a simple nerve circuit called the reflex arc, an uncomplicated neural loop that links a stimulus to a response in a direct way. A reflex arc shows the clear relationship between the central

and peripheral nervous systems. Reflex arcs require no conscious input from the brain and bring about behaviors that are generally rapid, involuntary, and nearly identical each time the stimulus is repeated—a knee jerk, for example, or the pullback of a toe from a tack or a finger from a hot stove.

Reflex arcs usually involve:

1. A *sensory neuron* in the peripheral nervous system that receives information from the external or internal environment—a tack stabbing a toe is this kind of information—and then transmits the message along a spinal nerve into the spinal cord (Fig. 21.7, Steps ①, ②).

2. *Interneurons* in the central nervous system that relay messages between nerve cells and integrate and coordinate incoming and outgoing messages (Step ③). Most of the brain is made up of interneurons.

3. *Motor neurons*, which relay messages from interneurons in the CNS out to muscles or secretory glands (Step ④). Motor neurons allow an organism to *act*—to respond to the information the sensory neuron brings in from the environment. In this case, the organism is you,

Figure 21.6
Organization of the Vertebrate Nervous System

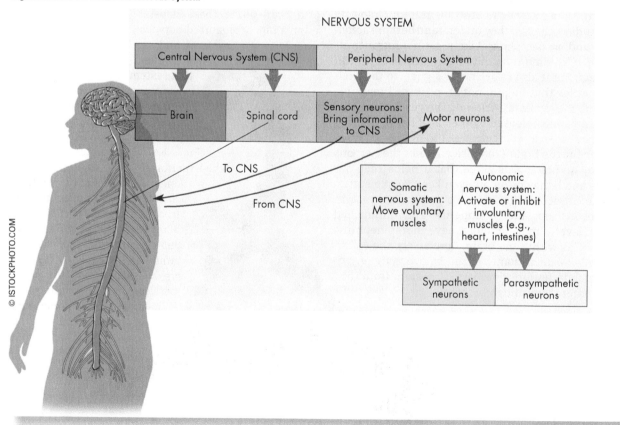

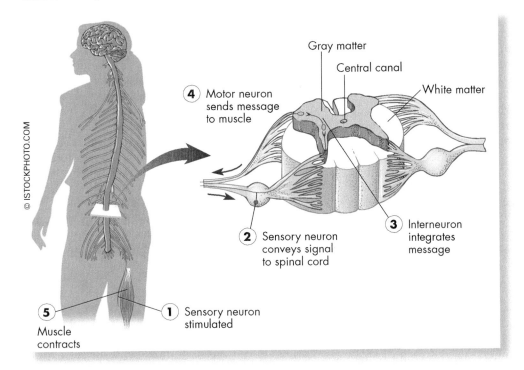

Figure 21.7
Reflex Arcs and Spinal Nerves

Gray matter

Central canal

White matter

4 Motor neuron sends message to muscle

2 Sensory neuron conveys signal to spinal cord

3 Interneuron integrates message

5 Muscle contracts

1 Sensory neuron stimulated

and the action is pulling your toe back from the tack (Step **5**).

The sensory and motor neurons enter or leave the spinal cord in pairs of nerves called spinal nerves, shown in Figures 21.6 and 21.7. Let's look more closely now at the motor neurons in these pairs of spinal nerves.

Motor Neurons

Some of your motor neurons are under voluntary control and activate muscles on command. Examples are Sherry Greer's motor neurons that allow her to make specific ASL signs during a conversation. These voluntarily controlled motor neurons form the somatic nervous system. A different set of motor neurons in the autonomic nervous system acts subconsciously and automatically to regulate the body's internal environment, controlling glands, the heart muscle, and smooth muscles in the digestive and circulatory systems.

The Autonomic System of Motor Neurons

A person's autonomic nervous system performs many of its duties through the spinal cord and lower cen-

ters of the brain (in or near the neck). There are two sets of autonomic neurons, called *parasympathetic* and *sympathetic neurons*, which function in opposition—a bit like the accelerator and brakes of a car.

In general, the parasympathetic nerves function as a housekeeping system for the body, stimulating the stomach to churn, the bladder to empty, and the heart to beat at a slow and even pace during most daily and nightly activities. During exercise or embarrassment, or when an emergency arises and generates intense anger, fear, or excitement, the sympathetic nerves dominate, increasing heart rate, dilating the pupils of the eyes (which lets in more light), expanding the bronchioles of the lungs (which improves O_2 and CO_2 exchange), and slowing down nonessential digestive activities until the emergency is past. Sympathetic and parasympathetic neurons often control the same organ and help to speed up or slow down its activity as needed. For example, most sympathetic neurons can speed and strengthen the heartbeat by secreting the neurotransmitter norepinephrine, while parasympathetic neurons can slow it by secreting acetylcholine.

Both branches of the autonomic system—the sympathetic and parasympathetic neurons—act primarily

spinal nerves
pairs of nerves in which the sensory and motor neurons enter or leave the spinal cord

somatic nervous system
motor neurons of the nervous system that are under voluntary control

autonomic nervous system
motor neurons of the nervous system that regulate the heart, glands, and smooth muscles in the digestive and circulatory systems

parasympathetic nerves
neurons of the autonomic nervous system that emanate from the spinal cord and act on the respiratory, circulatory, digestive, and excretory systems as a "housekeeping" system, conserving and restoring body resources

sympathetic nerves
neurons of the autonomic nervous system that emanate from the central spinal cord and act on the respiratory, circulatory, digestive, and excretory systems in response to stress or emergency, preparing for flight or fight

through reflex loops. Consider the loop that controls the emptying of the urinary bladder. Sympathetic motor neurons cause the bladder muscle to relax and the muscles that close the sphincter (through which the bladder empties) to shut tight. When the bladder fills, the bladder wall stretches. This activates stretch receptors, which signal the spinal cord via sensory neurons. These stimulate parasympathetic motor neurons that feed back to the bladder muscle and cause the urine-storing organ to contract and the sphincter to relax, and thus urine to be expelled. In infants, this reflex loop is the only control over bladder function, so the organ empties whenever it fills. With toilet training, the child's brain gradually learns to exert conscious control over the pelvic muscles that regulate urination.

The Central Nervous System

The sense receptors of the peripheral nervous system serve as windows to the environment. Without the central nervous system to interpret the data and coordinate the responses, however, an animal couldn't act appropriately. Important to this coordinating and responding is the neural thoroughfare that runs through the spinal cord.

Figure 21.8

Major Regions of the Brain

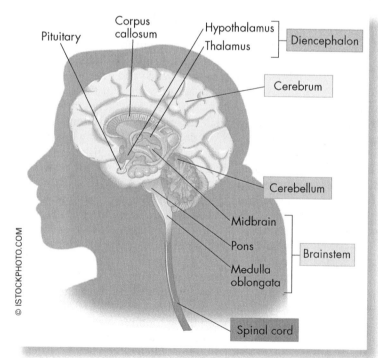

© ISTOCKPHOTO.COM

Pituitary
Corpus callosum
Hypothalamus
Thalamus
Diencephalon
Cerebrum
Cerebellum
Midbrain
Pons
Brainstem
Medulla oblongata
Spinal cord

The Spinal Cord: A Neural Highway

You've probably heard of "gray matter" and "white matter." But what are they? If you took a cross section from a human spinal cord, you'd see a butterfly-shaped core of gray material surrounded by an oval field of white (see Fig. 21.7). The gray matter contains nerve cell bodies and is a zone of many synapses, where local neural traffic occurs (such as the reflex arcs we discussed earlier). The white matter, on the other hand, is like an interstate freeway; it consists mainly of thin, mostly myelin-covered axons that transport information long distances up and down the spinal cord to and from the brain. Because many of these long axons are insulated with white, fatty myelin sheaths, (see Fig. 21.4), the entire white matter has a whitish color.

The integration of signals from sensory neurons and interneurons begins in the spinal cord. Most major data processing, however, occurs in the brain.

The Brain: The Ultimate Processor

We all know that the brain embodies our feelings and strivings, our knowledge and memories, our musical and verbal abilities, and our sense of the future. Biologists still do not fully understand, however, how it performs these tasks. Over many decades, studies of stroke patients or patients with injuries to particular, often small parts of the brain have revealed the seats of specific complex behaviors and specific emotions in individual brain regions. One of the big themes of modern neuroscience has been that brain anatomy can open a map to behavior.

The human brain consists of four interconnected parts (Fig. 21.8): (1) the brainstem, the "stalk" of the brain, which relays messages between the brain and spinal cord; (2) the highly rippled cerebellum attached and posterior to the brainstem; (3) the diencephalon, which sits just above the brainstem; and (4) the large, folded cerebrum, whose right and left halves sit atop the brainstem and span the inside of the head from just behind the eyes to the bony bump at the back of the skull.

The Brainstem: Fundamental Regulation

The brainstem plays three crucial roles: It helps integrate sensory and motor systems, it regulates body homeostasis, and it controls arousal. The lowest part of the brainstem, the *medulla oblongata*, lies inside the skull above the level of the mouth. The medulla oblongata helps keep body conditions constant (see Chapter 16) by receiving data about activities in various physiological systems and by regulating respiratory rate, heart rate, blood pressure, and many other subconscious body activities. Above the medulla lie the *pons*, a relay center that helps control breathing, and the *midbrain*, which contains fiber tracts running between the anterior and posterior brain, as well as structures involved in sight and hearing.

The Cerebellum: Muscle Coordinator

Attached to the pons, at the middle of the brainstem, is the cerebellum (Latin, *little brain*), a convoluted bulb that serves as a complex computer, comparing outgoing commands with incoming information about the status of muscles, tendons, joints, and the position of the body in space. The result is a fine-tuning of motor commands. Learning how to make the specific, rapid movements of sign language or how to run an offensive pattern in basketball involves the cerebellum.

The Diencephalon

The *diencephalon* (*di* = second + *cephalon* = brain) (Fig. 21.8) is an extension of the brainstem above the cerebellum, and it includes the thalamus, hypothalamus, and pineal gland (review Fig. 20.4). The *thalamus* makes up most of the diencephalon, and it is the main relay station for sensory signals moving between the cerebellum and other parts of the brain. It also plays a role in awareness and in the acquisition of knowledge.

Lying below the thalamus is the *hypothalamus*, which regulates the pituitary gland and provides the link we saw in Chapter 20 between the nervous and endocrine systems. The hypothalamus also has important roles in maintaining homeostasis: It helps to regulate body temperature, water balance, hunger, and the digestive system. By electrically stimulating different regions of the hypothalamus, researchers can make an animal behave as if it feels alternately hot and cold, hungry and satisfied, angry and content. Some regions of the hypothalamus seem to be pleasure centers: A rat with electrodes permanently implanted in those areas will continue pressing a foot pedal to stimulate its pleasure centers until the animal drops from exhaustion. The third part of the diencephalon is the *pineal gland*, shaped like a pea-sized pine cone. The pineal secretes melatonin and is involved in the operation of the body's biological clock (see Chapter 20).

Extending through the brainstem from the diencephalon down to the spinal cord is the *reticular formation*, a network of tracts that reaches into the cerebellum and cerebrum. When you're awake, specific neurons of the reticular formation are actively firing. When you're asleep or unconscious, those neurons fire more slowly. This selective shaping of neural input by the reticular formation and the diencephalon helps a person to concentrate on a dinner partner's conversation in a noisy restaurant, and plays a part in the groggy incoherence of an early-morning phone conversation.

The Cerebrum: Perception, Thought, Humanness

The two side-by-side hemispheres of the brain's cerebrum (Latin, *brain*) fit like a cap over most of the other brain regions (Fig. 21.8). This mass of tissue embodies not only the attributes we consider human, such as self-awareness, speech, and artistic ability, but also traits that we share with other vertebrates, such as sensory perception, motor output, and memory. In humans, the cerebral cortex, the cerebrum's highly creased and infolded surface layers, contains about 90 percent of the brain's neuron cell bodies. By looking at the brains of fish, birds, and cats (Fig. 21.9), you can see how this cap ballooned in size relative to

cerebellum
anterior portion of the vertebrate brain lying posterior to the cerebrum; integrates information about body position and motion, coordinates muscular activities, and maintains equilibrium

cerebrum
(L., *brain*) the topmost portion of the vertebrate brain; coordinates and processes sensory input and controls motor responses

cerebral cortex
the highly convoluted surface layers of the cerebrum, containing about 90 percent of a human brain's cell bodies; well-developed only in mammals and particularly prominent in humans; the region involved with our conscious sensations and voluntary muscular activity

Figure 21.9

Brain Differences in Various Vertebrates

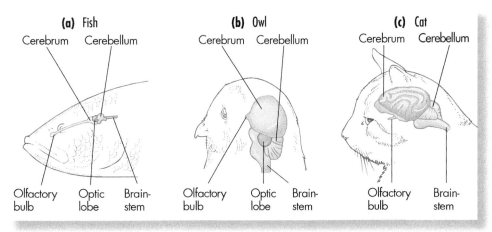

(a) Fish
Cerebrum   Cerebellum
Olfactory bulb   Optic lobe   Brainstem

(b) Owl
Cerebrum   Cerebellum
Olfactory bulb   Optic lobe   Brainstem

(c) Cat
Cerebrum   Cerebellum
Olfactory bulb   Brainstem

other brain regions during vertebrate evolution and became increasingly convoluted, with a massively enlarged surface area folded and fissured so it fits into the skull.

One of the great unsolved questions of modern biology is precisely *how* the cerebrum can control complicated traits. Biologists have many ideas but no single answer. One principle has been well established, however: Basic cerebral functions, including sensations (such as seeing or hearing), motor ability (movement), cognitive functions (such as language and perception), affective traits (emotions), and even some character traits (such as friendliness or shyness), can be mapped to specific regions of the cerebrum (Fig. 21.10).

Motor and Sensory Centers

Before the advent of modern brain imaging methods, researchers were limited to mapping the cerebral cortex primarily during surgery. Despite its billions of neurons, brain tissue has no pain receptors, so a surgeon can operate on this highly complex organ with only a local anesthetic for the scalp and skull incision. By inserting extremely fine, low-current electric probes into the exposed brain, neurosurgeons can stimulate specific regions and watch to see which muscles the patient moves or ask the alert patient to report the sensations he or she feels. Studies like these allowed neuroscientists to build maps of the brain regions that control feeling and movement in various parts of the body. If you run your right index finger from your left ear straight up to the top of your head, the arc traces the surface area devoted to the left hemisphere's motor cortex, the part of your brain that controls muscles on the right side of your body, including the ones that move your right hand (Fig. 21.10b). Likewise, the corresponding arc on the surface of the brain's right hemisphere moves the left side of your body.

Just behind the motor cortex lies the sensory cortex, which registers and integrates sensations from body parts (Fig. 21.10c). Again, the brain's left side receives sensations primarily from the body's right side, and vice versa.

On the maps of both the motor cortex and the sensory cortex, the body parts seem to have exaggerated proportions: Lips, face, and fingers appear extremely large, and the trunk too small. This distortion reflects the large number of delicate touch receptors in face and fingers and the large number of muscles we need for speech and manual dexterity compared to the small numbers of neurons we need for sensation and movement in the trunk. Other specific brain regions are dedicated to vision, hearing, and smell. Recent studies employing intense stimulation of a monkey's fingertips show that brain maps can change with use. People who lose their vision, for example, and then learn Braille, the raised-dot writing system for the blind, would have more cortical area devoted to fingertip sensation after Braille training than before.

Many higher cerebral functions map to specific regions, too. One area of the cerebral cortex, for example, is dedicated to recognizing faces (Fig. 21.10a). A person who suffers an injury to this part of the brain can no longer recognize loved ones' faces, even though he or she can still recognize their voices!

> **"** The brain's left side receives sensations primarily from the body's right side, and vice versa. **"**

Memory: Storage of Past and Present

Deep in each cerebral hemisphere lies a small bilateral structure called the hippocampus, which plays a crucial role in the formation of long-term memory. Have you ever been interrupted while trying to memorize a new phone number? You probably forgot the number because your hippocampus failed to fix it in long-term memory before the interruption occurred. A patient with a damaged hippocampus can recall events that happened even decades before the injury, but fails to remember new facts and experiences (including the shapes of objects, phone numbers, and people's names) for more than a few moments. Clearly, we need this area of the brain to help us lay down new memories, although the memories aren't actually stored there.

Researchers are making great strides in understanding how we learn and remember. They have found that when intense and/or repeated

Figure 21.10

Mapping the Human Brain: Specific Functions Reside in Specific Regions

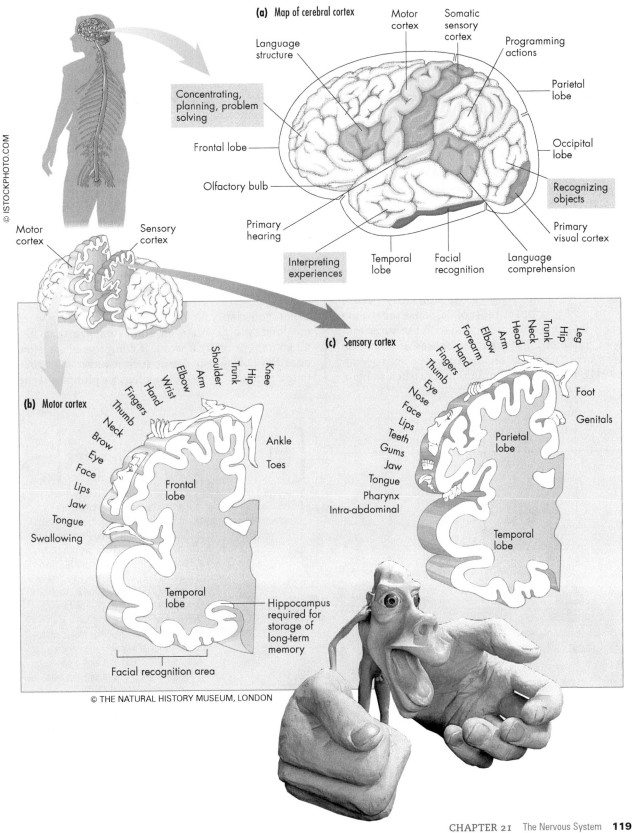

(a) Map of cerebral cortex

Language structure

Concentrating, planning, problem solving

Frontal lobe

Olfactory bulb

Primary hearing

Interpreting experiences

Temporal lobe

Facial recognition

Language comprehension

Motor cortex

Somatic sensory cortex

Programming actions

Parietal lobe

Occipital lobe

Recognizing objects

Primary visual cortex

Motor cortex

Sensory cortex

(b) Motor cortex

Fingers
Thumb
Neck
Brow
Eye
Face
Lips
Jaw
Tongue
Swallowing

Hand
Wrist
Elbow
Arm
Shoulder
Trunk
Hip
Knee

Frontal lobe

Ankle
Toes

Temporal lobe

Hippocampus required for storage of long-term memory

Facial recognition area

(c) Sensory cortex

Fingers
Thumb
Eye
Nose
Face
Lips
Teeth
Gums
Jaw
Tongue
Pharynx
Intra-abdominal

Hand
Forearm
Elbow
Arm
Head
Neck
Trunk
Hip
Leg

Foot

Genitals

Parietal lobe

Temporal lobe

© THE NATURAL HISTORY MUSEUM, LONDON

© ISTOCKPHOTO.COM

stimuli alter a neuron's normal impulse activity, the altered pattern can cause long-lasting changes in the expression of neurotransmitter genes. These changes, in turn, can alter communication between cells by revamping the activity needed to trigger impulses across specific synapses. Neurobiologists sometimes refer to the changes underlying learning and memory as "hard wiring," meaning that a memory is laid down or an item is learned only as long-term changes are physically inscribed in the way the neurons interact. These long-lasting changes seem to occur in many different brain regions, which suggests that memory involves far more than just the hippocampus.

LO⁴ How Do Sense Organs Perceive the World?

Sherry Greer, the young woman in our case study, moves through a world devoid of sounds, yet she has extraordinarily acute vision and touch. For most of us, sense organs are keys to knowing and interacting with the surrounding environment. But what *are* senses and how do they work? The sense organs are groups of specialized cells that receive stimulus energy (such as light, sound, odors or flavors, pressure, or heat) and convert it into another kind of energy—the kind that can trigger a neural impulse. Sensory neurons then relay the impulses to the brain, which, in turn, interprets (1) *what kind* of stimulus the sense organ received (what is the pitch of the sound, for example, the color of the light, or the nature of the chemical) and (2) *how strong* is the stimulus (for example, is it loud or soft, bright or dim, concentrated or dilute)? Our day-to-day survival depends on accurate answers to these questions.

Your eyes are generally tuned to visual stimuli, your ears to aural input, and so on. A strong enough mechanical, chemical, or electromagnetic stimulus, however, can often cause any sense organ to generate an action potential. Perhaps you've been bumped on the head or eye and "saw stars." You saw these flashes because cells in the visual pathway are sensitive to pressure as well as to light.

The Ear: Collector of Vibrations

When you clap your hands together or say a word out loud, you generate an aural message that, like all sounds, is really a wave of compressed air. How does the normal ear detect such a wave, analogous to the oscillations we create when we plunge a stone

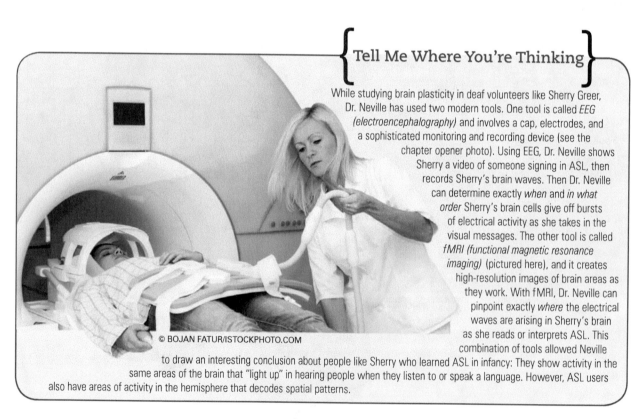

© BOJAN FATUR/ISTOCKPHOTO.COM

{ Tell Me Where You're Thinking }

While studying brain plasticity in deaf volunteers like Sherry Greer, Dr. Neville has used two modern tools. One tool is called *EEG (electroencephalography)* and involves a cap, electrodes, and a sophisticated monitoring and recording device (see the chapter opener photo). Using EEG, Dr. Neville shows Sherry a video of someone signing in ASL, then records Sherry's brain waves. Then Dr. Neville can determine exactly *when* and *in what order* Sherry's brain cells give off bursts of electrical activity as she takes in the visual messages. The other tool is called *fMRI (functional magnetic resonance imaging)* (pictured here), and it creates high-resolution images of brain areas as they work. With fMRI, Dr. Neville can pinpoint exactly *where* the electrical waves are arising in Sherry's brain as she reads or interprets ASL. This combination of tools allowed Neville to draw an interesting conclusion about people like Sherry who learned ASL in infancy: They show activity in the same areas of the brain that "light up" in hearing people when they listen to or speak a language. However, ASL users also have areas of activity in the hemisphere that decodes spatial patterns.

through the still surface of a pool of water? Sound waves first strike the flexible, sculptured outer ear (Fig. 21.11, Step ①). This, in turn, funnels sound waves to the *eardrum*, a taut membrane that stretches like a drumskin across each ear canal (Steps ② and ③). The eardrum vibrates in time with the sound waves, causing a chain of three tiny bones in each middle ear to vibrate. The last bone in the series causes a fluid to vibrate in the coiled cochlea (Greek, *kokhlos* = snail), the most complex mechanical structure in the human body, with over a million moving parts!

How Does the Ear Hear?

The cochlea is a trans-ducer: it changes one type of energy (sound vibrations) into another (nerve impulses). Here's how: The cochlea is shaped like three parallel tubes coiled like a snail shell (Fig. 21.11). Attached to a partition between two of the tubes are rows of box-shaped neurons called

cochlea
a spiral tube in the inner ear that contains sensory cells involved in detecting sound and analyzing pitch

Figure 21.11

How We Hear

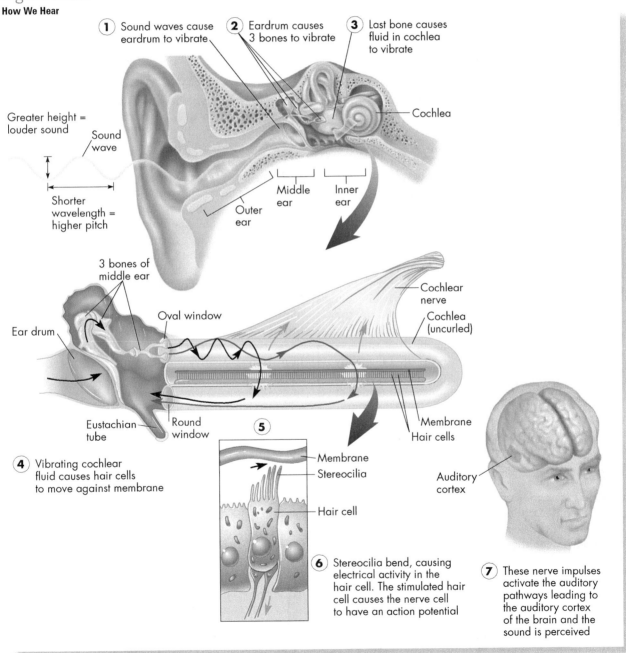

① Sound waves cause eardrum to vibrate

② Eardrum causes 3 bones to vibrate

③ Last bone causes fluid in cochlea to vibrate

Cochlea

Greater height = louder sound

Sound wave

Shorter wavelength = higher pitch

Middle ear

Inner ear

Outer ear

3 bones of middle ear

Oval window

Cochlear nerve

Cochlea (uncurled)

Ear drum

Eustachian tube

Round window

⑤

Membrane

Hair cells

④ Vibrating cochlear fluid causes hair cells to move against membrane

Membrane

Stereocilia

Hair cell

Auditory cortex

⑥ Stereocilia bend, causing electrical activity in the hair cell. The stimulated hair cell causes the nerve cell to have an action potential

⑦ These nerve impulses activate the auditory pathways leading to the auditory cortex of the brain and the sound is perceived

hair cell
box-shaped neurons containing cilia and attached to the cochlea; essential for hearing

cornea
the transparent outer portion of the vertebrate eye through which light passes

pupil
the central, shutter-like opening in the iris of the vertebrate eye through which light passes to the lens and the retina

iris
a pigmented ring of tissue in the vertebrate eye that regulates the size of the pupil and therefore controls the amount of light that enters

lens
a circular, crystalline structure in the eye of certain animals that focuses light onto the retina

retina
(L., *a small net*) a multi-layered region lining the back of the vertebrate eyeball containing light-sensitive cells

rod
one of the two types of photoreceptor (light-sensitive) cells in the retina of the vertebrate eye; rods are sensitive to low levels of light and to movement but cannot distinguish color (see also *cone*)

cone
one of the two types of photoreceptor (light-sensitive) cells in the retina of the vertebrate eye; cones are sensitive to high levels of light and to color (see also *rod*)

hair cells, each crowned by an elegant bundle of tiny extensions called *stereocilia* that stand erect like a Mohawk haircut (Fig. 21.11).

Vibrations in the fluid inside the cochlea cause the hair cells to move relative to a membrane that lies on top of them (Fig. 21.11, Steps ④ and ⑤). The movement bends the stereocilia, which are attached to their neighbors by thin, springlike links. The latest theory for how we hear says that sound vibrations affect these links and cause ion channels to open in the hair cell membrane (which, remember, is a specialized type of neuron). Ions enter the hair cell, trigger an impulse, and thereby convert the mechanical stimulation of the sound wave into an electrochemical signal (Step ⑥). Finally, the hair cell transmits the signal across one or more synapses to a sensory neuron in the cochlear nerve that leads to the brain (Step ⑦).

Receiving the signal, how does the brain know whether the incoming sound is the high-pitched whistle of a lovely song bird or the low growl of an angry grizzly bear? The answer involves the mechanical properties of the cochlea. Unlike a guitar string, which vibrates equally along its entire length when stimulated by the appropriate pitch, different parts of the cochlea vibrate maximally when stimulated by different pitches. High pitches excite motion in the membrane near the wide part of the cochlea, while low pitches cause movement near the cochlea's narrow tip. Because each region of membrane connects to a different part of the brain, different pitches stimulate different brain cells. Soft, soothing sounds cause the stereocilia on the hair cells to sway gently, and fewer neurons to fire action potentials. Loud sounds vibrate the stereocilia more vigorously and cause

more neural firing; very loud noises can actually vibrate the stereocilia until they break off. This can permanently damage the hair cells and along with them the sense of hearing.

The ear has jobs beyond hearing: It also helps us keep our balance and detects the rapid acceleration of an elevator as it drops or climbs or of a car speeding away from a green light.

The Eye: An Outpost of the Brain

Sherry's ability to communicate with others depends on her gestures and above all, her eyes. Visual sensations are possible because eyes convert light energy into neural energy.

How the Eye Detects Light

Picture a rose bush with huge, fragrant yellow blossoms. On a pitch-dark night, you might be able to smell the roses and feel the sharp thorns. But seeing it takes at least a low level of light. Light bouncing off the plant strikes the human eye and passes through the protective transparent outer layer, or cornea (Fig. 21.12a). If you gently place your finger over a closed eyelid and turn your eye from left to right, you can feel the bulge of your cornea. After penetrating the clear cornea, light passes through a transparent fluid and then through the pupil, which is a black, circular, shutterlike opening in the iris (the eye's colored portion). Next, light crosses the lens, a circular, crystalline structure that, together with the cornea, focuses light through another fluid onto the retina. The retina is a multilayered sheet that lines the back of the eyeball and contains light-sensitive *photoreceptor cells*; these begin converting light energy to electrochemical energy (nerve impulses) that can form brain patterns and create a visual image of a rose or other object. Because the lens is curved, it bends the light rays. As a result, the image of the object it projects on the retina is backwards (left and right are reversed) and upside down (Fig. 21.12a). Once the neural signal reaches the brain, however, it is integrated and sorted out so that we perceive the image in its actual orientation.

Within the three-layered retina, the rear layer (closest to the back of the eye and just inside the eye's tough outer covering) consists of jet-black pigment cells that protect the photoreceptors from extraneous light. In the second layer, nestled just in front of the pigment cells, are two types of photoreceptor cells called rods and cones because of their distinctive shapes (Fig. 21.12a). Rods are very

Figure 21.12
How Eyes Work

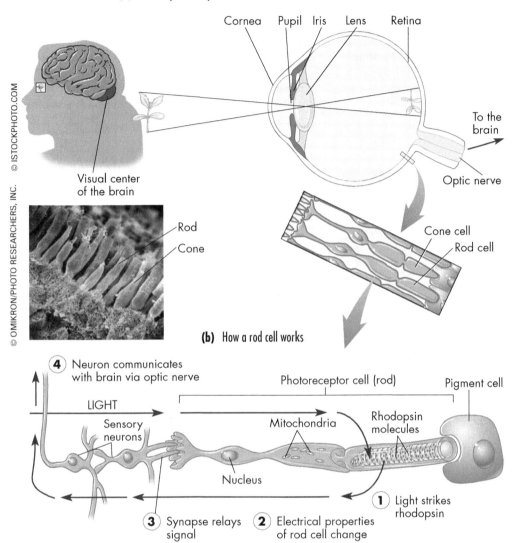

(a) Anatomy of the eye

Cornea Pupil Iris Lens Retina

Visual center of the brain

To the brain

Optic nerve

Rod
Cone

Cone cell
Rod cell

(b) How a rod cell works

4 Neuron communicates with brain via optic nerve

Photoreceptor cell (rod)

Pigment cell

LIGHT

Sensory neurons

Mitochondria

Rhodopsin molecules

Nucleus

1 Light strikes rhodopsin

3 Synapse relays signal

2 Electrical properties of rod cell change

© ISTOCKPHOTO.COM

© OMIKRON/PHOTO RESEARCHERS, INC.

sensitive to low levels of light, but can't distinguish color, whereas cones can detect color but need more light. (Remember cone for *color*.) Cones explain the trouble you have seeing colors in dim light. Night hunters such as owls and cats have a retina jam-packed with rods, allowing them to pick up the dim-mest reflections, but so few cones that their color vision is probably very poor.

In the retina's third layer, in front of the rods and cones, lie sensory neurons. These synapse with the rods and cones and with other neurons that send axons toward the brain. These axons collect into a bundle called the optic nerve, which exits the eye and leads to the brain.

The Visual Pigment

To understand how the eye works, let's concentrate on the rods and how they receive light. The front part of each rod contains the nucleus and forms synapses with other neurons. The rear part detects light by means of stacks of membranous disks housing millions of molecules of the light-sensitive pigment molecule *rhodopsin* (Fig. 21.12b). A protein part of each rhodopsin molecule snakes back and forth across the membrane and cradles the actual pigment portion, a small ring-and-chain molecule called *retinal*. (Eyes synthesize retinal from the compound that gives carrots their bright orange color; the old saying that carrots are good for your vision turns out to be true!) The structure of retinal is really the key to vision, since it changes shape when light hits it. This shape change unleashes a cascade of reactions that we eventually perceive as light.

We can tell bright light from dim because brighter light stimulates more neurons. These generate more action potentials in a shorter period of time; the action potentials travel down the optic nerve to the optic centers in the brain, and the brain then interprets these patterns as stronger light. We see the position of a light source because photoreceptors in different parts of the retina receive light from different parts of the visual field and link up with different parts of the brain. We see color because different cones are sensitive to light of different wavelengths.

Figure 21.13
The Nose Knows and So Does the Tongue

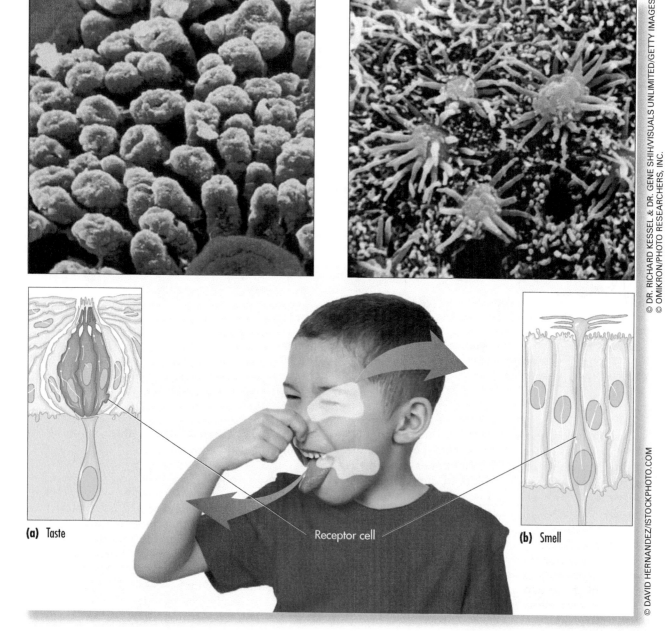

(a) Taste

Receptor cell

(b) Smell

© DR. RICHARD KESSEL & DR. GENE SHIH/VISUALS UNLIMITED/GETTY IMAGES

© OMIKRON/PHOTO RESEARCHERS, INC.

© DAVID HERNANDEZ/ISTOCKPHOTO.COM

Taste and Smell: Our Chemical Senses at Work

We humans are visual beings and sight seems to dominate our senses. Nevertheless, taste and smell probably play a far greater role in your daily life than you think. The tongue and nose receive and detect flavor and odor molecules—actual chemical tidbits of the environment. That's why biologists consider taste and smell to be our *chemical senses*.

People sometimes think of the tongue as a perceptual genius and the nose as a sensory dullard. However, precisely the opposite is true. The tongue is studded with taste buds, each of which consists of a pore leading to a nerve cell. The nerve cell is surrounded by accessory cells arranged in an overlapping pattern that resembles an artichoke or onion bulb (Fig. 21.13a). The nerve cells in taste buds have receptors capable of receiving flavor molecules, but they can distinguish only five general classes of flavors: sweet, salty, bitter, sour, and *umami* (savory flavors, such as in beef and cheese). We can tell similar foods apart—beef from pork, beets from turnips—and sense the subtle difference in their flavors partly because these foods stimulate different receptor types to different degrees, but mostly because aroma molecules from the food bind to receptors in the nose.

The *olfactory epithelium* consists of button-sized patches of yellowish mucous membrane high in the nasal passages. Olfactory neurons and their processes lie embedded in these patches. One end of the nerve cell, shaped somewhat like a flower, binds odor molecules (Fig. 21.13b). The other end is a long, spindly axon that carries signals to the olfactory bulb, or smell region, on the underside of the brain (Fig. 21.10a). If you take a bite of a sandwich and simultaneously pinch your nose shut, you can still perceive the four primary tastes, but not primary odors—and thus very little of the food's complex flavor.

For centuries, people have noticed the peculiarly intimate connections between smells, memories, and emotions. Who hasn't experienced a flood of memories, complete with appropriate emotions, when catching a whiff of a Christmas tree or a brand of sunscreen used on a particular beach in particular company. The explanation for such odor-stimulated *deja vu* lies in the anatomy of the nose and brain. The olfactory lobes are closely connected to the brain's limbic system, a series of small structures (including the hippocampus and hypothalamus) largely responsible for generating fear, rage, aggression, and pleasure and for regulating sex drives and reproductive cycles. A smell, therefore, directly stimulates the brain's centers of memory, emotion, and sexuality.

Smells can also affect the endocrine system. Women roommates, for example, often have synchronized menstrual cycles, and women with irregular periods often grow more regular when in a man's company on a routine basis. In both cases, the effects seem to be largely olfactory and due, perhaps, to pheromonelike molecules in the sweat, which act on the brain and its hormonal feedback loops with the body.

Our main message about sense organs is straightforward: An animal's brain can decipher the stimulus it receives as light, sound, taste, or smell because each sense organ is tuned to a different physical or chemical stimulus and sends a signal to a different part of the brain. And as we saw earlier, the brain's marvelous plasticity allows it to heighten one set of sensations if another set is dimmed. That explains why Sherry Greer can detect light and motion at the edges of her visual field with exceptional acuity, an ability that helps compensate for the absence of

> The brain's marvelous plasticity allows it to heighten one set of sensations if another set is dimmed.

taste buds
sensory organs studding the tongue that consist of pores leading to a nerve cell, which is surrounded by accessory cells arranged in an overlapping pattern that resembles an artichoke or onion bulb

limbic system
a series of small brain structures (including the hippocampus and hypothalamus) largely responsible for generating fear, rage, aggression, and pleasure and for regulating sex drives and reproductive cycles

Who knew?

Three common reflex responses are the withdrawal reflex, initiated when potentially damaging stimuli come in contact with the body; autonomic reflexes, which can make the heart pound; and the bladder-emptying urination reflex. Reflexes are predictable, involuntary responses to stimuli. They begin when receptors are stimulated, initiating a reflex arc through a control center in the nervous system that does not involve conscious decision making, and end when an effector organ carries out the response.

Learning Outcomes

LO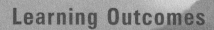**1** Identify the structure and functions of the skeleton

LO**2** Identify the structure and functions of muscles

LO**3** Understand the physiology and benefits of exercise

The Body
in Motion

> ❝ 'Use it or lose it' is an appropriate motto for the musculoskeletal system that generates the body's physical support and movement. ❞

An Almost Fall

Dr. Marjorie Woollacott is buckling Mary Walrod into a harness and is about to cause the 77-year-old woman to slip on an "electric banana peel." That's what Woollacott and her students affectionately call the unique equipment in her equally unique laboratory at the University of Oregon in Eugene. Woollacott studies balance and how so many of us start to lose it through age, inactivity, or lopsided exercise programs. What she is learning could have a major impact on college students, their parents, their grandparents, and the rest of society.

What do you know?

What are antagonistic muscles and why are they important?

Once snugly supported within the harness, Mary is in no danger, even when her feet slip out from beneath her as she steps gingerly along Woollacott's 20-meter (65-foot) long walkway. The test equipment has a hidden slip plate that moves forward just as a person's heel strikes it in a normal step. The effect, says Woollacott, is "just like stepping on a patch of ice on a cold day" or a banana peel on the sidewalk. As the harness prevents a tumble, the laboratory equipment simultaneously captures the "almost fall" on videotape and records electrical signals from the person's muscles.

"People used to think that your hip and trunk muscles mainly controlled your balance," says Dr. Woollacott. But her studies have shown that the strength, speed, and coordination of the ankles and legs is, in fact, the deciding factor in whether people have good balance or are unsteady on their feet. Moreover, by testing two kinds of runners, she and her students were able to trace the roots of balance to particular muscle fibers within the leg muscles.

When Dr. Woollacott tested sprinters in her lab—people who train for short, fast running events such as the 50-meter dash—she found that they exhibit superior balance. For example, one sprinter was scarcely affected by the slip plate track and merely took one small step to regain firm footing. This superior balance, says Woollacott, is based on a sprinter's high proportion of so-called fast-twitch muscle fibers, or special cells within the muscles that deliver quick power. However, when Woollacott tested marathoners on the slip plate, these runners lost their balance much more easily and staggered and wavered more than did the faster, stronger sprinters on the track. This, Woollacott explains, is due to the marathoner's high proportion of slow-twitch muscle fibers, or cells within the muscles that provide endurance but respond more slowly to a slip.

There is a surprising link between long-distance runners and senior citizens, and it's this: All of us naturally lose fast twitch fibers as we age. But the decline can be faster if we are generally sedentary or if we are selectively inactive—that is, build up just one set of muscles the way marathoners usually do with their legs. "Use it or lose it" is an appropriate motto for the musculoskeletal system that generates the body's physical support and movement. It helps explain why slips and falls are the seventh leading cause of death

skeleton
the rigid body support to which muscles attach and apply force, in vertebrates and invertebrates

in older Americans. And it underlies a number of Marjorie Woollacott's personal choices and opinions.

Dr. Woollacott's studies also help much younger people, including college-age athletes, plan training programs. "Their exercise regimens need to be focused," she says, "to help them build up the types of muscle fibers that are best for their particular sport." That's true whether their sport is swimming, ballet, rowing, tennis, basketball, sprinting, or ping pong, and whether they need quick power or greater endurance.

As we explore the musculoskeletal system in this chapter, we'll see how muscles and bones make exercise possible and how movement and physical work help most animals survive day-to-day. We'll see how bones grow and act as scaffolds and levers. We'll see how muscle fibers contract by means of organic motors. And we'll see why Americans—even at young ages—are growing more and more sedentary and how that lack of activity can strongly affect health.

As we go through the chapter, you'll discover the answers to these questions:

☑ How do skeletons work?

☑ How do muscles move skeletons?

☑ How does training for a sport affect the body's muscles and skeleton?

Here's a simple introduction to the muscles and bones: If you're sitting in a chair right now, swing your lower leg out in front of you, pivoting it about the knee, until your entire leg becomes straight. This is like the forward kicking movement in Figure 22.1b (red arrow). How does a small, natural movement like that take place? It involves a stiff rod (your upper leg bone) that has a stationary object at one end (your hips), a movable object at the other (your lower leg), and muscles pulling between them like a stretched rubber band. Crucial to this contraction is the **skeleton**, the rigid body support to which muscles attach and apply force. Most people think of the skeleton as a solid framework like a shrimp's outer

Figure 22.1

Tracings from an "Almost Fall"

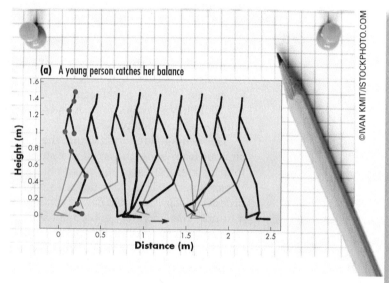

(a) A young person catches her balance

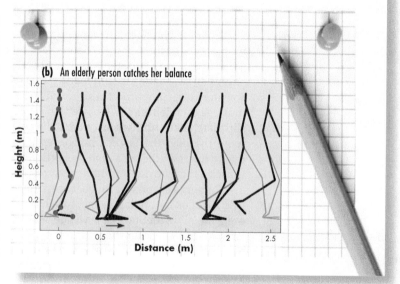

(b) An elderly person catches her balance

LO¹ The Skeleton: The Body's Framework

Take a look at Figure 22.1, which includes some of Dr. Woollacott's data from testing a young subject and an older subject on the slip plate. Can you see differences in how the two people responded? What happened to the arm? The knee? The angle of the upper body with respect to upright stance? How did their stride lengths compare? Our task in this chapter is to explore the body's system of muscles and bones in enough detail to be able to analyze the kinds of foot slips Dr. Woollacott studies and records. Our goal is to understand which muscles pull against which bones and in roughly what sequence to restore the balance we all need to walk upright.

hard shell or the rigid rods of bone in your arms and legs. And these *are* skeletons. But there's another less familiar type of skeleton, too, that depends on a liquid, like the hydraulic brake system in a car, rather than on a solid rod or shell to transmit force. Let's look for a moment at this simple type of skeleton.

Water as a Skeletal Support

Sea anemones in an ocean tide pool, earthworms in the backyard soil, and snails in a river bed all have the same kind of internal support based on a liquid core (made up of water or body fluid) wrapped in a muscular sheath. The two sea anemones in Figure 22.2 show how a water skeleton or hydroskeleton (*hydro* = water) works. This type of fluid internal skeleton is actually much like a water balloon: If you squeeze on one end, the fluid transmits force to the other end. The sea anemone's central digestive cavity is filled with seawater and its surrounding body wall contains two layers of muscles: One layer extends lengthwise from the animal's base to its tentacles; and the other encircles the wall. These two muscle layers act as antagonistic muscle pairs—groups of muscles that move the same object in opposite directions. When the lengthwise muscles contract, the animal becomes shorter and wider (as when you push a water-filled balloon from both ends simultaneously). When the circular muscles contract, the animal becomes longer and narrower (as when you wrap your hands around a balloon and squeeze).

Hydroskeletons are common among invertebrates, with their lack of bone, but even people rely on hydroskeletons in some situations. When we want to lift a heavy lamp or stack of books off the floor, we tend to hold our breath and tighten our abdominal muscles. The compressed fluid of the abdominal cavity contributes to the body's rigidity and helps support the load. The human penis and those of many other mammals are stiffened by a hydroskeleton, as well: valves allow blood to flow forcefully into the organ but not to flow out as freely, and the trapped fluid causes the penis to expand and become rigid.

hydroskeleton
a volume of fluid trapped within an animal's tissues that is noncompressible and serves as a firm mass against which opposing sets of muscles can act; for example, in earthworm segments

antagonistic muscle pair
two muscles that move the same object, such as a limb, in opposite directions

exoskeleton
the thick cuticle of arthropods, made of chitin

endoskeleton
(Gr., *endos* = within + *skeletos* = hard) an internal supporting structure, such as the bony skeleton of a vertebrate

Skeletons: Stiff Rods and Curved Plates

A simple hydroskeleton is fine for sea anemones living with the extra buoyant support of ocean water and for earthworms slithering inch by inch through the soil. A rapidly moving land animal, however, needs a solid framework made up of interlocked proteins, minerals, and polysaccharides. It can be an exoskeleton—a stiff external covering that surrounds the body, as in shrimp, beetles, grasshoppers, and other arthropods, or it can be an endoskeleton—like our own internal set of rigid rods and plates and those of other vertebrates (see Fig. 22.3 on the next page).

Figure 22.2
Sea Anemones and Water Skeletons

When the circular muscles contract, the animal becomes longer and narrower

When the longitudinal muscles contract, the animal becomes shorter and wider

Glossary

bone
the main supporting tissue of vertebrates, composed of a matrix of collagen hardened by calcium phosphate

collagen
a fibrous protein found extensively in connective tissue and bone; collagen also occurs in some invertebrates, as in the cuticle of nematode worms

coccyx
in vertebrates, the tailbone

skull
the skeleton of the vertebrate head

cranium
part of the skull that encloses and protects the brain

hyoid
a bone contained within the skull that is the only human bone not jointed with other bones; it is suspended under the back of the mouth by ligaments and muscles

vertebral column
the backbone

vertebra (pl., vertebrae)
one of a series of interlocking bones that makes up the vertebral column, or backbone, of vertebrate animals

process
a projecting part of an organism or organic structure, such as a bone

Figure 22.3

The Human Endoskeleton: Internal Support and Muscle Attachment

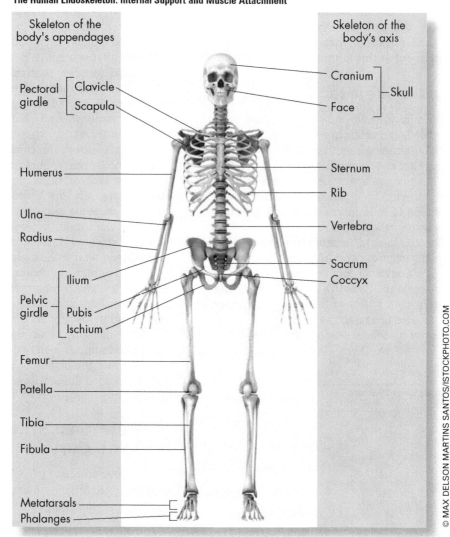

Skeleton of the body's appendages

Pectoral girdle — Clavicle, Scapula

Humerus

Ulna

Radius

Pelvic girdle — Ilium, Pubis, Ischium

Femur

Patella

Tibia

Fibula

Metatarsals
Phalanges

Skeleton of the body's axis

Cranium, Face — Skull

Sternum

Rib

Vertebra

Sacrum

Coccyx

© MAX DELSON MARTINS SANTOS/ISTOCKPHOTO.COM

A mammal's endoskeleton is made of bone, a living tissue that contains a meshwork of the long, stringy protein collagen hardened by calcium and phosphate. The human skeleton has 206 individual bones, and these are found in either the body's main axis, or in the limbs (appendages) that branch off that axis.

The Skeleton of the Body Axis

Virtually every human has a body axis made up of the skull, vertebral column, ribs, and coccyx (tailbone). Part of the skull is the cranium, which encloses and protects the brain, and part is a collection of face and middle ear bones (Fig. 22.3 and review Fig. 21.11). The skull also contains the hyoid bone, the only human bone not jointed with other bones, which is sus-pended under the back of the mouth by ligaments and muscles.

Since humans are upright animals, our head sits on top of our backbone, or vertebral column, rather than in front like a dog's or lizard's. The human back-bone is made up of 33 vertebrae (sing., vertebra) (Fig. 22.4a). Each vertebra is a rigid bone that fits together with other vertebrae in a stack and supports the trunk. An arch extends from the round box and encases and protects the spinal cord. Processes or protuberances provide attachment sites for muscles (Fig. 22.4b). Rubbery cartilage discs separate the vertebrae and allow the bones to move without grinding or pinch-ing each other. This movable stack of vertebrae and discs gives flexibility to the body axis, allowing a shortstop to bend forward and scoop up a line drive,

Figure 22.4
The Human Backbone

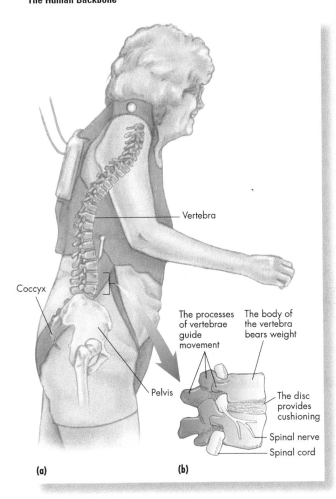

Vertebra

Coccyx

The processes of vertebrae guide movement

The body of the vertebra bears weight

Pelvis

The disc provides cushioning

Spinal nerve

Spinal cord

(a)   (b)

a gymnast to do a back walkover, or a person to flex to catch his or her balance. The vertebral column is a bit fragile, however, and requires special precautions as you lift, stand, or sit to avoid developing lower back problems. Curving forward from the vertebrae are 12 pairs of ribs, ten pairs of which meet in the front and attach at the breastbone (sternum) and form a protective compartment around the heart and lungs.

The Skeleton of the Body's Branches

Our human skeleton has appendages attached to the main axis. The pectoral (shoulder) girdle and pelvic (hip) girdle are branching-off points that support the arm and leg bones, and allow them to swing (see Fig. 22.3).

Bones: A Living Scaffold

As you walk, ride, drive, or bicycle today, the bones of your skeleton are supporting your body and anchor-ing your muscles. They also encase your vital organs, form your blood cells, and store your body's excess cal-cium and phosphate ions. You might think of your bones as nonliving mineral sticks and rods, but they're alive! A closer look at a large bone such as the femur, extend-ing between the hip and knee joints, shows how bones sup-port, anchor, encase, and store—as well as how they self-repair when broken.

The femur's long shaft (see Fig. 22.5a on the next page) allows it to support the body and transmit your weight to the ground. Bones aren't smooth pipes; they have projections, or processes, that serve as attachment sites for ligaments and tendons. Ligaments are connective bands linking bone to bone, while tendons con-nect bone to muscle. You can easily find and feel examples of these skeletal structures in your body. There is a large mus-cle attachment site on your skull bone where your head joins the back of your neck; this process (which feels like a bump) links to muscles that keep your head erect. If you tighten your quadriceps (thigh muscles), you can feel the ligament that attaches your patella (kneecap) to your tibia (shinbone) just below your knee. And you can easily feel tendons between the muscles in your upper arm and the bone in your forearm by putting your hand beneath the edge of a desk, lifting, and, with the other hand, touching the "cables" that project on the inside of your elbow.

Now let's zoom in still closer on the femur to see how it—and other bones—can perform so many important functions (Fig. 22.5b). A cross section through the thighbone reveals that bone has many small spaces between the hard parts. The spaces store fat or contain blood vessels. Regions with few, small spaces form compact bone. Generally toward the outside, compact bone is thick, strong, and resistant to bending; this enables the bone to provide support. Bone regions with larger, more numerous spaces form the tissue called spongy bone. The spaces in some

sternum
the breastbone; in birds, a blade-shaped anchor for the pectoral muscles that enables flight

pectoral (shoulder) girdle
the skeletal support to which front fins or limbs of vertebrates are attached

pelvic (hip) girdle
the skeletal support to which hind fins or limbs of vertebrates are attached

femur
the large bone extend-ing between the hip and knee joints

ligament
a band of connective tissue that links bone to bone

tendon
a band of connective tissue that connects bone to muscle

quadricep
thigh muscle

patella
kneecap

tibia
a large bone in the lower leg; shinbone

compact bone
bone with regions with few, small spaces

spongy bone
bone with regions with larger, more numerous spaces

areas of spongy bone contain red **marrow**, the major site of red blood cell manufacture in adults. A network of spongy bone crisscrosses each end of the femur and functions like girders providing strength near the joints. The tissue down the center of the femur bone's shaft is called the **marrow cavity**, a site of fat storage (Fig. 22.5c,d). Embedded within a matrix are specialized cells that *secrete* the proteins and minerals of the bone (Fig. 22.5e). Other specialized cells in the matrix *reabsorb* calcium and phosphate from bone for use in other parts of the body. After a bone breaks, these secreting cells and reabsorbing cells work together to build new bone tissue and remove regions of dead bone. Bone generally heals more rapidly than cartilage, ligaments, and tendons because bone has a richer blood supply.

Even in undamaged bone, the deposition and removal of protein and minerals go on continuously

Figure 22.5

A Short Tour of a Long Bone: The Femur

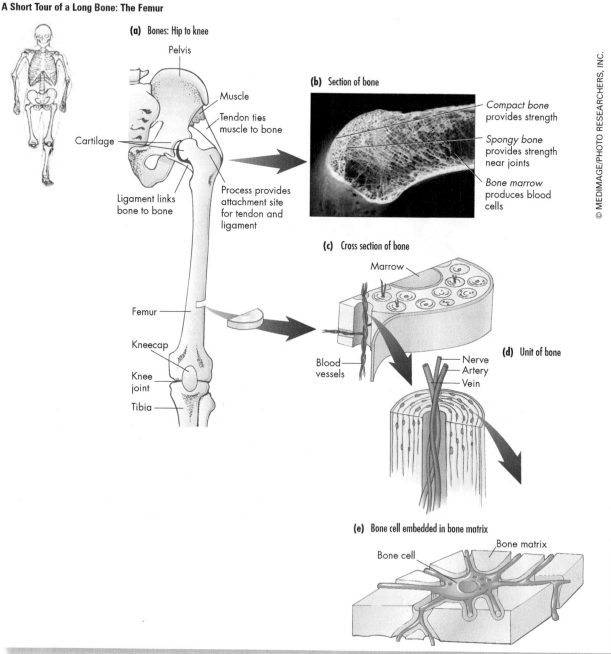

(a) Bones: Hip to knee

Pelvis

Muscle

Tendon ties muscle to bone

Cartilage

Ligament links bone to bone

Process provides attachment site for tendon and ligament

Femur

Kneecap

Knee joint

Tibia

(b) Section of bone

Compact bone provides strength

Spongy bone provides strength near joints

Bone marrow produces blood cells

© MEDIMAGE/PHOTO RESEARCHERS, INC.

(c) Cross section of bone

Marrow

Blood vessels

(d) Unit of bone

Nerve
Artery
Vein

(e) Bone cell embedded in bone matrix

Bone cell

Bone matrix

in a kind of remodeling process that lays down excess materials for storage and then returns them to the circulating blood when needed. Take, for example, the processes to which tendons attach. These grow larger and stronger when the attached muscles pull regularly and forcefully against them. Anthropologists excavating Italian cities buried centuries ago under ash and cinders from the eruption of Mt. Vesuvius could easily distinguish the skeleton of a slave girl from that of a nobleman's daughter simply by comparing the size of these processes on their arm and leg bones—processes that became remodeled during hard physical labor.

Bone remodeling can result in dangerously fragile bones, as well. Due partly to bone weakness, some older Americans have trouble keeping their balance. About 100,000 older people fall each year and fracture a hip, leg, or other large bone. All too often this fracture leads to permanent immobility or even death within a few weeks or months. Their condition of bone weakness is known as osteoporosis, and it occurs because cells specialized to remove stored calcium and phosphate from the existing bone matrix work faster than cells specialized to store the minerals and build bone. The result is porous, brittle bones. Osteoporosis is relatively common in inactive men and in men as they age, and it's especially common in women after menopause. Inactivity signals the need for diminished mineral stores in the bones. Also, in the years immediately following menopause, when a woman will no longer need extra calcium for milk production and breast feeding, her declining hormone levels signal the bones to eliminate up to half of her stored minerals. Recent research shows that drug therapy can help many men and women absorb calcium from their diets, store higher levels of bone minerals, and avoid osteoporosis.

Research also shows that regular exercise stimulates the deposition of calcium in bones. For example, professional baseball pitchers and tennis players have 35 to 50 percent more bone in their throwing or racket arms than in the arm on the other side. Likewise, postmenopausal women who hoisted 5-pound weights weekly for four years lost only half as much bone mass in their arms as did more sedentary women in the same age group. Luckily, with proper diet, exercise, and perhaps drug treatments, osteoporosis is not an inevitable result of aging.

Joints: Where Bone Meets Bone

The swinging of arms and legs as a person walks or falls on Dr. Woollacott's slip plate depends on joints. In fact, the movement of any bone with respect to an adjacent stationary bone requires a joint, or articulation—an expanded portion where the adjacent bones nearly touch. Slightly movable joints, such as those between adjacent vertebrae in the spine, have pads of cartilage that absorb shock but allow limited mobility (Fig. 22.4). Freely movable joints, such as the shoulder, hip, and knee (Fig. 22.5a), have pads of cartilage at the ends of the two adjoining bones. They also have a flattened sac called the *synovial membrane*, which is filled with a fluid (the synovial fluid) that cushions the joint and eases the gliding of bones across each other. Inflammation of this joint sac is called arthritis. In places where skin, tendons, muscles, and bone rub against one another, small sacs filled with fluid or bursae (*bursa* = purse; sing., bursa) cushion the movement. Inflammation of these sacs from overuse, such as in a weekend basketball game or dance session, can cause *bursitis*.

osteoporosis
a condition of bone thinning and weakness that occurs because cells specialized to remove stored calcium and phosphate from the existing bone matrix work faster than cells specialized to store the minerals and build bone

joint
the hinge, or point of contact, between two bones

arthritis
an inflammation of joints such as the shoulder, hip, knee, or knuckles of the fingers and toes; can be based on wear-and-tear or on the body's own autoimmune attack

bursa (pl., bursae)
(L., *bursa* = purse) small sac filled with fluid that cushions the movement in places where skin, tendons, muscles, and bone rub against one another

LO^2 Muscles: The Body's Movers

Bones provide support, but without muscles to move them, the body would be a static pile of sticks. This section investigates how muscles work at the level of the whole organism to recover balance. Then it explores the cellular construction of muscles and finally their molecular mechanism of action.

How Bones Act as Levers

When Marjorie Woollacott begins to test Mary Walrod (or another experimental subject) to see how her muscles and bones interact to maintain balance, the researcher places reflective markers on various parts of Mary's body. Then Woollacott trains a video camera on Mary's movements and records how they respond after she steps on the simulated "icy patch" or "banana peel" section of the laboratory walkway. The cameras and associated computers follow the positions of joints in space. Next, Dr. Woollacott makes stick figures of her subjects catching their balance based on the reflector patches she can track in her videotapes. These figures help her understand part of the story of why older people have a more difficult time keeping their balance than younger people. But there is more to it, and to understand the rest, she had to investigate the way bones pivot at joints, as well as how different people use their muscles, building on the basis of muscle structure and function.

Bones pivot at joints because of the way muscles pull on them. Animals with hard skeletons have muscles arranged in *antagonistic pairs*. For example, contraction (shortening) of the shin muscle (tibialis anterior) flexes your foot toward your body (Fig. 22.6a), while its antagonist, the calf muscle (gastrocnemius), extends your foot to point away from the body (Fig. 22.6b). Often, when a muscle contracts, its antagonist relaxes. Dr. Woollacott found, however, that when older people slip on her laboratory plate, they often contract both groups of muscles at the same time, stiffening the leg and preventing the small compensating movements it takes to restore balance.

We can produce the ordered movements of walking, lifting, throwing, and so on because of our skeletal muscles, muscles attached to bones that move the skeleton. One end of a skeletal muscle (called the origin) attaches to a bone that generally remains stationary during a contraction, like an anchor, while the other end (the insertion) attaches across a joint to a bone that moves. For example, reach down and feel your calf muscles at the back of your lower leg. These muscles attach to your femur just above the back of your knee, and at the opposite end, to your heel bone. When the calf muscles contract, the shortening forces the foot to rotate around a pivot, the ankle joint, exactly as a lever (here, the foot) rotates around a fulcrum (the ankle joint). Because of this arrangement, a small contraction of the muscle transmits a large movement to the bone. Figure 22.1b shows this change in angle during walking.

Figure 22.6

Muscles Move Bones to Action

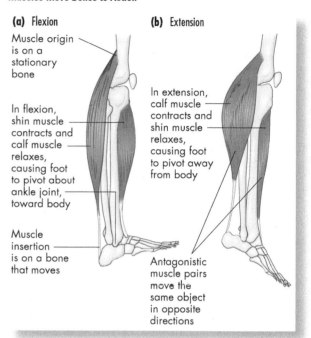

(a) Flexion

Muscle origin is on a stationary bone

In flexion, shin muscle contracts and calf muscle relaxes, causing foot to pivot about ankle joint, toward body

Muscle insertion is on a bone that moves

(b) Extension

In extension, calf muscle contracts and shin muscle relaxes, causing foot to pivot away from body

Antagonistic muscle pairs move the same object in opposite directions

The Body's Muscle System

Each muscle's arrangement and position is crucial to its function. Figure 22.7 shows many of the body's major skeletal muscles. Dr. Woollacott has found that several muscles are important for regaining balance after a slip, including parts of the "quads" (*quadriceps*) in the front of the thigh; three muscles running down the back of the thigh (the semitendinosus, semimembranosus, and biceps femoris) that form what we generally refer to as the "hamstrings"; a shin muscle in the front of the lower leg (*tibialis*); and the abdominals, or rectus abdominis ("abs"), (see Fig. 22.7). Dr. Woollacott knew that electrical events stimulate muscle contraction and that she could record the electrical activity in her subject's muscles by placing electrodes on the skin above the muscle in question. Figure 22.8 on page 136 shows data recorded from young and older adults during an unexpected slip. The signal is measured in volts and is displayed as a graph. When the "trace" or graphed line goes up, it means that the muscle has responded to the slip.

The technique for recording electrical changes in the muscles and plotting the changes on paper is called electromyograph, or EMG (Fig. 22.8). To learn how an EMG works, we need to first back up and look at the structure of individual muscle cells, since these allow entire muscles to shorten and hence to move the skeleton.

Muscle Cells, Muscle Proteins, and the Mechanism of Contraction

The muscles of your arms, legs, and trunk—indeed all of your skeletal muscles—are made up of muscle fibers: giant cells that have many nuclei and may extend the full length of the muscle, up to several centimeters (see Fig. 22.9a on page 137). If we took a small portion of a single muscle cell and enlarged it, we could see that the plasma membrane encloses several long bundles called fibrils (Fig. 22.9b). Each fibril is organized into units called sarcomeres (*sarco* = flesh). The sarcomeres in various fibrils line up and give the muscle cell a striped pattern leading to an alternate name for skeletal muscle: striated muscle. Surrounding each fibril is a network of modified endoplasmic reticulum, called the *sarcoplasmic reticulum* in muscle cells. Within each fibril are bundles of protein filaments (Fig. 22.9c). Mitochondria appear regularly between the fibrils. As we have seen, muscles work by shortening. This contraction happens because the sarcoplasmic reticulum acts like a car's electric system; the bundles of protein filaments act like the car's engine; and the mitochondria supply the energy system, the fuel for action.

Protein Filaments in Muscle Cells

The muscle protein filaments shown in Figure 22.9c actually do the job of contracting the muscle. From the dark line at the end of each sarcomere, numerous thin protein filaments project toward the middle of the sarcomere. These thin filaments are made mainly of many copies of the round protein actin. Toward the middle of the sarcomere lies a second type of filament, thicker than the first. These thick filaments are made of the

muscle fiber
a muscle cell; a giant cell with many nuclei and numerous myofibrils, capable of contraction when stimulated

fibril
long bundles found within a muscle cell, composed of sarcomeres

sarcomere
the contractile unit of a skeletal muscle consisting of repeating bands of actin and myosin

actin
(Gr., *actis* = a ray) a major component of microfilaments in contractile cells such as muscle

Figure 22.7
Skeletal Muscles of the Human Body

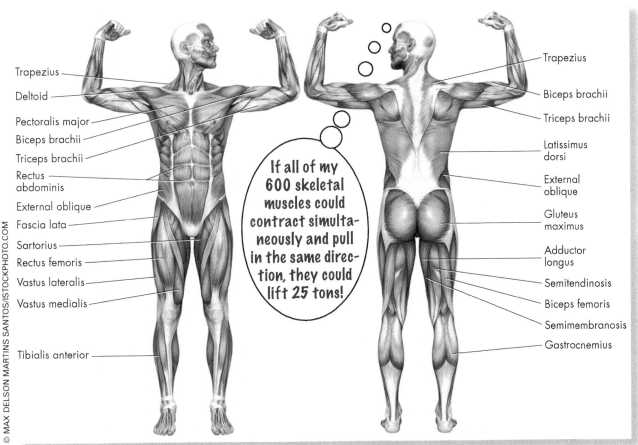

Trapezius
Deltoid
Pectoralis major
Biceps brachii
Triceps brachii
Rectus abdominis
External oblique
Fascia lata
Sartorius
Rectus femoris
Vastus lateralis
Vastus medialis
Tibialis anterior

If all of my 600 skeletal muscles could contract simultaneously and pull in the same direction, they could lift 25 tons!

Trapezius
Biceps brachii
Triceps brachii
Latissimus dorsi
External oblique
Gluteus maximus
Adductor longus
Semitendinosis
Biceps femoris
Semimembranosis
Gastrocnemius

© MAX DELSON MARTINS SANTOS/ISTOCKPHOTO.COM

myosin
a muscle protein that interacts with actin and causes muscles to contract

sliding filament mechanism
a mechanism of muscle contraction in which contraction is made possible by the unique arrangement and sliding of the thick filaments relative to the thin filaments, shortening the sarcomeres

Figure 22.8
EMG of Muscles During a Slip

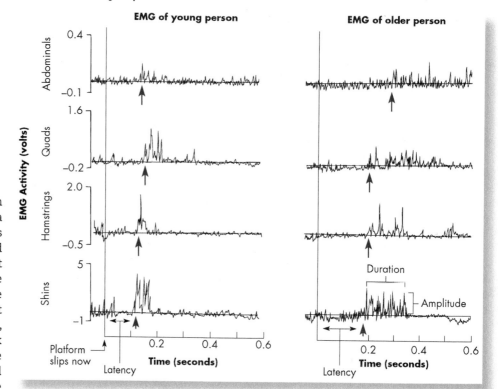

golf club-shaped protein myosin. If you grab a bundle of seven pencils and push the eraser end of the middle pencil out about half way, then the middle pencil would be like the thick filament in the middle of the cell, and the surrounding six pencils would be like the thin filaments attached to the end plate. Figure 22.9c shows one thick and one thin filament.

The Mechanism of Muscle Contraction

How do these neat arrays of actin and myosin filaments allow muscle cells to shorten and help stop you from falling after slipping on a banana peel? Biologists observing skeletal muscle tissue with an electron microscope noticed that as the muscle contracts, each sarcomere within the muscle cell becomes shorter. This causes the whole fiber to shorten. The *filaments* within each muscle cell, however, do *not* shorten during contraction. Instead, as each sarcomere shortens, the filaments *slide past each other*. To picture this, try thinking of putting your hands into the front pocket of your pullover sweatshirt on a cold day; your hands slide past the insides of the pocket, your elbows come nearer together, but neither the length of your forearms nor the length of the pocket changes. This process, going on right now in the muscles of your eyelids as they blink, your chest cavity as it expands with each breath, and your hands as they hold this book, is called the sliding filament mechanism of muscle contraction.

This filament sliding is made possible by a unique arrangement and behavior of the proteins in the thin and thick filaments. Within each thick filament, many

individual myosin protein molecules bind together, each with a long, straight tail at one end and a head at the other (Fig. 22.9c,d). The myosin head of the thick filament reaches out to a thin filament (made of actin) like an oar dipping into the water, and the two filaments attach temporarily (Fig. 22.9d, Step ①). The myosin head swings (Step ②), moving the actin past it (Step ③) like an oar moves water. This shortens the sarcomere and hence the entire muscle a tiny bit. The myosin head then releases the thin filament, swings back to its original position, and binds the thin filament again, this time in a different place, like a rower's oar taking another stroke. The process of reaching, attaching, swinging, and detaching happens over and over for each myosin molecule as the muscle contracts, literally sliding the actin thin filament past it.

Energy for Muscle Contraction

Not surprisingly, just as a rowing crew must eat heartily the night before a regatta, the reaching and swinging of myosin "oars" also requires energy. In muscle fibers at rest (Fig. 22.9d, Step ①), the myosin head is bound to ADP and a phosphate. After the power stroke (Step ②), the myosin head releases the ADP and phosphate (Step ④), and an energy packet, ATP, binds to the myosin head (Step ⑤). The binding of ATP causes the myosin head to release the thin filament and cleave the ATP to ADP and phosphate (Step ⑥). This delivers a burst of energy that powers the return of the myosin head to its original position, where it can bind to the thin filament once more (Step ⑦).

The mechanism of sliding protein filaments explains how muscles shorten, and muscle shortening explains how Mary Walrod can catch her balance on the laboratory slip plate. The sliding mechanism does not, however, explain how her muscles "know" *when* to contract and *how much* to contract to prevent a fall. That requires signals from cell membranes.

Controlling Muscle Contraction

Muscle contraction enhances an animal's survival only if that contraction is controlled and takes place at the appropriate time. If Mary Walrod's arms and legs started to react and contract *before* she got to the slip plate, she could fall—or at least "almost fall"—into the harness. The normal control over muscle contraction is exerted by electrical events—the very events, in fact, Dr. Woollacott detects with her electrodes (see Fig. 22.8). Motor neurons from the spinal cord run to and connect with all our skeletal muscles (Fig. 22.10a). The motor neuron releases a neurotransmitter substance onto the cell membrane of the muscle cell. This generates an action potential in the muscle cell that is similar to the one in a nerve cell (review Fig. 21.3). This signal causes sarcoplasmic reticulum to release calcium into the cell's cytoplasm. The calcium causes a blocking protein to "get out of the way," thus allowing the myosin head to associate with the thin filaments and hence start the contraction cycle shown in Figure 22.9d. When the muscle's action potential passes, ATP-fueled pumps bring the calcium ions back into the sarcoplasmic reticulum;

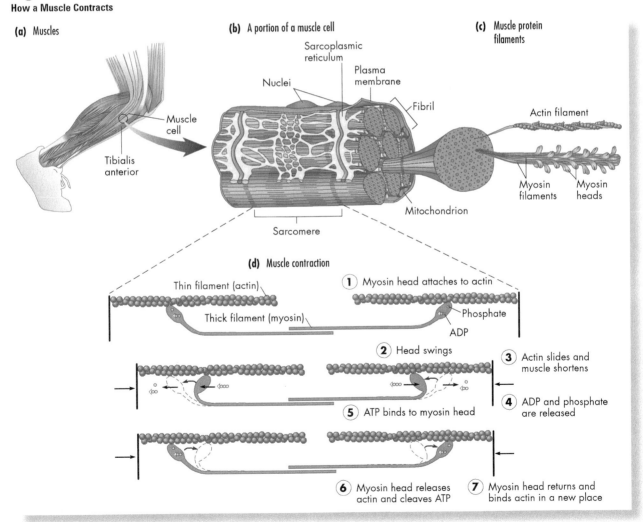

Figure 22.9
How a Muscle Contracts

(a) Muscles

Muscle cell

Tibialis anterior

(b) A portion of a muscle cell

Sarcoplasmic reticulum

Plasma membrane

Nuclei

Fibril

Mitochondrion

Sarcomere

(c) Muscle protein filaments

Actin filament

Myosin filaments

Myosin heads

(d) Muscle contraction

Thin filament (actin)

Thick filament (myosin)

① Myosin head attaches to actin

Phosphate

ADP

② Head swings

③ Actin slides and muscle shortens

④ ADP and phosphate are released

⑤ ATP binds to myosin head

⑥ Myosin head releases actin and cleaves ATP

⑦ Myosin head returns and binds actin in a new place

without calcium, the myosin can no longer bind and slide past the thin filaments, and so contraction stops and the muscle relaxes.

How Muscles Work to Help Control Balance

On the graphs in Figure 22.8, you can see the time it takes for a person's shin muscle to begin to respond to Dr. Woollacott's slip plate. This time delay is called the *latency*. What is the difference in latency between the younger and older person's shin muscles? How about the strength (or amplitude) of the response, which is revealed by the height of the tracing? The

Figure 22.10

Skeletal Muscle, Cardiac Muscle, and Smooth Muscle Compared

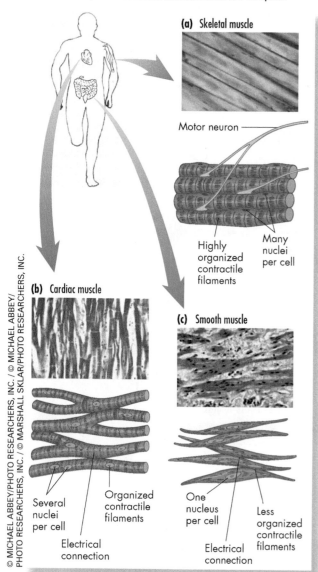

(a) Skeletal muscle

Motor neuron

Highly organized contractile filaments

Many nuclei per cell

(b) Cardiac muscle

(c) Smooth muscle

Several nuclei per cell

Organized contractile filaments

Electrical connection

One nucleus per cell

Less organized contractile filaments

Electrical connection

results showed that the older person responds later and with less strength than the younger person. To make up for this slower, weaker response, what happens to the duration of the muscle electric signal— the length of time it continues to stimulate the shin muscle? The graph shows that the older person compensates for the late, weak response by contracting for a longer period of time.

You can use this same graph to compare the order in which people's muscles in different parts of the body come into play during a slip (Fig. 22.8). Do the muscles start contracting high in the body and move down, or do they start low in the body and then move up? Do the younger and older subjects use their muscles in different orders during the slip plate experiments? In both age groups, people tend to start low and move up. However, infants who are learning to walk and are at the pull-up-and-stand stage use a very different balance-keeping strategy than the same children a few months later in the toddling stage.

Cardiac Muscle and Smooth Muscle

The mechanisms we just discussed for contracting, powering, and controlling apply to skeletal muscles that attach to bones and move the skeleton (Fig. 22.10a). Animals with backbones (vertebrates), however, have two additional types of muscles that move fluids rather than bones. Cardiac muscle, found only in the heart, drives blood through the circulatory system, while smooth muscle pushes food through the digestive tract and causes the urinary bladder, uterus, and blood vessel walls to contract.

Cardiac muscle consists of a network of heart muscle cells that are electrically connected to each other. These electrical connections allow adjacent cells to communicate back and forth (Fig. 22.10b). An impulse initiated any place on the heart muscle propagates through the entire organ, causing the whole heart to contract as a unit. The impulse usually begins inside the heart itself, in its pacemaker (review Fig. 17.8), not in nerves running to the heart. This quality allows the heart to keep beating during a heart transplant even though the vital organ is temporarily removed from the body.

In contrast to cardiac muscle, skeletal muscle fibers do not communicate with each other directly. Several skeletal muscle cells may contract at the same time because they are innervated by the same motor neuron coming from the spinal cord. This contractile group is a *motor unit* (Fig. 22.10a). The more motor units that fire, the more forceful the muscle contraction. Like skeletal muscle, cardiac muscle is striated, or striped, because of the way its thin and thick filaments are organized.

The smooth muscle cells of the digestive tract, urinary bladder, blood vessels, and other hollow body organs lack striations because their thick and thin filaments are not as well ordered as those in skeletal and cardiac muscle (Fig. 22.10c). Smooth muscle cells usually have a single nucleus, and many communicate with other smooth muscle cells electrically via gap junctions, as do cardiac muscle cells. This communication allows the rhythmic pushing of food down the digestive tract, the voiding of urine, the pushing of a baby through the birth canal, or the maintenance of blood pressure.

We've seen now how muscles and skeleton act together to keep balance and how smooth muscle and heart muscle propel other organs. Now let's see how major muscle groups act together when we do something fun, like play baseball or tennis or swim. At the same time, we'll see how the type of sport activity you choose can ultimately affect your body tone and your ability to stay in balance.

LO³ The Physiology of Sport and Exercise

Sport is big business—in colleges, in city stadiums, and on radio and television. Although owners spend billions of dollars promoting their teams, comparatively little funding is available for rigorously controlled experiments to discover how to improve athletic performance in people and other animals. The research that has been done, however, is beginning to present a clearer picture of how our muscles are fueled, about the body changes we can expect from training, and about the epidemic of diseases related to inactivity in our society. Let's explore some of those results now.

Getting Fuel to the Motor

While thick and thin filaments cause muscle cells to contract, we saw that the fuel for muscle cell contraction is ATP. We saw in Chapter 3 that mitochondria and certain enzymes in the cytoplasm are the powerhouses that make ATP and therefore provide cells with fuel. These cell parts cooperate in muscle cells to establish three energy systems: (1) the immediate system, (2) the glycolytic system, and (3) the oxidative system.

The duration of physical activity dictates which energy system the body uses at any given time. The immediate energy system is instantly available for a brief explosive action, such as one heave by a shot-putter. It depends on a muscle cell's stores of ATP plus the high-energy molecule creatine phosphate, and it can fuel muscle contraction for several seconds. The second energy system, the glycolytic energy system, is based on the splitting of glucose by glycolysis in the muscles. The glycolytic system can sustain heavy exercise for a few minutes, as in a 200-m swim. After that, the oxidative (or aerobic) energy system takes over for long periods of exercise. When a distance runner runs a 10-kilometer race, his muscles use the oxidative system throughout most of the race, until the final sprint. If enough oxygen is present, this aerobic energy system can produce energy by breaking down carbohydrates, fatty acids, and amino acids mobilized from other parts of the body. Clearly, anyone interested in melting away body fat should engage in aerobic activities like rapid walking, swimming, bicycling, cross-country skiing, or jogging, which rely primarily on the oxidative energy system and its ability to use fats as fuel.

Slow-Twitch Muscle Fibers

Not all muscle fibers use the three energy systems equally. We saw in the chapter introduction that long-distance runners have more slow-twitch muscle fibers while sprinters have more fast-twitch fibers. Here's what all of that means. Slow-twitch muscle fibers (also called *slow oxidative muscle fibers*) obtain most of their ATP from the oxidative system (see Fig. 22.11 on the next page). Slow-twitch fibers require about one-tenth of a second to contract fully, they are packed with mitochondria, they receive a rich supply of blood, and they have large quantities of the red protein myoglobin, which stores oxygen in muscle cells. These characteristics make slow-twitch fibers deep red, like the dark meat of a chicken (Fig. 22.11). Slow-twitch fibers are resistant to fatigue and thus are able to contract for long periods of time.

smooth muscle
muscle consisting of spindle-shaped, unstriated muscle cells; muscle type found in the digestive, reproductive, and circulatory systems

immediate energy system
energy in the body instantly available for a brief explosive action, such as one heave by a shot-putter

creatine phosphate
a high-energy molecule in the immediate energy system that can transfer energy to ATP

glycolytic energy system
energy system based on the splitting of glucose by glycolysis in the muscles; can sustain heavy exercise for a few minutes, as in a 200-m swim

oxidative (aerobic) energy system
the longest-sustaining energy system of the body that relies on the Krebs cycle and electron transport drain in mitochondria and its ability to use fats as fuel

slow-twitch muscle fibers
muscle fibers that obtain most of their ATP from the oxidative system; also called *slow oxidative muscle fibers*; provide power for most endurance sports

myoglobin
red protein that stores oxygen in muscle cells

fast-twitch muscle fibers
muscle fibers that obtain most of their ATP from glycolysis; also called *fast glycolytic muscle fibers*; provide quick power of the type needed for the 50-yard dash

fast oxidative-glycolytic muscle fibers
muscle fibers that have characteristics midway between those of fast-twitch and slow-twitch muscle fibers; these fibers are moderately powerful and moderately resistant to fatigue

Figure 22.11

Muscle Fibers and Sports Performance: Slow-Twitch and Fast-Twitch

Fiber types differ in their concentration of myosin

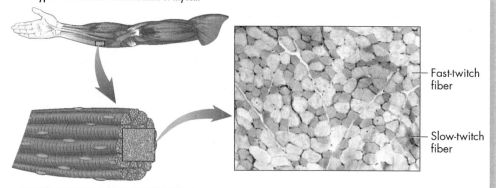

Fast-twitch fiber

Slow-twitch fiber

Athletes who have trained for endurance sports such as running marathons have a large proportion of slow-twitch muscles. Slow-twitch muscles also provide functions critical for survival, such as maintaining posture. Without the contraction of slow-twitch muscles in your jaw, your mouth would be wide open as you read this sentence.

Fast-Twitch Muscle Fibers

Whereas slow-twitch fibers bestow endurance, fast-twitch fibers, or *fast glycolytic muscle fibers*, provide quick power—the kind of power needed for a 50-yard dash, for example, or one clean jerk of a heavy barbell. Fast-twitch fibers derive most of their ATP from glycolysis, and they reach maximum contraction twice as quickly as slow-twitch fibers. They soon grow fatigued, however, since they quickly run through their limited stores of ATP. Fast-twitch fibers are white (Fig. 22.11) because they are packed with white actin and myosin filaments (which maximize contractile force), and they contain very little myoglobin for oxygen storage. The white meat in the breast of a chicken is the fast-twitch muscle that powers the wings and enables the chicken to suddenly burst away from a fox and fly to safety in a tree. By contrast, a duck's breast is dark meat, consisting of red, slow-twitch fibers that can sustain the beating of the wings without fatigue during long migratory flights. A third kind of muscle fiber, fast oxidative-glycolytic muscle fiber, has characteristics midway between fast glycolytic and slow oxidative fibers; these fibers are moderately powerful and moderately resistant to fatigue.

Although fiber types are genetically determined to a large degree, training can partly change how the muscle fibers function. For example, endurance training can cause both fast and slow fibers to develop an increased oxidative capacity but a reduced explosive strength. Clearly, a sprinter would want to avoid that type of training. In contrast, strength training improves immediate energy supply systems and suppresses oxidative capacity. Although it frustrates some body builders, the total *number* of muscle fibers is apparently genetically determined and is not affected by weight training. Lifting can, however, increase fiber *thickness* by increasing the number of thick and thin filaments in muscle cells.

Athletic Training and the Stress Response

For most animals, survival is linked to locomotion, and in nature, locomotion often must be rapid and coordinated if the animal is to survive. Heavy exercise, strenuous work, and the intensity of a basketball game or sprint workout stimulates the same fight-or-flight response that electrifies the escape of a field mouse from a diving hawk.

Recall our discussion of stress in Chapter 20. Stress initiates a cascade of hormone signals that raises the amount of vital fuels such as glucose and fatty acids in the blood; elevates heart rate and blood pressure; dilates air passages and increases breathing rate; and diverts blood from the skin and digestive organs to the skeletal muscles, supplying food and oxygen where they are needed the most (review Fig. 20.5). A strenuous athletic training session does the same things. As a result, the system adapts.

How Athletic Training Alters Physiology

Since heavy exercise evokes the fight-or-flight response, people who exercise several times a week enter this state of stress repeatedly. What effects do such repeated periodic challenges have on the body's homeostatic mechanisms? Training works by causing "breakdown" followed by "overshoot"— a breakdown of stored fuel, for example, followed by the increased deposition of fuel molecules; or a slight breakdown of muscle tissues, with an overall strengthening as the tissues are repaired. To increase fitness without injury, therefore, one must carefully, gradually, and *progressively* augment the *intensity*, *frequency*, and *duration* of workouts.

One goal of human athletic training is to boost the amount of oxygen a person can deliver to working muscles (the so-called maximal oxygen uptake). What changes occur after training that increase one's ability to take up oxygen? After training, hearts pump more blood per minute than before. This is due to an increase in the amount of blood pumped per beat, not an increase in the heart rate. Well-trained endurance athletes have enlarged heart cavities and thicker heart walls.

In addition, physically fit people can better use the increased oxygen pumped by their larger, stronger hearts because their muscles extract more oxygen from the blood. The muscle cell mitochondria grow larger and produce more ATP; the muscles build more myoglobin, which stores more oxygen; and there is an increase in the number of blood capillaries in the muscles. Together these phenomena provide the muscles with a greater oxygen supply.

Anyone still needing a nudge to begin or continue a regular exercise program can expect yet another benefit from it. Exercise stimulates the release of endorphins, naturally occurring morphines made in the pituitary gland and other brain regions. These peptide hormones reduce pain and enhance a feeling of well-being. The release of endorphins during strenuous exercise may explain, in part, why many people experience feelings of relaxation and contentment after a workout. Add to this the dramatic positive effects on the heart and on a person's chances of living a longer, more vigorous life, and it becomes more and more difficult to justify a sedentary life style.

Available evidence suggests that a physically inactive person is about twice as likely as an active one to die of heart disease. It is ironic that many people recognize the importance of diet and exercise to their pets' health, but fail to apply the same principles to their own human bodies. This inspired Swedish exercise physiologist Per Olof Astrand to advise sedentary adults to "Walk your dog whether you have one or not."

endorphins
peptides found in the anterior lobe of the pituitary and in several other regions of the brain and spinal cord that can act as a natural pain killer and are the source of the "runner's high"

Who knew?

Antagonistic muscles perform opposite actions. Since a single muscle can cause movement only by shortening, not lengthening, movement of a body part in the opposite direction requires a muscle on the opposite side.

" Walk your dog whether you have one or not. "

© BRANDON LAUFENBERG/ISTOCKPHOTO.COM

Chapter in Review

16

homeostasis
the maintenance of a constant internal balance despite fluctuations in the external environment

microgravity
state of near-weightlessness

anatomy
the study of biological structures such as bones and kidneys

physiology
the study of how biological structures function

epithelial tissue
a major tissue type that covers the body surface and lines the body cavities, ducts, and vessels

exocrine gland
a gland with its own transporting duct that carries its secretions to a particular region of the body, and includes the digestive and sweat glands; contrasts with endocrine glands

endocrine gland
a gland that secretes hormones directly into the extracellular fluid or blood rather than into a duct; includes the pituitary, adrenal, and thyroid glands; contrasts with exocrine glands

connective tissue
animal tissue that connects or surrounds other tissues and whose cells are embedded in a collagen matrix; bones and tendons are mainly connective tissue

muscle tissue
tissue that enables an animal to move; the three types are smooth muscle, cardiac muscle, and skeletal muscle

nervous tissue
animal tissue containing neurons, cells whose main function is the transmission of electro-chemical impulses

nervous system
an animal's network of nerves; includes the brain and spinal cord as well as the peripheral nerves, and integrates and coordinates the activities of all the body systems

neuron
a nerve cell that transmits messages through-out the body; made up of dendrites, cell body, and axon

receptor
[1] a protein of a specific shape that binds to a particular chemical; [2] in physiology, a structure that carries out one of three primary elements of a homeostatic system to sense environmental conditions; also see effector and integrator

integrator
one of three primary elements characteristic of a homeostatic system; an integrator evaluates the situation and makes decisions; also see effector and receptor

effector
one of three primary elements characteristic of a homeostatic system; an effector executes the decisions; also see integrator and receptor

feedback loop
a control system involving a series of steps that sense a change and, in turn, influence the functioning of the process; can be positive or negative

Introduction During Dr. Bernard Harris's 9 days in space, he lost over 10 percent of his muscle mass and 1 percent of his bone. His body literally disassembled itself in a normal, natural attempt to maintain a steady internal state—homeostasis—despite the very abnormal conditions of microgravity in space.

LO¹ Staying Alive: Problems and Solutions Essential life processes include capturing energy and materials, exchanging gases, and maintaining a body of a particular shape, fluid composition, and (usually) temperature range. Some body systems that help maintain homeostasis have a supply tube running from the outside environment to the inside; special regions of the tube where substances can be exchanged with body fluids; transport of essential materials by those fluids; and delivery of the materials to all cells.

LO² Body Organization: A Hierarchy An animal's cells are highly organized into a hierarchy of structures at increasingly complex levels: tissues, organs, and organ systems. The four tissue types are epithelial tissue, connective tissue (Bernard Harris's bone loss involves changes to the bone's connective tissue), muscle tissue, and nervous tissue.

LO³ How Do Our Bodies Maintain a Steady State? Homeostasis often works via feedback loops, which involve the action of a receptor, an integrator, and an effector. A negative feedback loop resists change by sensing a deviation from the baseline condition and opposing it. A household thermometer and furnace work this way, as do the human body's internal mechanisms for maintaining a steady temperature. A positive feedback loop brings about rapid change by sensing an initial environmental change, responding to it, and then amplifying the response further and further. This type of response brings about mammalian birth.

LO⁴ Homeostasis, Circulation, and Behavior The maintenance of body temperature in a homeotherm is a classic example of homeostasis involving specialized circulatory mechanisms. Vasoconstriction shunts blood away from the periphery and toward the body core, controlling heat loss. Vasodilation shunts blood to the body surface, promoting heat loss. Countercurrent flow promotes blood flow but also conserves heat. Adaptive behaviors also help prevent hypothermia or hyperthermia. These behaviors include hibernation, migration, huddling, building shelters, shedding heavy coats, and depositing fat layers. Poikilotherms have more fluctuation in core temperature and tend to bask in the sun or use other behavioral mechanisms to help control heat gain and loss. Some have enzymatic or tissue modifications that help tolerate cold or generate heat.

LO⁵ Maintaining Salt and Water Balance The kidney is an amazing filtration device that maintains the constitution of the blood and the level of water and salts in body fluids. The kidneys are part of the excretory system, which cleanses the blood and carries wastes out of the body as urine or its equivalent. Excretion removes the byproducts of metabolism and rids the organism of excess water and salts. The amino portion of amino acids, the building blocks of protein, is a leftover chemical

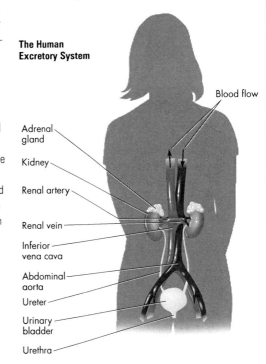

The Human Excretory System

Blood flow

Adrenal gland

Kidney

Renal artery

Renal vein

Inferior vena cava

Abdominal aorta

Ureter

Urinary bladder

Urethra

negative feedback loop
a series of steps used to resist change in a homeostatic system; first by sensing a deviation from the baseline condition, then by turning on mechanisms that oppose that trend and thus bring things back toward the baseline

hypothalamus
a collection of nerve cells at the base of the vertebrate brain just below the cerebral hemispheres; part of the diencephalon and responsible for regulating body temperature, many autonomic activities, and many endocrine functions

positive feedback loop
a series of steps that brings about rapid change in a homeostatic system; amplifies an initial change of the external or internal environment in one direction further and further in the same direction

homeotherm
a "warm-blooded animal" in which the internal body temperature is fairly constant, based on physiological mechanisms that also control the distribution of its large reservoir of warm, moving fluid when the environment is too hot or cold

vasoconstriction
contraction of blood vessel walls; regulates blood flow

vasodilation
relaxation of blood vessel walls; regulates blood flow

countercurrent flow (or countercurrent exchange)
a mechanism in which fluids with two different characteristics (such as temperature or solute concentrations) flow in opposite directions and can exchange energies or substances at points of contact along a concentration gradient

hypothermia
the state that sets in when the body's core temperature drops below 35°C (90°F)

hyperthermia
the state of elevated body temperature that sets in when environmental temperatures are too high and bodily exposure to heat is too prolonged

poikilotherm
an animal with variable internal temperature; colloquial synonym for poikilotherm is "cold-blooded animal"

water balance
a condition in which the amount of water entering the body equals the amount of water leaving

urine
a fluid that washes urea from the body

excretory system
system that [1] cleanses the blood of organic waste molecules and [2] carries them out of the body as urine or its equivalent through a special set of excretory tubes

intracellular fluid
the fluid inside cells

extracellular fluid
the fluid within the body but outside of cells

plasma
the liquid portion of blood

excretion
the elimination of metabolic waste products from the body; in vertebrates, the main excretory organs are the kidneys

waste product that can be removed as ammonia (by many aquatic animals); as uric acid (by birds, reptiles, insects, and land snails); or as urea (by mammals and a few kinds of fishes). In mammals, water balance is regulated by thirst, which is triggered by nerve activity in the hypothalamus of the brain, and by antidiuretic hormone (ADH) and aldosterone. The kidneys also help regulate normal blood pressure and volume.

An animal's excretory system is adapted to its environment: Animals inhabiting dry deserts, lush pastures, freshwater lakes or streams, or salty oceans each have adaptations appropriate to their surroundings that maintain the constancy of their internal fluids via osmoregulation. Land animals are in constant danger of dehydration. Body coverings help conserve moisture, and so do the kidneys by forming concentrated urine. Other adaptations can be behavioral or physiological. Aquatic invertebrates can have osmotic levels in which the contents of their body fluids follow that of the external environment, or they can have a more constant internal environment, maintained despite changes in the external surroundings.

uric acid
a water-insoluble nitrogenous waste product excreted by birds, land reptiles, and insects

urea
a water-soluble nitrogenous waste product formed during the breakdown of proteins, nucleic acids, and other substances, excreted by mammals and some fishes

kidney
the main excretory organ of the vertebrate body; filters nitrogenous wastes from blood and regulates the balance of water and solutes in blood plasma

ureter
the tube that carries urine from the kidney to the urinary bladder

kidney stones
crystals usually formed of calcium and organic compounds that painfully block the ureter

urinary bladder
a single storage sac into which the two ureters dump fluids for excretion; when full, it stretches local nerves, causing a feeling of urgency

renal cortex
one of the kidney's three distinct visible zones, where initial blood filtering takes place

renal medulla
the kidney's central zone, divided into a number of pyramid-shaped regions; helps conserve water and valuable dissolved materials (solutes)

nephron
the functional unit of the vertebrate kidney; each of the million nephrons in a kidney consists of a glomerulus enclosed by a Bowman's capsule and a long attached tubule; the nephron removes waste from the blood

filtration
the process in the vertebrate kidney in which blood fluid and small dissolved substances pass into the kidney tubule, but large proteins and blood cells are filtered out and remain in the blood

tubular reabsorption
in the vertebrate kidney, the process whereby nutrients are returned from the kidney tubule to the blood

tubular secretion
in the vertebrate kidney, the process whereby ions and drugs are secreted from the blood into the kidney tubule

Bowman's capsule
in the vertebrate kidney, the bulbous unit of the nephron that surrounds the blood capillaries of the glomerulus; the region that filters water and solutes from the blood

proximal tubule
in the vertebrate kidney, the convoluted tube between the Bowman's capsule and the loop of Henle

loop of Henle
U-shaped region of vertebrate kidney tubule chiefly responsible for reabsorption of water and salts from the filtrate by diffusion

distal tubule
the convoluted tubule in the vertebrate kidney that receives the forming urine after it has passed through the loop of Henle

glomerulus
(L., a little hall) in the vertebrate kidney, a collection of tightly coiled capillaries enclosed by the Bowman's capsule

podocytes
the epithelial cells of each Bowman's capsule (literally, "foot cells")

filtrate
in the vertebrate kidney, the fluid in the kidney tubule (nephron) that has been filtered through the Bowman's capsule

antidiuretic hormone (ADH)
a posterior pituitary gland hormone that regulates the amount of water passing from the kidney as urine

diuresis
abundant urine production

aldosterone
a steroid hormone released by the cortex of the adrenal gland that regulates salt reabsorption in the kidney

renin
an enzyme released by the kidney that converts a blood protein into the hormone angiotensin II

angiotensin II
a hormone that causes blood vessels to constrict, counteracting falling blood pressure; it can also trigger the adrenal glands to secrete aldosterone, which results in sodium and water reabsorption and thus even higher blood volume and pressure

osmoregulation
maintenance of a constant internal salt and water concentration in an organism

Chapter in Review

17

circulation
the path of blood or a blood equivalent such as hemo-lymph as it moves through an animal's body, carrying oxygen and nutrients to tissue cells and carrying wastes away

respiration
the process by which oxygen is drawn into the body and transferred to blood, and carbon dioxide is expelled

erythrocyte
a red blood cell; its main function is transport-ing oxygen to the tissues

leukocyte
a white blood cell; functions in the body's defense against invading microorganisms or other foreign matters

platelet
a disk-shaped cell fragment in the blood impor-tant in blood clotting; also called a *thrombocyte*

plasma
the liquid portion of blood

antibody
a protein produced by the immune system in response to the entry of specific antigens (foreign substances) into the body

albumin
a group of large blood proteins that helps maintain osmotic pressure and binds to toxic substances in the blood

fibrinogen
a protein in blood plasma that is converted to fibrin during clotting

carbonic anhydrase
an enzyme contained by red blood cells that speeds the conversion of carbon dioxide (CO_2) and water (H_2O) to bicarbonate (HCO_3^-) and hydrogen ion (H^+)

hemoglobin
a blood protein with iron-containing heme groups that bind and transport oxygen

erythropoietin
a hormone that stimulates the production of new red blood cells

open circulatory system
a system of fluid transport in spiders, insects, and many other invertebrates in which a clear blood equivalent called hemolymph circulates partially in vessels and partially unconfined by tubes or vessels

closed circulatory system
a fluid transport system in segmented worms and vertebrates in which blood is completely contained inside vessels

pulmonary circulation
the blood vessel system that carries oxygen-poor blood from the heart to the lungs, where gas exchange occurs, and carries oxygen-rich blood back to the heart

systemic circulation
the blood vessel system that carries oxygen-rich blood from the heart to the body and returns oxygen-poor blood to the heart

artery
a large blood vessel with thick, multilayered muscular walls, which carries blood from the heart to the body

Introduction Extra supplies of blood are short; artificial blood is a major research goal—and a difficult one. To understand why takes a knowledge of blood as a tissue, of how blood moves through the body delivering oxygen and removing wastes via the circulatory system, and how air is drawn into the body as an oxygen source and how carbon dioxide wastes are exhaled via the respiratory system.

LO¹ Blood: A Liquid Tissue for Transport Blood is made up of erythrocytes or red blood cells, leukocytes or white blood cells, small globular platelets, and the pale yellow fluid plasma surrounding the blood cells and platelets. Plasma contains antibodies, albumin, fibrino-gen, and other important dissolved proteins. One third of all your cells—25 trillion out of 75 trillion—are red blood cells. For every 500 red blood cells there is just one white blood cell or leukocyte.

LO² Circulatory Systems Tarantulas are typical of most invertebrates in that they have a clear blood equivalent called hemolymph that moves through an open circulatory system. A heart tube pumps hemolymph toward the brain, then the fluid percolates through the body cavity outside of tubes, bathing the internal tissues. Some invertebrates (such as earthworms) and all vertebrates have closed circulatory systems in which blood is completely contained inside vessels. These can efficiently shunt blood to needed areas and are pressurized.

LO³ The Human Circulatory System The right side of the heart pumps blood directly to the lungs and back to the left side of the heart. This "lung loop" is the pulmonary circulation. The left side of the heart pumps blood to all organs except the lungs and the blood returns to the right side of the heart; this "body loop" is the systemic circulation. These two loops prevent oxygen-rich blood from mixing with oxygen-poor blood.

There are several types of blood vessels. Arteries are large vessels with muscular walls that help keep up the blood pressure. Arteries branch into smaller arterioles, which branch into dense web-like networks of capillaries. The venous capillaries merge into venules, which merge into veins. Valves keep venous blood moving toward the heart, even though veins don't have muscu-lar, pulsating walls and the blood pressure in them is lower.

LO⁴ The Respiratory System The respiratory system is a set of tubes and organs that facilitate the exchange of oxygen and carbon dioxide at the level of the whole organ-ism. Humans have an in-and-out air flow or tidal ventilation, meaning that some stale air remains in the lungs. Lung ventilation is possible because the diaphragm pulls down during inhalation and relaxes during exhalation. A region of the brain stem sends nerve impulses to the diaphragm and rib muscles to contract, leading to inhalation. Levels of carbon dioxide inform this brain center, and it increases or decreases inhalation rates accordingly.

blood pressure
a force of liquid blood within the circula-tory system; created by blood moving within a closed system and propelled by contractions of the heart and muscular artery walls

arteriole
a thinner-walled, smaller branch of an artery, which carries blood from arteries to the capillaries in the tissues

capillary
tiny blood vessels with walls one cell thick that permeate the tissues and organs of the body

capillary bed
a network of capillaries that links arterial and venous blood vessels

venule
a small thin-walled blood vessel that arises from capillaries and carries blood from the tissues to the veins

vein
a large thin-walled blood vessel that brings blood from the body to the heart

valve
a tonguelike flap extending into the inter-nal space of a vein that helps regulate the flow of blood

heart
a muscular organ that pumps blood through vessels

atrium (pl., atria)
(L., hallway) a chamber of the heart that receives blood from the veins

ventricle
a muscular chamber of the heart that pumps blood to the lungs or to the rest of the body

pulmonary semilunar valve
one-way valve with three half-moon-shaped flaps through which the right ventricle of the heart pumps oxygen-poor blood toward the lungs

pulmonary artery
the artery that carries blood from the heart's right ventricle to the lungs

pulmonary veins
vessels that carry oxygenated blood from the lungs to the heart's left atrium

aorta
in a vertebrate animal, the main artery leading directly from the left ventricle of the heart; supplies blood to most of the animal's body

superior vena cava
one of the two largest veins in the human body; carries blood from the head, neck, and arms to the right atrium of the heart

inferior vena cava
one of the two largest veins in the human body; carries blood from the legs and most of the lower body to the right atrium of the heart

cardiac muscle
the specialized muscle tissue of the heart

intercalated disks
an intercellular connection that links heart muscle cells electrically

pacemaker cells
cells that set the rate of the heartbeat

sinoatrial (SA) node
a lump of modified heart muscle cells near the upper right atrium that is spontaneously electrically excitable; the pacemaker that governs the basic rate of heart contractions in vertebrates

atrioventricular (AV) node
a bundle of modified cardiac muscle cells between the heart's atria and ventricles that relays electrical activity to the ventricles

systole
the contraction phase of the heart muscle

diastole
the relaxation phase of the heart muscle

cardiac cycle
the contraction/relaxation (systolic/diastolic) sequence of atria and ventricles that makes up a single heartbeat

atherosclerosis
the formal name for cardiovascular disease, a condition in which waxy deposits or plaques build up inside the arteries and gradually obstruct blood flow

coronary arteries
the arteries of the heart

myocardial infarction (heart attack)
medical condition resulting from the blockage (from a blood clot) of the heart's arteries, causing complete cutoff of blood flow to a section of the heart muscle and subsequent damage or destruction of that muscle tissue

stroke
paralysis or numbness caused by destruction of brain tissue due to a blood clot or blood vessel break

precapillary sphincters
rings of smooth muscle around a capillary on the arterial (as opposed to venous) side of a capillary bed

nitric oxide
the simple chemical compound NO; it occurs as a gas under normal atmospheric conditions and has been found to act as a neurotransmitter during penile erection and certain other physiological processes

blood-clotting cascade
a series of actions involved in blood coagulation that converts fibrinogen to fibrin, and leads to a blood clot

coagulation
the formation of a blood clot

prothrombin
the inactive precursor of the enzyme thrombin, which produces fibrin, during the process of blood clotting

thrombin
a type of enzyme created from the inactive protein prothrombin during the process of blood clotting

fibrin
the activated form of the blood-clotting protein fibrinogen that combines into threads when forming a clot

hemophilia
genetic condition in which sufferers lack a functional copy of a gene encoding a protein in the clotting cascade; as a result, they do not form normal blood clots

lymphatic system
in vertebrates, a collective term for a system of vessels carrying lymph (fluid that has been forced out of the capillaries) back to the bloodstream

lymph
fluid forced out of capillaries, occupying spaces between cells, and draining into the lymphatic system

lymph node
a bean-shaped filtering organ and part of the immune system that stores lymphocytes and prevents debris in the lymph from mixing into the blood

lymphocyte
a white blood cell formed in lymph tissue; active in the immune responses that protect the body against infectious diseases

thymus
a gland in the neck or thorax of many vertebrates; makes and stores lymphocytes in addition to secreting hormones

spleen
organ about the size and shape of a banana in an adult person that lies just behind the stomach; the spleen filters blood, produces phagocytic (debris-gobbling) white blood cells, and stores platelets and some blood cells

organismal respiration
the manner in which a whole animal exchanges carbon dioxide and oxygen with the atmosphere

spiracle
a hole in the body wall of insects that forms the opening of the air tubes (tracheae)

tracheae
branching networks of hollow air passages used for gas exchange in insects

gill
a specialized structure that exchanges gases in water-living animals

gill filaments
tiny subdivisions of the gill bar that support many thin, platelike structures, which help extract dissolved oxygen from water

lamellae
tiny platelike structures supported by gill filaments; help aquatic animals respire efficiently in water

swim bladder
a bag of gas that can be inflated or deflated slightly and helps a fish maintain its depth in the water without sinking or floating

tidal ventilation
the in-and-out flow of air that characterizes mammalian respiration

pharynx
[1] in vertebrates, a tube leading from the nose and mouth to the larynx and esophagus; conducts air during breathing and food during swallowing; the *throat;* [2] in flatworms, a short tube connecting the mouth and intestine

esophagus
the muscular tube leading from the pharynx to the stomach

trachea
the "windpipe," the major airway leading into the lungs of vertebrates

larynx
a cartilaginous structure containing the vocal cords; it is also known as the voice box

epiglottis
a flap of tissue just above the larynx that closes during swallowing and prevents food from entering the lungs

bronchi (sing., bronchus)
two hollow passageways that branch off the trachea and enter the lungs

bronchiole
one of the thousands of small branches from the bronchi that lead to the alveoli in the lungs

alveoli (sing., alveolus)
in the lungs, tiny bubble-shaped sacs where gas exchange takes place

pleural sac
one of two fluid-filled sacs that enclose the lungs

thoracic cavity
the region within the rib cage directly over the heart, in which the lungs and heart are suspended

diaphragm
the muscle sheet that separates the thoracic cavity from the abdominal cavity and helps draw air into the lungs during breathing

ventilation
the process of inhalation and exhalation of the lungs of many vertebrates

inhalation
the drawing in of fresh air

exhalation
the passive release of air from the lungs

intercostal muscles
the muscles between ribs

medulla oblongata
the lowest region of the brainstem, the most posterior part of the brain; involved in keeping body conditions constant

hyperventilation
very rapid, deep breathing

Chapter in Review

18

immune system
the network of cells, tissues, and organs that defends the body against invaders

pathogen
a disease-causing agent

nonspecific resistance
cellular functions that fight disease in the same way regardless of the invader's characteristics

specific resistance
the body's ability to combat particular species or strains of pathogens and other invaders; works more slowly than nonspecific resistance

immunity
specific resistance, or immunity, is a slow series of reactions based on lymphocytes and antibodies (in vertebrates) that is more targeted to particular invaders or damaged cells within the organism than are nonspecific responses

interferons
a class of antimicrobial proteins that are released by certain virus-infected cells that diffuse to other cells and, in turn, cause them to produce proteins that inhibit viral replication

complement system
a group of about 20 plasma proteins (a type of antimicrobial protein) that attack and destroy microbes and stimulate inflammation

natural killer cell
a type of white blood cell that can kill many kinds of infectious microbes and some types of tumor cells; part of the nonspecific defense of the body

inflammatory response
the body's response to intruders, composed of a series of nonspecific internal resistance reactions including redness, pain, heat, and swelling

inflammation mediators
chemical signals released by damaged tissues that provoke inflammation reactions

prostaglandins
a fatty acid–derived hormone secreted by many tissues; for example, prostaglandin from the uterus produces strong contractions in the uterine muscle, causing menstrual cramps or inducing labor

cytokine
a short protein that acts as an inflammation mediator

mast cell
a round cell that occupies connective tissue in the skin and mucous membranes, contains little packets of chemicals, and releases histamine and heparin when triggered by certain antigens

histamine
a chemical released by mast cells that causes capillaries to dilate; part of the inflammatory response

heparin
a chemical released by mast cells that binds to clot-inhibiting proteins; part of the inflammatory response

Introduction Researchers are probing the secrets of the common cold and how our immune systems both contribute to the misery but also eventually end it. Resistance to disease involves a network of organs, cells, and molecules that defend the body from invaders of all kinds, including rhinoviruses (cold viruses). The most familiar part of this network is the immune system and the specifically targeted proteins or antibodies it produces.

LO¹ Disease Defense and Nonspecific Resistance Nonspecific resistance involves physical barriers such as skin, a first line of defense against intruders such as pathogens. Nonspecific responses also include the inflammatory response, with its generation of inflammation. The second line of defense includes nonspecific substances and cell activities. The molecules include interferons and proteins of the complement system. Inflammation mediators include prostaglandins and cytokines. Natural killer cells can kill many types of microbes by using perforins. The nonspecific molecules also (1) cause mast cells to release histamine and heparin, which cause tissue fluid leaking; (2) stimulate more mucus formation to float away virus and debris; (3) cause a hacking cough (prostaglandins) and/or a sore throat (cytokinins).

LO² Specific Resistance to Disease Specific resistance or immunity is a slower series of reactions than the nonspecific responses, but is more targeted to particular invaders or damaged cells within the organism. Any substance that can stimulate an immune response is an antigen, including viral and bacterial surface proteins. The antibody-mediated immune response responds to some invaders by producing protective proteins called antibodies. It has the remarkable feature of immunologic memory.

Several types of white blood cells, or lymphocytes, are part of the cell-mediated immune response. B cells or B lymphocytes arc formed in bone marrow and secrete antibody proteins and mark invaders for destruction. T cells or T lymphocytes come from the bone marrow but mature in the thymus and kill virus-infected or cancerous cells. Macrophages consume debris from intruders and present antigen to B and T cells.

Antibodies are able to mark and eliminate intruders because they are immunoglobulins. A person can make more than 100 million distinct types of antibody molecules, each with a unique binding site.

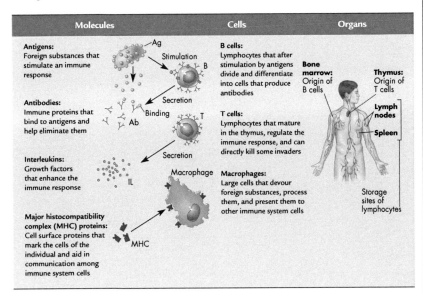

immunologic memory
the capability of memory B cells in vertebrates to produce a more rapid and vigorous immune response based on former encounters with antigens

antigen
(Gr. *anti* = against + *genos* = origin) any substance, including toxins, foreign proteins, and bacteria, that when introduced into a vertebrate animal causes antibodies to form

interleukin
a protein that speeds or slows the dividing and maturing of other immune cells

B cell or B lymphocyte
a type of white blood cell that makes and secretes antibodies in response to foreign substances (antigens)

T cell or T lymphocyte
a type of white blood cell that kills foreign cells directly and also regulates the activities of other lymphocytes

macrophage
an animal cell that ingests other organisms and substances; in the immune system, a cell that engulfs invaders and consumes debris

antibody-mediated immune response
a type of immunity in which antibody proteins circulate freely in the body, bind to invaders, and help eliminate them

plasma cell
a type of B cell clone that generates antibodies

immunoglobulin
globular proteins of the immune system that comprise antibodies; classes of immunoglobulins include IgG, IgA, IgM, and IgE

heavy chains
the two longest of the four polypeptides, or chains of amino acids, which compose an immunoglobulin molecule

light chains
the two shortest of the four polypeptides, or chains of amino acids, which compose an immunoglobulin molecule

gamma globulin
a blood protein fraction that is rich in the class of antibody (IgG) effective at eliminating viruses and bacteria

allergy
an extreme reaction to foreign substances or allergens that mimics a body's nonspecific resistance reaction

anaphylaxis
a life-threatening drop in blood pressure brought on by an extreme allergic reaction

cell proliferation
the body's process of duplicating B cells for the purpose of fighting off invaders such as the rhinoviruses that cause the common cold

clonal selection mechanism
the combined process of the binding of a B cell to an antigen and proliferation into a clone of B cells

memory cell
a type of B cell clone that can proliferate when stimulated by the type of antigen that triggered the original B cell, forming its own clone of both plasma and memory cells; also called *memory B cell*; responsible for the secondary immune response

primary response
the initial immune response to an invader

LO³ Regulating the Immune System B and T cells don't attack our own tissues because of self-tolerance, which develops when we are fetuses or newborns. If this tolerance goes awry, an autoimmune disease, such as multiple sclerosis or rheumatoid arthritis, can result. During pregnancy, a woman's immune system leaves the fetus—which is one-half foreign—undisturbed. An exception is Rh incompatibility.

LO⁴ Immunization Doctors can confer fast-acting immunity of short duration or slow-acting but longer-term immunity. Examples of passive immunization include an antivenin against snakebite or gamma globulin for a traveler. Active immunity involves vaccinations that safely stimulate the immune system to create antibodies against virus (such as smallpox) or bacteria to protect against potential future exposure. Researchers would like to create vaccines against the common cold but it is proving difficult because there are so many strains of rhinovirus and other cold viruses.

secondary response
a stronger, swifter reaction to an invader or other antigen when encountered a subsequent time

cell-mediated immune response
a type of immunity in which T cells directly attack invaders

cytotoxic T cell
a type of T cell that destroys foreign cells, including cells transplanted to a person from another individual or body cells transformed by virus infection or cancer

helper T cell
a type of T cell that communicates via chemical signals with B cells and the other types of T cells to trigger or to augment an immune response

suppressor T cell
a type of T cell that can stop or slow ongoing immune responses

T cell receptor
the receptor protein of a T cell

coreceptor
in a T cell, a molecule associated with the T cell receptor that enhances the T cell's ability to bind specific antigens

major histocompatibility (MHC) proteins
(Gr. *histos*, web of a loom, or tissue) cell surface proteins that mark an individual's cells for self-recognition and aid in communication among immune system cells

self-tolerance
the lack of an immune system response to components of one's own body

autoimmune disease
a disease in which a person's immune system attacks the body's own cells or tissues

rheumatoid arthritis
an autoimmune disease in which joints swell painfully; in hands affected by this condition, the fingers can become gnarled and twisted, and everyday movements such as buttoning a shirt can be painful or even impossible

multiple sclerosis (MS)
an autoimmune disease in which a person's immune system reacts to and damages or destroys the myelin sheaths that surround and protect nerve cells

Rh incompatibility
a situation in which a pregnant woman is Rh-negative but her fetus is Rh-positive, leading the mother's immune system to attack the fetus's red blood cells

passive immunization
the injection of antibodies generated in one individual into another individual

antivenin
an antibody that counteracts snake venom; antivenins are prepared by technicians who inject horses or rabbits with inactivated venom and then collect the antibodies produced by the mammal to fight the antigen

active immunity
the production of antibodies or antigen-specific T cells by an individual's own immune system

vaccination
a form of long-term protection produced by stimulating active immunity aimed at one microbe or toxin

booster shot
a second dose of a vaccine; can induce memory cells to differentiate and form still more antibody-producing and memory cells

Chapter in Review

19

nutrition
the science concerned with the amounts and kinds of nutrients needed by the body

dietary fiber
cellulose plant fibers and cell walls that cannot be digested; fiber is important for helping to propel wastes through the digestive system; also called *roughage*

essential fatty acid
an unsaturated fatty acid that cannot be manu-factured by the body and that therefore must be obtained from food; in humans, linoleic acid is an essential fatty acid

essential amino acid
any one of the eight amino acids that the human body cannot manufacture and that must be obtained from food

vitamin
(L. *vita* = life + *amine* = of chemical origin) an organic compound needed in small amounts for growth and metabolism and must be obtained in food

mineral
an inorganic element such as sodium or potassium that is essential for survival and is obtained in food

overweight
having body weight that is more than 10 per-cent above ideal

obese
having body weight that is more than 20 per-cent above ideal

basal metabolic rate
the rate at which the body uses energy while resting

anorexia nervosa
an eating disorder in which a person restricts food intake severely, becomes cadaverously thin, and yet still sees himself or herself as overweight

bulimia
an eating disorder in which a person secretly binges on high-calorie foods, then purges with self-induced vomiting, laxatives, diuretics, fast-ing, or vigorous exercise

intracellular digestion
the enzymatic breakdown of nutrient mol-ecules that occurs within cells

extracellular digestion
the enzymatic breakdown of nutrient mol-ecules that occurs outside of cells

gastrovascular cavity
the digestive cavity in cnidarians

mouth
the body opening where food enters the diges-tive tract

gut (gastrointestinal tract)
the food processing or alimentary canal made up of the mouth, esophagus, stomach, small intestine, and large intestine

anus
the end of the digestive tract where waste products exit the body

Introduction Koalas have a diet limited to tough, bitter eucalyptus leaves. The koala's anatomy and physiology, however, allow the animal to absorb all the water, nutrients, vitamins, and miner-als it needs from this single source. That makes the koala an interesting case history for studying nutrition and digestion.

LO¹ **Nutrients: Sources of Energy and Elements** The basic biological molecules we encountered in Chapter 2 are part of the nutrition story. Carbohydrates, including sugars, starches, and cellulose, are made up of glucose subunits and form the main source of energy and carbon atoms for most animal species.

LO² **How Animals Digest Food** The simplest animals, including the sponges, use intracellular digestion, taking particles into cells and breaking them down enzymati-cally. Most animals use extracellular digestion, the breakdown of larger pieces of food in a special body cavity or organ.

LO³ **The Digestive Tract** The five regions of the vertebrate diges-tive tract—the mouth, esopha-gus, stomach, small intestine, and large intestine—make up the alimentary canal or gastrointes-tinal tract (also called the gut). Accessory organs aid digestion, helping in the step-by-step conversion of foods into nutrients circulating in the bloodstream.

LO⁴ **The Human Digestive System** Your mouth and teeth are well suited to chewing food. Saliva moistens the food and contains a starch-breaking enzyme, amylase. The bolus then moves down the esophagus, passes through the cardiac sphincter, and en-ters the stomach, then passes through the pyloric sphincter to the small intestine. The small intestine is the main site of carbohydrate and fat digestion, and completes protein digestion.

Accessory Organs
Salivary glands
Epiglottis
Liver
Gall bladder
Pancreas
Jejunum

Alimentary Canal
Mouth
Tongue
Esophagus
Stomach
Duodenum
Small intestine
Large intestine (colon)
Ileum
Appendix
Rectum
Anus

① INGESTION AND MASTICATION Food ingested and broken down into small pieces

② DIGESTION Large molecules (macromolecules) split into subunits (monomers)

③ ABSORPTION Nutrients and water absorbed into blood or lymph

④ ELIMINATION Wastes eliminated

LO⁵ **Healthy Diets and Proper Nutrition** If you want to lose weight, eat foods with enough nutrients but with lower energy content and higher roughage content, then increase exercise to step up basal metabolic rate. New research on the action of the hormones leptin and insulin helps explain normal fat storage and obesity. Cutting fats and sugars helps, but exercising is the key to burning fat and turning up the metabolic level.

alimentary canal
the gastrointestinal tract; includes the mouth, esophagus, stomach, and small and large intestines

accessory organ
one of several organs that aid digestion, including the salivary glands, liver, gall-bladder, and pancreas

cecum
a feature of the large intestine; a dead-end sac that is vestigial in the human but can be large in other animals, including the koala

ingestion
the taking of food into the mouth; the first step of the digestive process

mastication
the physical breakdown of food into small pieces in the mouth

gizzard
a specialized muscular sac that grinds food in the digestive tracts of earthworms, chickens, and other animals

digestion
the mechanical and chemical breakdown of food into small molecules that an organism can absorb and use; the second step of the digestive process

absorption
in this, the third step of the digestive process, small molecules pass across the gut wall into the animal's lymphatic system or bloodstream, which transports the small molecules to each cell in the body

elimination
in this last step of the digestive process, most of the water in intestinal wastes is absorbed and undigested residues are eventually eliminated

mucosa
the innermost layer of the lining of many vertebrate canals and organs, such as the uterus, reproductive tracts, and alimentary canal; often consists of mucus-secreting cells; in the alimentary canal, the mucosa contains enzyme-secreting cells

mucus
a slimy coating secreted by mucosa cells that lubricates food passing through the gastrointestinal tract and that coats the respiratory and reproductive tract linings

submucosa
a connective tissue outside the mucosa of the digestive tract that is richly supplied with blood and lymph vessels and nerves

muscularis
a double layer outside the submucosa of the digestive tract that is made of muscle fibers, in longitudinal, circular, and oblique orientations

peristalsis
(Gr. *peristaltikos*, compressing around) in animals, successive waves of contraction and relaxation of muscles along the length of a tube, such as those in the digestive tract that help move food

serosa
the outermost layer of the alimentary canal

mesentery
the sheet of tissue that is joined to the serosa and attaches the gastrointestinal tract to the inner wall of the body cavity

lumen
the central cavity; in a blood vessel, the central space where the blood flows

enamel
the substance covering teeth that is composed of calcium salts and protein; the hardest substance in the body

tongue
a muscular organ on the floor of the mouth of most higher vertebrates that carries taste buds and manipulates food

bolus
a soft, round mass of chewed food, shaped by the tongue and suitable for swallowing

salivary gland
a gland that secretes saliva

saliva
a watery liquid secreted by the salivary glands that moistens food particles for swallowing; contains the starch-digesting enzyme amylase

amylase
a digestive enzyme that begins the breakdown of carbohydrates

hard palate
the part of the oral cavity that forms the floor of the nasal cavity and most of the roof of the mouth

soft palate
the posterior part of the roof of the mouth

epiglottis
a flap of tissue just above the larynx that closes during swallowing and prevents food from entering the lungs

glottis
the opening to the trachea, which is also known as the windpipe

pharynx
in vertebrates, a tube leading from the nose and mouth to the larynx and esophagus; conducts air during breathing and food during swallowing; the *throat*

esophagus
the muscular tube leading from the pharynx to the stomach

cardiac sphincter
a ring of muscle located at the junction of the stomach and esophagus

stomach
an expandable, elastic-walled sac of the gut that receives food from the esophagus

pepsinogen
a precursor to the protein-digesting enzyme pepsin

pepsin
an enzyme secreted by the stomach that digests proteins

chyme
the semifluid contents of the stomach consisting of partially digested food and gastric secretions

pyloric sphincter
a muscular ring located at the junction of the stomach and small intestine where chyme passes from the stomach to the small intestine

pancreas
a gland located behind the stomach that secretes digestive enzymes into the small intestine and secretes the hormones insulin and glucagon into the blood

protease
a pancreatic enzyme that breaks down proteins

lipase
a pancreatic enzyme that digests fats

insulin
a hormone made in the pancreas that causes cells to remove the sugar glucose from the blood

glucagon
a hormone made in the pancreas that causes glucose levels in the blood to rise, thus opposing the effect of insulin

liver
a large, lobed gland that destroys blood cells, stores glycogen, disperses glucose to the bloodstream, and produces bile

bile salts
molecules of modified cholesterol that break up fats in the small intestine

bile
a bitter, alkaline, yellow fluid produced by the liver that is stored in the gallbladder and released into the small intestine that aids in the digestion and absorption of fats

gallbladder
the sac beneath the right lobe of the liver that stores bile

small intestine
a coiled tube, about 6 meters (20 feet) long, that is the main site of carbohydrate and fat digestion and is also where protein digestion is completed, allowing nutrients to be absorbed into the blood

duodenum
the upper section of the small intestine

jejunum
the central section of the small intestine

ileum
the lower section of the small intestine

villus (pl., villi)
(L., a tuft of hair) a fingerlike projection of the intestinal wall that increases the surface area for absorption of nutrients

microvillus (pl., microvilli)
one of hundreds of tiny fingerlike projections extending from the surface of cells lining the walls of the intestine that increases the surface area available for absorption

colon (large intestine)
the last 1.2 meters (4 feet) of the human alimentary canal, which leads to the rectum

rectum
the terminal portion of the colon that stores and helps remove solid waste by defecation

appendix
finger-shaped vestigial organ that plays no known role in digestion, but may help fight infections in the gut

feces
semisolid undigested waste products that are stored in the rectum until excreted

gastrin
a digestive hormone secreted in the stomach that causes the secretion of other digestive juices

ulcers
craterlike sores in the mucosa of the stomach or small intestine

secretin
a digestive hormone secreted by the small intestine that causes the pancreas to secrete bicarbonate, which neutralizes stomach acid

cholecystokinin
a digestive hormone secreted by the small intestine that triggers the pancreas to release protein-digesting enzymes

leptin
a weight-regulating hormone produced by fat cells

Chapter in Review

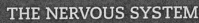

neuroscience
the study of the brain and nervous system

nervous system
an animal's network of nerves; includes the brain and spinal cord as well as the peripheral nerves; integrates and coordinates the activities of all the body systems

neuron
a nerve cell that transmits messages throughout the body; made up of dendrites, cell body, and axon

glial cell
a non-neural cell of the nervous system that surrounds the neurons and provides them with protection and nutrients

dendrite
(Gr., *dendron* = little tree) the branching projections of a neuron or nerve cell that transmit nerve impulses to the cell body

cell body
the major portion of the neuron; houses the nucleus and other organelles

axon
the portion of a nerve cell that carries the impulse away from the cell body

nerve
a group of axons and/or dendrites from many different neurons operating together in a bundle and held together by connective tissue

synapse
the region of communication between two neurons or between a neuron and a muscle cell

presynaptic cell
the neuron that sends a message down its axon and across a synapse to another cell, the postsynaptic cell

postsynaptic cell
the nerve cell that receives the message that has crossed a synapse from a presynaptic cell

nerve impulse
a change in ion permeabilities in a neuron's membrane that sweeps down the cell's axon to its terminal, where it can excite other cells

resting potential
potential energy that is the difference in electric charge between the cell's exterior and interior; measured in volts like a battery

potassium channel
a protein-lined pore in a cell's plasma membrane that permits potassium ions to flow in and out of the cell

sodium channel
a protein-lined pore in the plasma membrane through which sodium ions can pass

sodium-potassium pump
a protein that maintains the cell's osmotic balance by using ATP energy to transport sodium ions out of the cell and potassium ions into the cell

action potential
a temporary all-or-nothing reversal of the electrical charge across a cell membrane; occurs when a stimulus of sufficient intensity strikes a neuron

Introduction Sherry Greer was born deaf and her brain never received aural information during a critical early imprinting period. Sherry did learn languages (ASL from infancy and English in childhood) and went on to have a successful academic and business career. Dr. Helen Neville studies the effect of sensory input and deprivation on brain development. Her studies are part of the investigation of nervous system functioning, of brain plasticity, and of our species's unique ability to use language.

LO¹ The Structure and Function of Nerve Cells Most animals have a nervous system, a network of specialized cells that receives information, integrates it, and allows an effect—a change—to take place in the way the body functions. There can be over 1,000 types of nervous system cells, but each is either a neuron that participates in cell-to-cell communication or a glial cell that supports, surrounds, protects, and/or provides nutrients to neurons. A neuron has signal-receiving branches called dendrites, a cell body enclosing the nucleus, and a long, thin axon that transmits an impulse. A nerve is a group of axons from many different neurons bundled together. A synapse is a junction between neurons, including the synaptic cleft, a minute gap where a neural impulse crosses between two adjacent neurons. The nerve impulse is an electrochemical reaction that allows specific electrically charged atoms to rush into and out of the nerve cell. The difference in electric charge (based on charged sodium, potassium, and chloride ions) between the inside and outside of a neuron generates potential energy called the resting potential.

LO² Communication Between Nerve Cells When a nerve impulse reaches the terminal end of an axon, it triggers the release of a chemical signal or neurotransmitter. These molecules move into the narrow space separating sending and receiving cells, the neurotransmitter molecules diffuse across the cleft, and they bind to receptors in the receiving cell's plasma membrane. This can cause an action potential in the receiving cell. Enzymes clean up the neurotransmitter so a new round of reception and stimulation can occur. Cocaine blocks the cleanup of dopamine and can lead to addiction. Other neurotransmitters include acetylcholine and norepinephrine. Some neurons transmit signals directly through specialized gap junctions in electrical synapses.

LO³ Animal Nervous Systems Vertebrates such as ourselves have a central nervous system (CNS) or information processor that includes the brain and spinal cord. We also have a peripheral nervous system (PNS) or "middleman" that includes sensory neurons that sense the environment and motor neurons that control muscle contraction.

Major Regions of the Brain

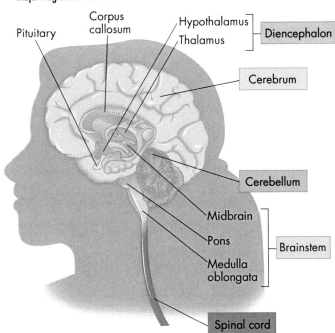

all-or-none response
a property of action potentials; they either don't occur at all, or they do occur and are always the same strength for a given neuron regardless of how powerful the stimulus may be

myelin sheath
a lipid membrane made up of Schwann cells that forms an insulating layer around neurons and speeds impulse travel

neurotransmitter
a chemical that transmits a nerve impulse across a synapse

central nervous system (CNS)
the part of the nervous system consisting of the brain and spinal cord that performs the most complex nervous system functions

brain
the body organ that performs complex neural integration and, along with the spinal cord, forms the central nervous system

spinal cord
a tube of nerve tissue that runs the full length of a vertebrate's spine

reflex
involuntary but predictable responses to stimuli

peripheral nervous system (PNS)
the part of the nervous system that consists of the sensory and motor neurons and connects the central nervous system with the sense organs, muscles, and glands of the body

sensory neuron
a nerve cell that receives information from the external or internal environment and transmits this information to the brain or spinal cord

motor neuron
a neuron that sends messages from the brain or spinal cord to muscles or secretory glands

reflex arc
an automatic reaction, involving only a few neurons and requiring no input from the brain, in which a motor response quickly follows a sensory stimulus

spinal nerves
pairs of nerves in which the sensory and motor neurons enter or leave the spinal cord

somatic nervous system
motor neurons of the nervous system that are under voluntary control

autonomic nervous system
motor neurons of the nervous system that regulate the heart, glands, and smooth muscles in the digestive and circulatory systems

parasympathetic nerves
neurons of the autonomic nervous system that emanate from the spinal cord and act on the respiratory, circulatory, digestive, and excretory systems as a "housekeeping" system, conserving and restoring body resources

sympathetic nerves
neurons of the autonomic nervous system that emanate from the central spinal cord and act on the respiratory, circulatory, digestive, and excretory systems in response to stress or emergency, preparing for flight or fight

brainstem
the lower portion of the vertebrate brain, relaying messages to and from the spinal cord and consisting of the medulla oblongata, pons, and midbrain

The brain has a brainstem, including the medulla oblongata, pons, and midbrain, which function mainly in homeostasis, control, sensory and motor integration, and arousal. The brain has a diencephalon, which includes the thalamus, hypothalamus, pituitary, and pineal gland. It also has a cerebellum, which monitors body position and times motor commands. And the brain has a cerebrum, a convoluted mass of tissue responsible for all our higher functions, including self-awareness and speech, as well as memory, sensation, and motor output. Various regions of the outer layer or cerebral cortex have specific functions in generating movement (the motor cortex, interpreting sensory input (the sensory cortex), creating language, and so on. The hippocampus is involved in forming both short- and long-term memories. Parts of both the left and right cerebral cortex are involved in language.

LO⁴ How Do Sense Organs Perceive the World? We hear because sound waves vibrate the eardrum, then a chain of tiny bones, then fluid in the coiled cochlea, a highly complex structure with over one million moving parts. The cochlea changes the energy from sound into nerve impulses. Hair cells crowned by stereocilia move in response to sound vibrations and trigger nerve impulses that the brain interprets as high, low, grating, melodious, and so on. The inner ear is also involved in maintaining balance.

We see because light passes through the transparent outer layer, or cornea; penetrates the pupil, or opening in the colored iris; traverses the crystalline lens; and is focused onto the retina. Photoreceptor cells—rods and cones—in the retina detect light and color, respectively, and send information to the brain via the optic nerve.

Taste and smell are our chemical senses because sensory cells in the olfactory epithelium and in the tongue's taste buds receive and detect flavor and odor molecules directly from the environment.

cerebellum
anterior portion of the vertebrate brain lying posterior to the cerebrum; integrates information about body position and motion, coordinates muscular activities, and maintains equilibrium

cerebrum
(L., *brain*) topmost portion of the vertebrate brain; coordinates and processes sensory input and controls motor responses

cerebral cortex
the highly convoluted surface layers of the cerebrum, containing about 90 percent of a human brain's cell bodies; well-developed only in mammals and particularly prominent in humans; the region involved with our conscious sensations and voluntary muscular activity

motor cortex
the part of the cerebral cortex of the brain that controls the movement of the body

sensory cortex
the part of the cerebral cortex of the vertebrate brain that registers and integrates sensations from body parts

hippocampus
a structure within the cerebrum of the brain that plays a crucial role in the formation of long-term memory

cochlea
a spiral tube in the inner ear that contains sensory cells involved in detecting sound and analyzing pitch

hair cell
box-shaped neurons containing cilia and attached to the cochlea; essential for hearing

cornea
the transparent outer portion of the vertebrate eye through which light passes

pupil
the central, shutterlike opening in the iris of the vertebrate eye through which light passes to the lens and the retina

iris
a pigmented ring of tissue in the vertebrate eye that regulates the size of the pupil and therefore controls the amount of light that enters

lens
a circular, crystalline structure in the eye of certain animals that focuses light onto the retina

retina
(L., *a small net*) a multilayered region lining the back of the vertebrate eyeball containing light-sensitive cells

rod
one of the two types of photoreceptor (light-sensitive) cells in the retina of the vertebrate eye; rods are sensitive to low levels of light and to movement but cannot distinguish color (see also *cone*)

cone
one of the two types of photoreceptor (light-sensitive) cells in the retina of the vertebrate eye; cones are sensitive to high levels of light and to color (see also *rod*)

optic nerve
the nerve leading from the eye to the brain

taste buds
sensory organs studding the tongue that consist of pores leading to a nerve cell, which is surrounded by accessory cells arranged in an overlapping pattern that resembles an artichoke or onion bulb

limbic system
a series of small brain structures (including the hippocampus and hypothalamus) largely responsible for generating fear, rage, aggression, and pleasure and for regulating sex drives and reproductive cycles

Chapter in Review

22

skeleton
the rigid body support to which muscles attach and apply force, in vertebrates and invertebrates

hydroskeleton
a volume of fluid trapped within an animal's tissues that is noncompressible and serves as a firm mass against which opposing sets of muscles can act; for example, in earthworm segments

antagonistic muscle pair
two muscles that move the same object, such as a limb, in opposite directions

exoskeleton
the thick cuticle of arthropods, made of chitin

endoskeleton
(Gr., *endos* = within + *skeletos* = hard) an internal supporting structure, such as the bony skeleton of a vertebrate

bone
the main supporting tissue of vertebrates, composed of a matrix of collagen hardened by calcium phosphate

collagen
a fibrous protein found extensively in connective tissue and bone; collagen also occurs in some invertebrates, as in the cuticle of nematode worms

coccyx
in vertebrates, the tailbone

skull
the skeleton of the vertebrate head

cranium
part of the skull that encloses and protects the brain

hyoid
a bone contained within the skull that is the only human bone not jointed with other bones; it is suspended under the back of the mouth by ligaments and muscles

vertebral column
the backbone

vertebra (pl., vertebrae)
one of a series of interlocking bones that makes up the vertebral column, or backbone, of vertebrate animals

process
a projecting part of an organism or organic structure, such as a bone

sternum
the breastbone; in birds, a blade-shaped anchor for the pectoral muscles that enables flight

pectoral (shoulder) girdle
the skeletal support to which front fins or limbs of vertebrates are attached

pelvic (hip) girdle
the skeletal support to which hind fins or limbs of vertebrates are attached

femur
the large bone extending between the hip and knee joints

ligament
a band of connective tissue that links bone to bone

Introduction   Dr. Marjorie Woollacott studies the muscles and bones involved in restoring balance after a slip on an "electric banana peel." Researchers like her help people prevent falls—a leading cause of death in the elderly—and plan for better exercise programs throughout life.

LO¹ The Skeleton: The Body's Framework   The skeleton is a rigid body support to which muscles attach and apply force. Many invertebrates have hydroskeletons with a liquid core wrapped in a muscular sheath. The layers act as antagonistic muscle pairs moving the same object (such as the animal with its enclosed liquid core) in opposite directions.

Arthropods have exoskeletons or stiff external coverings surrounding the body. Vertebrates have endoskeletons or rigid internal rods and plates surrounded by muscles and skin. A mammal's endoskeleton is made of bone, with its meshwork of collagen hardened by calcium and phosphate.

Marrow in the bone's center is the site of blood cell production. Some specialized bone cells secrete proteins and minerals, whereas others reabsorb the minerals for use elsewhere in the body when needed. Bone remodeling goes on continuously. When mineral-reabsorbing cells work faster than mineral-storing cells, bone thinning and weakness, called *osteoporosis*, can occur.

Bone movement requires a joint where adjacent bones nearly touch but are separated by shock-absorbing cartilage pads. Bones pivot at joints because muscles pull on them. Antagonistic pairs of muscle relax and contract to move a body part, as in pointing or flexing the foot.

LO² Muscles: The Body's Movers   Skeletal muscle connects to and moves the skeleton, with an origin on one bone and an insertion on another. Several muscles are needed to maintain and restore balance and to carry out physical activities. Skeletal muscles are made up of muscle fibers, giant cells with many nuclei that extend the length of the muscle. A contractile mechanism within each fiber allows it to shorten. Thin filaments made of the protein actin slide past thicker filaments made of the protein myosin. Skeletal muscle appears striated or striped because of the organization of thick and thin filaments.

Cardiac muscle contains networks of heart muscle cells electrically connected to each other. An impulse to contract propagates through the entire organ because of these connections. Cardiac muscle is also striated. Smooth muscle surrounds hollow organs, such as the intestines or urinary bladder, and lacks striations. The cells communicate with each other electrically, like cardiac muscle cells, and contract rhythmically, pushing food down the digestive tract, for example.

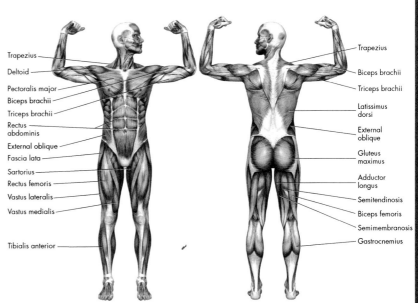

Trapezius
Deltoid
Pectoralis major
Biceps brachii
Triceps brachii
Rectus abdominis
External oblique
Fascia lata
Sartorius
Rectus femoris
Vastus lateralis
Vastus medialis
Tibialis anterior

Trapezius
Biceps brachii
Triceps brachii
Latissimus dorsi
External oblique
Gluteus maximus
Adductor longus
Semitendinosis
Biceps femoris
Semimembranosis
Gastrocnemius

tendon
a band of connective tissue that connects bone to muscle

quadricep
thigh muscle

patella
kneecap

compact bone
bone with regions with few, small spaces

spongy bone
bone with regions with larger, more numerous spaces

marrow
the major site of red blood cell manufacture in adults, found in the spaces of some spongy bone tissue

marrow cavity
the tissue down the center of the shaft in the femur and other bones that is a site of fat storage

osteoporosis
a condition of bone thinning and weakness that occurs because cells specialized to remove stored calcium and phosphate from the existing bone matrix work faster than cells specialized to store the minerals and build bone

joint
the hinge, or point of contact, between two bones

arthritis
an inflammation of joints such as the shoulder, hip, knee, or knuckles of the fingers and toes; can be based on wear-and-tear or on the body's own autoimmune attack

bursa (pl., bursae)
(L., *bursa* = purse) small sac filled with fluid that cushions the movement in places where skin, tendons, muscles, and bone rub against one another

skeletal muscle
muscle consisting of elongated, striated muscle cells; voluntary muscle

origin
the end of a skeletal muscle that generally remains stationary during a contraction, like an anchor

insertion
the end of a skeletal muscle that attaches across a joint to a bone that moves

tibialis
a shin muscle in the front of the lower leg

abdominals
rectus abdominis; muscles of the stomach area

EMG (electromyograph)
a tool used in studying muscle function; records electrical changes in the muscles during stimulation and plots the changes on paper

muscle fiber
a muscle cell; a giant cell with many nuclei and numerous myofibrils, capable of contraction when stimulated

fibril
long bundles found within a muscle cell, composed of sarcomeres

sarcomere
the contractile unit of a skeletal muscle consisting of repeating bands of actin and myosin

LO³ The Physiology of Sport and Exercise The immediate energy system provides power for one brief explosive action based on ATP and creatine phosphate. The glycolytic energy system can power heavy exercise for a few minutes. The oxidative energy system sustains an exerciser for long periods.

Slow-twitch muscle fibers get most of their ATP from the oxidative system. Marathoners have a large proportion of slow-twitch fibers. Fast-twitch muscle fibers provide quick power and get most of their ATP from glycolysis. Fast oxidative-glycolytic muscle fibers have in-between characteristics and are moderately powerful and moderately enduring.

actin
(Gr., *actis*, a ray) a major component of microfilaments in contractile cells such as muscle

myosin
a muscle protein that interacts with actin and causes muscles to contract

sliding filament mechanism
a mechanism of muscle contraction in which contraction is made possible by the unique arrangement and sliding of the thick filaments relative to the thin filaments, shortening the sarcomeres

smooth muscle
muscle consisting of spindle-shaped, unstriated muscle cells; muscle type found in the digestive, reproductive, and circulatory systems

immediate energy system
energy in the body instantly available for a brief explosive action, such as one heave by a shot-putter

creatine phosphate
a high-energy molecule in the immediate energy system that can transfer energy to ATP

glycolytic energy system
energy system based on the splitting of glucose by glycolysis in the muscles; can sustain heavy exercise for a few minutes, as in a 200-m swim

oxidative (aerobic) energy system
the longest-sustaining energy system of the body that relies on the Krebs cycle and electron transport drain in mitochondria and its ability to use fats as fuel

slow-twitch muscle fibers
muscle fibers that obtain most of their ATP from the oxidative system; also called *slow oxidative muscle fibers*; provide power for most endurance sports

myoglobin
red protein that stores oxygen in muscle cells

fast-twitch muscle fibers
muscle fibers that obtain most of their ATP from glycolysis; also called *fast glycolytic muscle fibers;* provide quick power of the type needed for the 50-yard dash

fast oxidative-glycolytic muscle fibers
muscle fibers that have characteristics midway between those of fast-twitch and slow-twitch muscle fibers; these fibers are moderately powerful and moderately resistant to fatigue

endorphins
peptides found in the anterior lobe of the pituitary and in several other regions of the brain and spinal cord that can act as a natural pain killer and are the source of the "runner's high"

Lab Manual

Structure and Function of Living Cells

OBJECTIVES

After completing this exercise, you will be able to

1. define *cell, cell theory, prokaryotic, eukaryotic, nucleus, cytomembrane system, organelle, multinucleate, cytoplasmic streaming, sol, gel, envelope;*

2. list the structural features shared by all cells;

3. describe the similarities and differences between prokaryotic and eukaryotic cells;

4. identify the cell parts described in this exercise;

5. state the function for each cell part;

6. distinguish between plant and animal cells;

7. recognize the structures presented in **boldface** in the procedure sections.

INTRODUCTION

Structurally and functionally, all life has one common feature: All living organisms are composed of **cells.** The development of this concept began with Robert Hooke's seventeenth-century observation that slices of cork were made up of small units. He called these units "cells" because their structure reminded him of the small cubicles that monks lived in. Over the next 100 years, the **cell theory** emerged. This theory has three principles: (1) All organisms are composed of one or more cells; (2) the cell is the basic *living* unit of organization; and (3) all cells arise from preexisting cells.

Although cells vary in organization, size, and function, all share three structural features: (1) All possess a **plasma membrane** defining the boundary of the living material; (2) all contain a region of **DNA** (deoxyribonucleic acid), which stores genetic information; and (3) all contain **cytoplasm,** everything inside the plasma membrane that is not part of the DNA region.

With respect to internal organization, there are two basic types of cells, **prokaryotic** and **eukaryotic.** Study Table 6-1, comparing the more important differences between prokaryotic and eukaryotic cells. The Greek word *karyon* means "kernel," referring to the nucleus. Thus, *prokaryotic* means "before a nucleus," while *eukaryotic* indicates the presence of a "true nucleus." Prokaryotic cells typical of bacteria, cyanobacteria, and archaea are believed to be similar to the first cells, which arose on Earth 3.5 billion years ago. Eukaryotic cells, such as those that comprise the bodies of protists, fungi, plants, and animals, probably evolved from prokaryotes.

This exercise will familiarize you with the basics of cell structure and the function of prokaryotes (prokaryotic cells) and eukaryotes (eukaryotic cells).

6.1   Prokaryotic Cells *(About 20 min.)*

MATERIALS

Per student:

- dissecting needle
- compound microscope
- microscope slide
- coverslip

Per student pair:

- distilled water (dH$_2$O) in dropping bottle

Per student group (table):

- culture of a cyanobacterium (either *Anabaena* or *Oscillatoria*)

Per lab room:

- 3 bacterium-containing nutrient agar plates (demonstration)
- 3 demonstration slides of bacteria (coccus, bacillus, spirillum)

TABLE 6-1 Comparison of Prokaryotic and Eukaryotic Cells

Characteristic	Cell Type	
	Prokaryotic	Eukaryotic
Genetic material	Located within cytoplasm, not bounded by a special membrane Consists of a single molecule of DNA	Located in **nucleus,** a double membrane-bounded compartment within the cytoplasm Numerous molecules of DNA combined with protein Organized into chromosomes
Cytoplasmic structures	Small ribosomes Photosynthetic membranes arising from the plasma membrane (in some representatives only)	Large ribosomes **Cytomembrane system,** a system of connected membrane structures **Organelles,** membrane-bounded compartments specialized to perform specific functions
Kingdoms represented	Bacteria Archaea	Protista Fungi Plantae Animalia

PROCEDURE

1. Observe the culture plate with bacteria growing on the surface of a nutrient medium. Can you see the individual cells with your naked eye?

    NOT A SHOT

2. Observe the microscopic preparations of bacteria on *demonstration* next to the culture plate. The three slides represent the three different shapes of bacteria. Which objective lenses are being used to view the bacteria?

    SP 100

Can you discern any detail within the cytoplasm?

    NO

   In the space provided in Figure 6-1, sketch what you see through the microscope. Record the magnification you are using in the blank provided in the figure caption. Then record the approximate size of the bacterial cells. (Return to page 34 of Exercise 3 if you've forgotten how to estimate the size of an object being viewed through a microscope.)

3. Study Figure 6-2, a three-dimensional representation of a bacterial cell. Now examine the electron micrograph of the bacterium *Escherichia coli* (Figure 6-3). Locate the **cell wall,** a structure chemically distinct from the wall of plant cells but serving the same primary function to contain and protect the cell's contents.

4. Find the **plasma membrane,** which is lying flat against the internal surface of the cell wall and is difficult to distinguish.

5. Look for two components of the **cytoplasm: ribosomes,** electron-dense particles (they appear black) that give the cytoplasm its granular appearance, and a relatively electron-transparent region (appears light) containing fine threads of DNA called the **nucleoid.**

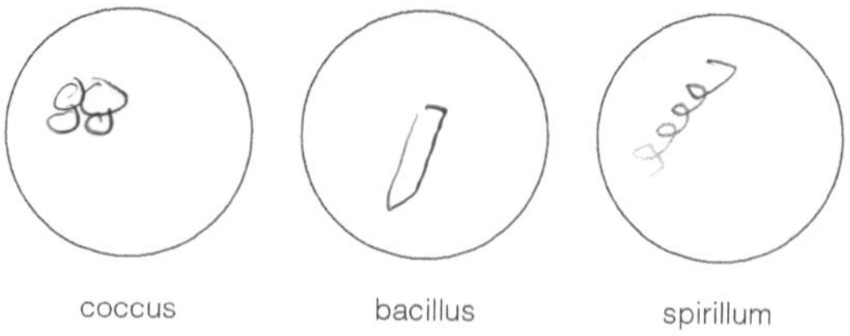

coccus   bacillus   spirillum

Figure 6-1 Drawing of several bacterial cells (*400* ×). Approximate size = _____ μm.

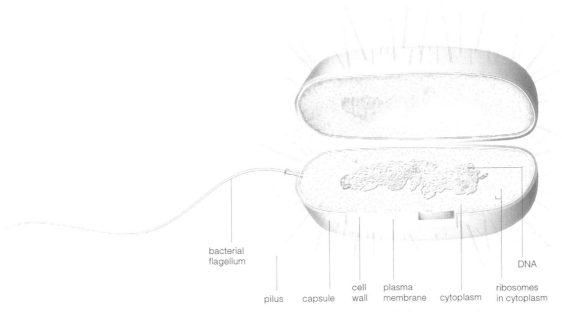

(After Starr, 2000.)

bacterial
flagellum

DNA

pilus   capsule   cell wall   plasma membrane   cytoplasm   ribosomes in cytoplasm

Figure 6-2   Three-dimensional representation of a bacterial cell as seen with the electron microscope.

Another type of prokaryotic cell is exemplified by cyanobacteria, such as *Oscillatoria* and *Anabaena*. Cyanobacteria (sometimes called blue-green algae) are commonly found in water and damp soils. They obtain their nutrition by converting the sun's energy through photosynthesis.

6. With a dissecting needle, remove a few filaments from the cyanobacterial culture, placing them in a drop of water on a clean microscope slide.

7. Place a coverslip over the material and examine it first with the low-power objective and then using the high-dry objective (or oil-immersion objective, if your microscope is so equipped).

8. In the space provided in Figure 6-4, sketch the cells you see at high power. Estimate the size of a *single* cyanobacterial cell and record the magnification you used to make your drawing.

9. Now examine the electron micrograph of *Anabaena* (Figure 6-5), which identifies the **cell wall, cytoplasm,** and **ribosomes.** The cyanobacteria also possess membranes that function in photosynthesis. Identify these **photosynthetic membranes,** which look like tiny threads within the cytoplasm.

10. Look at the captions for Figures 6-3 and 6-5. Judging by the magnification of each electron micrograph, which cell is larger, the bacterium *E. coli* or the cyanobacterium *Anabaena*?

    ANABAENA

cell wall

cytoplasm with ribosomes

DNA region

plasma membrane

(Photo courtesy of G. Cohen-Bazire.)

Figure 6-3   Electron micrograph of the bacterium *Escherichia coli* (28,300×).

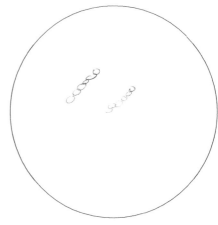

Figure 6-4   Drawing of several prokaryotic cells of a cyanobacterium (_490_ ×). Approximate size = _____ μm.

Because the electron micrograph of *Anabaena* is of relatively low magnification, the plasma membrane is not obvious, but if you could see it, it would be found just under the cell wall.

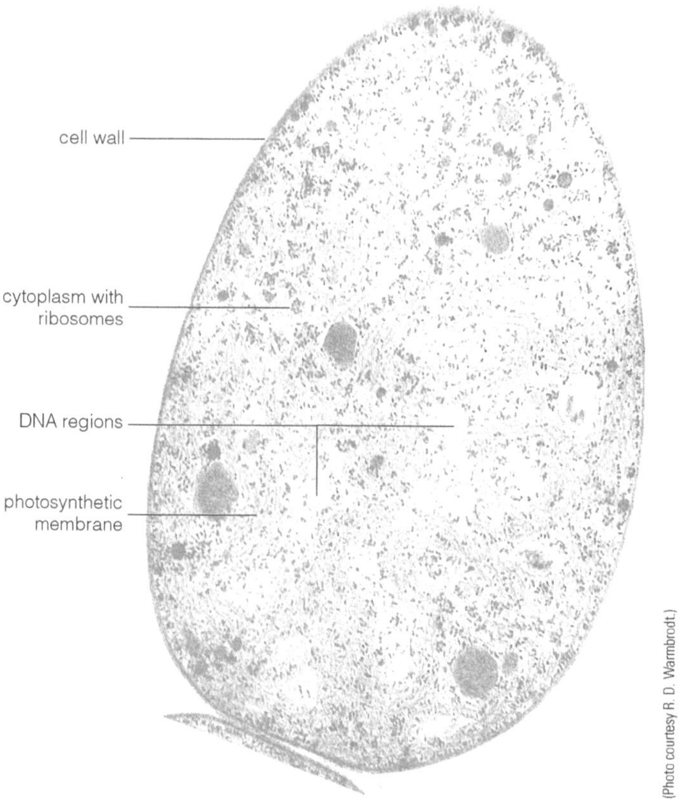

Eukaryotic Cells
(About 75 min.)

MATERIALS

Per student:

- textbook
- toothpick
- microscope slide
- coverslip
- culture of *Physarum polycephalum*
- compound microscope
- forceps
- dissecting needle

Per student pair:

- methylene blue in dropping bottle
- distilled water (dH_2O) in dropping bottle

Per student group (table):

- *Elodea* in water-containing culture dish
- onion bulb
- tissue paper

Per lab room:

- model of animal cell
- model of plant cell

(Photo courtesy R. D. Warmbrodt.)

Figure 6-5 Electron micrograph of *Anabaena* (11,600×).

Labels: cell wall; cytoplasm with ribosomes; DNA regions; photosynthetic membrane

A. Protist Cells as Observed with the Light Microscope

The slime mold *Physarum polycephalum* is in the Kingdom Protista. *Physarum* is a unicellular organism, so it contains all the metabolic machinery for independent existence.

PROCEDURE

1. Place a plain microscope slide on the stage of your compound microscope. This will serve as a platform on which you can place a culture dish.
2. Now obtain a petri dish culture of *Physarum,* remove the lid, and place it on the platform. Observe initially with the low-power objective and then with the medium-power objective. Place a coverslip over part of the organism before rotating the high-dry objective into place. (This prevents the agar from getting on the lens.)

Physarum is **multinucleate,** meaning that more than one nucleus occurs within the cytoplasm. Unfortunately, the nuclei are tiny; you won't be able to distinguish them from other granules in the cytoplasm.

3. Locate the **plasma membrane,** which is the outer boundary of the cytoplasm. Once again, the resolving power of your microscope is not sufficient to allow you to actually view the membrane.
4. Watch the cytoplasm of the organism move. This intracellular motion is known as **cytoplasmic streaming.** Although not visible with the light microscope without using special techniques, contractile proteins called **microfilaments** are believed responsible for cytoplasmic streaming.
5. Note that the outer portion of the cytoplasm appears solid; this is the **gel** state of the cytoplasm. Notice that the granules closer to the interior are in motion within a fluid; this portion of the cytoplasm is in the **sol** state. Movement of the organism occurs as the sol-state cytoplasm at the advancing tip pushes against the plasma membrane, causing the region to swell outward. The sol-state cytoplasm flows into the region, converting to the gel state along the margins.
6. In Figure 6-6, sketch the portion of *Physarum* that you have been observing and label it.

B. Experiment: Cytoplasmic Streaming (About 25 min.)

As you might predict, temperature affects many cellular processes. You may have observed that snakes and insects, being ectotherms (animals that gain heat from the environment and unlike humans, not primarily from metabolic activities), in nature are relatively sluggish during cold weather. Is the same true for other organisms, like the slime mold?

This simple experiment addresses the hypothesis that *cold slows cytoplasmic streaming in Physarum polycephalum.* Before starting this experiment, you may wish to review the discussion in Exercise 1, "The Scientific Method."

MATERIALS

Per experimental group:
- culture of *Physarum polycephalum*
- compound microscope
- container with ice *or* refrigerator
- timer *or* watch with second hand
- Celsius thermometer

Figure 6-6 Drawing of a portion of *Physarum* (_____×).

PROCEDURE

1. Place the *Physarum* culture on the stage of your compound microscope as described in Section A.
2. Time the duration of cytoplasmic streaming in one direction and then in the other direction. Do this for five cycles of back-and-forth motion. Calculate the average duration of flow in either direction. Record the temperature and your observations in Table 6-2.
3. Remove your culture from the microscope's stage, replace the cover, and place it and the thermometer in a refrigerator or atop ice for 15 minutes.
4. While you are waiting, in Table 6-2 write a prediction for the effect on the duration of cytoplasmic streaming by reducing the temperature of the culture of *Physarum polycephalum.*
5. After 15 minutes have elapsed, remove the culture from the cold treatment, record the temperature of the experimental treatment, and repeat the observations in step 2.
6. Record your observations and make a conclusion in Table 6-2, accepting or rejecting the hypothesis.

TABLE 6-2	Effect of Temperature on Cytoplasmic Streaming	
Prediction:		
Temperature (°C)	**Time**	**Observations and Duration of Directional Flow (sec.)**

A logical question to ask at this time is *why* temperature has the effect you observed. If you perform Exercise 8, "Enzymes: Catalysts of Life," you may be able to make an educated guess (another hypothesis).

C. Animal Cells Observed with the Light Microscope

PROCEDURE

1. *Human cheek cells.* Using the broad end of a clean toothpick, gently scrape the inside of your cheek. Stir the scrapings into a drop of distilled water on a clean microscope slide and add a coverslip. Dispose of used toothpicks in the jar containing alcohol.
2. Because the cells are almost transparent, decrease the amount of light entering the objective lens to increase the contrast. (See Exercise 3, page 33.) Find the cells using the low-power objective of your microscope; then switch to the high-dry objective for detailed study.

3. Find the **nucleus,** a centrally located spherical body within the **cytoplasm** of each cell.
4. Now stain your cheek cells with a dilute solution of methylene blue, a dye that stains the nucleus darker than the surrounding cytoplasm. To stain your slide, follow the directions illustrated in Figure 6-7.

Without removing the coverslip, add a drop of the stain to one edge of the coverslip. Then draw the stain under the coverslip by touching a piece of tissue paper to the *opposite* side of the coverslip.

5. In Figure 6-8, sketch the cheek cells, labeling the **cytoplasm, nucleus,** and the location of the **plasma membrane.** (A light microscope cannot resolve the plasma membrane, but the boundary between the cytoplasm and the external medium indicates its location.) Many of the cells will be folded or wrinkled due to their thin, flexible nature. Estimate and record in your sketch the size of the cells. (The method for estimating the size is found in Part I page 34.)

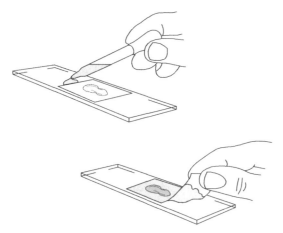

Figure 6-7 Method for staining specimen under coverslips of microscope slide.

Figure 6-8 Drawing of human cheek cells (_____×).
Approximate size = _____μm.
Labels: cytoplasm, nucleus, plasma membrane

D. Animal Cells as Observed with the Electron Microscope

Studies with the electron microscope have yielded a wealth of information on the structure of eukaryotic cells. Structures too small to be seen with the light microscope have been identified. These include many **organelles,** structures in the cytoplasm that have been separated ("compartmentalized") by enclosure in membranes. Examples of organelles are the nucleus, mitochondria, endoplasmic reticulum, and Golgi bodies. Although the cells in each of the six kingdoms have some peculiarities unique to that kingdom, electron microscopy has revealed that all cells are fundamentally similar.

PROCEDURE

1. Study Figure 6-9, a three-dimensional representation of an animal cell.
2. With the aid of Figure 6-9, identify the parts on the model of the animal cell that is on *demonstration.*
3. Figure 6-10 is an electron micrograph (EM) of an animal cell (kingdom Animalia). Study the electron micrograph and, with the aid of Figure 6-9 and any electron micrographs in your textbook, label each structure listed.
4. Pay particular attention to the membranes surrounding the nucleus and mitochondria. Note that these two are each bounded by *two* membranes, which are commonly referred to collectively as an **envelope.**
5. Using your textbook as a reference, list the function for the following cellular components:
   (a) plasma membrane _____

   _____

   (b) cytoplasm _____

   _____

   (c) nucleus (the plural is *nuclei*) _____

   _____

   (d) nuclear envelope _____

   _____

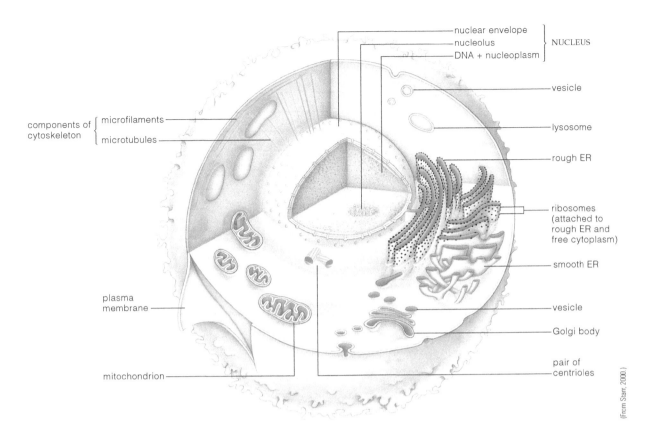

Figure 6-9 Three-dimensional representation of an animal cell as seen with the electron microscope.

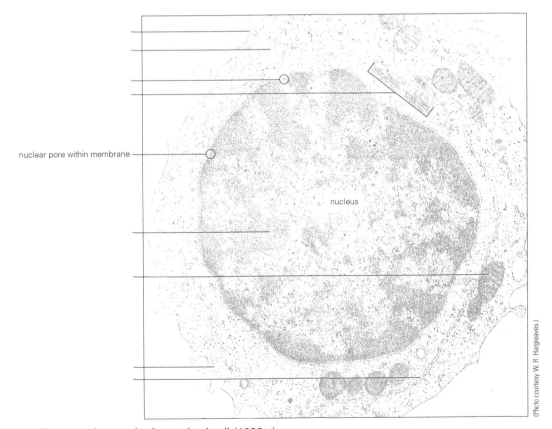

Figure 6-10 Electron micrograph of an animal cell (1600×).
Labels: plasma membrane, cytoplasm, nuclear envelope, nuclear pore, chromatin, rough ER, smooth ER, Golgi body, mitochondrion

(e) nuclear pores _____

_____

(f) chromatin _____

_____

(g) nucleolus (the plural is *nucleoli*) _____

_____

(h) rough endoplasmic reticulum (RER) _____

_____

(i) smooth endoplasmic reticulum (SER) _____

_____

(j) Golgi body _____

_____

(k) mitochondrion (the plural is *mitochondria*) _____

_____

E. Plant Cells Seen with the Light Microscope

E.1. Elodea leaf cells

Young leaves at the growing tip of *Elodea* are particularly well suited for studying cell structure because these leaves are only a few cell layers thick.

PROCEDURE

1. With a forceps, remove a single young leaf, mount it on a slide in a drop of distilled water, and cover with a coverslip.
2. Examine the leaf first with the low-power objective. Then concentrate your study on several cells using the high-dry objective. Refer to Figure 6-11.
3. Observe the abundance of green bodies in the cytoplasm. These are the **chloroplasts,** organelles that function in photosynthesis and that are typical of green plants.
4. Locate the numerous dark lines running parallel to the long axis of the leaf. These are the air-containing **intercellular spaces.**
5. Find the **cell wall,** a structure distinguishing plant from animal cells, visible as a clear area surrounding the cytoplasm.
6. After the cells have warmed a bit, notice the **cytoplasmic streaming** taking place. Movement of the chloroplasts along the cell wall is the most obvious visual evidence of cytoplasmic streaming. Microfilaments (much too small to be seen with your light microscope) are responsible for this intracellular motion.
7. Remember that you are looking at a three-dimensional object. In the middle portion of the cell is the large, clear **central vacuole,** which can take up from 50% to 90% of the cell interior. Because the vacuole in *Elodea* is transparent, it cannot be seen with the light microscope.
8. The chloroplasts occur in the cytoplasm surrounding the vacuole, so they will appear to be in different locations, depending on where you focus in the cell. Focus in the upper or lower surface and observe that the chloroplasts appear to be scattered throughout the cell.

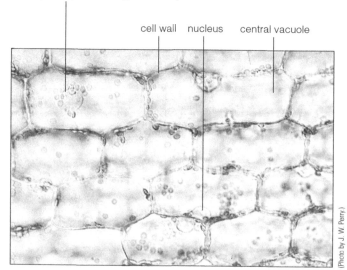

chloroplasts (surrounding a nucleus)

cell wall   nucleus   central vacuole

(Photo by J. W. Perry.)

Figure 6-11   *Elodea* cells (400×).

9. Now focus in the center of the cell (by raising or lowering the objective with the fine focus knob), and note that the chloroplasts lie in a thin layer of cytoplasm along the wall.

10. Locate the **nucleus** within the cytoplasm. It will appear as a clear or slightly amber body that is slightly larger than the chloroplasts. (You may need to examine several cells to find a clearly defined nucleus.)

11. Describe the three-dimensional shape of the *Elodea* leaf cell.

Very   lichy

_____

12. What are the shapes of the chloroplasts and nucleus? _Shpericel_____

_____

13. Now add a drop of methylene blue stain to make the cell wall more obvious. Add the stain as shown in Figure 6-7.

14. Look for the very, very tiny **mitochondria.** (If you have an oil-immersion lens on your microscope, you should use that lens.)

15. Compare the size of the mitochondria to chloroplasts:

The   mitochondria   is   Smaller

E.2. Onion scale cells

1. Make a wet mount of a colorless scale of an onion bulb, using the technique described in Figure 6-12. The *inner* face of the scale is easiest to remove, as shown in Figure 6-12d.

2. Observe your preparation with your microscope, focusing first with the low-power objective. Continue your study, switching to the medium-power and finally the high-dry objective. Refer to Figure 6-13.

3. Identify the **cell wall** and **cytoplasm.**

4. Find the **nucleus,** a prominent sphere within the cytoplasm.

5. Examine the nucleus more carefully at high magnification. Within it, find one or more nucleoli (the singular is *nucleolus*). Nucleoli are rich in a nucleic acid known as RNA (ribonucleic acid), while the nucleus as a whole is largely DNA (deoxyribonucleic acid), the genetic material.

6. You may see numerous **oil droplets** within the cytoplasm, visible in the form of granulelike bodies. These oil droplets are a form of stored food material. You may be surprised to learn that onion scales are actually leaves! Which cellular components present in *Elodea* leaf cells are absent in onion leaf cells?

_____

7. If you are using the pigmented tissue from a red onion, you should see a purple pigment located in the vacuole. In this case, the cell wall appears as a bright line.

8. In Figure 6-14, sketch and label several cells from onion scale leaves.

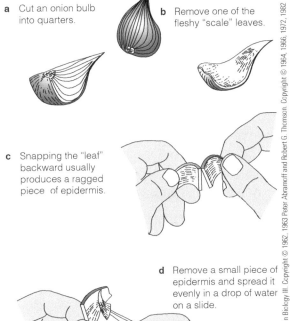

a Cut an onion bulb into quarters.

b Remove one of the fleshy "scale" leaves.

c Snapping the "leaf" backward usually produces a ragged piece of epidermis.

d Remove a small piece of epidermis and spread it evenly in a drop of water on a slide.

d Gently lower a coverslip to prevent trapping air bubbles. Examine with your microscope. Add more water to the edge of the coverslip with an eye dropper if the slide begins to dry.

Figure 6-12 Method for obtaining onion scale cells.

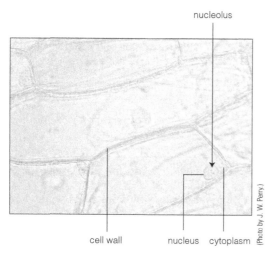

nucleolus

cell wall   nucleus   cytoplasm

(Photo by J. W. Perry.)

Figure 6-13   Onion bulb leaf cells (67×).
Labels: cell wall, cytoplasm, nucleus, nucleolus, oil droplets

Figure 6-14   Drawing of onion scale cells (_____×).
Labels: cell wall, cytoplasm, nucleus

F. Plant Cells as Seen with the Electron Microscope

The electron microscope has made obvious some of the unique features of plant cells.

PROCEDURE

1. Study Figure 6-15, a three-dimensional representation of a typical plant cell.
2. With the aid of Figure 6-15, identify the structures present on the model of a plant cell that is on _demonstration_.
3. Now examine Figure 6-16, a transmission electron micrograph from a corn leaf. Label all of the structures listed. _Caution: Many plant cells do not have a large central vacuole. This is one of them._ Notice that the chloroplast has an envelope, just as do the nucleus and mitochondria.
4. With the help of Figure 6-15 and any transmission electron micrographs and text in your textbook, list the function of the following structures.

   (a)   cell wall _____

   _____

   (b)   chloroplast _____

   _____

   (c)   vacuole _____

   _____

   (d)   vacuolar membrane _____

   _____

   (e)   plasma membrane _____

   _____

   (f)   cytoplasm _____

   _____

   (g)   nucleus _____

   _____

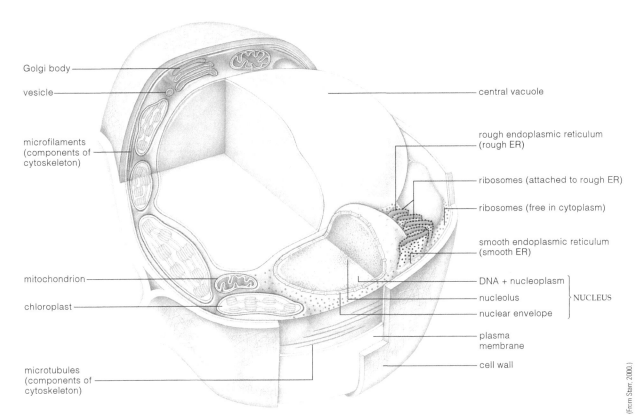

Golgi body

vesicle

microfilaments
(components of
cytoskeleton)

mitochondrion

chloroplast

microtubules
(components of
cytoskeleton)

central vacuole

rough endoplasmic reticulum
(rough ER)

ribosomes (attached to rough ER)

ribosomes (free in cytoplasm)

smooth endoplasmic reticulum
(smooth ER)

DNA + nucleoplasm

nucleolus } NUCLEUS

nuclear envelope

plasma
membrane

cell wall

(From Starr, 2000.)

Figure 6-15   Three-dimensional representation of a plant cell as seen with the electron microscope.

(h)   nuclear envelope _____

_____

(i)   nuclear pore _____

_____

(j)   chromatin _____

_____

(k)   nucleolus _____

_____

(l)   rough endoplasmic reticulum (RER) _____

_____

(m)   smooth endoplasmic reticulum (SER) _____

_____

(n)   Golgi body _____

_____

(o)   mitochondrion _____

_____

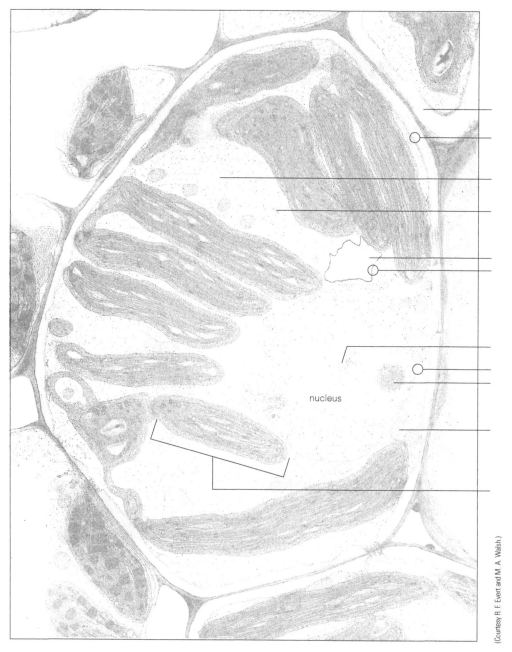

nucleus

Figure 6-16 Electron micrograph of a corn leaf cell (2700×).
Labels: cell wall, chloroplast, vacuole, vacuolar membrane, plasma membrane, nuclear envelope, chromatin, nucleolus, endoplasmic reticulum (ER), Golgi body, mitochondrion

_____ 1. The person who first used the term *cell* was
(a) Darwin
(b) Leeuwenhoek
(c) Hooke
(d) Watson

_____ 2. All cells contain
(a) a nucleus, plasma membrane, and cytoplasm
(b) a cell wall, nucleus, and cytoplasm
(c) DNA, plasma membrane, and cytoplasm
(d) mitochondria, plasma membrane, and cytoplasm

_____ 3. Prokaryotic cells *lack*
(a) DNA
(b) a true nucleus
(c) a cell wall
(d) none of the above

_____ 4. The word *eukaryotic* refers specifically to a cell containing
(a) photosynthetic membranes
(b) a true nucleus
(c) a cell wall
(d) none of the above

_____ 5. A bacterium is an example of a
(a) prokaryotic cell
(b) eukaryotic cell
(c) plant cell
(d) all of the above

_____ 6. Methylene blue
(a) is used to kill cells that are moving too quickly to observe
(b) renders cells nontoxic
(c) is a portion of the electromagnetic spectrum used by green plant cells
(d) is a biological stain used to increase contrast of cellular constituents

_____ 7. Components typical of plant cells but not of animal cells are
(a) nuclei
(b) cell walls
(c) mitochondria
(d) ribosomes

_____ 8. A central vacuole
(a) is found only in plant cells
(b) may take up between 50% and 90% of the cell's interior
(c) is both of the above
(d) is none of the above

_____ 9. The intercellular spaces between plant cells
(a) contain air
(b) are responsible for cytoplasmic streaming
(c) are nonexistent
(d) contain chloroplasts

_____ 10. An envelope
(a) surrounds the nucleus
(b) surrounds mitochondria
(c) consists of two membranes
(d) does all of the above

Nucleic Acids: Blueprints for Life

After completing this exercise, you will be able to

1. define *DNA, RNA, purine, pyrimidine, principle of base pairing, replication, transcription, translation, codon, anticodon, peptide bond, gene, genetic engineering, recombinant DNA, plasmid, bacterial conjugation;*

2. identify the components of deoxyribonucleotides and ribonucleotides;

3. distinguish between DNA and RNA according to their structure and function;

4. describe DNA replication, transcription, and translation;

5. give the base sequence of DNA or RNA when presented with the complementary strand;

6. identify a codon and anticodon on RNA models and describe the location and function of each;

7. give the base sequence of an anticodon when presented with that of a codon, and vice versa;

8. describe what is meant by the *one-gene, one-polypeptide hypothesis;*

9. describe the process of DNA recombination by bacterial conjugation;

10. explain the difference between DNA recombination by bacterial conjugation and the technique by which eukaryotic gene products are produced by bacteria.

INTRODUCTION

By 1900, Gregor Mendel had demonstrated patterns of inheritance, based solely on careful experimentation and observation. Mendel had no clear idea how the traits he observed were passed from generation to generation, although the seeds of that knowledge had been sown as early as 1869, when the physician-chemist Friedrich Miescher isolated the chemical substance of the nucleus. Miescher found the substance to be an acid with a large phosphorus content and named it "nuclein." Subsequently, nuclein was identified as **DNA,** short for **deoxyribonucleic acid.** Some 75 years would pass before the significance of DNA would be revealed.

Few would argue that the demonstration of DNA as the genetic material and the subsequent determination of its molecular structure are among the most significant discoveries of the twentieth century. Since the early 1950s, when James Watson and Francis Crick built on discoveries of others before them to construct their first model of DNA, tremendous advances in molecular biology have occurred, many of them based on the structure of DNA. Today we speak of gene therapy and genetic engineering in household conversations. In the minds of some, these topics raise hopes for curing or preventing many of the diseases plaguing humanity. For others, thoughts turn to "playing with nature," undoing the deeds of God, or creating monstrosities that will wipe humanity off the face of the earth.

This exercise will familiarize you with the basic structure of nucleic acids and their role in the cell. Understanding the function of nucleic acids—both DNA and **RNA (ribonucleic acid)**—is central to understanding life itself. We hope you will gain an understanding that will allow you to form educated opinions concerning what science should do with its newfound technology.

14.1   Isolation and Identification of Nucleic Acids *(About 30 min.)*

At the beginning of the twenty-first century, no scientific endeavor holds more promise for humanity than the Human Genome Project. This initiative by the National Institutes of Health and private companies has created a complete map of every gene in our chromosomes. With this knowledge, researchers are beginning to learn the function of each gene. This huge project, biology's "moon shot," has the potential to unlock the secrets of human life.

The first step in this undertaking is the isolation of DNA. In the following section, you'll isolate and identify a nucleic acid component of *Halobacterium salinarum*, a bacterium that grows in habitats with extremely high salt (NaCl) concentrations.

Halobacterium is able to live in its specialized environment because of its cell wall, which differs from that of most other bacteria by maintaining its rodlike shape *only* at high salt concentrations. As NaCl levels drop, the cell shape first becomes irregular and finally spherical. At still lower concentrations, the cell ruptures because of osmotic effects (Exercise 7). We will take advantage of this response to allow us to release the cells' contents, including the nucleic acids, for isolation.

MATERIALS

Per student pair:

- culture tube of *Halobacterium salinarum*
- cotton applicator stick
- 10 mL of 95% ethanol in a test tube
- glass rod
- inoculating needle
- 5- or 10-mL sterile pipette
- two 10-mL graduated cylinders
- 2 test tubes
- test tube rack
- china marker
- agarose gel plate with methylene blue stain
- dropping pipette

Per lab bench:

- TBE buffer solution bottle and in dropping bottle
- DNA standard solution in dropper bottle
- 1% albumin solution in dropper bottle
- paper towels

Per lab room:

- raw egg white in beaker
- source of dH_2O
- white light transilluminator or other source of white light

PROCEDURE

Work in pairs.

A. Isolation of Nucleic Acids

1. With the 10-mL graduated cylinder, measure 1.5 mL of distilled water into a clean test tube.
2. Remove the cap from the slant culture of *H. salinarum* and insert the cotton swab applicator stick into the culture tube. Gently swab the entire surface of the culture by carefully rotating the cotton swab over the pink bacterial colonies. Try to pick up as much of the bacterial colony as possible on the swab. Remove the cotton swab from the culture tube and replace the cap.
3. Transfer the cotton swab applicator stick to the test tube containing the distilled water. Release all the adhering cells by vigorously swirling the cotton swab in the distilled water and occasionally pressing the swab against the wall of the tube.

The bacterial cells rupture from osmotic shock, since the cell wall cannot withstand the change from conditions of extremely high salt concentration to those of salt absence.

4. Withdraw the swab from the test tube, pressing it against the tube wall to squeeze out as much fluid as possible. *The gelatinous fluid adhering to the swab's surface after wetting will contain a large concentration of nucleic acids. This fluid must be left in the test tube.* Discard the swab.
5. Wipe the surface of the glass rod with a piece of paper towel moistened with 95% ethanol. Insert the clean rod into the test tube containing the cell suspension and stir vigorously. This action will assure total cell lysis. Remove the glass rod.
6. Using the sterile pipet, add 3 mL of 95% ethanol one drop at a time down the *side* of the test tube containing the cell suspension. Any material adhering to the tube wall should be washed into the suspension. The alcohol should form a layer on top of the aqueous cell suspension; *be careful not to mix the water and alcohol layers.*
7. Clean the inoculating wire with a paper towel moistened in 95% ethanol. Insert the wire into the culture tube so that the hook is at the cell suspension–alcohol interface and rotate the wire in a circular motion. The rotation should mix the contents only at the partition layer between the alcohol and cell suspension.

Nucleic acids precipitate and are extracted at this boundary between alcohol and water. Notice that strands of material adhere to the wire and trail off into the solution. The long linear-chain molecules of DNA appear stringy and form a cottony, viscous cloud around the wire.

The nucleic acids you have extracted are not pure; they contain cellular debris as well as adhering proteins. Observe the appearance and texture of the raw egg white on demonstration. Egg white has a very high concentration of the protein albumin. You will test your extracted precipitate to identify its major component.

B. Identification—Test for DNA

1. Use a 10-mL graduated cylinder to measure 3 mL of TBE buffer solution into a clean test tube.
2. Place the nucleic acid from the wire winder into the test tube. Swirl the wire winder in the buffer solution to thoroughly dissolve the viscous material in the buffer solution.
3. Obtain an agarose plate with methylene blue stain. (Agarose is an inert gel-like substance; methylene blue stain binds specifically with DNA, causing a visible purplish color.) Turn the unopened plate over and use the marking pen to draw four small, widely separated circles on the *underside* of the plate. Label the circles P, D, A, and C. These will be visible when looking at the plate from above to mark the locations where different test substances will be applied.
4. Open the plate, and with a dropping pipette apply a drop of the precipitated bacterial material dissolved in TBE buffer solution onto the area marked P.
5. Similarly, apply a drop of DNA standard solution onto the area marked D.
6. Apply a drop of 1% albumin protein solution onto the area marked A.
7. Apply a drop of TBE buffer onto the area marked C.
8. Set the plate aside for 20–30 minutes to allow time for color development.
9. View the petri plate on the white light transilluminator. A purple color indicates the presence of DNA. (See Figure 14-1.) Record your results in Table 14-1.

(Photo by J. W. Perry.)

Figure 14-1 Agarose-methylene blue plate on white light transilluminator showing positive (left) and negative (right) tests for DNA.

TABLE 14-1 Identification of Contents Extracted from *Halobacterium*

Droplet Code	Droplet Contents	Color
P	Precipitate in TBE buffer	
D	DNA standard	
A	1% albumin	
C	TBE buffer	

Name the substance(s) present in the material you isolated from *Halobacterium*.

What is the purpose of the DNA standard droplet?

What is the purpose of the TBE buffer droplet?

14.2 **Modeling the Structure and Function of Nucleic Acids and Their Products** *(About 90 min.)*

MATERIALS

Per student pair or group:
- DNA puzzle kit

Per lab room:
- DNA model

PROCEDURE

Work in pairs or groups.

Note: Clear your work surface of everything except your lab manual and the DNA puzzle kit.

In this section, we are concerned with three processes: *replication, transcription,* and *translation.* But before we study these three *per se,* let's formulate an idea of the structure of DNA itself.

A. Nucleic Acid Structure

1. Obtain a DNA puzzle kit. It should contain the following parts:
   - 18 deoxyribose sugars
   - 9 ribose sugars
   - 18 phosphate groups
   - 4 adenine bases
   - 6 guanine bases
   - 6 cytosine bases
   - 4 thymine bases
   - 2 uracil bases
   - 3 transfer RNA (tRNA)
   - 3 amino acids
   - 3 activating units
   - ribosome template sheet

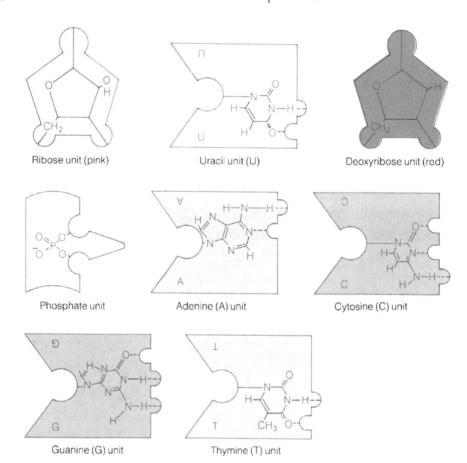

Ribose unit (pink)   Uracil unit (U)   Deoxyribose unit (red)

Phosphate unit   Adenine (A) unit   Cytosine (C) unit

Guanine (G) unit   Thymine (T) unit

2. Group the components into separate stacks. Select a single deoxyribose sugar, an adenine base (labeled A), and a phosphate, fitting them together as shown in Figure 14-2. This is a single nucleotide (specifically a *deoxy*ribonucleotide), a unit consisting of a sugar (deoxyribose), a phosphate group, and a nitrogen-containing base (adenine).

Let's examine each component of the nucleotide.

Deoxyribose (Figure 14-3) is a sugar compound containing five carbon atoms. Four of the five are joined by covalent bonds into a ring. Each carbon is given a number, indicating its position in the ring. (These numbers are read "1-prime, 2-prime," and so on. "Prime" is used to distinguish the carbon atoms from the position of atoms that are sometimes numbered in the nitrogen-containing bases.) This structure is usually drawn in a simplified manner, without actually showing the carbon atoms within the ring (Figure 14-4).

There are four kinds of nitrogen-containing bases in DNA. Two are **purines** and are double-ring structures. Specifically, the two purines are *adenine* and *guanine* (abbreviated A and G, respectively; Figure 14-5).

The other two nitrogen-containing bases are **pyrimidines,** specifically *cytosine* and *thymine* (abbreviated C and T, respectively). Pyrimidines are single-ring compounds, as shown in Figure 14-6.

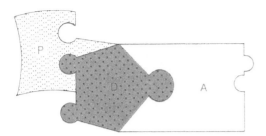

Figure 14-2 One deoxyribonucleotide.

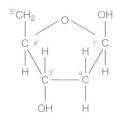

Figure 14-3 Deoxyribose.

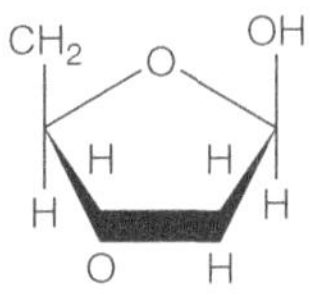

Figure 14-4 Simplified representation of deoxyribose.

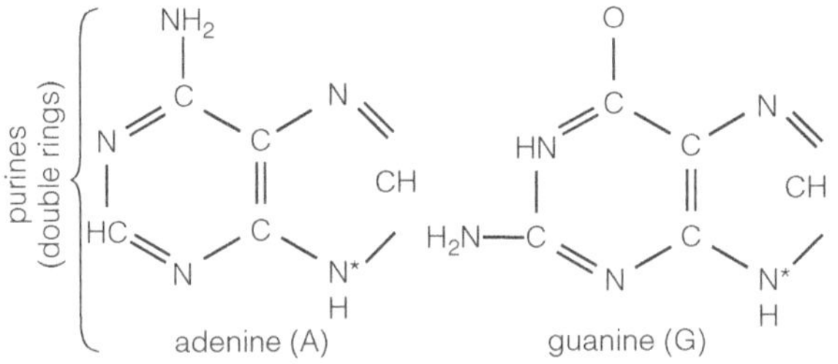

purines (double rings) { adenine (A)   guanine (G)

Figure 14-5 Double-ringed purines found in DNA.

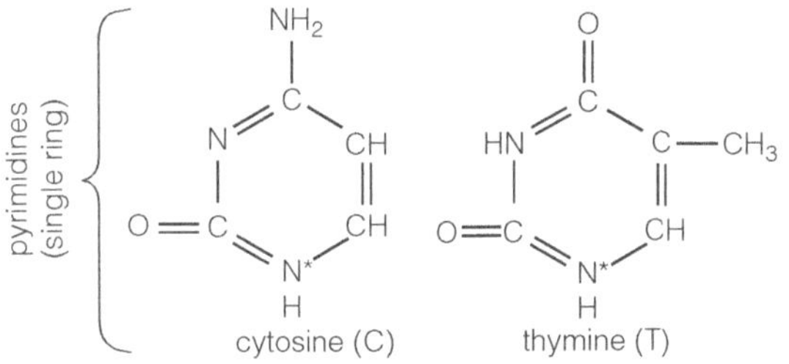

pyrimidines (single ring) { cytosine (C)   thymine (T)

Figure 14-6 Pyrimidines found in DNA.

The symbol * indicates where a bond forms between each nitrogen-containing base and the 1′ carbon atom of the sugar ring structure. Although deoxyribose and the nitrogen-containing bases are organic compounds (they contain carbon), the phosphate group is an inorganic compound, with the structural formula shown in Figure 14-7.

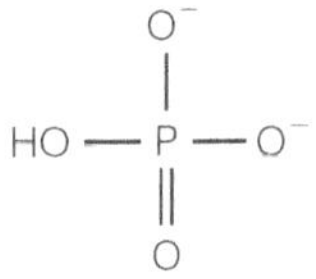

The phosphate end of the deoxyribonucleotide is referred to as the 5′ end, because the phosphate group bonds to the 5′ carbon atom.

There are four kinds of deoxyribonucleotides, each differing only in the type of base it possesses. Construct the other three kinds of deoxyribonucleotides, then draw them in Figures 14-8b–d. Rather than drawing the somewhat complex shape of the model, in this and other drawings, just give the correct position and letters. Use D for deoxyribose, P for a phosphate group, and A, C, G, and T for the different bases (as shown in Figure 14-8a).

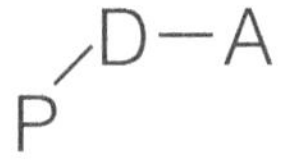

Note the small notches and projections in the nitrogen-containing bases. Will the notches of adenine and thymine fit together? _____

Will guanine and cytosine? _____
Will adenine and cytosine? _____
Will thymine and guanine? _____

The notches and projections represent bonding sites. Make a prediction about which bases will bond with one another.

_____

Will a purine base bond with another purine? _____
Will a purine base bond with both types of pyrimidines? _____

3. Assemble the three additional deoxyribonucleotides, linking them with the adenine-containing unit, to form a nucleotide strand of DNA. Note that the sugar backbone is bonded together by phosphate groups. Your strand should appear like that shown in Figure 14-9.

4. Now assemble a second four-nucleotide strand, similar to that of Figure 14-9. However, this time make the base sequence T-A-C-G, from bottom to top. DNA molecules consist of *two* strands of nucleotides, each strand the *complement* of the other.

Figure 14-7 Phosphate group found in nucleic acids.

P∕D—A

Deoxyribonucleotide containing adenine
a

Deoxyribonucleotide containing guanine
b

Deoxyribonucleotide containing cytosine
c

Deoxyribonucleotide containing thymine
d

Figure 14-8 Drawings of deoxyribonucleotides containing guanine, cytosine, and thymine.

5. Assemble the two strands by attaching (bonding) the nitrogen bases of complementary strands. Note that the adenine of one nucleotide always pairs with the thymine of its complement; similarly, guanine always pairs with cytosine. This phenomenon is called the **principle of base pairing.** On Figure 14-10, attach letters to the model pieces indicating the composition of your double-stranded DNA model.

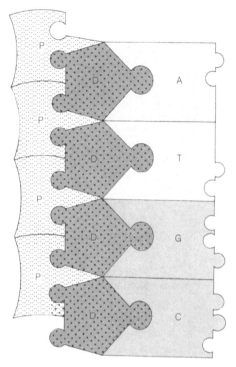

Figure 14-9   Four-nucleotide strand of DNA.

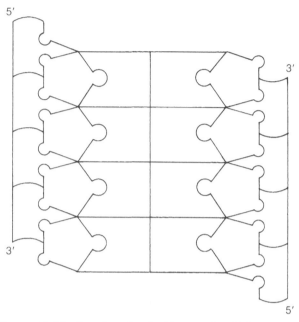

Figure 14-10   Drawing of a double strand of DNA.
Labels: A, T, G, C, D, P (all used more than once)

What do you notice about the *direction* in which each strand is running? (That is, are both 5′ carbons at the same end of the strands?)

_____

_____

_____

(Does the second strand of your drawing show this? It should.)

In life, the purines and pyrimidines are joined together by hydrogen bonds. Note again that the sugar backbone is linked by phosphate groups. Your model illustrates only a very small portion of a DNA molecule. The entire molecule may be tens of thousands of nucleotides in length!

6. Slide your DNA segment aside for the moment.
7. Examine the three-dimensional model of DNA on display in the laboratory (Figure 14-11). Notice that the two strands of DNA are twisted into a spiral-staircaselike pattern. This is why DNA is known as a *double helix.* Identify the deoxyribose sugar, nitrogen-containing bases, hydrogen bonds linking the bases, and the phosphate groups.

The second type of nucleic acid is RNA, short for ribonucleic acid. There are three important differences between DNA and RNA:
(a)   RNA is a *single strand* of nucleotides.
(b)   The sugar of RNA is **ribose.**
(c)   RNA lacks the nucleotide that contains thymine. Instead, it has one containing the pyrimidine uracil (U) (see Figure 14-12).

Compare the structural formulas of ribose (Figure 14-13) and deoxyribose (Figure 14-4). How do they differ?

_____

Why is the sugar of DNA called *deoxy*ribose? _____

_____

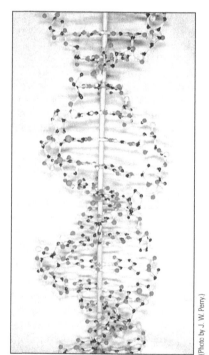

Figure 14-11   Three-dimensional model of DNA.

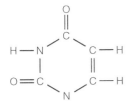

Figure 14-12 The pyrimidine uracil.

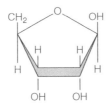

Figure 14-13 Ribose.

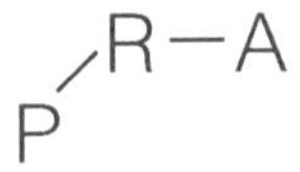

Ribonucleotide containing adenine

a

Ribonucleotide containing guanine

b

8. From the remaining pieces of your model kit, select four ribose sugars, an adenine, uracil, guanine, and cytosine, and four phosphate groups. Assemble the four **ribonucleotides** and draw each in Figure 14-14. (Use the convention illustrated in Figure 14-8 rather than drawing the actual shapes.)

Disassemble the RNA models after completing your drawing.

Ribonucleotide containing cytosine

c

Ribonucleotide containing uracil

d

Figure 14-14 Drawings of four possible ribonucleotides.

B. Modeling DNA Replication

DNA **replication** takes place during the S-stage of interphase of the cell cycle (see Exercise 11). Recall that the DNA is aggregated into chromosomes. Before mitosis, the chromosomes duplicate themselves so that the daughter nuclei formed by mitosis will have the same number of chromosomes (and hence the same amount of DNA) as did the parent cell.

Replication begins when hydrogen bonds between nitrogen bases break and the two DNA strands "unzip." Free nucleotides within the nucleus bond to the exposed bases, thus creating *two* new strands of DNA (as described below). The process of replication is controlled by enzymes called **DNA polymerases.**

1. Construct eight more deoxyribonucleotides (two of each kind) but don't link them into strands.
2. Now return to the double-stranded DNA segment you constructed earlier. Separate the two strands, imagining the zipperlike fashion in which this occurs within the nucleus.
3. Link the free deoxyribonucleotides to each of the "old" strands. When you are finished, you should have two double-stranded segments.

Note that one strand of each is the parental ("old") strand and the other is newly synthesized from free nucleotides. This illustrates the *semiconservative* nature of DNA replication. Each of the parent strands remains intact—it is *conserved*—and a new complementary strand is formed on it. Two "half-old, half-new" DNA molecules result.

Figure 14-15 Drawing of two replicated DNA segments, illustrating their semiconservative nature.

4. Draw the two replicated DNA molecules in Figure 14-15, labeling the old and new strands. (Once again, use the convention shown in Figure 14-8.)

C. Transcription: DNA to RNA

DNA is an "information molecule" residing *within* the nucleus. The information it provides is for assembling proteins *outside* the nucleus, within the cytoplasm. The information does not go directly from the DNA to the cytoplasm. Instead, RNA serves as an intermediary, carrying the information from DNA to the cytoplasm.

Synthesis of RNA takes place within the nucleus by **transcription.** During transcription, the DNA double helix unwinds and unzips, and a single strand of RNA, designated **messenger RNA (mRNA),** is assembled using the nucleotide sequence of *one* of the DNA strands as a pattern (template). Let's see how this happens.

1. Disassemble the replicated DNA strands into their component deoxyribonucleotides.
2. Construct a new DNA strand consisting of nine deoxyribonucleotides. With the purines and pyrimidines pointing away from you, lay the strand out horizontally in the following base sequence: T-G-C-A-C-C-T-G-C
3. Now assemble RNA ribonucleotides complementary to the exposed nitrogen bases of the DNA strand. Don't forget to substitute the pyrimidine uracil for thymine.

What is the sequence from left to right of nitrogen bases on the mRNA strand?

After the mRNA is synthesized within the nucleus, the hydrogen bonds between the nitrogen bases of the deoxyribonucleotides and ribonucleotides break.

4. Separate your mRNA strand from the DNA strand. (You can disassemble the deoxyribonucleotides now.) At this point, the mRNA moves out of the nucleus and into the cytoplasm.

By what avenue do you suppose the mRNA exits the nucleus? (*Hint:* Reexamine the structure of the nuclear membrane, as described in Exercise 6.)

To *transcribe* means to "make a copy of." Is transcription of RNA from DNA the formation of an *exact* copy? _____ Explain.

You will use this strand of mRNA in the next section. Keep it close at hand.

D. Translation—RNA to Polypeptides

Once in the cytoplasm, mRNA strands attach to *ribosomes,* on which translation occurs. To *translate* means to change from one language to another. In the biological sense, **translation** is the conversion of the linear message encoded on mRNA to a linear strand of amino acids to form a polypeptide. (A *peptide* is two or more amino acids linked by a peptide bond.)

Translation is accomplished by the interaction of mRNA, ribosomes, and **transfer RNA (tRNA),** another type of RNA. The tRNA molecule is formed into a four-cornered loop. You can think of tRNA as a baggage-carrying molecule. Within the cytoplasm, tRNA attaches to specific free amino acids. This occurs with the aid of activating enzymes, represented in your model kit by the pieces labeled "glycine activating" or "alanine activating." The amino acid–carrying tRNA then positions itself on ribosomes where the amino acids become linked together to form polypeptides.

1. Obtain three tRNA pieces, three amino acid units, and three activating units.
2. Join the amino acids first to the activating units and then to the tRNA. Will a particular tRNA bond with *any* amino acid, or is each tRNA specific? _____
3. Now let's do some translating. In the space below, list the sequence of bases on the *messenger* RNA strand, starting at the left.
   (left, 3′ end)_____(right, 5′ end)

Translation occurs when a *three*-base sequence on mRNA is "read" by tRNA. This three-base sequence on mRNA is called a **codon.** Think of a codon as a three-letter word, read right (5′) end to left (3′) end. What is the order of the rightmost (first) mRNA codon? (Remember to list the letters in the *reverse* order of that in the mRNA sequence.)
   The first codon on the mRNA model is (5′ end)_____ (3′ end)

4. Slide the mRNA strand onto the ribosome template sheet, with the first codon at the 5′ end.
5. Find the tRNA–amino acid complex that complements (will fit with) the first codon. The complementary three-base sequence on the tRNA is the **anticodon.** Binding between codons and anticodons begins at the P site of the 40s subunit (the smaller subunit) of the ribosome. The tRNA–amino acid complex with the correct anticodon positions itself on the P site.
6. Move the tRNA–amino acid complex onto the P site on the ribosome template sheet and fit the codon and anticodon together. In the boxes below, indicate the codon, anticodon, and the specific amino acid attached to the tRNA.

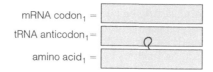

7. Now identify the second mRNA codon and fill in the boxes.

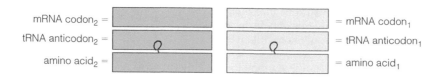

8. The second tRNA–amino acid complex moves onto the A site of the 40s subunit. Position this complex on the A site. An enzyme now catalyzes a condensation reaction, forming a **peptide bond** and linking the two amino acids into a dipeptide. (Water, HOH, is released by this condensation reaction.)

9. Separate amino acid$_1$ from its tRNA and link it to amino acid$_2$. (In reality, separation occurs somewhat later, but the puzzle doesn't allow this to be shown accurately; see below for correct timing.)

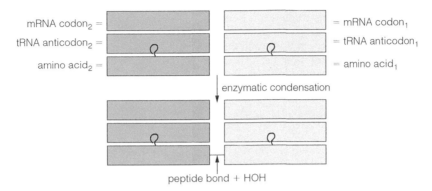

One tRNA–amino acid complex remains. It must occupy the A site of the ribosome in order to bind with its codon. Consequently, the dipeptide must move to the right.

10. Slide the mRNA to the right (so that tRNA$_2$ is on the P site) and fit the third mRNA codon and tRNA anticodon to form a peptide bond, creating a model of a tripeptide. At about the same time that the second peptide bond is forming, the first tRNA is released from both the mRNA and the first amino acid. Eventually, it will pick up another specific amino acid.

What amino acid will tRNA$_1$ pick up? _____.

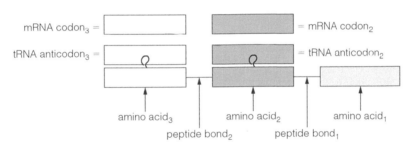

Record the tripeptide that you have just modeled. _____

You have created a short polypeptide. Polypeptides may be thousands of amino acids in length. As you see, the amino acid sequence is ultimately determined by DNA, because it was the original source of information.

Finally, let's turn our attention to the concept of a gene. A **gene** is a unit of inheritance. Our current understanding of a gene is that a gene codes for one polypeptide. This is appropriately called the **one-gene, one-polypeptide hypothesis.** Given this concept, do you think a gene consists of one, several, or many deoxyribonucleotides?

A gene probably consists of _____ deoxyribonucleotides.

Note: Please disassemble your models and return them to the proper location.

14.3 Principles of Genetic Engineering: Recombination of DNA *(About 15 min.)*

People suffering from Type 1 diabetes are unable to produce enough insulin, a hormone that is synthesized by the pancreas and that is instrumental in regulating the amount of blood sugar. Therapy for severe diabetes includes daily injections of insulin. Until recently, that insulin was extracted from the pancreas of slaughtered pigs and cows. With the advent of techniques commonly referred to as genetic engineering, human insulin is now produced by bacteria. These organisms grow and reproduce rapidly, hence producing quantities of insulin en masse.

Genetic engineering is a convenient phrase to describe what is more properly called methods in recombinant DNA. **Recombinant DNA** is DNA into which a set of "foreign" nucleotides has been inserted. In the case of insulin production, researchers first located on human chromosomes the gene (set of nucleotides) that codes for insulin production. Once identified, the nucleotides were removed from the human DNA and inserted into the DNA within a bacterium. As this bacterial cell reproduces, each new generation contains the gene coding for human insulin. The bacteria produce the hormone, which is harvested and purified. Thus these recombinant bacteria are "insulin factories."

Bacteria have been exchanging genes with each other for millennia. In the process, new genetic strains of bacteria may be produced. The following demonstration will familiarize you with genetic recombination in bacteria; these principles are the basis for genetic engineering.

Two strains of the bacterium *Escherichia coli* will be used in this experiment:

- Strain 1 carries a chromosomal gene that causes it to be resistant to the antibiotic drug streptomycin; it is susceptible to (killed by) another antibiotic, ampicillin. (See Figure 14-16a.)
- Strain 2 is resistant to the antibiotic drug ampicillin but susceptible to streptomycin; the gene for resistance to ampicillin is located on a small extrachromosomal (that is, not on its chromosome) loop of DNA called a **plasmid.** (See Figure 14-16b.)

Plasmids contain relatively few genes compared to the bacterial chromosome. Like chromosomal DNA, plasmids can replicate. Insertion of a nonbacterial DNA segment (set of nucleotides) results in the formation of a hybrid plasmid that can replicate the foreign DNA as well. This is the basis for human insulin production within bacteria, as mentioned above. Genes for resistance to various antibiotics are commonly found on plasmids as well.

Plasmids may also be transferred from a host (donor) bacterium to a recipient bacterial cell by a process called **bacterial conjugation.** Thus, the plasmid acts both as a carrier of foreign DNA and as an agent (vector) for the introduction of that DNA into the recipient cell. Once plasmid DNA is transferred to the recipient, the recipient bears the genes (and hence makes the gene products) formerly in the host.

Plasmid transfer between host and recipient (in this case, two bacterial cells) occurs through a bridge formed by the host cell that connects it to the recipient. Figure 14-17 illustrates bacterial conjugation. Note that genes on the bacterial chromosome are not transferred between cells.

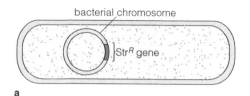
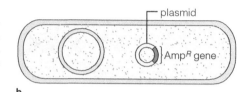

a

b

Figure 14-16 Genetic components of two strains of *Escherichia coli* bacteria. (**a**) Strain 1 has a gene for resistance to the antibiotic streptomycin (designated Str^R) on its chromosome. (**b**) Strain 2 has a gene for resistance to the antibiotic ampicillin (designated Amp^R) on a plasmid within the cell.

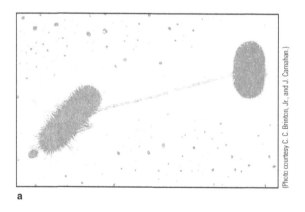

(Photo courtesy C. C. Brinton, Jr. and J. Carnahan.)

a

Figure 14-17 (**a**) Conjugation between two bacteria. (**b**) Plasmid gene transfer during bacterial conjugation. The bacterial chromosome is not shown.

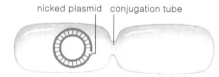

1 A conjugation tube has already formed between a donor and a recipient cell. An enzyme has nicked the donor's plasmid.

2 DNA replication starts on the nicked plasmid. The displaced DNA strand moves through the tube and enters the recipient cell.

3 In the recipient cell, replication starts on the transferred DNA.

4 The cells separate from each other; the plasmids circularize.

b

(After Starr, 2000.)

MATERIALS

Per student group (4):

- nutrient agar plate containing ampicillin, incubated with *E. coli* Strain 1 on one half, and *E. coli* Strain 2 on the other half
- nutrient agar plate containing streptomycin, incubated with *E. coli* Strain 1 on one half, and *E. coli* Strain 2 on the other half

- nutrient agar plate containing *both* ampicillin and streptomycin, incubated with a mating solution of both *E. coli* Strain 1 and *E. coli* Strain 2 spread across the plate (The mating solution is designed to allow bacterial conjugation to occur.)
- demonstration nutrient agar plates showing growth of *E. coli* Strain 1 and *E. coli* Strain 2

PROCEDURE

1. Examine the plates for growth. (Your instructor will provide demonstration plates for you to examine so that you can recognize bacterial growth.)
2. Record your observations in Table 14-2, using a + to indicate the growth of bacteria, a – to indicate absence of growth. A bacterium that is sensitive to (killed by) an antibiotic will be unable to grow on nutrient media containing that specific antibiotic.

TABLE 14-2   Bacterial Growth on Antibiotic-Containing Plates

Growth of Bacteria on Nutrient Agar Containing

Strain of *E. coli*	Ampicillin	Streptomycin	Ampicillin plus Streptomycin
Strain 2 (donor)			
Strain 1 (recipient)			
"Mating mixture"			

3. Discard your plates in the designated location.

Was Strain 2 susceptible *or* resistant to ampicillin? _____

To streptomycin? _____

Was Strain 1 susceptible *or* resistant to ampicillin? _____

To streptomycin? _____

Make a conclusion about the presence and location of a gene in each of the two strains of *E. coli* for resistance to each of the antibiotics.

    Strain 2

_____

_____

    Strain 1

_____

_____

    Make a conclusion about what happened when the two strains were mixed together. Incorporate your observations concerning antibiotic resistance into your conclusion.

_____

_____

_____

_____ 1. The individuals responsible for constructing the first model of DNA structure were
 (a) Wallace and Watson
 (b) Lamarck and Darwin
 (c) Mendel and Meischer
 (d) Crick and Watson

_____ 2. Deoxyribose is
 (a) a five-carbon sugar
 (b) present in RNA
 (c) a nitrogen-containing base
 (d) one type of purine

_____ 3. A nucleotide may consist of
 (a) deoxyribose or ribose
 (b) purines or pyrimidines
 (c) phosphate groups
 (d) all of the above

_____ 4. Which of the following is consistent with the principle of base pairing?
 (a) purine-purine
 (b) pyrimidine-pyrimidine
 (c) adenine-thymine
 (d) guanine-thymine

_____ 5. Nitrogen-containing bases between two complementary DNA strands are joined by
 (a) polar covalent bonds
 (b) hydrogen bonds
 (c) phosphate groups
 (d) deoxyribose sugars

_____ 6. The difference between deoxyribose and ribose is that ribose
 (a) is a six-carbon sugar
 (b) bonds only to thymine, not uracil
 (c) has one more oxygen atom than deoxyribose has
 (d) is all of the above

_____ 7. Replication of DNA
 (a) takes place during interphase
 (b) results in two double helices from one
 (c) is semiconservative
 (d) is all of the above

_____ 8. Transcription of DNA
 (a) results in formation of a complementary strand of RNA
 (b) produces two new strands of DNA
 (c) occurs on the surface of the ribosome
 (d) is semiconservative

_____ 9. An anticodon
 (a) is a three-base sequence of nucleotides on tRNA
 (b) is produced by translation of RNA
 (c) has the same base sequence as does the codon
 (d) is the same as a gene

_____ 10. Bacterial plasmids
 (a) are the only genetic material in bacteria
 (b) may carry genes for antibiotic resistance
 (c) may be transferred between bacteria during the process of conjugation
 (d) are both b and c

Evolutionary Agents

After completing this exercise, you will be able to

1. define *evolutionary agent, natural selection, fitness, directional selection, stabilizing selection, disruptive selection, gene flow, divergence, speciation, mutation, genetic drift, bottleneck effect, founder effect;*

2. determine the allele frequencies for a gene in a model population;

3. calculate expected ratios of phenotypes based on Hardy–Weinberg proportions;

4. describe the effects of nonrandom mating, natural selection, migration, genetic drift, and mutation on a model population;

5. describe the effects of different selection pressures on identical model populations;

6. identify the level at which selection operates in a population;

7. describe the impact of the founder effect on the genetic structure of populations.

INTRODUCTION

Heredity itself cannot cause changes in the frequencies of alternate forms of the same gene (alleles). If certain conditions are met, then the proportions of genotypes that make up a population of organisms should remain constant generation after generation according to the equation that describes the Hardy–Weinberg equilibrium:

$$p^2 + 2pq + q^2 = 1.0 \text{ (for two alleles)}$$

If p is the frequency of one allele, and q is the frequency of the other allele, then

$$p + q = 1.0$$

For example, if two alleles for coat color exist in a population of mice and the allele for white coats is present 70% of the time, then the alternate allele (black) must be present 30% of the time.

The Hardy–Weinberg equation describes the proportions of phenotypes present in succeeding generations, as long as conditions don't change. In our example, since $p = .7$, we would expect 49% (p^2) of the mice in our population to be homozygous for white coats. Thus, 42% ($2pq$) would have one of each allele and would appear gray if neither allele is dominant (that is, both alleles would have equal expression in the phenotype). What percentage of our population is homozygous for black coats? _____ %

In nature, however, the frequencies of genes in populations change over time. Natural populations never meet all of the conditions assumed for Hardy–Weinberg equilibrium. *Evolution is a process resulting in changes in the genetic makeup of populations through time;* therefore, factors that disrupt Hardy–Weinberg equilibrium are referred to as **evolutionary agents.** This exercise demonstrates the effect of these agents on the genetic structure of a simplified model population.

16.1 Natural Selection (75 min.)

The populations you will work with are composed of colored beads. White beads in our model represent individuals that are homozygous for the white allele ($C^W C^W$). Red beads are individuals homozygous for the red allele ($C^R C^R$), and pink beads are heterozygotes ($C^W C^R$). These beads exist in "ponds"—plastic dishpans filled with smaller beads. Counts of white, pink, and red individuals in the pond are made after straining the beads through a sieve. The smaller beads pass through the mesh, which retains the larger beads. Figure 16-1 shows the initial experimental setup.

When the individuals are recovered, the frequencies of the color alleles are determined using the Hardy–Weinberg equation. The alleles in our population are codominant. Thus, each white bead contains two white alleles; each pink bead, one white and one red allele; and each red bead, two red alleles. The total number of color alleles in a population of 40 individuals is 80. If such a population contains 10 white beads, 20 pink beads, and 10 red beads the frequency of the white allele is

$$p = \frac{(2 \times 10) + 20}{80} = .5$$

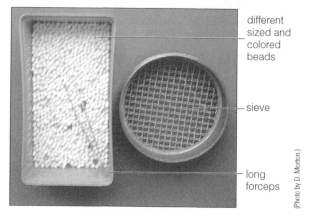

Figure 16-1 Experimental setup used to demonstrate natural selection.

(Photo by D. Morton.)

Because $p + q = 1.0$, the frequency of the red allele (q) must also be .5 if there are only two color alleles in this population.

MATERIALS

Per student group (4):

- plastic dishpan (12″ × 7″ × 2″)
- 50 large (10-mm-diameter) white beads
- 50 large red beads
- 50 large pink beads
- 4000 small (8-mm diameter) white beads
- 4000 small red beads (optional)

- ruler with a cm scale
- pair of long forceps
- coarse sieve (9.5 mm)
- scientific calculator

Per lab room:

- clock with a second hand

PROCEDURE

A. Experiment: Natural Selection Acting Alone

Natural selection disturbs the Hardy–Weinberg equilibrium by discriminating between individuals with respect to their ability to produce young. Those individuals that survive to reproduce perpetuate more of their genes in the population. These individuals exhibit greater **fitness** than do those who leave no offspring or fewer offspring.

This experiment addresses the hypothesis that *individuals are more likely to survive and reproduce when their coloration makes it easier to hide from predators in the environment.*

1. Work in groups of four with each group member assuming one of the following roles: Predator, Data Recorder/Timer, Calculator, or Caretaker. Predators search for prey. Data Recorders/Timers record numerical results and time events. Calculators use a scientific calculator to crunch numbers as needed. Caretakers look after and manipulate the experimental setup.

2. Create a white pond by filling a dishpan with small white beads to a depth of about 5 cm and establish an initial population by mixing into the pond 10 large white beads, 10 large red beads, and 20 large pink beads. The Predator will prey on the large beads, removing as many as possible in a limited amount of time. The survivors will then reproduce the next generation and predation will begin again. This cycle will be repeated several times. Make a prediction as to the changing frequency in the population of the red allele over time and write it in the Prediction (Selection Alone) row of Table 16-3.

3. Search the pond for prey (large beads) and, using a pair of long forceps, remove as many of them as possible in 30 seconds.

4. Strain the pond with the sieve, and count the number of large white, pink, and red beads. Record the totals in the After row under Initial in Table 16-1.

5. Calculate the frequencies of the white (p) and red (q) alleles remaining in the population after selection and record them in First generation after selection of Table 16-2. For example, if 6 white, 8 pink, and 8 red beads remain, the frequency of the white allele is

$$p = \frac{(2 \times 6) + 8}{44} = .45$$

TABLE 16-1 Large-Bead Counts Before and After Four Rounds of Simulated Predation

Population	White Beads	Pink Beads	Red Beads	Total Beads
Initial				
Before	10	20	10	40
After	_____	_____	_____	_____
Second Generation				
Before	_____	_____	_____	50
After	_____	_____	_____	_____
Third Generation				
Before	_____	_____	_____	50
After	_____	_____	_____	_____
Fourth Generation				
Before	_____	_____	_____	50
After	_____	_____	_____	_____

TABLE 16-2 Allele and Genotype Frequencies Due to Selection by Simulated Predation

Population	p	q	p^2	$2pq$	q^2
Initial	.5	.5	.25	.5	.25
First generation after selection					
Second generation after selection					
Third generation after selection					
Fourth generation after selection					

6. Using the new values for allele frequencies, calculate genotype frequencies for homozygous white (p^2), heterozygous pink ($2pq$), and homozygous red (q^2) individuals, and record them in Table 16-2. For example, if p now equals .45, the frequency of homozygous white individuals is

$$p^2 = (.45)^2 = .20$$

Assuming that 50 individuals comprise the next and succeeding generations (maximum number of individuals the pond can sustain), calculate the number of white, pink, and red individuals needed to create the population of a new pond and record these numbers in the Before row under Second Generation in Table 16-1. Here and in future calculations to generate new numbers of individuals, round up or down to the nearest whole number. For example, if $p^2 = .20$, the number of white beads needed is

$$p^2 \times 50 = .20 \times 50 = 10 \text{ white beads}$$

Using these numbers, construct a new pond.

7. Repeat steps 2–6 for three more rounds, filling in the remaining rows in Tables 16-1 and 16-2. When you are finished, copy the frequency of the red allele from Table 16-1 to Table 16-3 (Selection Alone column) and plot this data in Figure 16-2.

TABLE 16-3 Frequency of Red Allele (q) Due to Selection and Migration

Prediction (Selection Alone):

Prediction (Selection and Migration):

Generation	Selection Alone	Selection and Migration
1		
2		
3		
4		

Conclusion (Selection Alone):

Conclusion (Selection and Migration):

8. Write your conclusion as to your prediction in the Conclusion (Selection Alone) row of Table 16-3.
9. If you had started with a pond filled with small red beads as a background, how would the frequency of the red allele change?

_____

_____

_____

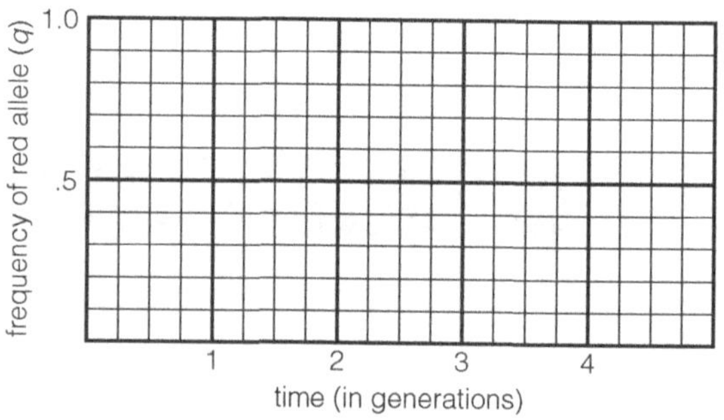

Figure 16-2 Effects of predation on allele frequencies.

10. Selection that favors one extreme phenotype over the other and causes allele frequencies to change in a predictable direction is known as **directional selection**. When selection favors an intermediate phenotype rather than one at the extremes, it's known as **stabilizing selection**. Selection that operates against the intermediate phenotype and favors the extreme ones is called **disruptive selection**. Which kind of selection is illustrated by simulated predation of white, pink, and red beads in a white pond? Explain why you made this choice.

_____

_____

_____

It is important to realize that selection operates on the entire phenotype so that the overall fitness of an organism is based on the result of interactions of thousands of genes.

11. If two identical populations (such as the mix of beads described in step 2) inhabited different environments (such as red and white ponds), how would the frequency of the color genes in each pond compare after a large number of generations?

_____

_____

As two populations become genetically different through time (**divergence**), individuals from these populations can lose the ability to interbreed. If this happens, two species form from one ancestral species. This process is called **speciation.**

The frequencies of alleles in a population also change if new organisms immigrate and interbreed, or when old breeding members emigrate. **Gene flow** due to *migration* may be a powerful force in evolution. This activity demonstrates its effect.

1. Establish an initial population as in the previous section, step 2.
2. Begin selection as before, *except* add five new red beads to each generation before the new allele frequencies are determined. These beads represent migrants from a population where the red allele confers greater fitness. This experiment addresses the hypothesis that *gene flow resulting from the migration of a significant number of individuals into a population undergoing predation affects the change in allele frequencies expected from selection alone.* Write your prediction as to how the change in frequency of the red allele will be affected in the Conclusion (Selection and Migration) row of Table 16-3.
3. For each generation, record the frequencies of the red allele obtained with both selection and migration in Table 16-3.
4. How does migration influence the effectiveness of selection in this example?

   _____

   _____

   _____

5. Write your conclusion as to your prediction in the Conclusion (Selection and Migration) row of Table 16-3.
6. How would migration have influenced the change in gene frequencies if white instead of red individuals had entered the population?

   _____

   _____

   _____

Gene flow keeps local populations of the same species from becoming more and more different from each other. Things that serve as barriers to gene flow can accelerate the production of new species. Migration can also introduce new genes into a population and produce new genetic combinations. Imagine the result of a black allele being introduced into our model population and the new heterozygotes (perhaps gray and dark red) it would produce.

Note: If time is short, any or all of the remaining sections may be done as thought experiments, i.e., doing it in your head rather than actually setting it up.

| 16.2 | **Mutation** *(About 15 min.)* |

Another way new genetic information enters a population is through **mutation.** This usually represents an actual change in the information encoded by the DNA of an organism. As such, most mutations are harmful and will be eliminated by natural selection. Nevertheless, mutations do provide the raw material for evolution.

MATERIALS

Per student group (4):

- small bowl
- 10 large white beads
- 10 large red beads

- 20 large pink beads
- 1 large gray bead
- scientific calculator

PROCEDURE

1. Establish an initial population by placing 10 large white beads, 10 large red beads, and 20 large pink beads in a small bowl (without the small beads).
2. For the sake of expediency, establish a new generation by one group member picking, without looking, 20 large beads from the bowl. Replace one white bead with a gray bead. This represents a mutation in a gamete that one parent contributed to this generation.
3. Calculate the allele frequencies of the new generation, including the frequency of the new color allele (r). Record them in Table 16-4.

TABLE 16-4 Change in Allele Frequencies Due to Mutation

Population	p	q	r
Initial	.5	.5	
New generation with mutation			

4. Three alleles are present ($p + q + r = 1.0$), so the Hardy–Weinberg equation is expanded to $p^2 + 2pq + q^2 + 2pr + 2qr + r^2 = 1.0$, and in addition to white, pink, and red phenotypes, we now have gray, dark red, and potentially, in subsequent generations, black. If the next generation contains 50 individuals, how many offspring of each phenotype would you expect? Use Table 16-5 to calculate these numbers.

TABLE 16-5 Numbers of Each Phenotype Two Generations After a Single Mutation

Color	Genotype	Frequency	× 50	Number of Individuals
White	p^2			
Pink	$2pq$			
Red	q^2			
Gray	$2pr$			
Dark red	$2qr$			
Black	r^2			

Imagine a population made up of individuals in these proportions. What effect will natural selection have on these phenotypes in a white pond?

_____

_____

_____

How could conditions change to favor the selection of the rare black allele?

_____

_____

16.3 **Genetic Drift** *(About 30 min.)*

Chance is also a factor that results in shifts in gene frequencies over several generations (**genetic drift**). This is primarily due to the random aspects of reproduction and fertilization. Genetic drift is often a problem for small populations in that they can lose much of their genetic variability. In very small populations, chance can eliminate an allele from a population, such that p becomes 0 and the other allele becomes fixed ($q = 1.0$). This loss of genetic variation due to a small population size is known as the **bottleneck effect**.

MATERIALS

Per student group (4):

- small bowl
- 10 large white beads
- 10 large red beads

- 20 large pink beads
- scientific calculator

PROCEDURE

1. As in the previous section, place 10 large white beads, 10 large red beads, and 20 large pink beads in a small bowl. Listed in Table 16-6 are the expected allele frequencies for color in this population given all individuals participate in reproduction.

TABLE 16-6 Allele Frequencies Produced by Genetic Drift

		Actual Frequency in	
	Expected Frequency	Small Cluster	Large Cluster
n			
p	.5		
q	.5		

2. Establish a cluster of reproductively lucky individuals by a group member choosing, without looking, 10 beads from the bowl.
3. In the second column of Table 16-6, record the allele frequencies present in this cluster.
4. Now replace the 10 beads you removed in step 2. Select beads at random again, but this time select 30 beads representing a larger cluster of reproductively lucky individuals.
5. Calculate the allele frequencies for this larger cluster and record them in the third column of Table 16-6.
6. Compare the allele frequencies in the three columns of Table 16-6. Sometimes chance determines whose gametes contribute to the next generation. What effect does the size of the number of individuals participating in reproduction have on gene flow to the next generation?

_____

_____

7. Another way in which chance affects allele frequencies in a population is when migrants from old populations establish new populations. To model this effect, choose at random six individuals from an initial population to represent the migrants.
8. Move these individuals to a new unoccupied pond. (It is not necessary to actually set up a new pond for this demonstration. Use your imagination.)
9. Now calculate the allele frequencies in the new pond and record them in Table 16-7. How do they compare with the frequencies that characterized the pond from which these migrants came?

_____

_____

The genetic makeup in future generations in the new population will more closely resemble the six migrants than the population from which the migrants came. This effect is known as the **founder effect.** The founder effect may not be an entirely random process because organisms that migrate from a population may be genetically different from the rest of the population to begin with. For example, if wing length in a population of insects is variable, we might expect insects with longer wings to be better at founding new populations because they can be carried farther by winds.

TABLE 16-7 Allele Frequencies in a Founder Population

	p	q
Initial Population	.5	.5
Founder Population		

Hardy–Weinberg equilibrium is also disturbed if individuals in a population don't choose mates randomly. Some members of a population may show a strong preference for mates with similar genetic makeups. This activity models this effect.

MATERIALS

Per student group (4):

- small bowl
- 10 large white beads
- 10 large red beads

- 20 large pink beads
- scientific calculator

PROCEDURE

1. Establish an initial population as in Section 16.3.
2. Assume that individuals will mate only with individuals of the same color. Arbitrarily assign sex to every bead so there are equal numbers of males and females in each color group.
3. If each pair of beads produces four offspring, record the number individuals with the same phenotype present in the next generation in Table 16-8. Remember that the pink pairs will produce one red, one white, and two pink individuals on average.

TABLE 16-8   Phenotype Changes Due to Nonrandom Mating Color

Color	Number in	
	Initial Generation	Next Generation
White	10	
Pink	20	
Red	10	

4. Calculate the genotype frequencies in this generation, record them in Table 16-9, and compare these with the frequencies in the initial generation.

TABLE 16-9   Genotype Frequency Changes Due to Nonrandom Mating

Genotype Frequency	Initial Generation	Next Generation
p^2		
$2pq$		
q^2		

5. What happens to the frequency of the heterozygote genotype in subsequent generations?

_____

_____

_____

PRE-LAB QUESTIONS

_____ 1. If all conditions of Hardy–Weinberg equilibrium are met,
  (a) allele frequencies move closer to .5 each generation
  (b) allele frequencies change in the direction predicted by natural selection
  (c) allele frequencies stay the same
  (d) all allele frequencies increase

_____ 2. If a population is in Hardy–Weinberg equilibrium and $p = .6$,
  (a) $q = .5$
  (b) $q = .4$
  (c) $q = .3$
  (d) $q = .16$

_____ 3. Natural selection operates directly on
  (a) the genotype
  (b) individual alleles
  (c) the phenotype
  (d) color only

_____ 4. The process that discriminates between phenotypes with respect to their ability to produce offspring is known as
  (a) natural selection
  (b) gene flow
  (c) genetic drift
  (d) migration

_____ 5. Two populations that have no gene flow between them are likely to
  (a) become more different with time
  (b) become more alike with time
  (c) become more alike if the directional selection pressures are different
  (d) stay the same unless mutations occur

_____ 6. A process that results in individuals of two populations losing the ability to interbreed is referred to as
  (a) stabilizing selection
  (b) fusion
  (c) speciation
  (d) differential migration

_____ 7. Two ways in which new alleles can become incorporated in a population are
  (a) mutation and genetic drift
  (b) selection and genetic drift
  (c) selection and mutation
  (d) mutation and gene flow

_____ 8. If a new allele appears in a population, the Hardy–Weinberg formula
  (a) cannot be used because no equilibrium exists
  (b) can be used but only for two alleles at a time
  (c) can be used by lumping all but two phenotypes in one class
  (d) can be expanded by adding more terms

_____ 9. A shift from expected allele frequencies, resulting from chance, is known as
  (a) natural selection
  (b) genetic drift
  (c) mutation
  (d) gene flow

_____ 10. Genetic drift is a process that has a greater effect on populations that
  (a) are large
  (b) are small
  (c) are not affected by mutation
  (d) do not go through bottlenecks

Human Respiration

OBJECTIVES

After completing this exercise, you will be able to

1. define *ventilation, inhalation, exhalation, breathing, cohesion, tidal volume, forced inhalation volume, forced exhalation volume, residual volume, vital capacity, chemoreceptor;*

2. list the skeletal muscles used in breathing and give the specific function of each;

3. trace the flow of air through the organs and structures of the respiratory system;

4. explain how air moves in and out of the lungs during respiration in the human;

5. explain how air moves in and out of the lungs during respiration in the frog;

6. distinguish among negative pressure inhalation, positive pressure exhalation, and positive pressure inhalation;

7. describe the relationship between vital capacity and lung volumes and the interrelationships among lung volumes;

8. explain the importance of CO_2 concentration in the blood and other body fluids to the control of respiration.

INTRODUCTION

In Exercise 10, we investigated carbohydrate metabolism and cellular respiration. Oxygen (O_2) is consumed, and carbon dioxide (CO_2) and water (H_2O) are produced during the breakdown of glucose to provide the energy (adenosine triphosphate, or ATP) to fuel cellular activities.

For cellular respiration to continue, O_2 must be replenished and CO_2 removed from cells by the process of diffusion (Exercise 7). The efficiency of diffusion to transport substances is great over short distances but decreases rapidly as distance increases. Evolution, however, has selected for organisms of different sizes—from one-celled species to the blue whale, the largest living animal. Because diffusion works well only over short distances, animals about the size of earthworms and larger have circulatory systems that move dissolved gases around the body, and animals a little larger have respiratory systems. For example, the clam and crayfish move water across gills to facilitate the body's gain of O_2 and loss of CO_2.

In humans and other air-breathing vertebrates, O_2 uptake and CO_2 elimination occur by diffusion across the moistened thin membranes of millions of alveoli (singular, *alveolus*) and their surrounding capillaries located in the lungs (Figure 41-1). These animals are protected from excessive water loss via evaporation from the very large, moist respiratory surface by having the lungs positioned inside the body.

The main function of the rest of the respiratory system is **ventilation**—the exchange of gases between the lungs and the atmosphere. The movement of gases in (**inhalation**) and out (**exhalation**) of the respiratory system requires the rhythmical contraction of skeletal muscles (**breathing**).

41.1 Breathing (50 min.)

Before we continue with this exercise, let's review some anatomical terms. The trunk of the body is divided into an upper *thorax*, which is supported by the rib cage and contains the *thoracic cavity*, and a lower *abdomen*. The thoracic and abdominal cavities are separated by a partition of skeletal muscle called the *diaphragm*. The thoracic cavity contains two *pleural cavities*, which contain the lungs and the *pericardial cavity* surrounding the heart.

The muscles of breathing and their roles in inhalation and exhalation are listed in Table 41-1. The external and internal intercostal muscles are located between the ribs. Contraction of the diaphragm increases the size of the thoracic cavity by lowering its floor. Relaxation of the diaphragm allows it to spring back to its original position. When they are contracted, the abdominal muscles can squeeze the internal organs, pushing up the diaphragm to decrease the size of the thoracic cavity.

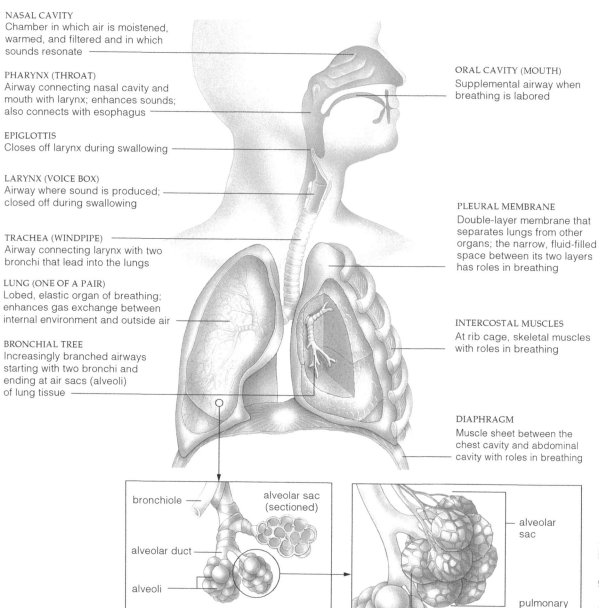

NASAL CAVITY
Chamber in which air is moistened, warmed, and filtered and in which sounds resonate

PHARYNX (THROAT)
Airway connecting nasal cavity and mouth with larynx; enhances sounds; also connects with esophagus

EPIGLOTTIS
Closes off larynx during swallowing

LARYNX (VOICE BOX)
Airway where sound is produced; closed off during swallowing

TRACHEA (WINDPIPE)
Airway connecting larynx with two bronchi that lead into the lungs

LUNG (ONE OF A PAIR)
Lobed, elastic organ of breathing; enhances gas exchange between internal environment and outside air

BRONCHIAL TREE
Increasingly branched airways starting with two bronchi and ending at air sacs (alveoli) of lung tissue

ORAL CAVITY (MOUTH)
Supplemental airway when breathing is labored

PLEURAL MEMBRANE
Double-layer membrane that separates lungs from other organs; the narrow, fluid-filled space between its two layers has roles in breathing

INTERCOSTAL MUSCLES
At rib cage, skeletal muscles with roles in breathing

DIAPHRAGM
Muscle sheet between the chest cavity and abdominal cavity with roles in breathing

bronchiole
alveolar sac (sectioned)
alveolar duct
alveoli

alveolar sac
pulmonary capillary

(After Starr and Taggart, 2001.)

Figure 41-1 Human respiratory system.

TABLE 41-1	Muscles Used to Breathe				
Stage of Respiratory Cycle	**Muscles**				
	External Intercostals	**Internal Intercostals**	**Diaphragm**	**Neck and Shoulder**	**Abdominal**
Restful inhalation	Relaxed	Relaxed	Contracted	Relaxed	Relaxed
Forced inhalation	Contracted	Relaxed	Contracted	Contracted	Relaxed
Restful exhalation	Relaxed	Relaxed	Relaxed	Relaxed	Relaxed
Forced exhalation	Relaxed	Contracted	Relaxed	Relaxed	Contracted

MATERIALS

Per student:

- 2 pieces of paper (each 14 × 21.5 cm—half of a sheet of notebook paper)

Per group (2):

- metric tape measure
- large caliper with linear scale (for example, Collyer pelvimeter)

Per group (4):

- functional model of lung
- models of the organs and structures of the respiratory system
- prepared slide of a section of mammalian lung

Per lab room:

- frogs in terrarium or video of breathing frog
- clock with second hand

PROCEDURE

A. Ventilatory Ducts and Lungs

The respiratory system consists of the lungs and the ducts that shuttle air between the atmosphere and the lungs. Its organs and structures from the outside in are the two **external nares** (nostrils), the **nasal cavity** (divided into right and left sides by a **nasal septum** or partition), the **pharynx** (shared with the digestive tract), the **glottis** (and its cover the **epiglottis**), the **larynx** (voice box), the **trachea** (windpipe), two **bronchi** (singular, bronchus), and its branches, which terminally open into myriad **alveoli** (singular, alveolus) in the **lungs.** Along with respiration, sound production is a major function of the respiratory tract.

1. Look at the various models of respiratory tract organs and structures and identify as many of the preceding boldfaced terms as possible.
2. Get your compound light microscope and examine a lung section at high power; identify the alveoli (Figure 41-2).

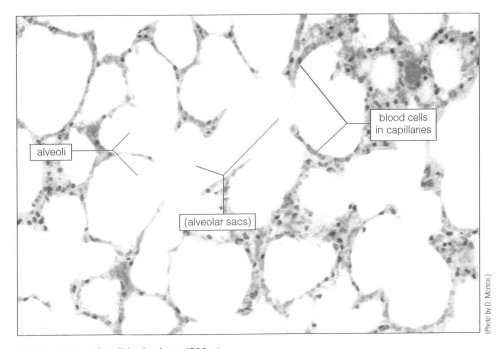

Figure 41-2 Alveoli in the lung (500×).

B. Ventilation

All flow occurs down a pressure gradient. When you let go of an untied inflated balloon, it flies away, propelled by the jet of air flowing out of it. The air flows out because the pressure is higher inside the balloon. The high pressure inside the balloon is maintained by the energy stored in its stretched elastic wall.

When the thoracic cavity expands during inspiration, first the pressure in the pleural sacs decreases, and then the pressure within the lungs decreases. Because the pressure outside the body is now higher than that in the lungs, and assuming the connecting *ventilatory ducts* (trachea and so on) are not blocked, air flows into the lungs (Figure 41-3). This is called **negative pressure inhalation.**

The opposite occurs during expiration. The size of the thorax and pleural sacs decreases, the pressure in the lungs increases, and air flows out of the body down its concentration gradient. This is called **positive pressure exhalation.**

The pressure in the pleural sacs is actually always below atmospheric pressure, which means the lungs are always partially inflated after birth. Thus, a hole in a pleural sac or lung will result in a collapsed lung. **Cohesion** (sticking together) of the wet pleural membranes lining the outsides of the lungs and insides of the body walls of the pleural cavities aids inhalation. Exhalation depends in part on the *elastic recoil* (like letting go of a stretched rubber band) of lung tissue.

1. Work in groups of four. Look at the functional lung model. The "Y" tube is analogous to the ventilatory ducts. The balloons represent the lungs. The space within the transparent chamber represents the thoracic spaces and its rubber floor (rubber "diaphragm"), the muscular diaphragm.
2. Pull down the rubber diaphragm. Describe what happens to the balloons.

_____

As you pull down the rubber diaphragm, does the volume of the space in the container increase or decrease?

_____

As the volume changes, does the pressure in the container increase or decrease?

_____

As the balloons inflate, does the volume of air in the balloons increase or decrease?

_____

Why do the balloons inflate?

_____
_____
_____
_____
_____

3. Push up on the rubber diaphragm. Describe what happens to the balloons and why it takes place.

_____
_____
_____
_____
_____

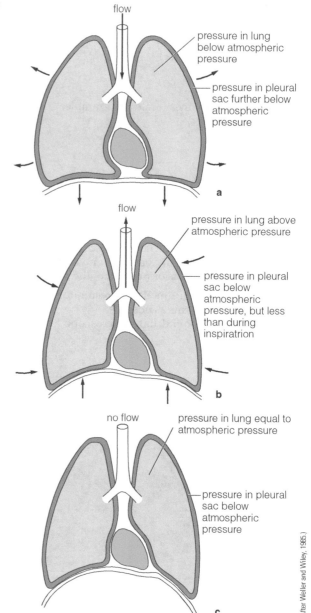

Figure 41-3 Changes in the thoracic cavity during (**a**) negative pressure inhalation and (**b**) positive pressure exhalation, and corresponding movements of air. (**c**) The thoracic cavity at the end of an expiration.

(After Weller and Wiley, 1985.)

4. Pull the rubber diaphragm down and push it up several times in succession to simulate breathing.
5. Pucker up your lips and inhale. As you inhale, place one piece of paper directly over your lips. What occurs?

_____
_____

The negative pressure created in your lungs by the contraction of the muscles of inhalation causes this suction.

6. Fold the narrow ends of the two pieces of paper to produce 2- to 3-cm flaps. Open the flaps and use them as handles. Hold a piece of paper with each hand and touch the papers' flat surfaces together in front of you (Figure 41-4). Pull them apart.

Now, thoroughly wet both pieces of paper with water and again touch their flat surfaces together in front of you. Pull them apart. What difference did the water make?

_____

_____

7. Some vertebrates, such as the frog, inhale by pushing air into the lungs. This is the positive pressure inhalation. Observe a frog out of water or watch a video of a breathing frog.

The frog inhales by sucking in air through the nostrils by lowering the floor of the mouth. Valves in the nostrils are then closed and the floor of the mouth raised, thus increasing the pressure and forcing the air into the lungs. The upper portion of the ventilatory duct can be closed to keep the air in the lungs. Exhalation occurs by elastic recoil of the lungs with the ventilatory duct open. In the frog, both inhalation and exhalation are the result of positive pressure.

What is the frog's respiratory rate (breaths per minute)? Count and record how many times the frog lowers and raises the floor of the mouth (one breath) in 3 minutes. _____ breaths/3 minutes

Divide by 3 to calculate the average respiratory rate and record it: _____ breaths/minute

Respiration in the frog is supplemented by gas exchange across the moist skin. Also, as they are ectotherms (do not maintain a high body temperature using physiological means), frogs generally have a lower metabolic rate and, therefore, a lesser demand for O_2 than a mammal of the same size.

C. Breathing Movements

1. Place your hands on your abdomen and take three deep breaths—three inspirations followed by three expirations. What do you feel during each inspiration?

_____

_____

each expiration?

_____

_____

2. Place your hands on your chest and repeat step 1. What do you feel during each inspiration?

_____

_____

each expiration?

_____

_____

(Photo by D. Morton.)

Figure 41-4 Use of two pieces of paper to demonstrate cohesion.

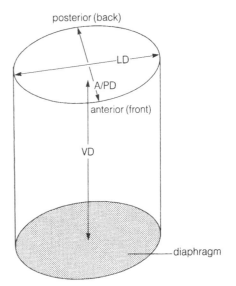

Figure 41-5 Thoracic diameters: LD, lateral diameter; A/PD, anterioposterior diameter; and VD, vertical diameter.

D. Measurements of the Thorax

The size of the thorax can be described by three so-called diameters: the lateral diameter (LD), the anterioposterior diameter (A/PD), and the vertical diameter (VD; Figure 41-5). The vertical diameter is the only one that can't be measured easily.

Make the following observations and record them in Table 41-2.

1. Work in pairs. Take turns measuring the circumference of each other's chest with a tape measure at two levels, under the armpits (axillae, C_{AX}) and at the lower tip of the sternum (xiphoid process, C_{XP}) for the conditions listed in Table 41-2. While the measurements are being taken, it's extremely important not to tense muscles other than those used for respiration. For example, do not raise the arms.

TABLE 41-2 Chest Measurements (cm)

Subject	Condition	C_{AX}	C_{XP}	A/PD	LD
You	At the end of a restful inhalation				
	At the end of a restful (passive) exhalation				
	At the end of a forced (maximum) inhalation				
	At the end of a forced (maximum) exhalation				
Your lab partner	At the end of a restful inhalation				
	At the end of a restful (passive) expiration				
	At the end of a forced (maximum) inhalation				
	At the end of a forced (maximum) exhalation				

2. With calipers, also measure the A/PD and LD at the nipple line for these same conditions. The distance between the tips of the calipers is read off the scale in centimeters.

3. About two-thirds of the air inhaled during a restful inhalation is due to contraction of the diaphragm. Interpret the data in Table 41-2 and in your own words describe changes in the size of the thorax during

    a. a restful inhalation:

       C_{AX} _____

       C_{XP} _____

       A/PD _____

       LD _____

    b. a passive exhalation:

       C_{AX} _____

       C_{XP} _____

       A/PD _____

       LD _____

    c. a forced inhalation:

       C_{AX} _____

       C_{XP} _____

       A/PD _____

       LD _____

    d. a forced exhalation:

       C_{AX} _____

       C_{XP} _____

       A/PD _____

       LD _____

Does the size of the thorax change significantly during a restful inhalation or a passive exhalation? _____ (yes or no)

How does the shape of the thorax change during a forced inhalation?

_____

_____

_____

_____

How does the shape of the thorax change during a subsequent forced exhalation?

_____

_____

_____

_____

Spirometry *(30 min.)*

Air in the lungs is divided into four mutually ex-clusive volumes (Figure 41-6): tidal volume (TV), forced inhalation volume (FIV), forced exhalation volume (FEV), and residual volume (RV).

Tidal volume is the volume of air inhaled or exhaled during breathing. It normally varies from a minimum at rest to a maximum during strenuous exercise.

Forced inhalation volume is the volume of air you can voluntarily inhale after inhalation of the tidal volume. **Forced exhalation volume** is the volume of air you can voluntarily exhale after an exhalation of the tidal volume. FIV and FEV both decrease as TV increases.

Residual volume is the volume of air that cannot be exhaled from the lungs. That is, normal lungs are always partially inflated.

There are four capacities derived from the four volumes:

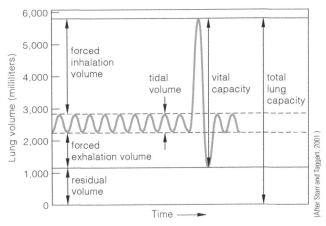

Figure 41-6 Spirogram shows the defined lung volumes and capacities.

(After Starr and Taggart, 2001)

inspiratory capacity (IC) = TV + FIV

functional residual capacity (FRC) = FEV + RV

vital capacity (VC) = TV + FIV + FEV

total lung capacity (TLC) = total of all four lung volumes

All the lung volumes except the residual volume can be measured or calculated from measurements obtained using a simple spirometer or lung volume bag. A more sophisticated recording spirometer plots respi-ration over time (a spirogram). Figure 41-5 shows a spirogram and the relationships of the lung volumes and capacities.

Caution

Always use a sterile mouthpiece and do not inhale air from either a simple spirometer or a lung volume bag.

MATERIALS

Per group (4):

- noseclip (optional)
- simple spirometer or lung volume bags

PROCEDURE

1. Work in groups of four. Sit quietly and breathe restfully. Use a noseclip or hold your nose. After you feel comfortable, start counting as you inhale. After the fourth inhalation, exhale normally into the spirometer or lung volume bag. Read the volume indicated by the spirometer or squeeze the air to the end of the lung volume bag and read the volume from the wall of the bag. Record the volume below (trial 1). Reset the spirometer or squeeze the air out of the lung volume bag. Repeat this procedure two more times (trials 2 and 3) and calculate the total and average tidal volume at rest.

   trial 1 _____ mL   trial 3 _____ mL

   trial 2 _____ mL   total = _____ mL

   Divide the total by 3 = _____ mL to calculate the average TV at rest. Record the TV in Table 41-3.

TABLE 41-3 Vital Capacity and Lung Volumes at Rest (mL)	
Measure	**Volume (mL)**
Tidal volume	_____
Forced inhalation volume	_____
Forced exhalation volume	_____
Vital capacity	_____

2. Determine the volume of air you can forcibly exhale after a restful inhalation (average of three trials).
   trial 1 _____ mL   trial 3 _____ mL
   trial 2 _____ mL   total = _____ mL
   Divide the total by 3 = _____ mL. This is the average sum of FEV and TV at rest.
3. Determine the volume of air you can forcibly exhale after a forceful inhalation (average of three trials).
   trial 1 _____ mL   trial 3 _____ mL
   trial 2 _____ mL   total = _____ mL
   Divide the total by 3 = _____ mL to calculate the average VC. Record VC in Table 41-3.
4. Calculate the FEV at rest by subtracting step 1's result from step 2's result.
   _____ mL (step 2) − _____ mL (step 1) = _____ mL.
   Record FEV in Table 41-3.
5. Calculate the FIV at rest by subtracting step 2's result from step 3's result.
   _____ mL (step 3) − _____ mL (step 2) = _____ mL.
   Record the FIV in Table 41-3.
6. Does **vital capacity** change as tidal volume increases or decreases? _____ (yes or no)
7. Measure and record your height in centimeters. _____ cm

Write your vital capacity/height on the board—your name isn't necessary.

Plot the vital capacity of each student in your lab section on the following graph.

Is there a relationship between vital capacity and height? If so, describe it mathematically using a graphing calculator or with words.

_____

_____

_____

The control of respiration, both the rate and depth of breathing, is very complex. Simply stated, **chemoreceptors** (receptors for chemicals such as O_2, CO_2, and hydrogen ions, or H^+), stretch receptors in the ventilatory ducts, and centers in the brain stem (part of the brain that connects to the spinal cord) control respiration.

Your own experience has taught you that respiration is to some extent under the control of the conscious mind. We can decide to stop breathing or to breathe more rapidly and deeply. However, the unconscious mind can override voluntary control. The classic example of this is the inability to hold one's breath for more than a few minutes. In this section you will make further pertinent observations related to the hypothesis that CO_2 concentration in the blood and other body fluids is the most important stimulus for the control of respiration.

MATERIALS

Per student pair:
- small mirror

Per lab room:
- a safe place to exercise
- clock with second hand

PROCEDURE

Caution

Do not do the following activities if you have any medical problems with your lungs or heart. All subjects should stop immediately if they feel faint.

1. Work in pairs. Write two predictions in Table 41-4. In prediction 1 forecast the effects on respiratory rate and the ability to hold one's breath after hyperventilation (overventilating the lungs by forced deep breathing). (For example, if I hyperventilate, then. . . .) In prediction 2, forecast the effects on respiratory rate and the ability to hold one's breath after exercise.
2. Sit down and after you feel comfortable, have your lab partner count the number of times you breathe in 3 minutes. If it's difficult to see you breathe, have your partner place a small mirror under your nose. Record the number of breaths: _____ breaths

Divide this number by 3 to calculate the average respiratory rate *at rest* and write it in the second column of Table 41-4.

3. Determine how many minutes you can hold your breath after a restful inhalation and record the time in the third column of Table 41-4.

TABLE 41-4   Respiratory Data

Prediction 1:

Prediction 2:

	Condition	Respiratory Rate (breaths/minute)	Breath Holding (minutes)
You	At rest		
	After hyperventilation		
	After exercise		
Your lab partner	At rest		
	After hyperventilation		
	After exercise		

Conclusions:

4. Now breathe as deeply and as rapidly as possible (*hyperventilate*). Try to take at least 10 breaths but stop as soon as you can answer the following question. (In any case, do not continue for more than 20 breaths.) As times goes on, does it become easier or more difficult to continue rapid deep breathing?

   _____

   Immediately have your lab partner count and record the number of breaths you take in the next 3 minutes: _____ breaths

5. Now determine how many minutes you can hold your breath *immediately* after hyperventilating. Record this time in the third column of Table 41-4.

6. Divide the number in step 4 by 3 to calculate the average respiratory rate *after hyperventilation* and write it in the second column of Table 41-4.

Does hyperventilation increase, decrease, or have no effect on the CO_2 concentration of the blood?

_____

7. When fully recovered from step 2, carefully run in place for 2 minutes in the area designated by your lab instructor. Immediately after sitting down, again have your lab partner count how many breaths you take in 3 minutes and record it: _____ breaths

Now determine how long you can hold your breath *immediately* after 2 minutes of exercise and record it in the third column of Table 41-4.

As you did earlier, calculate the average respiratory rate *after exercise* and record it in the second column of Table 41-4.

Does running in place increase or decrease the CO_2 concentration of the blood? _____

What causes the CO_2 concentration to change while you are running in place?

_____

_____

_____

8. Switch roles with your lab partner and repeat steps 1–7, recording this data in Table 41-4.
9. Use Table 41-4 to summarize your results:

   _____

   _____

   _____

   _____

   _____

Write a conclusion in Table 41-5 as to whether your results supported your predictions.

| 41.4 | **Experiment: Physiology of Exercise** *(40 min.)* |

When an animal increases its activity, its muscles need more O_2 to support their higher level of cellular metabolism. Increasing both breathing and the circulation of blood through the lungs, heart, and skeletal muscles enhances oxygen delivery.

From observing our own bodies, we know that exercise is accompanied by increases in the rate of breathing, the depth of breathing, and the heart rate. Intuitively, we also expect a similar elevation in arterial blood pressure because this would increase the blood pressure difference between the elastic arteries near the heart and the arterioles near the capillaries. This steeper pressure gradient would result in a higher blood velocity—the speed at which blood flows—just as a boulder rolls faster down a steeper hill. Higher blood velocity along with increased activity of the respiratory system means more O_2 is transported to the heart and skeletal muscles.

So, how do heart rate, systolic blood pressure, respiratory rate, and tidal volume change as the intensity of exercise increases? This experiment addresses the hypothesis that *all these factors will increase as the intensity of exercise increases to contribute to delivering more and more O_2 to the skeletal muscles.*

MATERIALS

Per student:

■ calculator

Per lab room:

■ television or monitor
■ video cassette or DVD player
■ video cassette or DVD: "Experiment: Biology; The Physiology of Exercise"

PROCEDURE

As a class you will watch a video of a young man on a stationary bicycle. After recording his heart rate, systolic blood pressure, respiratory rate, and tidal volume at rest, you will record data for these same observations after four periods of work—pedaling against a constant resistance at 10, 15, 20, and 25 km/hour.

1. State a prediction for this experiment and write it in Table 41-5.
2. Watch the video and record the data in Table 41-5. Certain numbers need to be multiplied by 10 or 100 to convert them to the units used in the table. However, don't convert any of the values read off the various meters in the video, because the conversion factors are included in the table.
3. List the experimental variables.
   Independent variable _____
   Dependent variables _____
   Controlled variables (as many as you can identify)
   _____
   _____

TABLE 41-5 Physiology of Exercise

Prediction:

Intensity of exercise	Heat rate (beats/min.)	Systolic pressure (mm Hg)	Respiratory rate (breaths/min.)	Tidal volume (L)
0 km/hr (rest)	_____ × 10	_____	_____ × 10	_____
10 km/hr	_____ × 10	_____	_____ × 10	_____
15 km/hr	_____ × 100	_____	_____ × 10	_____
20 km/hr	_____ × 100	_____	_____ × 10	_____
25 km/hr	_____ × 100	_____	_____ × 10	_____

Conclusion:

4. Plot these results in the following graphs:

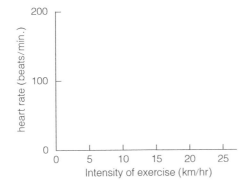

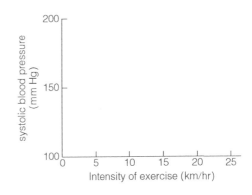

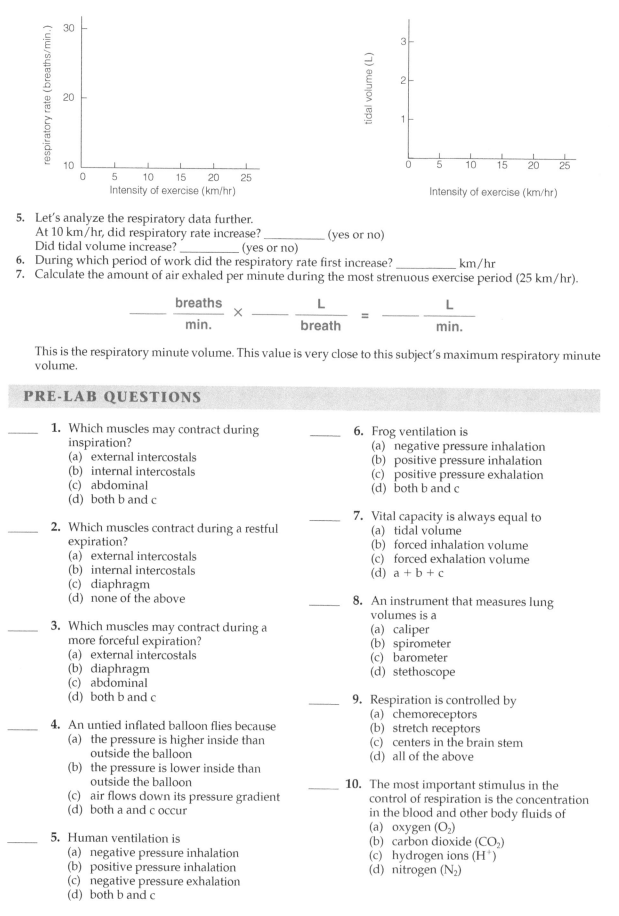

5. Let's analyze the respiratory data further.
   At 10 km/hr, did respiratory rate increase? _____ (yes or no)
   Did tidal volume increase? _____ (yes or no)
6. During which period of work did the respiratory rate first increase? _____ km/hr
7. Calculate the amount of air exhaled per minute during the most strenuous exercise period (25 km/hr).

$$\underline{\hspace{2cm}} \frac{\text{breaths}}{\text{min.}} \times \underline{\hspace{2cm}} \frac{\text{L}}{\text{breath}} = \underline{\hspace{2cm}} \frac{\text{L}}{\text{min.}}$$

This is the respiratory minute volume. This value is very close to this subject's maximum respiratory minute volume.

PRE-LAB QUESTIONS

_____ 1. Which muscles may contract during inspiration?
(a) external intercostals
(b) internal intercostals
(c) abdominal
(d) both b and c

_____ 2. Which muscles contract during a restful expiration?
(a) external intercostals
(b) internal intercostals
(c) diaphragm
(d) none of the above

_____ 3. Which muscles may contract during a more forceful expiration?
(a) external intercostals
(b) diaphragm
(c) abdominal
(d) both b and c

_____ 4. An untied inflated balloon flies because
(a) the pressure is higher inside than outside the balloon
(b) the pressure is lower inside than outside the balloon
(c) air flows down its pressure gradient
(d) both a and c occur

_____ 5. Human ventilation is
(a) negative pressure inhalation
(b) positive pressure inhalation
(c) negative pressure exhalation
(d) both b and c

_____ 6. Frog ventilation is
(a) negative pressure inhalation
(b) positive pressure inhalation
(c) positive pressure exhalation
(d) both b and c

_____ 7. Vital capacity is always equal to
(a) tidal volume
(b) forced inhalation volume
(c) forced exhalation volume
(d) a + b + c

_____ 8. An instrument that measures lung volumes is a
(a) caliper
(b) spirometer
(c) barometer
(d) stethoscope

_____ 9. Respiration is controlled by
(a) chemoreceptors
(b) stretch receptors
(c) centers in the brain stem
(d) all of the above

_____ 10. The most important stimulus in the control of respiration is the concentration in the blood and other body fluids of
(a) oxygen (O_2)
(b) carbon dioxide (CO_2)
(c) hydrogen ions (H^+)
(d) nitrogen (N_2)

EXERCISE 41

Human Respiration

POST-LAB QUESTIONS

41.1 Breathing

1. Which skeletal muscles are contracted during
   a. restful inhalation?

   b. forced inhalation?

   c. restful exhalation?

   d. forced exhalation?

2. How does the size of the thorax change during
   a. inhalation?

   b. exhalation?

3. How does the potential volume of the pleural sacs change during
   a. inhalation?

   b. exhalation?

4. Define these terms:
   a. negative pressure inhalation

   b. positive pressure exhalation

5. How does breathing in a human differ from that in a frog?

41.2 Spirometry

6. Explain the relationship among vital capacity, tidal volume, forced inhalation volume, and forced exhalation volume.

41.3 Control of Respiration

7. What substance is the most important stimulus in the control of respiration? How is its production linked to changes in metabolic rate, such as occur during exercise?

41.4 Experiment: Physiology of Exercise

8. Give an explanation for the fact that athletes' resting heart rates are usually slower than the average rate for healthy humans.

Food for Thought

9. Explain why hyperventilation can prolong the time you can hold your breath. Can this be dangerous (for example, hyperventilation followed by swimming under water)?

10. Search the World Wide Web for sites about emphysema. List two sites below and briefly summarize their contents.

http://

http://

Human Sensations, Reflexes, and Reactions

After completing this exercise, you will be able to

1. define *consciousness, sensory neurons, receptors, stimulus, motor neurons, effectors, somatic motor neurons, autonomic motor neurons, interneurons, chemical synapse, integration, proprioception, sensations, modality, free neuron endings, encapsulated neuron endings—Meissner's and Pacinian corpuscles, projection, phantom pain, adaptation, reflex, reflex arc, stretch reflexes, patella reflex, muscle spindle, pupillary reflex, swallowing reflex, reaction;*

2. describe the flow of information through the nervous system;

3. state the nature and function of sensations;

4. describe a stretch reflex;

5. describe the pupillary reflex;

6. distinguish between a reflex and a reaction;

7. measure visual reaction time.

INTRODUCTION

How do you interact with the external environment? To answer this question, you first have to be able to analyze your interactions. This means you have to be conscious. **Consciousness** is the state of being aware of the things around you, your responses, and your own thoughts. Being conscious allows you to learn, to remember, and to feel and show emotion. Second, you have to understand the flow of information through the nervous system (Figure 37-1).

Sensory neurons carry messages from **receptors** to the spinal cord and brain, which comprise the central nervous system (CNS). Receptors are located both within the body and on its surface. Receptors within the body receive information from the internal environment, while those on the surface of the body receive information from the external environment. Each piece of information received by a receptor is called a **stimulus** (plural, *stimuli*).

Motor neurons carry messages from the CNS to **effectors**. Effectors are muscles or glands that respond to stimuli. **Somatic motor neurons** control skeletal muscles, and **autonomic motor neurons** control smooth muscles, cardiac muscle, and glands.

In the CNS, a sensory neuron can directly stimulate a motor neuron across a *chemical synapse;* more frequently, though, one or more **interneurons** (*association neurons*) connect the sensory and motor neurons.

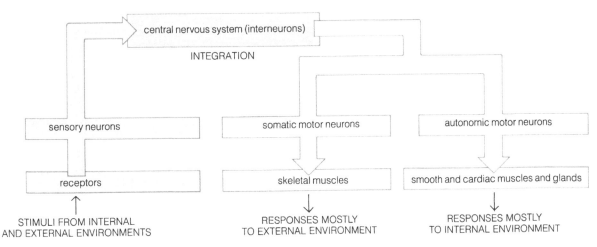

Figure 37-1 Flow of information through the nervous system.

A **chemical synapse** is a junction between two neurons (or between a neuron and an effector) that are separated by a small gap. A chemical transmitter substance released from the first neuron diffuses across the gap and then binds to (and produces changes in) the receiving cell.

The function of the interneurons is **integration.** At this level, integration is the processing of messages received from receptors via sensory neurons and the activation of the appropriate motor neurons, if any, to initiate responses by effectors. Your conscious mind is located in the cerebral cortex of the brain and is aware of (and indeed plays a part in) some of this activity.

37.1   Sensations *(50 min.)*

A receptor is the smallest part of a sense organ (such as skin) that can respond to a stimulus. The receptor is linked to the CNS by a single sensory neuron. Our bodies have receptors for light, sound waves, chemicals, heat, cold, tissue damage, and mechanical displacement. Senses for which we have sensations include sight, hearing, taste, smell, pain, touch, pressure, temperature, vibration, equilibrium, and **proprioception** (knowledge of the position and movement of the various body parts). **Sensations** are that portion of the sensory input to the CNS that is perceived by the conscious mind. There are also a number of complex sensations such as thirst, hunger, and nausea.

Most sensations inform the conscious mind about the state of the external environment. Sensations from the internal environment inform the conscious mind about problems such as dehydration. If you are thirsty, you will make a conscious decision to find and drink water.

Receptors and the sensations they produce have three characteristics: *modality, projection,* and *adaptation.* These characteristics can be easily demonstrated by investigating the skin's receptors.

MATERIALS

Per student pair:

- compound microscope
- prepared slide of mammalian skin stained with hematoxylin and eosin
- felt-tip, nonpermanent pen
- bristle
- dissecting needle
- scientific calculator
- 2 blunt probes in a 250-mL beaker of ice water
- 2 blunt probes in a 250-mL beaker of hot tap water (the hot water will have to be changed every 5 minutes)

- ice bag
- camel-hair brush
- reflex hammer
- three 1000-mL beakers containing
  ice water
  45°C water
  room-temperature water
- tissue paper

Per lab room:

- demonstration slide of a Pacinian corpuscle

PROCEDURE

A. Modality

Modality is the particular sensation that results from the stimulation of a particular receptor. For example, the modalities of taste—bitter, salty, sour, and sweet—are associated with four different types of taste buds. However, although every receptor has evolved to be most sensitive to one type of stimulus, modality actually depends on where in the brain the sensory neurons from the receptor (or the interneurons to which they connect) terminate. Modality cannot be encoded in the messages carried by sensory neurons, because every impulse in that message is identical. The only information neurons transmit is the absence or presence of a stimulus and (if one is present) its intensity—low stimulus-intensities produce a low frequency of impulses and high stimulus-intensities produce a high frequency of impulses.

   1. Examine a prepared section of skin (Figure 37-2). Two categories of receptors are present: **free neuron endings** and **encapsulated neuron endings.**

Free neuron endings are almost impossible to see in typically stained sections, but note their distribution in Figure 37-2. Stimulating different free neuron endings produces sensations of pain, crude touch, and perhaps cold and hot. Encapsulated neuron endings consist of neuron endings surrounded by a connective tissue capsule.

Find **Meissner's corpuscles** in the *dermal papillae* (Figure 37-2). Meissner's corpuscles are receptors for fine touch and low-frequency vibration. Now look for **Pacinian corpuscles** between the dermis and hypodermis. Pacinian corpuscles look like a cut onion and are receptors for pressure and high-frequency vibration. Not all skin sections will contain a Pacinian corpuscle. If you cannot locate one, look at the demonstration slide.

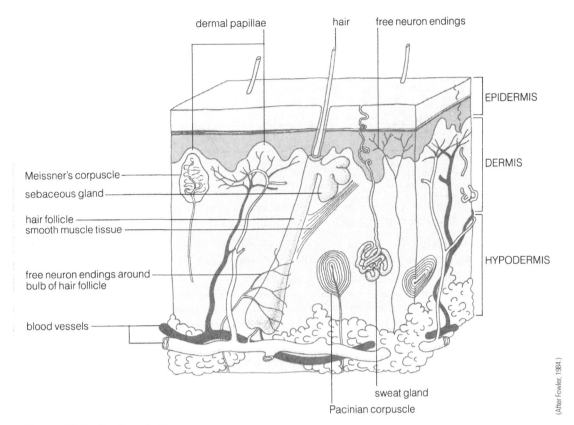

dermal papillae · · · · hair · · · · free neuron endings

EPIDERMIS

DERMIS

Meissner's corpuscle ——
sebaceous gland ——

hair follicle ——
smooth muscle tissue ——

HYPODERMIS

free neuron endings around ——
bulb of hair follicle

blood vessels ——

sweat gland
Pacinian corpuscle

(After Fowler, 1984.)

Figure 37-2 Section of skin.

2. With a felt-tip, nonpermanent ink pen, draw a 25-cell, 0.5-cm grid (Figure 37-3) on the inside of your lab partner's forearm, just above the wrist.
3. You are now the investigator, and your lab partner is the subject. At this point, ask your lab partner to close his or her eyes. Using a bristle, touch the center of each box in the grid. If the bristle bends, you are pressing too hard. Ask your lab partner to announce when the touch is felt. Do not count responses given when you remove the bristle. Just count those that coincide with the initial touch. Mark each positive response with a T in the upper left-hand corner of the corresponding box in Figure 37-3.
4. Repeat the above with a clean dissecting needle. This time, if you feel a prick, mark P for "pain" in the upper right-hand corner of the corresponding box in Figure 37-3.

Caution

Do not press; simply let the tip of the dissecting needle rest on the surface of the skin.

Figure 37-3 Grid for testing skin stimuli and recording modality data.

5. Repeat the above with a chilled blunt probe. Before using the blunt probe, dry it with tissue paper. The blunt probe will warm up over time, so switch it with the second chilled blunt probe every five trials. This time, mark each positive response with a C for "cold" in the lower left-hand corner of the corresponding box in Figure 37-3.
6. Repeat the above with a heated blunt probe. Before using the blunt probe, dry it with tissue paper. Use the two blunt probes alternately every five trials. This time, mark each positive response with an H for "hot" in the lower right-hand corner of the corresponding box in Figure 37-3.
7. Record the total number of positive responses for each stimulus in Table 37-1. Calculate the density of receptors for each modality (multiply the number of positive responses for each stimulus by 4) and record them in the third column of Table 37-1.
8. Repeat this procedure for your lab partner.
9. Does each cell in the grid contain a receptor for all four modalities studied? _____ (yes or no)

TABLE 37-1	Positive Identifications to Stimuli Applied to 25 Cells in a 0.25-cm² Patch of Skin	
Stimulus	Number of Responses	Density (Responses/cm²)
Touch		
Pain		
Cold		
Hot		

10. Can you see a pattern or patterns in the distribution of positive responses marked in Figure 37-3? _____ If yes describe the pattern(s): _____

11. Are the densities for the receptors for each modality the same? _____ (yes or no)

B. Projection

All sensations are felt in the brain. However, before the conscious mind receives a sensation, it is assigned back to its source, the receptor. This phenomenon is called **projection.** This is a very important characteristic of sensations because it allows the conscious mind to perceive the body as part of the world around it. You have probably experienced projection. A common example is the "pins and needles" you feel in your hand and forearm when you accidentally jar the nerve that passes over the inside of the elbow (so-called funny bone). The sensory neurons in the nerve are stimulated, and your brain projects the sensation back to the receptors. Another example is the **phantom pain** and other sensations that recent amputees sometimes "feel" in missing limbs. This occurs because the sensory neurons that once served the missing body part are activated by the trauma of the amputation.

1. Obtain an ice bag from the freezer.
2. Your lab partner holds the ice bag against the inside of your elbow for 2–5 minutes.
3. Describe any sensations felt in the hand or forearm to your lab partner who records them in Figure 37-4.
4. While the ice bag is applied to your elbow, your lab partner checks you for any loss of sensation by gently stroking your forearm and hand with a camel-hair brush. Sensations may also be felt after the ice bag is removed.
5. If no results are obtained, try tapping the inside of the elbow with the reflex hammer.
6. Similarly test your lab partner.
7. What can you conclude about projection and the receptors on the surface of the hand and forearm?

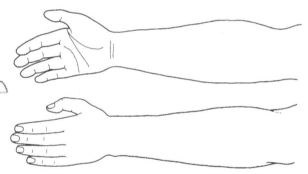

Figure 37-4 Front and back views of forearm and hand for recording projection data.

C. Adaptation

The intensity of the signal produced by a receptor depends in part on the strength of the stimulus and in part on the degree to which the receptor was stimulated before the stimulus. Receptors undergo **adaptation** to a constant stimulus over time. For example, when you first enter a dark room after being in bright light, you cannot see. After a while, your photoreceptors adapt to the new light conditions, and your vision improves.

1. Partially fill each of three 1000-mL beakers with ice water, water at room temperature, and water at 45°C.
2. Place one hand in the ice water and one in the warm water. After 1 minute, place both hands simultaneously in the water at room temperature.
3. Describe the sensation of temperature in each hand to your lab partner, who records these descriptions in Table 37-2.

TABLE 37-2	Sensations Felt When Preadapted Hands Are Placed in Room-Temperature Water
Relative Temperature of Preadaption	**Result**
Cold	
Warm	

4. What can you conclude about the skin receptors for temperature and their capacity for adaptation?

_____

_____

_____

What about the ability of other kinds of receptors to adapt? Use your own experiences for smell, touch, and pain to answer this question. (Hints for touch: Can you feel your clothes? How about when you first get dressed after a shower?)

_____

_____

_____

_____

_____

37.2   Reflexes (25 min.)

A **reflex** is an involuntary response to the reception of a stimulus. A **reflex arc** consists of the nervous system components activated during the reflex. The simplest reflex arc consists of a receptor, sensory neuron, motor neuron, and effector. Involuntary means that your conscious mind does not decide the response to the stimulus. However, the conscious mind may be aware after the fact that the reflex has taken place. Reflexes of which we are not aware occur most often in the internal environment (for example, reflexes involved in adjustments of blood pressure).

MATERIALS

Per student pair:
- reflex hammer
- penlight

PROCEDURE

A. Stretch Reflexes

Stretch reflexes are the simplest type of reflex because the interneurons are not directly involved (Figure 37-5). The sensory neuron connects directly with the motor neuron in the spinal cord. Stretch reflexes are important in controlling balance and complex skeletal muscular movements such as walking. Physicians often test these reflexes during physicals to check for spinal nerve damage. You've probably experienced one of these tests, the **patella reflex.** In this test, the receptor is the **muscle spindle** in the quadriceps femoris muscle of the front of the thigh, which is attached through its tendon and the patellar ligament to the top of the front surface of the tibia. The tibia is the larger of the two lower leg bones. The patella (kneecap) is embedded in the middle of the combined tendon/ligament. The muscle spindle detects any stretching of the muscle. The effector is the muscle itself.

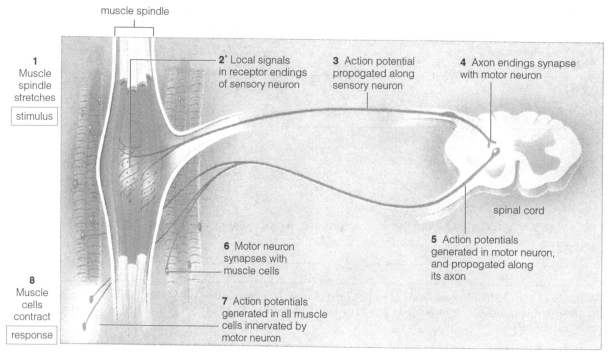

muscle spindle

1 Muscle spindle stretches
stimulus

2° Local signals in receptor endings of sensory neuron

3 Action potential propogated along sensory neuron

4 Axon endings synapse with motor neuron

spinal cord

6 Motor neuron synapses with muscle cells

5 Action potentials generated in motor neuron, and propogated along its axon

8 Muscle cells contract
response

7 Action potentials generated in all muscle cells innervated by motor neuron

Figure 37-5 The stretch reflex.

1. Sit on a clean lab bench and shut your eyes.
2. Your lab partner taps the patella ligament with a reflex hammer (Figure 37-6). Describe the response.

_____

_____

_____

If you have trouble producing a response, distract yourself by counting backward from 10. During this count, your lab partner again taps the patella ligament.

3. Even with your eyes shut, are you aware of the stimulus and the response? _____ (yes or no) This is because of pressure receptors that sense the tap and because of proprioceptors that sense movement of the leg.
4. Stretch reflexes are _somatic reflexes_ because they involve somatic motor neurons and skeletal muscles. Can you willfully inhibit a stretch reflex? _____ (yes or no)
5. Similarly test your lab partner.

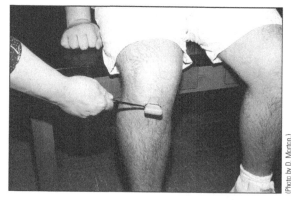

Figure 37-6 Area to tap to produce patella reflex.

(Photo by D. Morton.)

B. Pupillary Reflex

1. Shine the penlight into your lab partner's eyes. Does the size of the pupil (the diameter of the opening into the eye that is surrounded by the pigmented iris) get larger or smaller? _____
2. Now turn off the penlight. Does the size of the pupil get larger or smaller? _____
3. Repeat steps 1 and 2. Which is faster, constriction of the iris (which makes the pupil smaller) or dilation of the iris (which makes the pupil larger)? _____
4. Are you aware of the pupil's changing diameter? _____ (yes or no)
5. The **pupillary reflex** is an autonomic reflex because it involves an autonomic motor neuron and, in this case, smooth muscle. Can you willfully inhibit the pupillary reflex? _____ (yes or no)
6. Similarly test your lab partner.

Complex reflexes involve many reflex arcs and interneurons. A good example is swallowing. The stimulus in the **swallowing reflex** is the movement of saliva, food, or drink into the posterior oral cavity. The response is swallowing.

1. Cup your hand around your neck and swallow. Feel the complex skeletal muscular movements involved in swallowing. Do you consciously control all these muscles? _____ (yes or no)
2. Is it possible to swallow several times in quick succession? _____ (yes or no)
3. Explain this result. It has something to do with the stimulus.

   _____

   _____

   _____

   _____

   _____

4. What part of swallowing does your conscious mind control, and what part is a reflex?

   _____

   _____

   _____

37.3   Reactions *(20 min. or longer)*

A **reaction** is a voluntary response to the reception of a stimulus. *Voluntary* means that your conscious mind initiates the reaction. An example is swatting a fly once it has landed in an accessible spot. Because neurons must carry the sensory message to the cerebral cortex and the message to react back to the motor neuron, a reaction takes more time than a reflex. *Reaction time* is the sum of the time it takes for

- the stimulus to reach the receptive unit,
- the receptor to process the message,
- a sensory neuron to carry the message to the integration center,
- the integration center to process the information,
- a motor neuron to carry the response to the effector, and
- the effector to respond.

Visual reaction time can easily be measured with a reaction-time ruler. This device makes use of the principle of progressive acceleration of a falling object.

MATERIALS

Per student pair:
- Reaction Time Kit (Carolina Biological Supply Company)
- chair or stool
- scientific calculator

PROCEDURE

The following instructions are modified from the *Reaction Time Kit Instructions* booklet.

1. Sit on a chair or stool (Figure 37-7).
2. Your lab partner stands facing you and holds the *release end* of the reaction-time ruler with the thumb and forefinger of the dominant hand, at eye level or higher.
3. Position the thumb and forefinger of your dominant hand around the *thumb line* on the ruler. The space between the thumb and forefinger should be about 1 inch.
4. Tell your lab partner when you are ready to be tested.

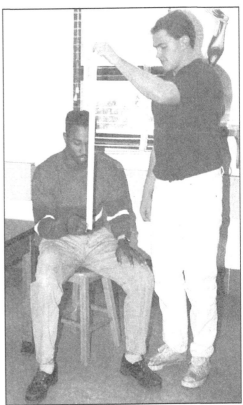

Figure 37-7 Two students measuring visual reaction time.

(Photo by D. Morton.)

5. Any time during the next 10 seconds, your lab partner lets go of the ruler.
6. Catch the ruler between the thumb and forefinger as soon as it starts to fall. The line under your thumb represents visual reaction time in milliseconds.
7. Read the reaction time from the ruler out loud, and your lab partner records the data in Table 37-3.
8. Repeat steps 1–7 ten times and calculate the average reaction time from the ten trials.
9. Similarly test your lab partner.
10. The reaction times of most of the ten trials should be similar, but perhaps the first few or one at random may be relatively different from the others. If this is true for your own or your lab partner's data, suggest some reasons for this variability.

_____

_____

_____

_____

_____

11. If opportunity and interest allow, the _Reaction Time Kit Instructions_ booklet has a number of suggestions for other experiments that you can easily do with the reaction-time ruler.

TABLE 37-3 Reaction-Time Data

Trial	Subject 1	Subject 2
1		
2		
3		
4		
5		
6		
7		
8		
9		
10		
Total		
Average (Total/10)		

_____ 1. Neurons that carry messages from receptors to the CNS are
(a) sensory
(b) motor
(c) interneurons
(d) autonomic

_____ 2. Neurons that carry messages from the CNS to effectors are
(a) sensory
(b) motor
(c) interneurons
(d) both a and b

_____ 3. Neurons that carry messages within the CNS are
(a) sensory
(b) motor
(c) interneurons
(d) autonomic

_____ 4. Knowledge of the position and movement of the various body parts is
(a) modality
(b) projection
(c) adaptation
(d) proprioception

_____ 5. Skin contains
(a) free neuron endings
(b) encapsulated neuron endings
(c) no nervous tissue
(d) both a and b

_____ 6. Which characteristic of receptors does phantom pain illustrate?
(a) modality
(b) projection
(c) adaptation
(d) proprioception

_____ 7. A simple reflex arc is made up of a receptor and
(a) a sensory neuron
(b) a motor neuron
(c) an effector
(d) all of the above

_____ 8. A stretch reflex is
(a) somatic
(b) autonomic
(c) both a and b
(d) none of the above

_____ 9. A pupillary reflex is
(a) somatic
(b) autonomic
(c) both a and b
(d) none of the above

_____ 10. A reaction is
(a) a reflex
(b) involuntary
(c) voluntary
(d) both a and b